THE ACT OF CREATION

ALSO BY ARTHUR KOESTLER

NOVELS

The Gladiators

Darkness at Noon

Arrival and Departure

Thieves in the Night

The Age of Longing

AUTOBIOGRAPHY

Dialogue with Death

Scum of the Earth

Arrow in the Blue

The Invisible Writing

The God That Failed (with others)

ESSAYS

The Yogi and the Commissar

Insight and Outlook

Promise and Fulfilment

The Trial of the Dinosaur

Reflections on Hanging

The Sleepwalkers

The Lotus and the Robot

Suicide of a Nation? (edit.)

THEATRE

Twilight Bar

The Act of

ARTHUR KOESTLER

Creation

The Macmillan Company ★ New York

CONTENTS

*

BOOK ONE

THE ART OF DISCOVERY
AND THE DISCOVERIES OF ART

*

PART ONE

THE JESTER

PART THREE

THE ARTIST

A. THE PARTICIPATORY EMOTIONS

B. VERBAL CREATION

C. VISUAL CREATION

BOOK TWO

HABIT AND ORIGINALITY

★

FOREWORD

BY PROFESSOR SIR CYRIL BURT

From time immemorial the gift of creativity has been venerated almost as if it were divine. There is more than a grain of truth in the romance of old Euhemerus, which relates how the gods and demigods of the ancient myths were really 'men of pre-eminent accomplishments deified out of flattery or gratitude'. Prometheus, the discoverer of fire, Vulcan, the first of the smiths, Hermes, the inventor of writing, Aesculapius, the founder of the most ancient school of medicine—each was welcomed into the classical Pantheon, much as today an outstanding scientist is elected to the Royal Society. In the Middle Ages the scientific pioneers—the leading alchemists, anatomists, and physicists—were almost as frequently suspected of owing their miraculous knowledge and skill to the devil rather than to the deity. Even as late as the nineteenth century relics of the old superstitious awe still lingered on, translated into the biological jargon of the day. These intellectual prodigies, it was argued, were plainly endowed, not with supernatural, but certainly with superhuman powers: they must therefore be either congenital sports or members of a rare anthropological species. Cynics, like Nordau and Lombroso, retorted that the much-vaunted superman was nothing but an unbalanced pathological freak, suffering from a hypertrophied cerebrum, or else the victim of some mental degeneracy, akin no doubt to the 'sacred disease' of epilepsy. 'After all,' it was said, 'who could be more original than a lunatic, and what is more imaginative than a dream?' Perhaps the so-called genius is just a 'sleepwalker' whose dreams have hit upon the truth.

As Mr. Koestler has so clearly indicated in his earlier volumes, in *Insight and Outlook*, and again in *The Sleepwalkers*, each of these views —once we have allowed for naïvetés resulting from the system of thought in which it appeared—brings out an important aspect of the problem. It is therefore curious, as he goes on to observe, that not until the close of the nineteenth century were any systematic attempts made

13

to investigate the matter scientifically. By collecting pedigrees, measuring abilities, and applying statistical techniques, Sir Francis Galton proved, or thought he could prove, that the most important element in genius was simply an exceptionally high degree of the all-round mental capacity which every human being inherits—'general intelligence'. And, reviving a proposal that originated with Plato, he contended that the surest way to manufacture geniuses would be to breed them, much as we breed prize puppies, Derby winners, and pedigree bulls.

Galton, however, in his later years came to lay almost equal stress on certain supplementary qualitites, which he believed were likewise very largely the outcome of innate disposition. Of these 'special aptitudes' the most important was what he called 'fluency'—that is, 'an unusual and spontaneous flow of images and ideas': the creative mind seemed 'always pullulating with new notions'. He added two further characteristics—'receptivity' and 'intuition or insight', i.e. what James has called 'sagacity' and T. S. Eliot 'sense of fact'— characteristics that are said to distinguish the 'useful inventiveness' of the genius from the 'useless fancies of the eccentric and the crank'. McDougall, Galton's most enthusiastic follower, discerned a fourth and still more elusive characteristic which he described as 'productive' or 'deviant association'. (What all these terms really cover is still a problem for intensive inquiry.) And then finally, as they all insist, there is also a motivational ingredient which Galton described by the somewhat ambiguous label—'zeal': the enthusiasm of the genius over his problems keeps him working late into the night long after the clerks and the factory-workers have gone home to their evening relaxations.

Galton's view, or rather the oversimplified version of it which appears in the popular textbooks, has of late been vigorously challenged by psychologists and educationists in America. To begin with, as might be expected in a democracy founded on the thesis that 'all men are created equal', many of them insist that genius is 'not born but made'. 'Give me', said Professor Watson, the apostle of behaviourism, 'half a dozen healthy infants and my own world to bring them up in, and I will guarantee to turn each one of them into any kind of man you please—artist, scientist, captain of industry, soldier, sailor, beggar-man, or thief.' We may willingly grant that without the necessary environment and the appropriate training even those who are most richly endowed by nature will fail to bring their gifts to full fruition. Heredity at best can provide only the seed; the seed must be planted in suitable soil, tended, watered, and cultivated before it can mature and blossom. But the question then arises—what kind of soil is needed? What sort of a world would Watson have provided? What type of training or what special brand of education can we ourselves supply to develop these latent potentialities to the utmost?

On all these points there is a conflict of doctrine which Mr. Koestler's arguments should do much to resolve. And there is a further point of disagreement. According to what has been called the British view, and contrary to the traditional notion, the difference between the creative genius and the plain man is not qualitative but merely quantitative: the so-called genius owes his outstanding achievements merely to the fortunate concurrence of a variety of factors, partly innate and partly environmental, all quite ordinary in themselves, but in his case developed to an exceptional degree. During the past few years, however, an alternative view has been put forward in America, which maintains that there are two distinct types of intellectual ability, differing not in degree but in kind. The commoner intelligence tests, it is argued—those, for example, which are in regular use in our 11-plus examination—measure only one rather superficial type of ability. There is a second, which Professor Guilford, as a result of his researches on 'high-level personnel', has suggested should be christened 'creativity'; and this in his opinion is 'far more fundamental'. As to what exactly is the nature of this second capacity we are still left rather in the dark. If you look up this useful word in the earlier editions of the *Oxford English Dictionary* you will fail to find it; and yet during the last two or three years it has attained something of the status of a glamour term among both English and American educationists.

At the moment, therefore, the views of professional psychologists regarding 'the act of creation' seem mainly to be in a state of bewildered confusion; and there is a crying need for an entirely fresh examination of the subject from top to bottom. However, psychologists are by no means the only people to maintain that 'creativity' (or whatever we like to term it) is in some sense or other an 'individual property'. In most civilized countries the importance attached to its results has been recognized by the laws of patent and of copyright. Both in war and in peace rewards have been offered and bestowed for what are known as 'original inventions'. And the various legal arguments to which these proprietary rights have led may furnish some preliminary notion of what such phrases are intended to convey. First, there must be the basic idea or conception; secondly, the idea must be embodied in concrete and articulate form—a literary, musical, or dramatic work, the specifications for a machine, a manufacturing process, or a material product; thirdly, the outcome as thus embodied must be new; and finally—a point which, curiously enough, is often forgotten in psychological and educational discussions—it must have value; the novelty must be a useful novelty.

If there is such a thing as creativity as thus defined, then it is clear that civilization must owe much, if not everything, to the individuals so gifted. The greater the number and variety of genuinely creative minds a nation can produce and cultivate, the faster will be its rate of progress. However, the pastime of debunking the 'cult of great men', which became so popular when Spencer and Buckle were laying the foundations of social and political theory, has once again become fashionable; and in these egalitarian days it requires some courage to pick up a pen and defend the concept of 'creative genius' against the onslaughts of the scientific sceptic. It is, so the critics assure us, not the gifted individual, but the spirit of the age and the contemporary trends of society—what Goethe called the *Zeitgeist*—that deserve the credit for these cumulative achievements: had Julius Caesar's grand-nephew succumbed to the illness which dogged his early youth, another son of Rome would have reorganized the State, borne the proud title of Augustus, and been duly deified. Had Copernicus, Kepler, and Newton fallen victims to the plague, one of their contemporaries would sooner or later have hit upon the scientific laws now coupled with their names. Certainly, *Aut Caesar aut nullus* is not an axiom to which the modern historian would subscribe either in these or any other instances. Yet to build up an empire on the ruins of a republic, to devise the theories which govern modern astronomy, would still have needed the vigour and the brain of an individual genius. And can anyone believe that, if William Shakespeare, like his elder sisters, had died in the cradle, some other mother in Stratford-upon-Avon or Stratford-atte-Bow would have engendered his duplicate before the Elizabethan era ended?

However, it is scarcely profitable to discuss the relative importance of genetic constitution and social environment until we have first determined in what precisely the 'act of creation' really consists. Here, as it seems to me, is one of the greatest gaps in the psychology of today. It is not an issue that can be satisfactorily solved by the tools and techniques which present-day psychologists commonly employ—

mental testing, experimental research, planned observations on men and animals. What is really needed is a systematic study carried out by one of those rare individuals who himself happens to possess this peculiar gift of creativity. And here, I venture to suggest, Mr. Koestler enjoys an advantage which few, if any, of the professional psychologists who have touched upon the subject can genuinely claim. This does not mean that the book is just based on the author's 'introspective reflections' about his methods of working as an essayist or novelist; on the contrary, he has been at pains to keep personal introspection, as the phrase is commonly understood, out of his chapters. The ground which he has covered and the evidence which he offers for his main conclusions are very much wider and more varied. He has in fact undertaken a new and comprehensive analysis of the whole problem; and is, so I believe, the first to make such an attempt.

The impartial reader will scarcely need any independent witness to testify in advance that Mr. Koestler is admirably equipped for the task. Although most widely known as a creative artist in the field of general literature, he received his early training as a scientist at the University of Vienna. In the course of travels in both hemispheres he has visited most of the more progressive places of learning where psychological research is being carried out. His knowledge of the relevant literature, both psychological and non-psychological, is unusually extensive and fully up to date. Moreover, he has enjoyed the intimate friendship of some of the most original investigators in contemporary branches of science, from nuclear physics to experimental neurology; and he has thus been able to watch the daily workings of their minds.

He begins with human creativity as exemplified in art, science, and literature; and to these fascinating topics the first half of his book is devoted. But he holds that creativity is by no means a peculiarly human gift; it is merely the highest manifestation of a phenomenon which is discernible at each successive level of the evolutionary hierarchy, from the simplest one-celled organism and the fertilized egg to the adult man and the highest human genius. It is, to adopt his phraseology, an 'actualization of surplus potentials'—of capacities, that is to say, which are untapped or dormant under ordinary conditions, but which, when the conditions are abnormal or exceptional, reveal themselves in original forms of behaviour. This 'actualization' he seeks to trace through morphogenesis, neurogenesis, and regeneration, and the various departures from simple instinctive behaviour in lowlier

creatures, up to the more 'insightful' forms of learning and of problem-
solving exhibited by animals and man. At every stage, so he maintains,
much the same 'homologue principles', derived from the hierarchical
nature of the basic part-whole relation, can be seen to operate. This
is of necessity the most technical and the most controversial part of his
work, but it is also the most original and illuminating. The outcome
is a wide and an entirely novel synthesis; and Mr. Koestler's book will
at once take its place as a classic among recent contributions to the
science of the human mind.

Technicalities are unavoidable, particularly when we pass from
first-hand observation to explanatory interpretations couched in precise biological, neurological, or psychological terms. Mr. Koestler
has overcome the problem by relegating the more erudite and speculative parts of his exposition to the second half of his book; and in his
prefatory remarks he suggests that those who feel more at home in the
Arts and Humanities than in the Sciences can skip the more technical
chapters. I hope, however, that all such readers will disregard this
advice as merely a symptom of the author's own modesty. Psychology,
more than any other branch of study, requires us to break down the
barriers between the two cultures. In my youth psychology was
regarded as a department of philosophy; and in my own university
the only way of studying it was by registering as an Arts student and
taking a degree in what were traditionally styled the Humaner
Letters. But the true student of humanity must study, not the Humanities only, but the relevant branches of science as well. However, I
suspect that my advice will turn out to be superfluous: most readers
on reaching the end of Book One will find themselves so intrigued
that they will be unable to resist pushing on to the next.

On the other hand, the specialist may perhaps feel tempted to turn
to the second half first of all: for, now that the pendulum has swung in
the opposite direction, the royal road to psychology usually starts
from elementary science. And, since the science taught in the preliminary stages is not only elementary but too often out of date, the
intending psychologist is still more severely penalized. A scientific
training may suffice for studying the behaviour of rats and robots.
The student of human nature is nowadays too apt to forget that most
of what we know about the mind of man is to be learnt from the
writings not of scientists but of men of letters—the poets and the
philosophers, the biographers and the historians, the novelists and the
literary critics. I tell my own students to read Pope's *Essay on Man* as

well as Skinner's textbook on *Science and Human Behaviour*. But indeed the modern psychologist, like the youthful Bacon, needs to 'take all knowledge for his province'.

Many of those who find Mr. Koestler's arguments completely convincing on all essential points may nevertheless be inclined, as I myself, to query minor details here and there. My own hesitations arise, not so much from definable objections, but rather from doubts requiring further information or factual evidence which is at present unobtainable. Indeed, the most valuable feature of Mr. Koestler's book is that it suggests so many problems and provisional hypotheses for direct scientific inquiry in a deplorably neglected field. In particular it would be highly instructive to note how far the views he has independently reached resemble those already outlined, in their own cumbersome language, by earlier British writers such as Bain, Ward, Stout, and McDougall, and, more important still, where precisely they differ.

Meanwhile, his theory of the creative process carries with it a number of practical corollaries of first importance to the teacher and the social and educational reformer. Most of the earlier discussions of creativity were based on accounts of the intellectual processes of creative adults. It is, however, with the work of children in our schools that we ought really to begin. Viewed in the light of Mr. Koestler's analysis, three salient questions call urgently for special investigation. How can we best detect the individuals who are endowed by nature with creative ability of this or that specific type? How are they to be trained and educated? And what are the existing social and scholastic barriers which hide or hinder the emergence of creative talent? Educational psychologists have of late woken up to the fact that the kind of examinations and intelligence tests which they still habitually employ tend to select the efficient learner and the verbal reasoner rather than intuitive observers or constructive and critical thinkers. With most of the mechanically scored tests handed out year by year, the child who gives an original answer, or hits on an alternative solution which the psychologist has missed (by no means a rare occurrence), is automatically marked wrong. Even when by some happy chance our methods of selection have picked out a potential inventor or a budding genius, we still have no notion how he should be encouraged and instructed so as to develop to the utmost his unusual latent powers. The problem has at last been recognized; but the remedy is still to seek. During the past year or two there have been an increasing number of conferences and papers, especially in the United States, devoted to 'the identification of creative individuals' and 'the cultivation of creative talents'. There has, too, been a small but growing amount of experimental research. Nevertheless, apart from a few unconvincing speculations, varying with the prepossessions of each writer, there is as yet no sound psychological basis either for the theorist or the practitioner. Mr. Koestler's eclectic survey is thus as timely in its appearance as it is far-reaching in its implications. It supplies a fertile set of premisses from which the practical teacher as well as the psychological research-worker can reap a rich harvest of fruitful ideas.

But his book is not merely a highly original contribution to present-day psychology. It is also a richly documented study in the history of scientific discovery and an essay in the analysis of literary and artistic creation. It will, therefore, present an irresistible challenge, and should appeal, not only to psychological or educational specialists, but also to every cultivated reader who is interested in 'the proper study of mankind'.

AUTHOR'S PREFACE

The first part of this book proposes a theory of the act of creation —of the conscious and unconscious processes underlying scientific discovery, artistic originality, and comic inspiration. It endeavours to show that all creative activities have a basic pattern in common, and to outline that pattern.

The aim of Book Two is to show that certain basic principles operate throughout the whole organic hierarchy—from the fertilized egg to the fertile brain of the creative individual; and that phenomena analogous to creative originality can be found on all levels.

Anyone who writes on a complex subject must learn that he cannot aim one arrow at two targets. Book One is aimed at the general reader; some of the chapters in Book Two presuppose a closer acquaintance with current trends in biology and experimental psychology, and are rather technical. There is an unavoidable difference in style between the two parts: in the first I avoided pedantry at the cost of occasional lapses into a loose terminology; in the second this was not possible. Readers who find certain passages in the second part too technical can safely skip them and pick up the thread later on without losing sight of the general idea. Its leitmotifs are restated on various levels throughout the book.

It may seem a presumptuous undertaking to inquire into the biological origins of mental creativity when we are still unable to define the chemistry of a simple muscle twitch. But often in the history of ideas we find two opposite methods at work: the 'downward' approach from the complex to the elementary, from the whole to its component parts, and the 'upward' approach from part to whole. The emphasis on either of these methods may alternate according to philosophical fashion, until they meet and merge in a new synthesis. It would have been as impossible to build theoretical physics on a foundation of its elementary particles (which turn out to be more and more baffling) as it has proved impossible to build a theory of psychology on 'elementary reflexes' and 'atoms of behaviour'. Vice versa, without the

21

assumption that complex matter consisted of atomic parts, whatever they are, physics and chemistry could not have evolved.

I have tried to combine both methods by choosing as my starting point a phenomenon which is at the same time complex and simple, in which a subtle intellectual process is signalled by a gross physiological reflex: the phenomenon of laughter. Humour is an elusive thing, so is the rainbow; yet the study of coloured spectra provided clues to the elementary structure of matter.

A preliminary outline of this theory was published in 1949 under the title *Insight and Outlook*. It was intended as the first of two volumes, and its preface contained the optimistic sentence: 'Volume Two is in preparation and will, it is hoped, appear twelve months after the first.'

The twelve months have grown into fifteen years. Partly because I became involved with other subjects; but mainly because I felt dissatisfied with that first attempt, and felt the need to base the theory on a broader foundation. I kept returning to it in between other books, but each time the broadening process necessitated an excursion into some related field and, as often happens, these excursions acquired a momentum of their own. One chapter on 'man's changing vision of the universe' grew into a separate book of more than six hundred pages;[1] so did another chapter, on Eastern mysticism.[2] And when at last I felt ready to write that long-postponed second volume I found that I had to scrap the first and begin again at the beginning. The whole theoretical framework had to be revised and even the terminology changed. Readers acquainted with *Insight and Outlook* will notice, however, that I have taken over, or paraphrased, passages from it which seem to have weathered the time; to avoid tedium I have omitted quotation marks. I have also incorporated into the text extracts from lectures given at English and American universities, with the kind permission of the authorities concerned.

Summaries appear at irregular intervals at the ends of chapters or sections where I felt that they might be helpful. Asterisks refer to text notes, index numbers to source references.

I have no illusions about the prospects of the theory I am proposing: it will suffer the inevitable fate of being proven wrong in many, or most, details, by new advances in psychology and neurology. What I am hoping for is that it will be found to contain a shadowy pattern of truth, and that it may stimulate those who search for unity in the diverse manifestations of human thought and emotion.

I am deeply indebted to Professor Sir Cyril Burt, and to Professor Holger Hyden, University of Gothenburg, for reading the manuscript, for their corrections, criticisms and encouragement; to Professor Dennis Gabor, Imperial College, London, Dr. Alan McGlashan, St. George's Hospital, and Professor Michael Polanyi, Oxford, for many stimulating discussions on the subject of this book. My grateful thanks are further due to Dr. J. D. Cowan, Imperial College, for his criticism from the standpoint of Communication Theory; to Dr. Rodney Maliphant for surveying the literature on the psycho-physiology of weeping; to Dr. Christopher Wallis for compiling a bibliography on the same subject; and to Miss Edith Horsley for her patient and careful editorial work.

London, December 1963

comic simile ←→ hidden analogy ←→ poetic image

witticism ←→ epigram ←→ trouvaille

satire ←→ social analysis ←→ allegory

impersonation ←→ empathy ←→ illusion

caricature ←→ schematisation ←→ stylisation

pun ←→ word-puzzle ←→ rhyme

riddle ←→ problem ←→ allusion

debunking ←→ discovering ←→ revealing

coincidence ←→ "trigger" ←→ fate

SA.   S.Tr.

←— bathos —— SHORT CUT —— pathos —→

BOOK ONE
THE ART OF DISCOVERY
AND THE DISCOVERIES OF ART

PART ONE

THE JESTER

I

THE LOGIC OF LAUGHTER

The Triptych

The three panels of the rounded triptych shown on the frontispiece indicate three domains of creativity which shade into each other without sharp boundaries: Humour, Discovery, and Art. The reason for this seemingly perverse order of arrangement—the Sage flanked by the Jester and the Artist on opposite sides—will become apparent as the argument unfolds.

Each horizontal line across the triptych stands for a pattern of creative activity which is represented on all three panels; for instance: comic comparison—objective analogy—poetic image. The first is intended to make us laugh; the second to make us understand; the third to make us marvel. The logical pattern of the creative process is the same in all three cases; it consists in the discovery of hidden similarities. But the emotional climate is different in the three panels: the comic simile has a touch of aggressiveness; the scientist's reasoning by analogy is emotionally detached, i.e. neutral; the poetic image is sympathetic or admiring, inspired by a positive kind of emotion. I shall try to show that all patterns of creative activity are tri-valent: they can enter the service of humour, discovery, or art; and also, that as we travel across the triptych from left to right, the emotional climate changes by gradual transitions from aggressive to neutral to sympathetic and identificatory—or, to put it another way, from an absurd through an abstract to a tragic or lyric view of existence. This may look like a basketful of wild generalizations but is meant only as a first indication of the direction in which the inquiry will move.

The panels on the diagram meet in curves to indicate that there are no clear dividing lines between them. The fluidity of the boundaries between Science and Art is evident, whether we consider Architecture, Cooking, Psychotherapy, or the writing of History. The mathematician talks of 'elegant' solutions, the surgeon of a 'beautiful' operation, the literary critic of 'two-dimensional' characters. Science is said to aim at Truth, Art at Beauty; but the criteria of Truth (such as verifiability and refutability) are not as clean and hard as we tend to believe, and the criteria of Beauty are, of course, even less so. A glance at the chart on p. 332 will indicate that we can arrange neighbouring provinces of science and art in series which show a continuous gradient from 'objective' to 'subjective', from 'verifiable truth' to 'aesthetic experience'. One gradient, for instance, leads from the so-called exact sciences like chemistry through biochemistry to biology, then through medicine—which is, alas, a much less exact science—to psychology, through anthropology to history, through biography to the biographical novel, and so on into the abyss of pure fiction. As we move along the sloping curve, the dimension of 'objective verifiability' is seen to diminish steadily, and the intuitive or aesthetic dimension to increase. Similar graded series lead from construction engineering through architecture and interior design to the hybrid 'arts and crafts' and finally to the representative arts; here one variable of the curve could be called 'utility', the second 'beauty'. The point of this game is to show that regardless of what scale of values you choose to apply, you will move across a continuum without sharp breaks; there are no frontiers where the realm of science ends and that of art begins, and the *uomo universale* of the Renaissance was a citizen of both.

On the other side of the triptych the boundaries between discovery and comic invention are equally fluid—as the present chapter will show —although at first sight this is less obvious to see. That the Jester should be brother to the Sage may sound like blasphemy, yet our language reflects the close relationship: the word 'witticism' is derived from 'wit' in its original sense of ingenuity, inventiveness.* Jester and savant must both 'live on their wits'; and we shall see that the Jester's riddles provide a useful back-door entry, as it were, into the inner workshop of creative originality.

The Laughter Reflex

Laughter is a reflex. The word reflex, as Sir Charles Sherrington said, is a useful fiction. However much its definitions and connotations differ according to various schools—it has in fact been the central battleground of psychology for the last fifty years—no one is likely to quarrel with the statement that we are the more justified to call an organism's behaviour 'reflex' the more it resembles the action of a mechanical slot-machine; that is to say, the more instantaneous, predictable, and stereotyped it is. We may also use the synonyms 'automatic', 'involuntary', etc., which some psychologists dislike; they are in fact implied in the previous sentence.

Spontaneous laughter is produced by the co-ordinated contraction of fifteen facial muscles in a stereotyped pattern and accompanied by altered breathing. The following is a description abridged from Sully's classic essay on the subject.

Smiling involves a complex group of facial movements. It may suffice to remind the reader of such characteristic changes as the drawing back and slight lifting of the corners of the mouth, the raising of the upper lip, which partially uncovers the teeth, and the curving of the furrows betwixt the corners of the mouth and the nostrils (the naso-labial furrows). To these must be added the formation of wrinkles under the eye, which is a further result of the first movement . . . and the increased brightness of the eyes.

These facial changes are common to the smile and the laugh, though in the more violent forms of laughter the eyes are apt to lose under their lachrymal suffusion the sparkle which the smile brings.

We may now pass to the larger experience of the audible laugh. That this action is physiologically continuous with the smile has already been suggested. . . . How closely connected are smiling and moderate laughing may be seen by the tendency we experience when we reach the broad smile and the fully open mouth to start the respiratory movements of laughter. As Darwin and others have pointed out, there is a series of gradations from the faintest and most decorous smile up to the full explosion of the laugh.

. . . The series of gradations here indicated is gone through, more or less rapidly, in an ordinary laugh. . . . The recognition of this identity of the two actions is evidenced by the usages of speech. We see in the classical languages a tendency to employ the same word for the two. . . . This is particularly clear in the case of the Latin *ridere*, which means to smile as well as to laugh, the form *subridere* being rare (Italian, *ridere* and *sorridere*; French *rire* and *sourire*; German *lachen* and *lächeln*).

We may now turn to the distinguishing characteristics of laughing; that is, the production of the familiar series of sounds. . . .[1]

But these do not concern us yet. The point to retain is the continuity of the scale leading from the faint smile to Homeric laughter, confirmed by laboratory experiments. Electrical stimulation of the *zygomatic major*, the main lifting muscle of the upper lip, with currents of varying intensity, produces expressions ranging from smile to broad grin to the facial contortions typical of loud laughter.[2] Other researchers made films of tickled babies and of hysterics to whom tickling was conveyed by suggestion. They again showed the reflex swiftly increasing from the first faint facial contraction to paroxysms of shaking and choking—as the quicksilver in a thermometer, dipped into hot water, rapidly mounts to the red mark.

These gradations of intensity not only demonstrate the reflex character of laughter but at the same time provide an explanation for the rich variety of its forms—from Rabelaisian laughter at a spicy joke to the rarefied smile of courtesy. But there are additional reasons to account for this confusing variety. Reflexes do not operate in a vacuum; they are to a greater or lesser extent interfered with by higher nervous centres; thus civilized laughter is rarely quite spontaneous. Amusement can be feigned or suppressed; to a faint involuntary response we may add at will a discreet chuckle or a leonine roar; and habit-formation soon crystallizes these reflex-plus-pretence amalgams into characteristic properties of a person.

Furthermore, the same muscle contractions produce different effects according to whether they expose a set of pearly teeth or a toothless gap—producing a smile, a simper, or smirk. Mood also superimposes its own facial pattern—hence gay laughter, melancholy smile, lascivious grin. Lastly, contrived laughter and smiling can be used as a conventional signal-language to convey pleasure or embarrassment, friendliness or derision. We are concerned, however, only with spontaneous laughter as a specific response to the comic; regarding which we can conclude with Dr. Johnson that 'men have been wise in very different modes; but they have always laughed in the same way'.

The Paradox of Laughter

I have taken pains to show that laughter is, in the sense indicated above, a true reflex, because here a paradox arises which is the starting point of our inquiry. Motor reflexes, usually exemplified in textbooks by

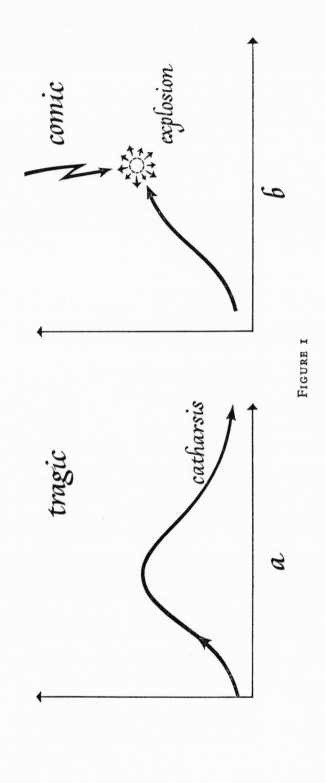

FIGURE I

'Worried about money?'

'No . . . nothing like that.'

'Trouble with the kids?'

'Well, if you must know, it's my little Jimmy.'

'What's wrong with him, then?'

'Nothing is wrong. His teacher said he must see a psychiatrist.'

Pause. 'Well, well, what's wrong with seeing a psychiatrist?'

'Nothing is wrong. The psychiatrist said he's got an Oedipus complex.'

Pause. 'Well, well, Oedipus or Shmoedipus, I wouldn't worry so long as he's a good boy and loves his mamma.'

The next one is quoted in Freud's essay on the comic.

Chamfort tells a story of a Marquis at the court of Louis XIV who, on entering his wife's boudoir and finding her in the arms of a Bishop, walked calmly to the window and went through the motions of blessing the people in the street.

'What are you doing?' cried the anguished wife.

'Monseigneur is performing my functions,' replied the Marquis, 'so I am performing his.'

Both stories, though apparently quite different and in their origin more than a century apart, follow in fact the same pattern. The Chamfort anecdote concerns adultery; let us compare it with a tragic treatment of that subject—say, in the Moor of Venice. In the tragedy the tension increases until the climax is reached: Othello smothers Desdemona; then it ebbs away in a gradual catharsis, as (to quote Aristotle) 'horror and pity accomplish the purgation of the emotions' (see Fig. 1, a, on next page).

In the Chamfort anecdote, too, the tension mounts as the story progresses, but it never reaches its expected climax. The ascending curve is brought to an abrupt end by the Marquis' unexpected reaction, which debunks our dramatic expectations; it comes like a bolt out of the blue, which, so to speak, decapitates the logical development of the situation. The narrative acted as a channel directing the flow of emotion; when the channel is punctured the emotion gushes out like a liquid through a burst pipe; the tension is suddenly relieved and exploded in laughter (Fig. 1, b):

surprising that Psychology has not considered the possible gains which
could result from the reversal of that step.

The bibliography of Greig's *Psychology of Laughter and Comedy*,
published in 1923, mentioned three hundred and sixty-three titles of
works bearing partly or entirely on the subject—from Plato and
Aristotle to Kant, Bergson, and Freud. At the turn of the century
T. A. Ribot summed up these attempts at formulating a theory of the
comic: 'Laughter manifests itself in such varied and heterogeneous
conditions . . . that the reduction of all these causes to a single one
remains a very problematical undertaking. After so much work spent
on such a trivial phenomenon, the problem is still far from being
completely explained.'[3] This was written in 1896; since then only two
new theories of importance have been added to the list: Bergson's
Le Rire and Freud's *Wit and its Relations to the Unconscious*. I shall have
occasion to refer to them.*

The difficulty lies evidently in the enormous range of laughter-
producing situations—from physical tickling to mental titillation of
the most varied kinds. I shall try to show that there is unity in this
variety; that the common denominator is of a specific and specifiable
pattern which is of central importance not only in humour but *in all
domains of creative activity*. The bacillus of laughter is a bug difficult to
isolate; once brought under the microscope, it will turn out to be a
yeast-like, universal ferment, equally useful in making wine or vinegar,
and raising bread.

The Logic of Laughter: A First Approach

Some of the stories that follow, including the first, I owe to my late
friend John von Neumann, who had all the makings of a humorist:
he was a mathematical genius and he came from Budapest.

Two women meet while shopping at the supermarket in the
Bronx. One looks cheerful, the other depressed. The cheerful one
inquires:
'What's eating you?'
'Nothing's eating me.'
'Death in the family?'
'No, God forbid!'

knee-jerk or pupillary contraction, are relatively simple, direct responses to equally simple stimuli which, under normal circumstances,
function autonomously, without requiring the intervention of higher
mental processes; by enabling the organism to counter disturbances of
a frequently met type with standardized reactions, they represent
eminently practical arrangements in the service of survival. But what
is the survival value of the involuntary, simultaneous contraction of
fifteen facial muscles associated with certain noises which are often
irrepressible? Laughter is a reflex, but unique in that it serves no
apparent biological purpose; one might call it a luxury reflex. Its only
utilitarian function, as far as one can see, is to provide temporary
relief from utilitarian pressures. On the evolutionary level where
laughter arises, an element of frivolity seems to creep into a humourless universe governed by the laws of thermodynamics and the survival
of the fittest.

The paradox can be put in a different way. It strikes us as a reasonable
arrangement that a sharp light shone into the eye makes the pupil
contract, or that a pin stuck into one's foot causes its instant withdrawal—because both the 'stimulus' and the 'response' are on the same
physiological level. But that a complicated mental activity like the
reading of a page by Thurber should cause a specific motor response
on the reflex level is a lopsided phenomenon which has puzzled philosophers since antiquity.

There are, of course, other complex intellectual and emotional activities which also provoke bodily reactions—frowning, yawning, sweating, shivering, what have you. But the effects on the nervous system
of reading a Shakespeare sonnet, working on a mathematical problem,
or listening to Mozart are diffuse and indefinable. There is no clear-
cut predictable response to tell me whether a picture in the art gallery
strikes another visitor as 'beautiful'; but there is a predictable facial
contraction which tells me whether a caricature strikes him as 'comic'.

*Humour is the only domain of creative activity where a stimulus on a high
level of complexity produces a massive and sharply defined response on the
level of physiological reflexes.* This paradox enables us to use the response as an indicator for the presence of that elusive quality, the
comic, which we are seeking to define—as the tell-tale clicking of the
geiger-counter indicates the presence of radioactivity. And since the
comic is related to other, more exalted, forms of creativity, the back-
door approach promises to yield some positive results. We all know
that there is only one step from the sublime to the ridiculous; the more

But these do not concern us yet. The point to retain is the continuity of the scale leading from the faint smile to Homeric laughter, confirmed by laboratory experiments. Electrical stimulation of the *zygomatic major*, the main lifting muscle of the upper lip, with currents of varying intensity, produces expressions ranging from smile to broad grin to the facial contortions typical of loud laughter.[2] Other researchers made films of tickled babies and of hysterics to whom tickling was conveyed by suggestion. They again showed the reflex swiftly increasing from the first faint facial contraction to paroxysms of shaking and choking—as the quicksilver in a thermometer, dipped into hot water, rapidly mounts to the red mark.

These gradations of intensity not only demonstrate the reflex character of laughter but at the same time provide an explanation for the rich variety of its forms—from Rabelaisian laughter at a spicy joke to the rarefied smile of courtesy. But there are additional reasons to account for this confusing variety. Reflexes do not operate in a vacuum; they are to a greater or lesser extent interfered with by higher nervous centres; thus civilized laughter is rarely quite spontaneous. Amusement can be feigned or suppressed; to a faint involuntary response we may add at will a discreet chuckle or a leonine roar; and habit-formation soon crystallizes these reflex-plus-pretence amalgams into characteristic properties of a person.

Furthermore, the same muscle contractions produce different effects according to whether they expose a set of pearly teeth or a toothless gap—producing a smile, a simper, or smirk. Mood also superimposes its own facial pattern—hence gay laughter, melancholy smile, lascivious grin. Lastly, contrived laughter and smiling can be used as a conventional signal-language to convey pleasure or embarrassment, friendliness or derision. We are concerned, however, only with spontaneous laughter as a specific response to the comic; regarding which we can conclude with Dr. Johnson that 'men have been wise in very different modes; but they have always laughed in the same way'.

The Paradox of Laughter

I have taken pains to show that laughter is, in the sense indicated above, a true reflex, because here a paradox arises which is the starting point of our inquiry. Motor reflexes, usually exemplified in textbooks by organism's behaviour 'reflex' the more it resembles the action of a mechanical slot-machine; that is to say, the more instantaneous, predictable, and stereotyped it is. We may also use the synonyms 'automatic', 'involuntary', etc., which some psychologists dislike; they are in fact implied in the previous sentence.

Spontaneous laughter is produced by the co-ordinated contraction of fifteen facial muscles in a stereotyped pattern and accompanied by altered breathing. The following is a description abridged from Sully's classic essay on the subject.

Smiling involves a complex group of facial movements. It may suffice to remind the reader of such characteristic changes as the drawing back and slight lifting of the corners of the mouth, the raising of the upper lip, which partially uncovers the teeth, and the curving of the furrows betwixt the corners of the mouth and the nostrils (the naso-labial furrows). To these must be added the formation of wrinkles under the eye, which is a further result of the first movement . . . and the increased brightness of the eyes.

These facial changes are common to the smile and the laugh, though in the more violent forms of laughter the eyes are apt to lose under their lachrymal suffusion the sparkle which the smile brings.

We may now pass to the larger experience of the audible laugh. That this action is physiologically continuous with the smile has already been suggested. . . . How closely connected are smiling and moderate laughing may be seen by the tendency we experience when we reach the broad smile and the fully open mouth to start the respiratory movements of laughter. As Darwin and others have pointed out, there is a series of gradations from the faintest and most decorous smile up to the full explosion of the laugh.

. . . The series of gradations here indicated is gone through, more or less rapidly, in an ordinary laugh. . . . The recognition of this identity of the two actions is evidenced by the usages of speech. We see in the classical languages a tendency to employ the same word for the two. . . . This is particularly clear in the case of the Latin *ridere*, which means to smile as well as to laugh, the form *subridere* being rare (Italian, *ridere* and *sorridere*; French *rire* and *sourire*; German *lachen* and *lächeln*).

We may now turn to the distinguishing characteristics of laughing; that is, the production of the familiar series of sounds. . . .[1]

I said that this effect was brought about by the Marquis' unexpected reaction. However, unexpectedness alone is not enough to produce a comic effect. The crucial point about the Marquis' behaviour is that it is both unexpected and perfectly logical—but of a logic not usually applied to this type of situation. It is the logic of the division of labour, the *quid pro quo*, the give and take; but our expectation was that the Marquis' actions would be governed by a different logic or code of behaviour. It is the clash of the two mutually incompatible codes, or associative contexts, which explodes the tension.

In the Oedipus story we find a similar clash. The cheerful woman's statement is ruled by the logic of common sense: if Jimmy is a good boy and loves his mamma there can't be much wrong. But in the context of Freudian psychiatry the relationship to the mother carries entirely different associations.

The pattern underlying both stories is *the perceiving of a situation or idea, L, in two self-consistent but habitually incompatible frames of reference, M_1 and M_2* (Fig. 2). The event L, in which the two intersect, is made to vibrate simultaneously on two different wavelengths, as it were. While this unusual situation lasts, L is not merely linked to one associative context, but *bisociated* with two.

I have coined the term 'bisociation' in order to make a distinction between the routine skills of thinking on a single 'plane', as it were, and the creative act, which, as I shall try to show, always operates on

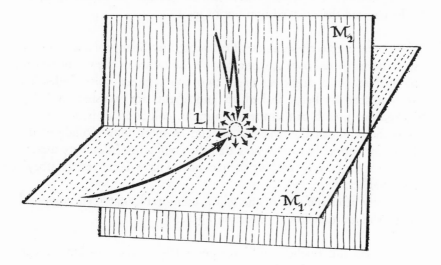

FIGURE 2

more than one plane. The former may be called single-minded, the latter a double-minded, transitory state of unstable equilibrium where the balance of both emotion and thought is disturbed. The forms which this creative instability takes in science and art will be discussed later; first we must test the validity of these generalizations in other fields of the comic.

At the time when John Wilkes was the hero of the poor and lonely, an ill-wisher informed him gleefully: 'It seems that some of your faithful supporters have turned their coats.' 'Impossible,' Wilkes answered. 'Not one of them has a coat to turn.'

In the happy days of *La Ronde*, a dashing but penniless young Austrian officer tried to obtain the favours of a fashionable courtesan. To shake off this unwanted suitor, she explained to him that her heart was, alas, no longer free. He replied politely: 'Mademoiselle, I never aimed as high as that.'

'High' is bisociated with a metaphorical and with a topographical context. The coat is turned first metaphorically, then literally. In both stories the literal context evokes visual images which sharpen the clash.

A convict was playing cards with his gaolers. On discovering that he cheated they kicked him out of gaol.

This venerable chestnut was first quoted by Schopenhauer and has since been roasted over and again in the literature of the comic. It can be analysed in a single sentence: two conventional rules ('offenders are punished by being locked up' and 'cheats are punished by being kicked out'), each of them self-consistent, collide in a given situation —as the ethics of the *quid pro quo* and of matrimony collide in the Chamfort story. But let us note that the conflicting rules were merely *implied* in the text; by making them explicit I have destroyed the story's comic effect.

Shortly after the end of the war a memorable statement appeared in a fashion article in the magazine *Vogue*:

Belsen and Buchenwald have put a stop to the too-thin woman age, to the cult of undernourishment.[4]

It makes one shudder, yet it is funny in a ghastly way, foreshadowing the 'sick jokes' of a later decade. The idea of starvation is bisociated with one tragic, and another, utterly trivial context. The following quotation from *Time* magazine[5] strikes a related chord:

REVISED VERSION

Across the first page of the Christmas issue of the *Catholic Universe Bulletin*, Cleveland's official Catholic diocesan newspaper, ran this eight-column banner head:

'It's a boy in Bethlehem.

Congratulations God—congratulations Mary—congratulations Joseph.'

Here the frames of reference are the sacred and the vulgarly profane. A technically neater version—if we have to dwell on blasphemy —is the riposte which appeared, if I remember rightly, in the *New Yorker*:

'*We wanted a girl.*'

The samples discussed so far all belong to the class of jokes and anecdotes with a single point of culmination. The higher forms of sustained humour, such as the satire or comic poem, do not rely on a single effect but on a series of minor explosions or a continuous state of mild amusement. Fig. 3 is meant to indicate what happens when a

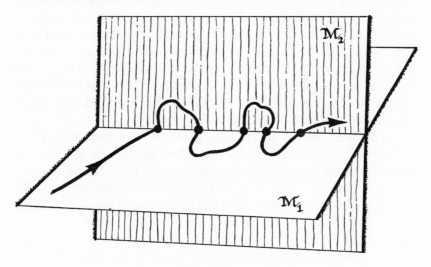

FIGURE 3

humorous narrative oscillates between two frames of reference—say, the romantic fantasy world of Don Quixote. and Sancho's cunning horse-sense.

Matrices and Codes

I must now try the reader's patience with a few pages (seven, to be exact) of psychological speculation in order to introduce a pair of related concepts which play a central role in this book and are indispensable to all that follows. I have variously referred to the two planes in Figs. 2 and 3 as 'frames of reference', 'associative contexts', 'types of logic', 'codes of behaviour', and 'universes of discourse'. Henceforth I shall use the expression 'matrices of thought' (and 'matrices of behaviour') as a unifying formula. I shall use the word '*matrix*' to denote any ability, habit, or skill, any pattern of ordered behaviour governed by a '*code*' of fixed rules. Let me illustrate this by a few examples on different levels.

The common spider will suspend its web on three, four, and up to twelve handy points of attachment, depending on the lie of the land, but the radial threads will always intersect the laterals at equal angles, according to a fixed *code of rules* built into the spider's nervous system; and the centre of the web will always be at its centre of gravity. The *matrix*—the web-building skill—is flexible: it can be adapted to environmental conditions; but the rules of the code must be observed and set a limit to flexibility. The spider's choice of suitable points of attachment for the web are a matter of *strategy*, depending on the environment, but the form of the completed web will always be polygonal, determined by the code. The exercise of a skill is always under the dual control (a) of a fixed code of rules (which may be innate or acquired by learning) and (b) of a flexible strategy, guided by environmental pointers—the 'lie of the land'.

As the next example let me take, for the sake of contrast, a matrix on the lofty level of verbal thought. There is a parlour game where each contestant must write down on a piece of paper the names of all towns he can think of starting with a given letter—say, the letter 'L'. Here the code of the matrix is defined by the rule of the game; and the *members* of the matrix are the names of all towns beginning with 'L' which the participant in question has ever learned, regardless whether at the moment he remembers them or not. The task before him is to fish these names out of his memory. There are various strategies for doing this. One person will imagine a geographical map, and then scan this imaginary map for towns with 'L', proceeding in a given direction —say west to east. Another person will repeat sub-vocally the syllables Li, La, Lo, as if striking a tuning fork, hoping that his memory circuits (Lincoln, Lisbon, etc.) will start to 'vibrate' in response. His strategy determines which member of the matrix will be called on to perform, and in which order. In the spider's case the 'members' of the matrix were the various sub-skills which enter into the web-building skill: the operations of secreting the thread, attaching its ends, judging the angles. Again, the order and manner in which these enter into action is determined by strategy, subject to the 'rules of the game' laid down by the web-building code.

All coherent thinking is equivalent to playing a game according to a set of rules. It may, of course, happen that in the course of the parlour game I have arrived via Lagos in Lisbon, and feel suddenly tempted to dwell on the pleasant memories of an evening spent at the night-club La Cucaracha in that town. But that would be 'not playing the game', and I must regretfully proceed to Leeds. Drifting from one matrix to another characterizes the dream and related states; in the routines of disciplined thinking only one matrix is active at a time.

In word-association tests the code consists of a single command, for instance 'name opposites'. The subject is then given a stimulus word— say, 'large'—and out pops the answer: 'small'. If the code had been 'synonyms', the response would have been 'big' or 'tall', etc. Association tests are artificial simplifications of the thinking process; in actual reasoning the codes consist of more or less complex sets of rules and sub-rules. In mathematical thinking, for instance, there is a great array of special codes, which govern different types of operations; some of these are hierarchically ordered, e.g. addition—multiplication—exponential function. Yet the rules of these very complex games can be represented in 'coded' symbols: $x + y$, or $x.y$ or x^y or $x\sqrt{y}$, the sight of which will 'trigger off' the appropriate operation—as reading a line in a piano score will trigger off a whole series of very complicated finger-movements. Mental skills such as arithmetical operations, motor skills such as piano-playing or touch-typing, tend to become with practice more or less automatized, pre-set routines, which are triggered off by 'coded signals' in the nervous system— as the trainer's whistle puts a performing animal through its paces.

This is perhaps the place to explain why I have chosen the ambiguous word 'code' for a key-concept in the present theory. The reason is precisely its nice ambiguity. It signifies on the one hand a set of rules which must be obeyed—like the Highway Code or Penal Code; and it indicates at the same time that it operates in the nervous system through 'coded signals'—like the Morse alphabet—which transmit orders in a kind of compressed 'secret language'. We know that not only the nervous system but all controls in the organism operate in this fashion (starting with the fertilized egg, whose 'genetic code' contains the blue-print of the future individual. But that blue-print in the cell nucleus does not show the microscopic image of a little man; it is 'coded' in a kind of four-letter alphabet, where each letter is represented by a different type of chemical molecule in a long chain; see Book Two, I).*

Let us return to reasoning skills. Mathematical reasoning is governed by specific rules of the game—multiplication, differentiation, integration, etc. Verbal reasoning, too, is subject to a variety of specific codes: we can discuss Napoleon's defeat at Waterloo 'in terms of' (a) historic significance, (b) military strategy, (c) the condition of his liver, (d) the constellation of the planets. We can call these 'frames of reference' or 'universes of discourse' or 'associative contexts'—expressions which I shall frequently use to avoid monotonous repetitions of the word 'matrix'. The jokes in the previous section can all be described as universes of discourse colliding, frames getting entangled, or contexts getting confused. But we must remember that each of these expressions refers to specific patterns of activity which, though flexible, are governed by sets of fixed rules.

A chess player looking at an empty board with a single bishop on it does not see the board as a uniform mosaic of black and white squares, but as a kind of magnetic field with lines of force indicating the bishops' possible moves: the board has become patterned, as in Fig. 4 a; Fig. 4 b shows the pattern of the rook.

When one thinks of 'matrices' and 'codes' it is sometimes helpful to bear these figures in mind. The *matrix* is the pattern before you, representing the ensemble of permissible moves. The *code* which governs the matrix can be put into simple mathematical equations which contain the essence of the pattern in a compressed, 'coded' form; or it can be expressed by the word 'diagonals'. The code is the fixed, invariable factor in a skill or habit; the matrix its variable aspect. The two words do not refer to different entities, they refer to different *aspects* of the same activity. When you sit in front of the chessboard your *code* is the rule of the game determining which moves are permitted, your

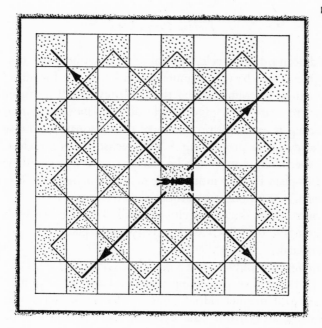

FIGURE 4

matrix is the total of possible choices before you. Lastly, the choice of the actual move among the variety of permissible moves is a matter of *strategy*, guided by the lie of the land—the *'environment'* of other chessmen on the board. We have seen that comic effects are produced by the sudden clash of incompatible matrices: to the experienced chess player a rook moving bishopwise is decidedly 'funny'.

Consider a pianist playing a set-piece which he has learned by heart. He has incomparably more scope for 'strategy' (tempo, rhythm, phrasing) than the spider spinning its web. A musician transposing a tune into a different key, or improvising variations of it, enjoys even greater freedom; but he too is still bound by the codes of the diatonic or chromatic scale. Matrices vary in flexibility from reflexes and more or less automatized routines which allow but a few strategic choices, to skills of almost unlimited variety; but all coherent thinking and behaviour is subject to some specifiable code of rules to which its character of coherence is due—even though the code functions partly or entirely on unconscious levels of the mind, as it generally does. A bar-pianist can perform in his sleep or while conversing with the barmaid; he has handed over control to the automatic pilot, as it were.

Hidden Persuaders

Everybody can ride a bicycle, but nobody knows how it is done. Not even engineers and bicycle manufacturers know the formula for the correct method of counteracting the tendency to fall by turning the handlebars so that 'for a given angle of unbalance the curvature of each winding is inversely proportional to the square of the speed at which the cyclist is proceeding'.[6] The cyclist obeys a code of rules which is specifiable, but which he cannot specify; he could write on his number-plate Pascal's motto: *'Le cœur a ses raisons que la raison ne connaît point.'* Or, to put it in a more abstract way:

The controls of a skilled activity generally function below the level of consciousness on which that activity takes place. The code is a hidden persuader.

This applies not only to our visceral activities and muscular skills, but also to the skill of perceiving the world around us in a coherent and meaningful manner. Hold your left hand six inches, the other twelve inches, away from your eyes; they will look about the same size, although the retinal image of the left is twice the size of the right.

Trace the contours of your face with a soapy finger on the bathroom mirror (it is easily done by closing one eye). There is a shock waiting: the image which looked life-size has shrunk to half-size, like a head-hunter's trophy. A person walking away does not seem to become a dwarf—as he should; a black glove looks just as black in the sunlight as in shadow—though it should not; when a coin is held before the eyes in a tilted position its retinal projection will be a more or less flattened ellipse; yet we see it as a circle, because we *know* it to be a circle; and it takes some effort to see it actually as a squashed oval shape. Seeing is believing, as the saying goes, but the reverse is also true: knowing is seeing. 'Even the most elementary perceptions', wrote Bartlett,[7] 'have the character of inferential constructions.' But the inferential process, which controls perception, again works unconsciously. Seeing is a skill, part innate, part acquired in early infancy.* The selective codes in this case operate on the input, not on the output. The stimuli impinging on the senses provide only the raw material of our conscious experience—the 'booming, buzzing confusion' of William James; before reaching awareness the input is filtered, processed, distorted, interpreted, and reorganized in a series of relay-stations at various levels of the nervous system; but the processing itself is not experienced by the person, and the rules of the game according to which the controls work are unknown to him.

The examples I mentioned refer to the so-called 'visual constancies' which enable us to recognize that the size, brightness, shape of objects remain the same even though their retinal image changes all the time; and to 'make sense' out of our sensations. They are shared by all people with normal vision, and provide the basic structure on which more personal 'frames of perception' can be built. An apple looks different to Picasso and to the greengrocer because their visual matrices are different.

Let me return once more to verbal thinking. When a person discusses, say, the problem of capital punishment he may do so 'in terms of' social utility or religious morality or psychopathology. Each of these universes of discourse is governed by a complex set of rules, some of which operate on conscious, others on unconscious levels. The latter are axiomatic beliefs and prejudices which are taken for granted and implied in the code. Further implied, hidden in the space between the words, are the rules of grammar and syntax. These have mostly been learned not from textbooks but 'by ear', as a young gypsy learns to fiddle without knowing musical notation. Thus when one is engaged in ordinary conversation, not only do the codes of grammar and syntax, of courtesy and common-or-garden logic function unconsciously, but even if consciously bent on doing so we would find it extremely difficult to define these rules which define our thinking. For doing that we need the services of specialists—the semanticists and logicians of language. In other words, there is less difference between the routines of thinking and bicycle-riding than our self-esteem would make us believe. Both are governed by implicit codes of which we are only dimly aware, and which we are unable to specify.*

Habit and Originality

Without these indispensable codes we would fall off the bicycle, and thought would lose its coherence—as it does when the codes of normal reasoning are suspended while we dream. On the other hand, thinking which remains confined to a single matrix has its obvious limitations. It is the exercise of a more or less flexible skill, which can perform tasks only of a kind already encountered in past experience; it is not capable of original, creative achievement.

We learn by assimilating experiences and grouping them into ordered schemata, into stable patterns of unity in variety. They enable us to cope with events and situations by applying the rules of the game appropriate to them. The matrices which pattern our perceptions, thoughts, and activities are condensations of learning into habit. The process starts in infancy and continues to senility; the hierarchy of flexible matrices with fixed codes—from those which govern the breathing of his cells, to those which determine the pattern of his signature, constitute that creature of many-layered habits whom we call John Brown. When the Duke of Wellington was asked whether he agreed that habit was man's second nature he exclaimed: 'Second nature? It's ten times nature!'

Habits have varying degrees of flexibility; if often repeated under unchanging conditions, in a monotonous environment, they tend to become rigid and automatized. But even an elastic strait-jacket is still a strait-jacket if the patient has no possibility of getting out of it. Behaviourism, the dominant school in contemporary psychology, is inclined to take a view of man which reduces him to the station of that patient, and the human condition to that of a conditioned automaton. I believe that view to be depressingly true up to a point. The argument of this book starts at the point where, I believe, it ceases to be true.

There are two ways of escaping our more or less automatized routines of thinking and behaving. The first, of course, is the plunge into dreaming or dream-like states, when the codes of rational thinking are suspended. The other way is also an escape—from boredom, stagnation, intellectual predicaments, and emotional frustration—but an escape in the opposite direction; it is signalled by the spontaneous flash of insight which shows a familiar situation or event in a new light, and elicits a new response to it. The bisociative act connects previously unconnected matrices of experience; it makes us 'understand what it is to be awake, to be living on several planes at once' (to quote T. S. Eliot, somewhat out of context).

The first way of escape is a regression to earlier, more primitive levels of ideation, exemplified in the language of the dream; the second an ascent to a new, more complex level of mental evolution. Though seemingly opposed, the two processes will turn out to be intimately related.

Man and Machine

When two independent matrices of perception or reasoning interact with each other the result (as I hope to show) is either a *collision* ending in laughter, or their *fusion* in a new intellectual synthesis, or their *confrontation* in an aesthetic experience. The bisociative patterns found in any domain of creative activity are tri-valent: that is to say, the same pair of matrices can produce comic, tragic, or intellectually challenging effects.

Let me take as a first example 'man' and 'machine'. A favourite trick of the coarser type of humour is to exploit the contrast between these two frames of reference (or between the related pair 'mind' and 'matter'). The dignified schoolmaster lowering himself into a rickety chair and crashing to the floor is perceived simultaneously in two incompatible contexts: authority is debunked by gravity. The savage, wistfully addressing the carved totem figure—'Don't be so proud, I know you from a plum-tree'—expresses the same idea: hubris of mind, earthy materiality of body. The variations on this theme are inexhaustible: the person slipping on a banana skin; the sergeant-major attacked by diarrhoea; Hamlet getting the hiccoughs; soldiers marching like automata; the pedant behaving like a mechanical robot; the absent-minded don boiling his watch while clutching the egg, like a machine obeying the wrong switch. Fate keeps playing practical jokes to deflate the victim's dignity, intellect, or conceit by demonstrating his dependence on coarse bodily functions and physical laws—by degrading him to an automaton. The same purpose is served by the reverse technique of making artefacts behave like humans: Punch and Judy, Jack-in-the-Box, gadgets playing tricks on their masters, hats in a gust of wind escaping the pursuer as if with calculated malice.

In Henri Bergson's book on the problem of laughter this dualism of subtle mind and inert matter ('the mechanical encrusted on the living') is made to serve as an explanation of *all* forms of the comic; whereas in the present theory it applies to only one variant of it among many others. Surprisingly, Bergson failed to see that each of the examples just mentioned can be converted from a comic into a tragic or purely intellectual experience, based on the same logical pattern— i.e. on the same pair of bisociated matrices—by a simple change of emotional climate. The fat man slipping and crashing on the icy pavement will be either a comic or a tragic figure according to whether the spectator's attitude is dominated by malice or pity: a callous schoolboy will laugh at the spectacle, a sentimental old lady may be inclined to weep. But in between these two there is the emotionally balanced attitude of the physician who happens to pass the scene of the mishap, who may feel both amusement and compassion, but whose primary concern is to find out the nature of the injury. Thus the victim of the crash may be seated in any of the three panels of the triptych. Don Quixote gradually changes from a comic into a puzzling figure if, instead of relishing his delusions with arrogant condescension, I become interested in their psychological causes; and he changes into a tragic figure as detached curiosity turns into sympathetic identification—as I recognize in the sad knight my brother-in-arms in the fight against windmills. The stock characters in the farce—the cuckold, the miser, the stutterer, the hunchback, the foreigner—appear as comic, intellectually challenging, or tragic figures according to the different emotional attitudes which they arouse in spectators of different mental age, culture, or mood.

The 'mechanical encrusted on the living' symbolizes the contrast between man's spiritual aspirations and his all-too-solid flesh subject to the laws of physics and chemistry. The practical joker and the clown specialize in tricks which exploit the mechanical forces of gravity and inertia to deflate his humanity. But Icarus, too, like the dinner guest whose chair collapsed, is the victim of a practical joke—the gods, instead of breaking the legs of his chair, have melted away his wings.

The second appeals to loftier emotions than the first, but the logical structure of the two situations and their message is the same: whatever you fancy yourself to be you are subject to the inverse square law like any other lump of clay. In one case it is a comic, in the other a tragic message. The difference is due to the different character of the emotions involved (malice in the first case, compassionate admiration in the second); but also to the fact that in the first case the two frames of reference collide, exploding the tension, while in the second they remain juxtaposed in a tragic confrontation, and the tension ebbs away in a slow catharsis. The third alternative is the reconciliation and synthesis of the two matrices; its effect is neither laughter, nor tears, but the arousal of curiosity: just *how* is the mechanical encrusted on the living? How much acceleration can the organism stand, and how does zero gravity affect it?

According to Bergson, the main sources of the comic are the mechanical attributes of inertia, rigidity, and repetitiveness impinging on life; among his favourite examples are the man-automaton, the puppet on strings, Jack-in-the-Box, etc. However, if rigidity contrasted with organic suppleness were laughable in itself, Egyptian statues and Byzantine mosaics would be the best jokes ever invented. If automatic repetitiveness in human behaviour were a necessary and sufficient condition of the comic there would be no more amusing spectacle than an epileptic fit; and if we wanted a good laugh we would merely have to feel a person's pulse or listen to his heart-beat, with its monotonous tick-tack. If 'we laugh each time a person gives us the impression of being a thing'[8] there would be nothing more funny than a corpse.

In fact, every one of Bergson's examples of the comic can be transposed, along a horizontal line as it were, across the triptych, into the panels of science and art. His *homme-automate*, man and artefact at the same time, has its lyric counterpart in Galatea—the ivory statue which Pygmalion made, Aphrodite brought to life, and Shaw returned to the comic domain. It has its tragic counterpart in the legends of Faust's Homunculus, the Golem of Prague, the monsters of Frankenstein; its origins reach back to Jehovah manufacturing Adam out of *adamāh*, the Hebrew word for earth. The reverse transformation—life into mechanism—has equally rich varieties: the pedant whom enslavement to habit has reduced to an automaton is comic because we despise him; the compulsion-neurotic is not, because we are puzzled and try to understand him; the catatonic patient, frozen into a statue, is tragic because we pity him. And so again back to mythology: Lot's wife turned into a pillar of salt, Narcissus into a flower, the poor nymph Echo wasting away until nothing is left but her voice, and her bones changed into rocks.

In the middle panel of the triptych the *homme-automate* is the focal, or rather bi-focal, concept of all sciences of life. From their inception they treated, as the practical joker does, man as both mind and machine. The Pythagoreans regarded the body as a musical instrument whose soul-strings must have the right tension, and we still unwittingly refer to our mortal frame as a kind of stringed guitar when we speak of 'muscle *tone*', or describe John as 'good tempered'. The same bifocal view is reflected in the four Hippocratic 'humours'—which were both liquids of the body and moods of the spirit; and *spiritus* itself is, like *pneuma*, ambiguous, meaning also breath. The concept of *catharsis* applied, and still does, to the purgation of either the mind or the bowels. Yet if I were to speak earnestly of halitosis of the soul, or of laxatives to the mind, or call an outburst of temper a humourrhage, it would sound ludicrous, because I would make the implicit ambiguities explicit for the purpose of maliciously contrasting them; I would tear asunder two frames of reference that our Greek forbears had managed to integrate, however tentatively, into a unified, psychosomatic view which our language still reflects.

In modern science it has become accepted usage to speak of the 'mechanisms' of digestion, perception, learning, and cognition, etc., and to lay increasing or exclusive stress on the automaton aspect of the *homme-automate*. The mechanistic trend in physiology reached its symbolic culmination at the beginning of the century in the slogan 'Man a machine'—the programmatic title of a once famous book by Jacques Loeb; it was taken over by behaviouristic psychology, which has been prominent in the Anglo-Saxon countries for half a century. Even a genial naturalist like Konrad Lorenz, whose *King Solomon's Ring* has delighted millions, felt impelled to proclaim that to regard Newton and Darwin as automata was the only permissible view for 'the inductive research worker who does not believe in miracles'.[9] It all depends, of course, on what one's definition of a miracle is: Galileo, the ideal of all 'inductive research workers', rejected Kepler's theory that the tides were due to the moon's attraction as an 'occult fancy'.[10] The intellectual climate created by these attitudes has been summed up by Cyril Burt, writing about 'The Concept of Consciousness' (which behaviourists have banned, as another 'occult fancy', from the vocabulary of science): 'The result, as a cynical on-looker might be tempted to say, is that psychology, having first bargained away its soul and then gone out of its mind, seems now, as it faces an untimely end, to have lost all consciousness.'[11]

I have dwelt at some length on Bergson's favourite example of the comic, because of its relevance to one of the leitmotifs of this book. The man-machine duality has been epitomized in a laconic sentence—'man consists of ninety per cent water and ten per cent minerals'—which one can regard, according to taste, as comic, intellectually challenging, or tragic. In the first case one has only to think of a caricature showing a fat man under the African sun melting away into a puddle; in the second, of the 'inductive research worker' bent over his test-tube; in the third, of a handful of dust.

Other examples of Bergson's man-automaton need be mentioned only briefly. The puppet play in its naïve Punch and Judy version is comic; the sophisticated marionette theatre is a traditional form of art; life-imitating contraptions are used in various branches of science and technology: from the dummy figures of dressmakers to the anatomical models in medical schools; from the artificial limbs of the orthopaedist to robots imitating the working of the nervous system (such as Grey Walter's electronic tortoises). In the metaphorical sense the puppet on strings is a timeless symbol, either comic or tragic, of man as a plaything of destiny—whether he is jerked about by the gods or suspended on his own chromosomes and glands. In the neutral zone between comedy and tragedy philosophers have been tireless in their efforts to reconcile the two conflicting aspects of the human puppet: his experience of free will and moral responsibility on the one hand; the strings of determinism, religious or scientific, on the other.

An extreme variant of the puppet motif is Jack-in-the-Box, symbol of the stubborn, mechanical repetitiveness, but also of the indestructibility, of life. Its opposite number is the legendary monster who instantly grows a new tentacle or head when the hero has cut it off; or the old woman in Raskolnikof's dream who, after each stroke of the axe on her skull, turns round and laughs in his face. In the biological sciences Jack-in-the-Box is a familiar figure, represented in all processes of the trigger-release type—the muscle-twitch, the epileptic fit, the 'sign-releasers' of the animal kingdom, whose symbolic message activates the springs of hopping mad or tenderly amorous, innate behaviour patterns.

To p. 28. 'Wit' stems from *witan*, understanding; whose roots go back (via *videre* and εἰδῶ) to the Sanskrit *veda*, knowledge. The German *Witz* means both joke and acumen; it comes from *wissen*, to know; *Wissenschaft*—science, is a close kin to *Fürwitz* and *Aberwitz*—presumption, cheek, and jest. French teaches the same lesson. *Spirituel* may either mean witty or spiritually profound; to amuse comes from to muse (*à-muser*), and a witty remark is a *jeu d'esprit*—a playful, mischievous form of discovery.

The word 'jester', too, has a respectable ancestry. The *chansons de geste* played a prominent part in medieval literature from the eleventh to the fifteenth centuries. They were epics centred on heroic events; their name is derived from the Latin *gesta*: deeds, exploits. With the coming of the Renaissance, satire tended to replace the epics of chivalry, and in the sixteenth century the heroic 'geste' turned into 'jest'.

To p. 32. A critical discussion of both theories can be found in Appendix I of *Insight and Outlook*.

To p. 40. The choice of the term 'matrix' is less easy to explain. In an earlier version I used 'field' and 'framework', but 'field' is too vague, and 'frame' too rigid. 'Matrix' is derived from the Latin for womb and is figuratively used for any pattern or mould in which things are shaped and developed, or type is cast. Thus the exercise of a habit or skill is 'moulded' by its matrix. In mathematics, matrices are rectangular arrays of numbers capable of all sorts of magic; they can be subjected to various transformations without losing their identity—i.e. they are both 'flexible' and 'stable'. Also, matrices have a constant attached to them, called their 'determinant', which remains unaffected by any of these transformations. But the analogy between 'determinant' and 'code' is extremely loose and in more than one respect misleading.

To p. 43. Congenitally blind patients, who acquire vision after surgical operations at a mature age, have great difficulties in recognizing patterns and faces, and in orienting themselves in space. Cf. Senden (1932), quoted by Hebb (1949).

To p. 44. The dual concepts of matrices and codes were designed with one eye on psychology, the other on physiology. Their theoretical implications in this wider context are discussed in Book Two.

The reader versed in experimental psychology will have been reminded by now of such old friends from the Würzburg School as *Aufgabe*, *Einstellung*, *Bewusstseinslage*; and of their Anglo-Saxon relatives: 'determining tendency', 'expectancy', 'task', 'schema' and 'set'. He will probably also remember that J. J. Gibson in a famous article (quoted by Humphrey, 1951, p. 105) listed some forty different meanings in which the word 'set' was used. I hope to show that 'matrices' and 'codes' are concepts at the same time more precise, and of more general validity, than *Aufgaben* or 'sets'.

II

LAUGHTER AND EMOTION

The sudden bisociation of an idea or event with two habitually incompatible matrices will produce a comic effect, provided that the narrative, the semantic pipeline, carries the right kind of emotional tension. When the pipe is punctured, and our expectations are fooled, the now redundant tension gushes out in laughter, or is spilled in the gentler form of the sou-rire.

Aggression and Identification

Laughter, as the cliché has it, is 'liberating', i.e. tension-relieving. Relief from stress is always pleasurable, regardless whether it was caused by hunger, sex, anger, or anxiety. Under ordinary circumstances such relief is obtained by some purposeful activity which is appropriate to the nature of the tension. When we laugh, however, the pleasurable relief does not derive from a consummatory act which satisfies some specific need. On the contrary: laughter prevents the satisfaction of biological drives, it makes a man equally incapable of killing or copulating; it deflates anger, apprehension, and pride. The tension is not consummated—it is frittered away in an apparently purposeless reflex, in facial grimaces, accompanied by over-exertion of the breathing mechanism and aimless gestures. To put it the other way round: the sole function of this luxury reflex seems to be the disposal of excitations which have become redundant, which cannot be consummated in any purposeful manner.

But *why* has the excitation suddenly become 'redundant'; and why is it discharged in laughter and not, say, in weeping—which is an equally 'purposeless' activity? The answer to the second half of the question

51

seems obvious: the kind of excitation exploded in laughter has a different quality or chemical composition, as it were, from the emotions which overflow in tears. But the very obviousness of this answer is deceptive, for the attempt to define this difference in 'quality and composition' necessitates a new approach to the theory of human emotions.

At first sight there seems to be a bewildering variety of moods involved in different types of humour. The practical joke is frankly aggressive; the lavatory jokes of children are scatological; blue jokes are sexual; the Charles Addams type of cartoon and the 'sick' joke play on feelings of horror and disgust; the satirist on righteous indignation. Moreover, the same type of semantic pipeline can be made to carry different types of fluid under varying degrees of pressure: for instance, 'they haven't got a coat to turn' and 'I never aimed as high as that' are both bisociations of metaphorical and direct meaning—jokes of the same logical pattern but with different emotional colouring. The more sophisticated forms of humour evoke mixed, and sometimes contradictory, feelings; but whatever the mixture, it must contain one ingredient whose presence is indispensable: an impulse, however faint, of aggression or apprehension. It may be manifested in the guise of malice, derision, the veiled cruelty of condescension, or merely as an absence of sympathy with the victim of the joke—a 'momentary anaesthesia of the heart', as Bergson put it. I propose to call this common ingredient the *aggressive-defensive* or *self-asserting* tendency—the reasons for choosing this clumsy term will be seen later on. In the subtler types of humour this tendency is so faint and discreet that only careful analysis will detect it, like the presence of salt in a well-prepared dish—which, however, would be tasteless without it.

It is the aggressive element, the detached malice of the parodist, which turns pathos into bathos, tragedy into comedy. It may be combined with affection, as in friendly teasing; in civilized humour aggression is sublimated and often unconscious. But in jokes which appeal to children and primitives cruelty and boastful self-assertion are much in evidence, and the same is true of the historically earlier forms and theories of the comic. 'As laughter emerges with man from the mists of antiquity it seems to hold a dagger in its hand. There is enough brutal triumph, enough contempt, enough striking down from superiority in the records of antiquity and its estimates of laughter to presume that original laughter may have been wholly animosity.'[1] In the Old Testament there are (according to Mitchell[2]) twenty-nine references to laughter, out of which thirteen are linked with scorn, derision, mocking, or contempt, and only two are 'born out of a joyful and merry heart'. A survey among American schoolchildren between the ages of eight and fifteen led to the conclusion (which could hardly have surprised anybody) that 'mortification or discomfort or hoaxing of others very readily caused laughter, while a witty or funny remark often passed unnoticed'.[3]

Among the theories of laughter that have been proposed since the days of Aristotle, the 'theory of degradation' appears as the most persistent. For Aristotle himself laughter was closely related to ugliness and debasement; for Cicero 'the province of the ridiculous . . . lies in a certain baseness and deformity'; for Descartes laughter is a manifestation of joy 'mixed with surprise or hate or sometimes with both'; in Francis Bacon's list of laughable objects, the first place is taken by 'deformity'. The essence of the 'theory of degradation' is defined in Hobbes's *Leviathan*:

> The passion of laughter is nothing else but sudden glory arising from a sudden conception of some eminency in ourselves by comparison with the infirmity of others, or with our own formerly.

Bain, one of the founders of modern psychology, followed on the whole the same theory: 'Not in physical effects alone, but in everything where a man can achieve a stroke of superiority, in surpassing or discomforting a rival, is the disposition of laughter apparent.'[4]

For Bergson laughter is the corrective punishment inflicted by society upon the unsocial individual: 'In laughter we always find an unavowed intention to humiliate and consequently to correct our neighbour.'[5] Max Beerbohm found 'two elements in the public's humour: delight in suffering, contempt for the unfamiliar'. McDougall believed that 'laughter has been evolved in the human race as an antidote to sympathy, a protective reaction shielding us from the depressive influence of the shortcomings of our fellow men.'[6]

Thus on this one point there is agreement among the theorists, ancient and modern; and not only agreement but exaggeration. One has only to think of Aristophanes or Calderon; *A Midsummer Night's Dream* or Chateaubriand's *Maximes et Pensées*, to realize that the aggressive charge detonated in laughter need not be gunpowder; a grain of Attic salt is enough to act as a catalyst. Furthermore, we must remember

that aggression and self-defence, rage and fear, hostility and apprehension, are as pairs of twins in their psychology and physiology. One
of the typical situations in which laughter occurs is the moment of the
sudden cessation of danger, real or imaginary; and rarely is the character
of laughter as a discharge-mechanism for redundant tensions more
strikingly manifested than in the sudden change of expression on the
small child's face from anxious apprehension to the happy laugh of
relief.

Whatever the composition of the emotional charge which a narrative carries, it will produce a comic effect only if an aggressive-defensive
tendency, however sublimated, is present in it. You may be deeply
moved by a person's predicament, and yet unable to suppress a smile
at its ludicrous aspect; and the impression of the 'ludicrousness' of
another person's behaviour always implies an assertion—conscious
or unconscious—of your own superiority; you smile at his expense.

The emotions which dominate on the opposite side of the triptych
do not concern us as yet; but I must briefly mention them for the sake
of contrast. Listening to Mozart, watching a great actor's performance,
being in love or some other state of grace, may cause a welling up of
happy emotions which moisten the eye or overflow in tears. Compassion and bereavement may have the same physical effect. The
emotions of this class, whether joyous or sad, include sympathy,
identification, pity, admiration, awe, and wonder. The common
denominator of these heterogeneous emotions is a feeling of participation, identification, or belonging; in other words, the self is experienced
as being a *part of a larger whole*, a higher unity—which may be Nature,
God, Mankind, Universal Order, or the *Anima Mundi*; it may be an
abstract idea, or a human bond with persons living, dead, or imagined.
I propose to call the common element in these emotions the *participatory* or *self-transcending* tendencies. This is not meant in a mystical
sense (though mysticism certainly belongs to this class of emotion); the
term is merely intended to convey that in these emotional states the
need is felt to behave *as a part* of some real or imaginary entity which
transcends, as it were, the boundaries of the individual self; whereas
when governed by the self-assertive class of emotions the ego is experienced as a self-contained whole and the ultimate value.

As a rule our emotions are complex mixtures in which both tendencies participate. Thus the emotion called 'love'—whether sexual
or maternal—usually contains an aggressive or possessive, self-asserting

component, and an identificatory or self-transcending component. If emotions were represented by different colours, then the two opposite tendencies would appear as brightness values (black-white mixtures) superimposed on them.

The subject will be discussed in more detail later (Chapters XI–XV); readers irritated by these repeated anticipatory excursions may find some excuse for them in the consideration that the painful vivisection of the comic, in which they are asked to participate, is not an end in itself, but a means to uncover the pattern which unites the apparently so heterogeneous creative activities in humour, art, and discovery.

The Inertia of Emotion

The first to make the suggestion that laughter is a discharge mechanism for 'nervous energy' seems to have been Herbert Spencer. His essay on the 'Physiology of Laughter' (1860) starts with the proposition: 'Nervous energy always *tends* to beget muscular motion; and when it rises to a certain intensity always does beget it. . . . Emotions and sensations tend to generate bodily movements, and . . . the movements are violent in proportion as the emotions or sensations are intense.' Hence, he concludes, 'when consciousness is unawares transferred from great things to small' the 'liberated nerve force' will expend itself along the channels of least resistance, which are the muscular movements of laughter.

The details of Spencer's theory (parts of which Freud incorporated into his own)[7] have become obsolete; but its basic thesis that 'emotion tends to beget bodily motion' has not only been confirmed, but has become so much of a commonplace in contemporary neurophysiology that the need to qualify it is often forgotten. For there exist, of course, emotional states—looking at the sea, or engaging in religious contemplation—which, on the contrary, tend to promote relaxation and bodily passivity. The title of Walter B. Cannon's pioneer work, which had a decisive influence on the modern approach to the problem of emotions—*Bodily Changes in Pain, Hunger, Fear, and Rage*—ought to have acted as a warning that the emotions which mobilize the body into action all belong to an important, but nevertheless limited, category—that which enters the service of the self-assertive tendencies. Cannon himself warned—with little success—against the lumping together of all emotions into a kind of red rag drenched with adrenalin.* However, for the moment we are concerned only with precisely this limited category—the aggressive-defensive type of emotion which enters into the comic.

When the Marquis in the Chamfort story rushes to the window, our intellect turns a somersault and enters with gusto into the new game; but the piquant expectations which the narrative carried, including perhaps an unconscious admixture of sadism, cannot be transferred to the other, the *quid-pro-quo* matrix; they are disposed of through channels of least resistance. When Othello, on the point of strangling Desdemona, breaks into hiccoughs and is transformed into a poor, sodden ham, our thoughts are again capable of performing the jump from one associative context into another, but our tension, now deprived of its logical justification, must somehow be worked off. In a word, laughter is aggression (or apprehension) robbed of its logical *raison d'être;* the puffing away of emotion discarded by thought.

To give another example: one of the popular devices of sustained humour is impersonation. Children imitating adults, the comedian impersonating a public figure, men disguised as women and women as men—in all these cases the impersonator is perceived as himself and somebody else at the same time. While this situation lasts the two matrices are bisociated in the spectator's mind; and while his intellect is capable of swiftly oscillating from one matrix to the other and back, his emotions are incapable of following these acrobatic turns; they are spilled into the gutters of laughter as soup is spilled on a rocking ship.

What these metaphors are meant to convey is that the *aggressive-defensive class of emotions has a greater inertia, persistence, or mass momentum than reason.* This assumption is tacitly shared by most psychological theories, but it needs to be explicitly stated in order to appreciate its consequences. The most important among these is that quite frequently our emotions are incapable of keeping step with our reason and become divorced from reason. In psychopathology this phenomenon is taken for granted, but its significance in less extreme situations is generally overlooked—although both common experience and neurophysiology ought to make it obvious. Emotions of the self-asserting type involve a wide range of bodily changes, such as increased secretion of the adrenal glands, increase of blood sugar, acceleration of heart rate, speedier clotting of the blood, altered breathing, inhibition of digestive activity, changes in electric skin resistance, sweating, 'goose-pimples' which make the hair of the skin stand on end, dilation of the pupils, muscle tension, and tremor. The joint effect of these so-called emergency reactions is to put the whole organism into a state of readiness for come what may; sweating, for instance, disposes of the heat generated by fight or flight, and the abundance of blood sugar in the circulation provides the muscles with excess energy. Hence the remarkable feats of force of which people are capable in danger; but more important from our point of view is the lowering of the threshhold of motor responses—the increased excitability of the muscles by nervous impulses, and the resulting tendency to violent movement, to 'work off', or at least 'shake off', the physiological effects of emotion. The chief mediators of this general mobilization of the resources of the body are the so-called sympathetic division of the autonomous nervous system, and the hormones secreted by the medulla of the suprarenal glands: adrenalin and nor-adrenalin, the 'humours' of fear and anger. Since these nervous and glandular processes are interrelated, it is convenient to refer to them jointly as activities of the sympathico-adrenal system. (To avoid confusion, I must underline that the sympathetic nervous system has nothing to do with the friendly emotion of sympathy; rather, as I have just said, with its opposites: rage and fear. However, by a lucky coincidence the initials of *S*ympathico-*A*drenal system are the same as those of the *S*elf-*A*ssertive emotions which are aroused by it.)

It follows from the above that these emotions involve incomparably heavier machinery, acting on the whole body, than the process of thinking which, physiologically speaking, is confined to the roof of the brain. The chemical and visceral states induced by the action of the sympathico-adrenal system tend to persist; once this massive apparatus is set in motion it cannot be called off or 'change its direction' at a moment's notice. Common observation provides daily, painful confirmation of this. We are literally 'poisoned' by our adrenal humours; reason has little power over irritability or anxiety; it takes time to talk a person out of a mood, however valid the arguments; passion is blind to better judgement; anger and fear show physical after-effects long after their causes have been removed. If we could change our moods as quickly as we jump from one thought to another we would be acrobats of emotion.

Thinking, in its physiological aspect, is based on electro-chemical activities in the cerebral cortex and related regions of the brain, involving energy transactions which are minute compared to the massive glandular, visceral, and muscular changes that occur when emotions are aroused. These changes are governed by phylogenetically much older parts of the brain than the roof-structures which enable man to think in verbal symbols. Behaviour at any moment is the outcome of complex processes which operate simultaneously on several levels of the nervous system, from the spinal cord to our latest acquisition, the pre-frontal lobes. There is probably no formal thinking without some affective colouring; but it is nevertheless legitimate to distinguish between form and colour—in our case between the *logical pattern* of a comic narrative and the *emotive charge* which it carries.

The sympathico-adrenal system might be compared to the body of a piano which gives resonance to the cortical strings of thought. When all is well the huge wooden box lends depth and colour and warmth to the vibrations of the strings. But if you play a humorous scherzo with full pedal on, the resonating body is unable to follow the swift modulations of the chords—thought and emotion have become dissociated. It is *emotion deserted by thought* which is discharged in laughter. For emotion, owing to its greater mass momentum, is unable to follow the sudden switch of ideas to a different type of logic or a new rule of the game; less nimble than thought, it tends to persist in a straight line. Ariel leads Caliban on by the nose: she jumps on a branch, he crashes into the tree.

It could be objected that the faint emotive charge of a joke, the slight malice or salaciousness which it arouses, would not be sufficient to bring the massive sympathico-adrenal machinery into action. The answer lies in the anachronistic character of our autonomous responses to stimuli which carry an echo, however faint, of situations that held a threat or promise in the remote past of the species; which once were biologically relevant, though they no longer are. These reactions lag by many millennia behind the conditions in which we live: we jump at a sudden sound; we develop gooseflesh in response to a screeching noise, to make our long-lost body hair bristle at the attack of some extinct beast; we sweat before an examination—to dispose of the excessive heat our bodies might develop in the impending struggle with the examiner. I like to call these innate, anachronistic responses the *over-statements of the body*. One of the remarkable things about them is that they can be triggered off by certain stimuli in minute, quasi-homeopathic doses.

To sum up, the grain of salt which must be present in the narrative to make us laugh turns out to be a drop of adrenalin.

In the first chapter I discussed the logic of humour; in the previous section its emotional dynamics. Fitting the two together, we can now expand the formula on page 35 as follows: The sudden bisociation of a mental event with two habitually incompatible matrices results in an abrupt transfer of the train of thought from one associative context to another. The emotive charge which the narrative carried cannot be so transferred owing to its greater inertia and persistence; discarded by reason, the tension finds its outlet in laughter.

But that still leaves the question open why the excess energy should be worked off in the particular form of laughter and not, say, by flapping one's arms or wiggling one's toes. The somewhat tentative answer is that the muscular contractions and breathing actions in laughter seem to offer natural channels of least resistance for the overflow. To quote Freud:

> According to the best of my knowledge, the grimaces and contortions of the corners of the mouth that characterize laughter appear first in the satisfied and over-satiated nursling when he drowsily quits the breast. . . . They are physical expressions of the determination to take no more nourishment, an 'enough' so to speak, or rather a 'more than enough'. . . . This primal sense of pleasurable saturation may have provided the link between the smile —that basic phenomenon underlying laughter—and its subsequent connection with other pleasurable processes of de-tension.[8]

In other words, the muscle-contractions of the smile, as the earliest manifestations of relief from tension, would thereafter become channels of least resistance.

The peculiar breathing in laughter, with its repeated, explosive exhalations, seems designed to 'puff away' surplus tension in a kind of respiratory gymnastics; and the vigorous gestures and slapping of thighs obviously serve the same function. Often these massive reactions seem to be quite out of proportion to the feeble stimuli which provoke them—particularly when we do not like the type of joke which causes such hilarity in others:

> A thousand Edinburgh schoolchildren burst into laughter when David Oistrakh, the Russian violinist, snapped a string while playing

Schubert's Fantasy in C Major during a recital of a city housing estate yesterday. Their studious attention broke when Mr. Oistrakh —guest of honour at the Edinburgh Festival—held up the violin and looked with consternation at his accompanist.[9]

Let us try to understand what those brats found so funny. Firstly, there is the familiar pattern of the practical joke which the laws of physics play on the artist, suddenly revealing that his magic strings are made of common cat-gut—'I know you from a plum-tree'. The 'consternation' on Oistrakh's face is the consternation of the man slipping on the banana skin; exaltation is debunked by the sudden impact of triviality. But all this does not account for that unexpected, barbaric outburst of hilarity which schoolmasters know only too well —unless one realizes that what I call, somewhat abstractly, 'the emotional charge of the narrative' contains here a mass of resentment, mostly perhaps unconscious, at having to sit still and listen 'with studious attention' to that Russian with the unpronounceable name; a repressed emotion, tending to beget fidgety motions, until the tension snaps with the string, releasing the outburst, instantly transforming the hushed class into a horde of savages.

In other words, all discussions of the comic remain bloodless abstractions unless we bear in mind that laughter is a phenomenon of the trigger-release type, where a minute cause can open the tap of surprisingly large stores of energy from various sources: repressed sadism; repressed sex; repressed fear; even repressed boredom. Here is a list of 'occasions for laughter' recorded by American undergraduates in reply to a questionnaire:

A pillow fight in the dormitory
A girl friend tore her dress
I fell during skating
A dog came in during a lecture
A mispronounced word in rhetoric class
Being teased about my corpulence
Lizzie trying to do a fairy dance
My opponents in a bridge game bidding four spades when I held
   two aces and the king, jack and five of spades
An article by a priest on the sex life of H. G. Wells.[10]

This ought to be enough to make one realize that laughter may be entirely mirthless and humourless;* it can be contrived as a means of social communication or in lieu of a rude noise. It can also serve to cover up sexual or sadistic gloating, as in the forced, tumescent laughter of the spectators at a strip-tease—or in the jolly manifestations of English popular humour at public hangings in the last century.

Surprisingly, Bergson believed that one can only laugh in the presence of others—presumably because this fitted his theory of laughter as an act of social correction ('one has no taste for the comic when one feels isolated. It seems that laughter needs an echo. Our laughter is always the laughter of a group.').[11] No doubt, collective giggling fits do occur in dormitories at girls' schools, and no doubt one laughs with more gusto in company than alone. But the infectiousness of emotive manifestations is a well-known phenomenon in group behaviour, which equally applies to hysteria, panic, even to infectious coughing of theatre audiences; it is not a specific characteristic of laughter, and contributes nothing to its explanation.

Lastly, laughter or smiling frequently occur in response to stimuli which in themselves are not comic, but merely signs or symbols for comic stimuli, or even symbols of symbols—Chaplin's boots, Groucho Marx's cigar, caricatures of celebrities reduced to a few visual hints, catch-phrases and allusions to familiar situations. The analysis of these oblique cases often requires tracing back a long and involved thread of associations to its source, which is not much fun; yet the procedure is essentially the same as the literary critic's or the art historian's when they try to analyse the evocative power of a poetic image or a land-scape. The task is made more complicated by the fact that the effect of such comic symbols—the sight of Colonel Blimp on a cartoon, the appearance of Falstaff on the stage—appears to be instantaneous; there seems to be no time for first accumulating and then discharging ten-sion. But in these cases memory serves as an accumulator, a storage battery whose electric charge can be sparked off any time: the smile which greets Papageno strutting on to the scene is derived from a mixture of memories and expectations. All of which goes to show that to find the explanation why we laugh may be a task as delicate as analysing the chemical composition of a perfume, with its multiple ingredients—some of which are never perceived, while others, sniffed in isolation, would make us wince.

Discussing the problem of man's innate aggressive tendencies, Aldous Huxley once said:

> On the physiological level I suppose the problem is linked with the fact that we carry around with us a glandular system which was admirably well adapted to life in the Paleolithic times but is not very well adapted to life now. Thus we tend to produce more adrenalin than is good for us, and we either suppress ourselves and turn destructive energies inwards or else we do not suppress ourselves and we start hitting people.[12]

A third alternative, which Huxley overlooked, is to laugh at people. There are, of course, other outlets for tame aggression: sport, politics, book-reviewing, and so forth; but these are conscious, voluntary activities, whereas laughter is a spontaneous, physiological reflex, a gift of nature included in our native equipment as part of the evolutionary package deal. Not only the functions of our glands, but the whole autonomous nervous system and the emotion-controlling centres in the mid-brain, are much older than the Paleolithic Age, and reflect conditions at a stage of human evolution when the struggle for existence was more deadly than at present and when any unusual sight or sound had to be answered by jumping, bristling, fight, or flight. As security and comfort increased in the species, the affect-generating emergency mechanisms of the sympathico-adrenal system gradually became an anachronism. But organs and their functions do not atrophy at the rate at which they become redundant; and thus the biological evolution of *homo sapiens* (if it has not stopped altogether) lags dangerously behind his mental evolution. One consequence of this is that our brains have become 'divided houses of faith and reason', of thinking at odds with emotions; another, that our emotive responses have become 'over-statements of the body' out of all proportion with the reactions biologically required or socially permitted—and cannot be worked off through their original channels. Fortunately, at some point along the evolutionary line, the luxury reflexes of laughter and weeping emerged as overflow mechanisms for the disposal of at least part of our redundant emotions. They are obviously twin reflexes: laughter serving the disposal of aggressive emotions cast off by the intellect, while crying (to anticipate once more) facilitates the overflow of participatory emotions accepted by the intellect.

It follows that two conditions had to be fulfilled before *homo ridens*, the laughing animal, could emerge: first a relative security of existence, which called for new outlets for excess energies; second and more important, a level of evolution had to be reached where reasoning had gained a certain degree of autonomy from the 'blind' urges of emotion; where thought had acquired that independence and nimbleness which enable it to detach itself from feeling—and to confront its glandular humours with a sense of humour. Only at this stage of 'cortical emancipation' could man perceive his own emotions as redundant, and make the smiling admission 'I have been fooled'.

Beneath the human level there is neither the possibility nor the need for laughter; it could arise only in a biologically secure species with redundant emotions and intellectual autonomy.* The sudden realization that one's own excitement is 'unreasonable' heralds the emergence of self-criticism, of the ability to see one's very own self *from outside*; and this bisociation of subjective experience with an objective frame of reference is perhaps the wittiest discovery of *homo sapiens*.

Thus laughter rings the bell of man's departure from the rails of instinct; it signals his rebellion against the singlemindedness of his biological urges, his refusal to remain a creature of habit, governed by a single set of 'rules of the game'. Animals are fanatics; but 'O / How the dear little children laugh / When the drums roll and the lovely / Lady is sawn in half. . . .'[13]

NOTES

To p. 56. Criticizing a paper read by a neurologist to a learned society, he remarked: 'The author spoke of emotions in very general terms. . . . There are features which he mentioned which I could recognize as characteristic of major emotions, as anger and rage; but after all, love is an emotion. . . . I think that when we discuss emotion we ought to specify the sorts of emotion we have in mind' (Cannon, 1929).

To p. 61. The article in which this list appeared is characteristic of the behaviourist approach; it ennumerated three 'basic principles' of laughter: (a) 'as an expression of joy', (b) 'laughter makes for group cohesion through homogeneity of feeling within the group', (c) 'laughing can be used as a weapon in competitive situations'. The word 'humour' was not mentioned in the article; laughing at 'jokes, antics, etc.', was mentioned only in passing, as obviously not a phenomenon worthy of the psychologists' attention.

To p. 63. Some domesticated animals—dogs, chimpanzees—seem to be capable of a humorous expression and to engage in teasing activities. These may be regarded as evolutionary forerunners of laughter.

III

VARIETIES OF HUMOUR

The tools have now been assembled which should enable the reader to dissect any specimen of humour. The procedure to be followed is: first, determine the nature of M_1 and M_2 in the diagrams on pages 35 and 37 by discovering the type of logic, the rules of the game, which govern each matrix. Often these rules are implied, as hidden axioms, and taken for granted—the code must be de-coded. The rest is easy: find the 'link'—the focal concept, word, or situation which is bisociated with both mental planes; lastly, define the character of the emotive charge and make a guess regarding the unconscious elements that it may contain. In the sections which follow I shall apply this technique to various types of humour.

Pun and Witticism

Our spacemen, Mrs. Lamport fears, are 'heading for the "lunar bin".' The ageing libertine, she tells us, 'feels his old Krafft Ebbing'. The Reverend Spooner had a great affection, or so he said, for 'our queer old dean'.

One swallow, the proverb says, does not make a summer—nor quench the thirst. Elijah's ravens, according to Milton, were 'though ravenous taught to abstain from what they brought'. Not so Napoleon, who, shortly after his coronation, confiscated the estates of the house of Orléans, which caused a contemporary to remark: *'C'est le premier vol de l'aigle.'* Equally to the point was Mr. Paul Jenkin's discovery regarding the pros and cons of Britain's entry into the Common Market: 'The Cons were pro, while Lab has turned con.'

The pun is the bisociation of a single phonetic form with two meanings—two strings of thought tied together by an accoustic knot. Its immense popularity with children, its prevalence in certain forms of mental disorder ('punning mania'), and its frequent occurrence in the dream, indicate the profound unconscious appeal of association based on pure sound. Its opposite number is the rhyme. In between these two, on the central panel, the bisociation of sound and sense assumes a playful form in word games like Lexicon, anagram, and crossword puzzle; and a serious form in comparative philology and paleography, the deciphering of ancient inscriptions (pp. 186–7).

Whether the two meanings associated with the pun are derived from the same root as in 'lunar bin'; or are homonyms as *vol* = flight and *vol* = theft, is irrelevant provided the two derivations have drifted apart far enough to become incompatible. In fact, there is a continuous series stretching from the pun through the play of words (*jeu de mots*) to the play of ideas (*jeu d'esprit*). Let me quote a few more examples of the latter.

'The super-ego is that part of the personality which is soluble in alcohol.' The concept 'soluble' is bisociated (a) with the context of the chemical laboratory and (b) with the (metaphorical) dissolution of one's high principles in one's cups. The first few words of the sentence arouse perhaps a mild irritation with the Freudian jargon—or apprehension, as the case may be; which is then tittered away through the now familiar mechanism.

Here is another sample from this game of definitions: 'What is a sadist? A sadist is a person who is kind to a masochist.' The link-concept is 'kindness', bisociated with two diametrically opposed meanings; moreover the whole definition is open to two different interpretations:

(a) the sadist does a kindness to the masochist by torturing him;

(b) the sadist is torturing the masochist by being kind to him.

In both cases the sadist must go against his own nature, and the definition turns out to be in fact a variant of the logical paradox about the Cretan who asserts that all Cretans are liars. But we can get around it by deciding that in either interpretation 'kind' should be understood both literally and metaphorically at the same time; in other words, by playing simultaneously two games governed by opposite rules. We shall see that such *reversals of logic* play a considerable part in scientific discovery (pp. 191–9). They are also a recurrent motif in poetry and literature. One of my favourite Donne quotations is a line from the Litany: 'For O, for some, not to be martyrs is a martyrdom.'

I have given examples of the bisociation of professional with commonsense logic, of metaphorical with literal meaning, of contexts linked by sound affinities, of trains of reasoning travelling, happily joined together, in opposite directions. The list could be extended beyond the limits of patience. In fact *any* two matrices can be made to yield a comic effect of sorts, by finding an appropriate link between them and infusing a drop of adrenalin. Take as a random example two associative contexts centred on the unpromising key-words 'alliteration' and 'hydrotherapy'. (The example actually originated in a challenge following a discussion; I am merely quoting it, with apologies, to show that in principle it can be done):

> *Gossip Column Item:* Lady Smith-Everett, receiving me in her sumptuous boudoir, explained that she had always suffered from 'the most maddening rashes' until she met her present physician, a former professor of psycho-hydrotherapy at the University of Bucharest. By employing a new test which he invented, the Professor discovered that she had 'a grade 4 allergy' against sojourning in spas and holiday resorts with the initial letter C. No more visits to Capri and Carlsbad for Lady S-E.!

It is not even necessary that the two matrices should be governed by incompatible codes. One can obtain comic effects by simply confronting quantitatively different scales of operations, provided that they differ sufficiently in order of magnitude for one scale to become negligible compared with the other. The result is the type of joke made according to the formula: the mountains laboured, the birth was a mouse.

With an added twist you get this kind of dotty dialogue—between a nervous bus-passenger and the conductor:

'What's the time?'

'Thursday.'

'Good Lord! I must get off.'

This is a serial affair in which not two but three matrices are successively involved, each with a different scale of measurement. M_1 has a grid of hours and minutes; M_2 of days of the week. The two differ in fact only in quantity but provide qualitatively different frames of reference; the third matrix has spatial instead of temporal co-ordinates —where to get off, not when. It would be impossible to orientate one's behaviour with reference to these three different grids at the same time; yet that is precisely what the tri-sociated passenger is trying to do.

Let me repeat: any two universes of discourse can be used to fabricate a joke. Lewis Carroll sent the following contribution to a philosophical symposium:

'Yet what mean all such gaieties to me
Whose life is full of indices and surds?
$$X^2 + 7X + 53$$
$$= 11/3'$$

The universes of verbal and mathematical symbols are linked by pure sound-affinity—with rhyme but without reason. When T. E. Lawrence joined the ranks as Private Shaw, Noël Coward wrote to him that famous letter beginning 'Dear 338171 (may I call you 338?)'.

Man and Animal

In the previous chapter I discussed the bisociation of man and machine; related to it is the hybrid man-animal. Disney's creatures behave as if they were human without losing their animal appearance, they live on the line of intersection of the two planes; so do the cartoonist's piggy or mousy humans. This double-existence is comic, but only so long as the confrontation has the effect of a slightly degrading exposure of one or the other. If sympathy prevails over malice even poor Donald Duck's misfortunes cease to be laughable; and as you move over to the right-hand panel of the triptych, the man-animal undergoes a series of transformations: from the cloying lyricism of Bambi to the tragedy of Orwell's Boxer; from the archetypal menace of the werewolf to the Metamorphosis of Kafka's hero into a filth-devouring cockroach. As for science, the importance of learning about man by the experimental study of animal physiology need not be stressed; in psychology it has been rather overstressed to the point where the salivary reflexes of dogs came to be regarded as paradigmatic for human behaviour.

Impersonation

The various categories of the comic shade into each other: Disney's animals acting like humans could as well be classified under the heading 'imitation, impersonation, and disguise'. The impersonator is two different people at one time. If the result is degrading, the spectator will laugh. If he is led to sympathize or identify himself with the impersonated hero, he will experience that state of split-mindedness known as dramatic illusion or the magic of the stage. Which of the two possibilities will occur depends of course partly on the actor, but ultimately 'a jest's prosperity lies in the ear / Of him that hears it, never in the tongue / Of him that makes it'.[1] The same 'narrative', a Victorian melodrama or a Chinese opera, acted in both cases in precisely the same way, will make some spectators giggle, others weep. The same dramatic devices may serve either a comic or a tragic purpose: Romeo and Juliet are the victims of absurd coincidences, Oedipus's marriage to his mother is due to mistaken identity; Rosalind in *As You Like It* and Leonora in *Fidelio* are both disguised as men, yet in one case the result is drama, in another comedy. The technique of creating character-types is also shared by both: in the classical form of tragedy, whether Greek, Indian, or Japanese, characterization is often achieved by standardized masks; in the comedy, down to Molière, by the creation of types: the miser, the glutton, the hypocrite, the cuckold. In the centre panel (where impersonation appears in the form of empathy, the act of self-projection which enables one to understand others, see below pp. 187-8) the classification of character-types has been the aim of incessant efforts—from the 'four temperaments' of the Greeks, to Kretschmer, Jung, Sheldon, and so on.

The Child-Adult

Why are puppies droll? Firstly, their helplessness, trustingness, attachment, and puzzled expression make them more 'human' than grown-up dogs; in the second place the ferocious growl of the puppy strikes us as an impersonation of adult behaviour (like the little boy with stuck-on beard and bowler-hat, pretending to be the family doctor); thirdly, the puppy's waddling and tumbling makes it a choice victim of nature's practical jokes; furthermore, its bodily disproportions, the huge padded paws, wrinkled brow, and Falstaffian belly, give it the appearance of a caricature; and so on. The delighted laughter which greets the puppy's antics seems so simple to explain; but when we try to analyse it we find several interlocking causes; and while the word 'delighted' indicates a pure emotion, free from the ugly taint of aggressiveness, the grain of self-satisfied condescension, the conviction of our own superiority is nevertheless present, even if we are not aware of it.

A simple shift of emphasis will move the bisociation of child and adult into the centre panel where it becomes a concern of pedagogues and psychiatrists. A further shift to the right, and the relation will be reversed, the child will be seen as an adult in disguise, immersed in the hidden tragedies of the nursery and boarding school—an inexhaustible subject of the autobiographical novel.

The Trivial and the Exalted

Parody is the most aggressive form of impersonation, designed not only to deflate hollow pretence but also to destroy illusion in all its forms; and to undermine pathos by harping on the trivial, all-too-human aspects of the victim. Stage props collapsing, wigs falling off, public speakers forgetting their lines, dramatic gestures remaining suspended in the air—the parodist's favourite points of attack are all situated on the line of intersection between two planes: the Exalted and the Trivial.

The artist reverses this technique by conferring on trivial experiences a new dignity and wonder: Rembrandt painting the carcass of a flayed ox, Manet his skinny, insipid Olympia; Hemingway drawing tragedy out of the repetitive, inarticulate stammer of his characters; Chekhov focussing the reader's attention on a fly crawling on a lump of sugar while Natasha is contemplating suicide.

When 'consciousness is unawares transferred from great things to small'—which Spencer regarded as the prime cause of laughter—the result will be *either* a comic or an aesthetic experience, depending on whether the person's emotions are of the type capable of participating in the transfer or not. The artist, reversing the parodist's technique, walks on a tightrope, as it were, along the line where the exalted and the trivial planes meet; he 'sees with equal eye, as God of all, / A hero perish or a sparrow fall'. The scientist's attitude is basically similar in situations where he suddenly discovers the connection between a banal event and a general law of nature—Newton's apple or the boiling kettle of James Watt.

When F. W. H. Myers became interested in people's attitudes to religion he questioned an elderly widow on what she thought about the whereabouts of her departed husband's soul. She replied: 'Oh well, I suppose he is enjoying eternal bliss, but I wish you wouldn't talk about such unpleasant subjects.' I would call this an illustration of the peaceful coexistence of the tragic and trivial planes in our humble minds. Equally convincing is this statement made by a schoolboy to his mathematics master:

'Infinity is where things happen which don't.'[2]

Caricature and Satire

The political cartoon, at its best, is a translation into visual imagery of a witty topical comment; at its worst, a manipulation of symbols—John Bull, Uncle Sam, the Russian bear—which, once comic, have degenerated into visual clichés. The symbols trigger off memories and expectations; the narrative content of the cartoon is taken in by visual scanning, with possibly a delayed-action effect due to the time needed for 'seeing the joke'. The analysis of such mixed forms is a lengthy affair.*

The portrait caricature, on the other hand, relies for its effects on purely visual means. Its method recalls the distorting mirrors at fun-fairs, which reflect the human form elongated into a candle-shape, or absurdly compressed, or as a vague phantom with wavy outlines. As a result we see ourselves and yet something else; our familiar shapes being transformed as if the body were merely an elastic surface that can be stretched in all directions.

The mirror distorts by exaggerating mechanically in one spatial direction at the expense of others; the caricaturist distorts by exaggerating features which he considers characteristic of his victim's appearance or personality. His second main trick is over-simplification: he minimizes or leaves out features which are not relevant for his purpose. A prominent nose, for instance, such as General de Gaulle's, can be exploited to the extent that the rest of the face shrinks to insignificance: the part has been detached from the whole and has become a nose *an sich*. The product of the clever caricaturist's distortions is something physiologically impossible, yet at the same time visually convincing—he has superimposed his frame of perception on our own. For a caricature is comic only if we know something of the victim, if we have a mental image, however vague, of the person, or type of person, at which it is aimed—even if it is an Eskimo, a cave-man, or a Martian robot. The unknown cannot be distorted or misrepresented. The caricature of the more ferocious type is the rape of an image, an optical debunking of the victim; in its gentler form, a semi-affectionate kick at the heel of Achilles.

Thus the malicious pleasure derived from a good caricature originates in the confrontation of a likeness, distorted according to the artist's rules of the game, with reality or our image thereof. But it is a rather harmless form of malice because we know that the caricaturist's monster with the cucumber nose or enormous belly is a biological impossibility, that it is *not real*. Illustrations of elephantiasis and pathological obesity are not comic because these distortions of the human shape are known to be real, and therefore arouse pity. The knowledge that the deformities of the caricature are merely pretence acquits us of all charitable obligations and allows us to laugh at the victim's expense.

The exaggeration and simplification of features selected according to his judgement of what is to be considered relevant is a technique shared by both the caricaturist and the artist—who calls it stylization. (Needless to say, a caricature is also a form of art; but for convenience' sake I am using throughout this book the term 'art' to refer to its non-comic varieties.) Stylization has been carried to extreme length in a number of ancient and modern art forms without destroying the aesthetic effect: that is to say, without sliding from art into caricature. The elongated skulls of certain Egyptian sculptures reflect a contemporary practice of deforming the princely babies' heads, but they obviously exaggerate the result. Nevertheless it would hardly occur to one to call Tutankhamen an egghead—because one feels that the sculptor exaggerated not with a hostile but with a worshipful intent, and this attitude is communicated to the spectator. Once more the polarity between comic and aesthetic experience is seen to derive from the polarity between the self-assertive and self-transcending tendencies.

This still holds true even when communication between artist and spectator breaks down. In the eyes of the Philistine all experimental art is ludicrous, because the Philistine's attitude is aggressive-defensive. When Picasso shuffles round the eyes and limbs of his figures in a manner which is biologically impossible and yet has a visual logic of its own, he juxtaposes the seen and the known—he is walking, precariously balanced, on the borderline between two universes of experience, each governed by a different code. The conservative-minded spectator, unable to follow, suspects the artist of pulling his leg by deliberately distorting the human shape as the caricaturist does; and so the two-faced woman with three breasts becomes in his eyes a caricature. The ambiguity is perhaps most strikingly illustrated in some of the character-studies by Leonardo, Hogarth, and Daumier. The passions reflected in them are so violent, the grimaces so ferocious, that it is impossible to tell whether they were meant as portraits or caricatures, and the distinction becomes a purely theoretical one. If you feel that such distortions of the human face do not really exist, that Daumier, deliberately exaggerating, merely *pretended* that they exist, then you are absolved from horror and pity and can laugh at his grotesques. But if you feel that this is indeed what Daumier saw in those de-humanized faces, then you are looking at a work of art. The humorist thrives on deformity; the artist deforms the world to re-create it in his own image.

The technique of exaggerating the relevant and simplifying or ignoring the irrelevant aspects of reality is shared not only by the artist and caricaturist but is equally indispensable to the scientist. The motivations of each of the three differ, of course, and with them their criteria of relevance. The humorist's motives are aggressive, the artist's participatory, the scientist's exploratory. The scientist's criteria of relevance are 'objective' in the sense of being emotionally neutral, but they still depend on the particular aspect of reality in which he is interested. Every drawing on the blackboard—whether it is meant to represent the wiring diagram of a radio set or the circulation of the blood, the structure of a molecule or the weather over the Atlantic—is based on the same method as the cartoonist's: selective emphasis on the relevant factors and omission of the rest. A map bears the same relation to a landscape as a character-sketch to a face; every chart, diagram, or model, every schematic or symbolic representation of physical or mental processes, is an unemotional caricature of reality. At least, 'unemotional' in the sense that the bias is not of an obvious kind; although some models of the universe as a rigid, mechanical clockwork which, once wound up, must follow its unalterable course, or of the human mind as a slot-machine, have turned out to be crude caricatures inspired by unconscious bias.

The *satire* is a verbal caricature which distorts characteristic features of an individual or society by exaggeration and simplification. The features picked out for enlargement by the satirist are, of course, those of which he disapproves: 'If Nature's inspiration fails', wrote Juvenal, 'indignation will beget the poem.' The comic effect of the satire is derived from the simultaneous presence, in the reader's mind, of the social reality with which he is familiar, and of its reflection in the distorting mirror of the satirist. It focusses attention on abuses and deformities in society of which, blunted by habit, we were no longer aware; it makes us suddenly discover the absurdity of the familiar and the familiarity of the absurd.

The same effect is achieved if, instead of magnifying objectionable features in customs and institutions, the satirist projects them by means of the *allegory* onto a different background, such as an animal society— e.g. Aristophanes, Swift, Orwell. In either case we are made suddenly conscious of conventions and prejudices which we have unquestioningly accepted, which were tacitly implied in the codes in control of our thinking and behaviour. The confrontation with an alien matrix reveals in a sharp, pitiless light what we failed to see in following our dim routines; the tacit assumptions hidden in the rules of the game are dragged into the open. The bisociative shock shatters the frame of complacent habits of thinking; the seemingly obvious is made to yield its secret.

'In this world of perfect justice, rich and poor alike have the right to sleep under bridges.' Anatole France's classic epigram is a confrontation of abstract democracy with the brutal facts of life; it conjures up the image of a well-dressed *bourgeois* making use of his constitutional rights to doss down, in the name of *Liberté*, *Egalité*, and *Fraternité*, under the arches of the Pont de la Concorde. In its higher reaches the satirist's art merges into the social scientist's quest for truth; *Brave New World* and *1984* are extrapolations of present trends into the future; *Gulliver's Travels* and *Erewhon*, on the other hand, follow the method of the anthropologist, who deepens our understanding of our own society by confronting it with the equally 'self-evident' beliefs and customs of exotic civilizations.

Thus, as we travel across the triptych, satire shades into social science; and this, in turn, branches out into the tragic allegory—Plato's Cave and Kafka's Castle—or into poetic Utopia. The artistic hazards of the latter are perhaps due to a conflict of emotions. Writers of Utopias are motivated by revulsion against society as it is, or at least by a rejection of its values; and since revulsion and rejection are aggressive attitudes, it comes more naturally to them to paint a picture of society with a brush dipped in adrenalin than in syrup or aspirin. Hence the contrast between Huxley's brilliant, bitter *Brave New World* and the goody-goody bores on his *Island*.

The satirist's most effective weapon is *irony*. Its aim is to defeat the opponent on his own ground by pretending to accept his premises, his values, his methods of reasoning, in order to expose their implicit absurdity. 'All animals are equal, but some are more equal than others.' Irony purports to take seriously what it does not; it enters into the spirit of the other person's game to demonstrate that its rules are stupid or vicious. It is a subtle weapon, because the person who wields it must have the imaginative power of seeing through the eyes of his opponent, of projecting himself into the other's mental world. The psychiatrist who goes patiently along with the patient's fantasies, the teacher who adapts his language to the level of comprehension of the child, the dramatist who speaks through his characters' voices, employ the same procedure with the opposite intent and effect.

The Misfit

Both Cicero and Francis Bacon gave deformity a high place on their lists of causes for laughter. The princes of the Renaissance collected midgets, hunchbacks, monsters, and Blackamoors for their merriment. We have become too civilized for that kind of thing, but children still jeer and laugh at people with a limp or a stammer, at foreigners with a funny pronunciation, at people oddly dressed—at any form of appearance or behaviour which deviates from the familiar norm. The more backwoodish a social group, juvenile or adult, the stricter its conception of the normal, and the readier it will ridicule any departure from it.

Consider for a moment the curious fact that to a civilized person a stutterer causes sympathetic embarrassment, whereas a person of normal speech giving an imitation of stuttering makes us laugh. So does the youngster in love who stutters only under the effect of a momentary surge of emotion. Again, a person with a foreign accent is accepted with tolerance, but the imitation of a foreign accent is comic. The explanation is that we know the imitator's stutter or mis-prononunciation to be mere pretence; this makes sympathy both un-necessary and impossible, and enables us to be childishly cruel with a clear conscience. We have met the same phenomenon (page 71) in our attitude towards the bodily deformities imputed by the caricaturist to his victim.

The tolerant acceptance of physical or mental malformations in our fellow creatures, though of relatively recent origin, has become deeply engrained in Western society; we are no longer aware of the fact that it requires a certain imagination and a good deal of empathy to recognize in a dwarf, or a 'thick-lipped Blackamoor', a human being which, though different in appearance, exists and feels as one-self does. In the small child this kind of projective mechanism is absent or rudimentary. Piaget, among others, has strikingly shown how late the child accords to its fellow beings a conscious ego like its own. The more a person deviates from the familiar norm of the child's surroundings, the more difficult it is for the child to project into him life and feelings, to grant him the faculty of having experiences like his own. The same applies to the attitudes shown by tribal or parochial societies to foreigners, slaves, members of the 'lower classes' (almost inevitably treated as comic figures in literature up to and including Dickens); as well as to criminals, the mentally disordered and physically deformed. The creature who does not 'belong' to the tribe, clan, caste, or parish is not really human; he only aspires or pretends to be 'like us'. To civilized man, a dwarf is comic only if he struts about pretending to be tall, which he is not; in the primitive's eye the dwarf is comic because he pretends to be human, which he is not. The Greek word 'barbarian' means both foreigner and stutterer (bar-bar-ous); the uncouth, repetitive, barking sounds he uttered were a grotesque imitation of true human speech. Bodily and functional deformities are laughable to the uncouth mind for the same reasons as impersonation and caricature.

The Paradox of the Centipede

However, an additional factor enters into the comic effect of some disorders of behaviour such as stuttering, mispronunciation, misspelling: one might call it the bisociation of structure and function, or of part and whole. The stammering barbarian was a comic figure to the Greeks for reasons just mentioned; but the comedian's stage-stutter is funny in a different way. When he struggles with a consonant, trying to take the same hurdle again and again, eyes bulging and face convulsed, we become suddenly aware of the complicated motions of lips and tongue required to produce the sound 'M'; our attention becomes focussed on these physiological details torn from their functional context and placed under a magnifying glass, as it were. Much the same happens when the gramophone needle gets stuck in a groove, and the soprano's voice keeps repeating the same word on the same quaver. The part has become detached from the whole and monopolizes attention as if it existed in its own right, as an independent structural entity, regardless of its function in the larger context from which alone its meaning is derived. In one of Silone's novels an innocent peasant boy from the Abruzzi drifts into a crowd in front of Mussolini's new forum, and cannot understand why everybody keeps chanting in a chorus: '*Ce-du*, *ce-du, ce-du, ce-du* . . .' The isolated quaver or consonant which has made a declaration of independence, the syllables 'du' and 'ce' torn from their context, are examples of the conflict which can arise between part and whole, structure and function, when—to put it in a different way —the dependent part pretends to be an independent whole and forces our attention to regard it as such.

When we exercise a well-practised skill the parts must function smoothly and automatically—they must never occupy the focus of attention. This is true whether the skill in question is riding a bicycle, playing the violin, ennunciating the letter 'M', or forming sentences according to the rules of grammar and syntax. The code which controls the performance functions, as we repeatedly saw, on a lower level of consciousness than the performance itself—on the fringes of awareness or, in completely automatized skills, even beyond the fringe. The moment attention is focussed on a normally auto-matized part-function such as ennunciating consonants, the matrix breaks down, the needle gets stuck, and the performance is paralysed— like the centipede who was asked in which order he moved his hundred legs, and could walk no more.

The paradox of the centipede is a consequence of the hierarchic organization of the nervous system which demands that the highest centres should be occupied with the task in hand conceived as a whole, and leave the execution of the component sub-tasks and sub-sub-tasks to the sub-centres, etc., on lower levels of the nervous system. A brigadier does not give orders to, and concentrate his attention on, individual soldiers during action; if he does the action goes haywire. The paradox of the centipede will be seen to play an important part in discovery and the theory of thinking in general; in humour, apart from the examples mentioned, it accounts for the comic effect of the 'self-conscious' (in fact, detail-conscious) behaviour of the person who does not know what to do with his hands; and also explains why the comedian's clothes, and some foreign or bygone fashions, are funny. Conventional articles of apparel are perceived as parts of a person's appearance as a whole, whereas the comedian's checked trousers and the Victorian lady's bustle disrupt the unity and force attention on textiles and starched draperies leading an independent life. Except when we are in a romantic mood: then a historical costume on the stage is no longer seen detached from its wearer but attaches him to the period.

Since I mentioned mispronunciation, I must add the obvious remark that if the maltreated word assumes a different meaning, we get the involuntary pun; and even if it does not, mispronunciation can be funny if it follows its own logic which exposes the absurdities of conventional spelling. Try on an innocent foreigner the sequence: a coughing plough and a soughing trough; then see what happens.

Displacement

A car dealer is boosting a new sports model to a prospective client:

'You get into this car at midnight and at 4 a.m. you are in Grimsby.'

The customer is indignant: 'And what am I to do in the middle of the night in *Grimsby*?'

The question is perfectly logical, but irrelevant to the subject under discussion, which is the speed of the car. The link-concept is 'Grimsby at 4 a.m.'—which in one context plays the accidental part of an improvised example, in the second an essential part. This sudden shift of emphasis—or displacement of attention—to a seemingly irrelevant aspect of a bisociated concept is frequently found not only in humour, but also in art and discovery (Chapters VIII, XXIII). It is related to the paradox of the centipede, but instead of displacing attention from the *whole* to the *part* it is displaced from a dominant to a previously *neglected aspect* of the whole, showing it in a new light.

In the *Ballad of Reading Gaol* there are two unforgettable lines:

> How else but through a broken heart
> May Lord Christ enter in?

The broken heart has become such a cliché that its physical implications—splitting apart and creating a gap—are never thought of. Wilde shifts our attention to that forgotten physical image; he lets salvation enter through the aching gap, like a thief in the night. When the White

Queen complains: 'It's a poor sort of memory which only works backwards,' she is putting her finger on an aspect of reality—the irreversibility of time—which we normally take for granted; her apparently silly remark carries metaphysical intimations, and appeals to our secret yearning for the gift of prophecy—matters which would never occur to Alice, that little paragon of stubborn common sense.

Coincidence

It was once usual to classify comedies into those relying on situations, manners, or characters. In his discussion of the first, Bergson came closest to the essence of humour: 'A situation is always comic', he wrote, 'if it participates simultaneously in two series of events which are absolutely independent of each other, and if it can be interpreted in two quite different meanings.' One feels like crying 'Fire', but a couple of pages further on Bergson has dropped the clue and gone back to his hobby: the interference of two independent series in a given situation is merely a further example of the 'mechanization of life'.

In fact the crossing of two independent causal chains through coincidence, mistaken identity, confusion of time and occasion, is the most clean-cut example of bisociated contexts. The chance-coincidence on which they are hinged is the *deus ex machina*, the intervention of providence in both tragedy and comedy; and, needless to say, lucky hazards play an equally conspicuous part in the history of scientific discovery.

Nonsense

One type of comic verse lives on the bisociation of exalted form with trivial content. Certain metric forms, such as hexameter and Alexandrine, arouse expectations of pathos, of the heroic and exalted; the pouring of homely, trivial contents into these epic moulds—'beautiful soup, so rich and green'—creates a comic effect of the same type as the parody. The rolling dactyls of the first line of the limerick, carrying, instead of Hector and Achilles, a young lady from Stockton as their passenger, make her already appear ridiculous, regardless of the calamities which are sure to befall her. In this atmosphere of malicious expectation whatever witticism the text has to offer will have a much enhanced effect.

Instead of an epic mould, a soft, lyrical one will equally do:

> ... And what could be moister
> Than tears from an oyster?

Another variant is what one might call the pseudo-proverb: 'The rule is: jam tomorrow and jam yesterday—but never jam today.' Two logically incompatible statements have been telescoped into a line whose rhythm and syntax gives the impression of being a popular adage or golden rule of life. Sometimes the trick is done by the sub-stitution of a single word in a familiar text: 'One should never work between meals.' The homely, admonitory structure lulls the mind into bored acquiescence until the preposterous subterfuge is discovered. Oscar Wilde was a master of this form: 'In married life three is com-pany and two none'; 'the only way to get rid of a temptation is to yield to it', etc., etc. My own favourite coinage is: 'One should not carry moderation to extremes.'

Nonsense humour—as Max Eastman has pointed out—is only effective if it pretends to make sense: 'It's a fact the whole world knows That Pobbles are happier without their toes.' Even with rhymed gibberish the illusion of meaning is essential. 'The slithy toves' that 'gyre and gimble in the wabe' evoke sound associations which suggest some kind of action even though we are unable to say what exactly the action is—perhaps some small creatures gyrating and gambolling on a brilliant day in the web of some flowery bush. The meaning varies with the person as the interpretation of the ink blots in a Rohrschach test; but without this illusory meaning projected into the phonetic pattern, without the simultaneous knowledge of being fooled, and of fooling oneself, there would be no enjoyment of 'the jabberwock with eyes of flame' who 'came whiffling through the tulgey wood / And burbled as it came'.

Tickling

The harmless game of tickling has resisted all attempts to find a unitary formula for the causes of laughter; it has been the stumbling block which made the theorists of the comic give up, or their theories break down.

It was at one time believed that the laughter caused by tickling is a purely mechanical reflex in response to a purely physical stimulation.

But—as Darwin has pointed out—the response to tickling is squirming, wriggling, and straining to withdraw the tickled part— activities which may or may not be accompanied by laughter. The squirming response was interpreted by Darwin and Crile as an innate defence mechanism to escape a hostile grip on vulnerable areas which are not normally exposed to attack: the soles of the feet, the neck, arm-pits, belly, and flank. If a fly settles on the belly of a horse a kind of contractile wave may pass over the skin—the equivalent of the squirming of the tickled child. But the horse does not laugh when tickled, and the child not always. As Gregory has put it:

A child fingers the pepper-pot, waves pepper into its nose, and sneezes violently. Touch it under the arm-pits, or finger its waist, and it wriggles vigorously. It sneezes to dislodge the pepper from its nose, and its wriggle suggests a sneeze to relieve its whole body. The violent squirm of the tickled child so obviously tries to avoid the tickling hand that, when the truth is perceived, it is difficult to understand how tickling and laughter could ever be identified or confused.[3]

Thus tickling a child will call out a wriggling and squirming response. But the child will laugh only—and this is the crux of the matter—if an additional condition is fulfilled: it must perceive the tickling *as a mock attack*, a caress in a mildly aggressive disguise. This explains why people laugh only when tickled by others but not when they tickle themselves. (The question why this should be so was once put to a B.B.C. Brains Trust which, after some humming, hawing, and giggling, decided that it was one of the insoluble mysteries of human nature.) Not only must there be a second person to do the tickling, but her expression and attitude must be mock-aggressive—as mothers and nurses instinctively know. Battle cries like 'peekaboo' and 'bow-wow' pay guaranteed dividends, like the comedian's imitation of the lion's roar. As in every attack, the element of surprise plays an important part: the expert tickler's tactics never let the victim guess when and where the next pressure or pincer movement will occur. Experiments in tickling on babies under one year old showed that babies laughed fifteen times more often when tickled by their mothers than when they were tickled by strangers. For naturally the mock-attack will make the baby laugh only if it knows that it is a mock-attack; and with strangers one never knows. Even with its own mothe there is an ever-so-slight feeling of uncertainty and apprehension, the expression of which alternates with laughter in the baby's behaviour; and it is precisely this element of apprehension between two tickles which is relieved in the laughter accompanying the squirm. The rule of the game is 'let me be just a little frightened so that I can enjoy the relief'.

Thus the mechanism is essentially the same as in comic impersonation: the tickler impersonates an aggressor, but is simultaneously known not to be one. It is probably the first situation encountered in life which makes the infant live on two planes at once, the first delectable experience in bisociation—a foretaste of pleasures to come at the pantomime show, of becoming a willing victim to the illusions of the stage, of being tickled by the horror-thriller.

In adolescence, erotic elements enter into the game, and tickling assumes the role of a sexual mock-attack—acknowledged with giggles which betray their origin in infantile apprehensions. Some homosexuals claim to be extremely ticklish and display a tendency to squirming and wriggling as an expression of mock-fright. But these are secondary developments which partly illuminate, partly confuse the original pattern—the tickled child's laughter is a discharge of apprehensions recognized as unfounded by the intellect.

The Clown

Most of the comic techniques I have discussed can be found in the repertory of the circus clown—the classic incarnation of the coarser type of humour. His face is a richly exaggerated caricature of stupidity, sometimes with an infectious grimace of laughter painted on it; in each piece of his apparel form battles against function; each of his movements is a parody of grace. He is the victim and perpetrator of preposterous practical jokes; he is both human and inert matter, for to survive all the slaps, whacks, and cracks, his skull must be made of ebony. He is the image in the distorting mirror, the clumsy impersonator of acrobats, ballet dancers, and fairies: Caliban imitating Ariel. He is a collection of deformities, bodily and functional; he stumbles over obstacles and words; he is timid, gauche, eccentric, and absentminded. Above all, he is the man of gigantic efforts and diminutive accomplishments: the midwife who aids the mountain to deliver the mouse.

The clown's domain is the coarse, rich, overt type of humour: he leaves nothing to be guessed, he piles it on. A good deal of the enjoyment he causes is a mild gloating, the discharge of sadistic, sexual, scatalogical impulses by way of the purifying channels of laughter. One means of producing and prolonging this effect is *repetition*. The clown and the clowning kind of music-hall comedian will tell, or act out, a long-drawn narrative in which the same type of flash, the same pattern, the same situation, the same key-words, recur again and again. Although repetition diminishes the effect of surprise, it has a cumulative effect on the emotive charge. The logical pattern is the same in each repeat, but new tension is easily drawn into the familiar channel. It is as if more and more liquid were being pumped into the same punctured pipeline.

Originality, Emphasis, Economy

I have discussed the logic of humour and its emotive dynamics, and have tried to indicate how to analyse a joke. But nothing has been said so far about the criteria which decide whether it is a good, bad, or indifferent joke. These are, of course, partly a matter of personal taste, partly dependent on the technique of the humorist; only the second is our concern.

There are, I shall suggest, three main criteria of comic technique: originality, emphasis, and economy. In the light of the previous chapters we shall expect them to play also a significant part in the techniques of scientific theorizing and artistic creation.

An art dealer (this story is authentic) bought a canvas signed 'Picasso' and travelled all the way to Cannes to discover whether it was genuine. Picasso was working in his studio. He cast a single look at the canvas and said: 'It's a fake'.

A few months later the dealer bought another canvas signed Picasso. Again he travelled to Cannes and again Picasso, after a single glance, grunted: 'It's a fake.'

'But *cher maître*,' expostulated the dealer, 'it so happens that I saw you with my own eyes working on this very picture several years ago.'

Picasso shrugged: 'I often paint fakes.'

One measure of originality is its surprise effect. Picasso's reply—as the Marquis' in the Chamfort story—is truly unexpected; with its perverse logic, it cuts through the narrative like the blade of the guillotine.

But creative originality is not so often met with either in art or in humour. One substitute for it is suggestiveness through *emphasis*. The cheap comedian piles it on; the competent craftsman plays in a subtler way on our memories and habits of thought. Whenever in the *Contes Drolatiques* Balzac introduces an abbé or a monk, our associations race ahead of the narrative in the delectable expectation of some venal sin to be committed; yet when the point of the story is reached we still smile, sharing the narrator's mock-indignation and pretended surprise. In other words, anticipations of the type of joke or point to come do not entirely destroy the comic effect, provided that we do not know when and how exactly it will strike home. It is rather like a game: cover my eyes and I shall pretend to be surprised. Besides, the laughter provoked by spicy jokes is, as already said, only partly genuine, partly a cloak to cover publicly less demonstrable emotions —regardless whether the story in itself is comic or not.

Suggestive techniques are essential; they create suspense and facilitate the listener's flow of associations along habit-formed channels. A comic idea of a given logical pattern can be transposed into any number of different settings; local colour and dialect help to establish the atmosphere. The most effective stories are regional: Scottish, Marseillais, Cockney; the mere mention of 'a man from Aberdeen' establishes the matrix, the desired frame of mind. Thus suggestiveness depends firstly on *the choice of relevant stimuli*—as the biologist would say. Next, all non-essential elements should be omitted, even at the price of a certain sketchiness, otherwise attention will be sidetracked, the tension frittered away: this is the technique of *simplification*. In the third place the effect is increased by certain emphatic gestures, inflections, a stress on dialect and slang: in a word, by *exaggeration*. We have met these three related factors: selection, exaggeration, simplification, in the technique of the caricature (and of the portrait and blue-print); taken together they provide the means of highlighting aspects of reality considered to be significant. It is not surprising that the same techniques enter into the artist's and humorist's efforts to communicate with his audience.

However, except in the coarsest type of humour and the trashiest forms of art, suggestion through emphasis is not enough; and it can defeat its own purpose. It must be compensated by the opposite kind of virtue: the exercise of *economy*, or, more precisely: the technique of *implication*.

Picasso's 'I often paint fakes' is at the same time original, emphatic, and implicit. He does not say: 'Sometimes, like other painters, I do something second-rate, repetitive, an uninspired variation on a theme, which after a while looks to me as if somebody had imitated my technique. It is true that this somebody happened to be myself, but that makes no difference to the quality of the picture, which is no better than if it were a fake; in fact you could call it that—an uninspired Picasso apeing the style of the true Picasso.'

None of this was said; all of it was implied. But the listener has to work out by himself what is implied in the laconic hint; he has to make an imaginative effort to solve the riddle. If the answer were explicitly given, on the lines indicated in the previous paragraph, the listener would be both spared the effort and deprived of its reward; there would be no anecdote to tell.

To a sophisticated audience any joke sounds stale if it is entirely explicit. If this is the case the listener's thoughts will move faster than the narrator's tale or the unfolding of the plot; instead of tension it will generate boredom. 'Economy' in this sense means the use of hints in lieu of statements; instead of moving steadily on, the narrative jumps ahead, leaving logical gaps which the listener has to bridge by his own effort: he is forced to co-operate.

The operation of bridging a logical gap by inserting the missing links is called *interpolation*. The series A, C, E, . . . K, M, O shows a gap which is filled by interpolating G and I. On the other hand, I can extend or *extrapolate* the series by adding to it R, T, V, etc. In the more sophisticated forms of humour the listener must always perform either or both of these operations before he can 'see the joke'. Take this venerable example, quoted by Freud:

> The Prince, travelling through his domains, noticed a man in the cheering crowd who bore a striking resemblance to himself. He beckoned him over and asked: 'Was your mother ever employed in my palace?'
>
> 'No, Sire,' the man replied. 'But my father was.'

The logical pattern of the story is quite primitive. Two implied codes of behaviour are brought into collision: feudal lords were supposed to have bastards; feudal ladies were not supposed to have bastards; and there is a particularly neat, quasi-geometrical link provided by the reversible symmetry of the situation. The mild amusement which the story offers is partly derived from the malicious pleasure we take in the Prince's discomfiture; but mainly from the fact that it is put in the form of a riddle, of two oblique hints which the listener must complete under his own steam, as it were. The dotted lines in the figure below indicate the process (the arrow in M_1 may be taken to represent the Prince's question, the other arrow, the reply).

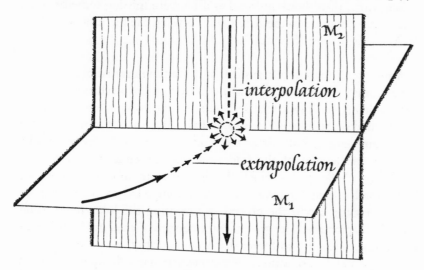

FIGURE 5

Incidentally, Wilde has coined a terser variation on the same theme: '*Lord Illingworth:* "You should study the Peerage, Gerald. . . . It is the best thing in fiction the English have ever done." '

Nearly all the stories that I have quoted show the technique of implication—the hint, the oblique allusion—in varying degrees: the good little boy who loves his mama; the man who never aimed as high as that; the kind sadist, etc. Apart from inter- and extrapolation (there is no need for our purposes to make a distinction between them) a third type of operation is often needed to enable one to 'see the joke': *transformation*, or reinterpretation, of the given data into some analogous terms. These operations comprise the transformation of metaphorical into literal statements, of verbal hints into visual terms, and the interpretation of visual riddles of the *New Yorker* cartoon type. A good example ('good', I am afraid, only from a theoretical point of view) is provided by another story, quoted from Freud:

> Two shady business men have succeeded in making a fortune and were trying to elbow their way into Society. They had their portraits painted by a fashionable artist; framed in gold, these were shown at a reception in the grand style. Among the guests was a well-known art critic. The beaming hosts led him to the wall on which the two portraits were hanging side by side. The critic looked at them for a long time, then shook his head as if he were missing something. At length he pointed to the bare space between the pictures and asked: 'And where is the Saviour?'

A nice combination of transformation with interpolation.

Economy, in humour as in art, does not mean mechanical brevity but implicitness. 'Implicit' is derived from the Latin word for 'folded in'. To make a joke like Picasso's 'unfold', the listener must fill in the gaps, complete the hints, trace the hidden analogies. Every good joke contains an element of the riddle—it may be childishly simple, or subtle and challenging—which the listener must solve. By doing so, he is lifted out of his passive role and compelled to co-operate, to repeat to some extent the process of inventing the joke, to re-create it in his imagination. The type of entertainment dished out by the mass media makes one apt to forget that true recreation is re-creation.

Emphasis and implication are complementary techniques. The first bullies the audience into acceptance; the second entices it into mental collaboration; the first forces the offer down the consumer's throat; the second tantalizes, to whet his appetite.

In fact, both techniques have their roots in the basic mechanisms of communicating thoughts by word or sign. Language itself is never completely explicit. Words have suggestive, evocative powers; but at the same time they are merely stepping stones for thought. Economy means spacing them at intervals just wide enough to require a significant effort from the receiver of the message; the artist rules his subjects by turning them into accomplices.

NOTE

To p. 70. Cf. the analysis of an Osbert Lancaster cartoon in *Insight and Outlook*, p. 80 f.

IV

FROM HUMOUR TO DISCOVERY

Explosion and Catharsis

Primitive jokes arouse crude, aggressive, or sexual emotions by means of a minimum of ingenuity. But even the coarse laughter in which these emotions are exploded often contains an additional element of admiration for the cleverness of the joke—and also of satisfaction with one's own cleverness in seeing the joke. Let us call this additional element of admiration plus self-congratulation the intellectual gratification offered by the joke.

Satisfaction presupposes the existence of a need or appetite. Intellectual curiosity, the desire to understand, is derived from an urge as basic as hunger or sex: the exploratory drive (see below, XI, and Book Two, VIII). It is the driving power which makes the rat learn to find its way through the experimental maze without any obvious incentive being offered in the form of reward or punishment; and also the prime-mover behind human exploration and research. Its 'detached' and 'disinterested' character—the scientists' self-transcending absorption in the riddles of nature—is, of course, often combined with ambition, competition, vanity. But these self-assertive tendencies must be restrained and highly sublimated to find fulfilment in the mostly unspectacular rewards of his slow and patient labours. There are, after all, more direct methods of asserting one's ego than the analysis of ribonucleic acids.

When I called discovery the emotionally 'neutral' art I did not mean by neutrality the absence of emotion—which would be equivalent to apathy—but that nicely balanced and sublimated blend of motivations, where self-assertiveness is harnessed to the task; and where on the other hand heady speculations about the Mysteries of Nature must be submitted to the rigours of objective verification.

We shall see that there are two sides to the manifestation of emotions at the moment of discovery, which reflect this polarity of motivations.

One is the triumphant explosion of tension which has suddenly become redundant since the problem is solved—so you jump out of your bath and run through the streets laughing and shouting Eureka! In the second place there is the slowly fading after-glow, the gradual catharsis of the self-transcending emotions—a quiet, contemplative delight in the truth which the discovery revealed, closely related to the artist's experience of beauty. The Eureka cry is the explosion of energies which must find an outlet since the purpose for which they have been mobilized no longer exists; the carthartic reaction is an inward un-folding of a kind of 'oceanic feeling', and its slow ebbing away. The first is due to the fact that 'I' made a discovery; the second to the fact that a discovery has been made, a fraction of the infinite revealed. The first tends to produce a state of physical agitation related to laughter; the second tends towards quietude, the 'earthing' of emotion, some-times a peaceful overflow of tears. The reasons for this contrast will be discussed later; for the time being, let us remember that, physiologically speaking, the self-assertive tendencies operate through the massive sympathico-adrenal system which galvanizes the body into activity—whereas the self-transcending emotions have no comparable trigger-mechanism at their disposal, and their bodily manifestations are in every respect the opposite of the former: pulse and breathing are slowed down, the muscles relax, the whole organism tends towards tranquillity and catharsis. Accordingly, this class of emotions is devoid of the inertial momentum which makes the rage-fear type of reactions so often fall out of step with reasoning; the participatory emotions do not become dissociated from thought. Rage is immune to understand-ing; love of the self-transcending variety is based on understanding, and cannot be separated from it.

Thus the impact of a sudden, bisociative surprise which makes reasoning perform a somersault will have a twofold effect: part of the tension will become detached from it and exploded while the remain-ing part will slowly ebb away. The symbols

FIGURE 6

on the triptych are meant to refer to these two modes of the discharge of tension: the *explosion* of the aggressive-defensive and the gradual *catharsis*, or 'earthing', of the participatory emotions.

'Seeing the Joke' and 'Solving the Problem'

The dual manifestation of emotions at the moment of discovery is reflected on a minor and trivial scale in our reactions to a clever joke. The pleasant after-glow of admiration and intellectual satisfaction, gradually fading, reflects the cathartic reaction; while the self-congratulatory impulse—a faint echo of the Eureka cry—supplies added voltage to the original charge detonated in laughter: that 'sudden glory' (as Hobbes has it) 'arising out of our own eminency'.

Let our imagination travel once more across the triptych of creative activities, from left to right, as it were. We can do this, as we have seen, by taking a short-cut from one wing to another, from the comic to the tragic or sublime; or alternatively by following the gradual transitions which lead from the left to the centre panel.

On the extreme left of the continuum—the infra-red end of the emotive spectrum—we found the practical joke, the smutty story, the lavatory humour of children, each with a heavy aggressive or sexual or scatalogical load (which may be partly unconscious); and with a logical structure so obvious that it required only a minimum of intellectual effort to 'see the joke'. Put into a formula, we could say that the ratio A : I—where A stands for crude emotion, and I for intellectual stimulation—is heavily loaded in favour of the former.

As we move across the panel towards the right, this ratio changes, and is ultimately reversed. In the higher forms of comedy, satire, and irony the message is couched in implicit and oblique terms; the joke gradually assumes the character of an epigram or riddle, the witticism becomes a challenge to our wits:

'Psychoanalysis is the disease for which it pretends to be the cure.'

'Philosophy is the systematic abuse of a terminology specially invented for that purpose.'

'Statistics are like a bikini. What they reveal is suggestive. What they conceal is vital.'

Or, Heine's description of a young virgin:

'Her face is like a palimpsest—beneath the Gothic lettering of the monk's sacred text lurks the pagan poet's half-effaced erotic verse.'

The crude aggression of the practical joke has been sublimated into malicious ingenuity; gross sexuality into subtle eroticism. Incidentally, if I had not mentioned that the last quotation was by Heine, whose name combined with 'virgin' arouses ominous expectations, but had pretended instead that it was from a novel by D. H. Lawrence, it would probably have impressed the reader as profoundly poetic instead of malicious—a short-cut from wing to wing, by reversal of the charge from minus to plus. Again, imagine for a moment that the quotation occurred in an essay by a Jungian psychologist—and it will turn into an emotionally neutral illustration of 'the intrusion of archetypes into perception'.

In cases like this the wording of the narrative (or the picture on the canvas) can remain unaltered, and its transformation from a comic into a poetic or intellectually enlightening message depends entirely on the subjective attitude of the percipient.* However, the lines of correspondence across the panels are meant to indicate more general *patterns* of creative activity. Thus, as we move from coarse humour towards the neutral zone, we find the bisociation of *sound and meaning* first exemplified in the pun, then in word games (ranging from the crossword puzzle to the decyphering of the Rosetta stone); lastly in alliteration, asonance, and rhyme. The *mind-matter* theme we found expressed in countless variations on all three panels; and each variation of it—the puppet on strings or Jack-in-the-Box—was again seen as tri-valent. *Impersonation* is used both in comedy and tragedy; but in between them the medicine man in his mask, the cassocked priest in the confessional, the psychiatrist in the role of the father, each impersonate a person or power other than himself. The distorting mirror, with its emphasis on one significant aspect to the exclusion of others, is used alike in the *caricature* and in the scientist's diagrams and schemata; when Clavdia in the *Magic Mountain* offers her lover an X-ray portrait of her chest as a souvenir we hardly know on which of the three panels we are. Nor can we draw a sharp line between social satire and sociological discovery: *Animal Farm* and *1984* taught a whole generation more about the nature of totalitarianism than academic science did. One last example:

In 1960 an anecdote in the form of an imaginary dialogue circulated in the satellite countries of the East:

'Tell me, Comrade, what is capitalism?'
'The exploitation of man by man.'
'And what is Communism?'
'The reverse.'

.   .   .   .   .

The *double entendre* on 'reverse'—'it *pretends* to be the opposite, but it comes down to the same, only the exploiting is done by a different gang'—casts a new, sharp light on a hoary problem; it has the same power of sudden illumination as an epigram by Voltaire.

Similar borderline cases are brain-twisters, logical paradoxes, mathematical games. Even chess problems can be both 'witty' and 'funny' if they contain some sudden reversal of logic, an ironical twist, or an affront to chess common sense; the connoisseur will smile, or even laugh, when he is shown the solution, and the tension suddenly snaps. His laughter may signify 'how stupid of me not to have seen it' or 'not to have seen it at once' or 'how clever of me', etc. To distinguish between these cases would be splitting hairs, for the basic process is the same: the tension has been dissociated from its original purpose and must find some other outlet. When the string of the guitar snaps it gives out a twang—for precisely the same reason.

But this tension is no longer comparable to the emotions aroused in the grosser types of humour. The intellectual challenge, which in the coarse joke played such a subsidiary part, now dominates the picture; the A : I ratio has been reversed. There may be vanity and competitiveness in rising to the challenge; but they are sublimated and held in balance by a self-forgetting absorption in the problem.

As we cross the fluid boundary leading into the central panel of the triptych, the task of 'seeing the joke' becomes the task of 'solving the problem'. And when we succeed we no longer roar with laughter as at the clown's antics; laughter gradually shades into an amused, then an admiring smile—reflecting the harmonic balance of opposites, the sudden glory and quiet glow of intellectual satisfaction.

The Creation of Humour

Up to now I have been discussing the effects of humour on the audience: the reader, listener, spectator. Let me turn from the consumer's reactions to the processes which go in on the mind of the producer—the inventor of the joke, the creator of humour.

Humour depends primarily on its surprise effect: the bisociative shock. To cause surprise the humorist must have a modicum of originality—the ability to break away from the stereotyped routines of thought. Caricaturist, satirist, the writer of nonsense-humour, and even the expert tickler, each operates on more than one plane. Whether his purpose is to convey a social message, or merely to entertain, he must provide mental jolts, caused by the collision of incompatible matrices. To any given situation or subject he must conjure up an appropriate— or appropriately inappropriate—intruder which will provide the jolt.

The first schoolboy to have the idea of sawing through the legs of the master's chair must have been a genius (such practices were not uncommon in my school-days in Hungary). His habitual outlets for aggression being barred by the heavy penalties they would entail, he must have been labouring under a creative stress which initiated his search for an original solution of his problem. A chance observation— like the fall of Newton's apple—may have provided the link to a different frame of reference, where the object of his resentment was merely a mass subject to the pull of gravity. Now all he had to do was to transfer the scene of operations from the blocked matrix M_1 to this auxiliary matrix M_2. If this sounds facetious let us remember that Bergson's theory of humour is based on this single facet.

In all forms of malicious wit there is an aggressive tendency at work which, for one reason or another, cannot be satisfied by the usual methods of reasoned argument, physical violence, or straight invective. I shall call a matrix 'blocked' when its 'rules of the game' prove inapplicable to the existing situation or problem in hand; when none of the various ways of exercising a skill, however plastic and adaptable that skill is, leads to the desired goal. The young officer in the Viennese anecdote, resenting the courtesan's pretentious reply, is in the same position as the frustrated schoolboy: he cannot reply: 'Come off the high horse, I know that cash is all that matters to you,' without incurring the penalties of vulgarity. Chamfort's Marquis cannot kill the Bishop—it would be an unpardonable lack of *savoir-faire*. Picasso cannot tell the dealer that he is an insufferable bore who does not know a Kokoschka from a Klee; that would be unkind.

But how do they discover the inspired reposte which saves the situation? It sounds a simple question, but if psychology knew the answer to it there would be no point in writing this book.

As a first step let us note a trivial fact: the officer's mental leap from the metaphorical to the literal plane indicates a phenomenon already discussed: the *displacement of attention* to a seemingly irrelevant feature —in this case from the poetic connotations of the lady's heart to its concrete spatial location. (We remember that Wilde used a similar displacement effect for a different purpose in 'How else but through a broken heart . . .'). The Marquis achieves his aim—to kill by ridicule—

by transferring his attention from the glaringly obvious consideration that the Bishop is usurping his *privileges*, to an irrelevant side-line—that he is doing another man's *job*; as if the issue were a demarcation dispute between the Boilermakers' and the Shipwrights' Unions on who should drill the holes.

Thus in some of the cases we have discussed, the solution is arrived at by a kind of 'thinking aside', a shift of attention to some feature of the situation, or an aspect of the problem, which was previously ignored, or only present on the fringes of awareness. The humorist may stumble on it by chance; or, more likely, guided by some intuition which he is unable to define. This gives us a first intimation of unconscious processes intervening in the creative act. The humorist's achievement, represented on the neat diagrams in previous chapters, appears as an exercise in pure intellectual geometry: 'Construct two planes inclined at a given angle and generate two curves which intersect in a given point.' In actual fact, however, the bisociative act, in humour as in other branches of creativity, depends in varying degrees on assistance from fringe-conscious or unconscious processes. Picasso's illuminating grunt was certainly inspired by a process of this kind. On the other hand, the mediocre cartoonist and other professional craftsmen of the comic operate mostly with the same familiar matrices, fixed at a given angle, as it were, governed by familiar rules of the game; and their task is reduced to devising new links—puns, gags, pegs for parody. It is a mechanized kind of bisociative technique, which also has its practitioners in science and art.

Paradox and Synthesis

There is an obvious contrast between the emotive reactions of creator and consumer: the person who invents the joke or comic idea seldom laughs in the process. The creative stress under which he labours is not of the same kind as the emotions aroused in the audience. He is engaged in an intellectual exercise, a feat of mental acrobatics; even if motivated by sheer venom it must be distilled and sublimated. Once he has hit on the idea and worked out the logical structure, the basic pattern of the joke, he uses his tricks of the trade—suspense, emphasis, implication—to work up the audience's emotions; and to make these explode in laughter when he springs his surprise-effect on them.

Now the humorist may also experience surprise at the moment

when the idea hits him—particularly if it was generated by the unconscious. But there is a basic difference between a shock imposed from outside and a quasi self-administered shock. The humorist has solved his problem by joining two incompatible matrices together in a paradoxical synthesis. His audience, on the other hand, has its expectations shattered and its reason affronted by the impact of the second matrix on the first; instead of fusion there is collision; and in the mental disarray which ensues, emotion, deserted by reason, is flushed out in laughter.

In the humorist's mind no such divorce occurs; he has nothing to laugh about. At most he may, at the moment of inspiration, hit his desk: 'I have got it.' But the creative stress which is relieved in such minor gestures, symbolic of victory, of opposition vanquished, is of a sublimated nature—quite unlike the more primitive emotions puffed away in the massive laughter of the audience. The contrast is further illustrated in situations where a person fails to find the solution of a brain-teaser—and, on being told it, starts hitting, not the desk, but his own benighted head. The redundant tension is worked off in a symbolic gesture of self-punishment—again a more specific outlet for energies harnessed to intellectual tasks, than the laughter-channels of least resistance.

The less suggestive and the more implicit the joke, the more will the consumer's reactions approximate the producer's—whose mental effort he is compelled to re-create. When the witticism is transformed into epigram, and teasing into challenge, the overflow reflex for primitive emotions is no longer needed, and de-tension assumes more individualized and sophisticated forms; the roar of Homeric laughter is superseded by Archimedes's piercing cry or Kepler's holy ravings.

The creative act of the humorist consisted in bringing about a momentary fusion between two habitually incompatible matrices. Scientific discovery, as we shall presently see, can be described in very similar terms—as the permanent fusion of matrices of thought previously believed to be incompatible. Until the seventeenth century the Copernican hypothesis of the earth's motion was considered as obviously incompatible with commonsense experience; it was accordingly treated as a huge joke by the majority of Galileo's contemporaries. One of them, a famous wit, wrote: 'The disputes of Signor Galileo have dissolved into alchemical smoke. So here we are at last, safely back on a solid earth, and we do not have to fly with it as so many ants crawling around a balloon.'[1]

The history of science abounds with examples of discoveries greeted with howls of laughter because they seemed to be a marriage of incompatibles—until the marriage bore fruit and the alleged incompatibility of the partners turned out to derive from prejudice. The humorist, on the other hand, deliberately chooses discordant codes of behaviour or universes of discourse to expose their hidden incongruities in the resulting clash. Comic discovery is paradox stated—scientific discovery is paradox resolved.

But here again we find, instead of a clear dividing line, continuous transitions. The paradoxes of Achilles and the Tortoise, or of the Cretan Liar, have, during two millennia, tickled philosophers and teased mathematicians into creative efforts; and Juvenal's *Si Natura negat, facit indignatio versum* remains as true as ever.

Summary

I have started this inquiry with an analysis of humour because it is the only domain of creative activity where a complex pattern of intellectual stimulation elicits a sharply defined response in the nature of a physiological reflex.

The pattern underlying all varieties of humour is 'bisociative'—perceiving a situation or event in two habitually incompatible associative contexts. This causes an abrupt transfer of the train of thought from one matrix to another governed by a different logic or 'rule of the game'. But certain emotions, owing to their greater inertia and persistence, cannot follow such nimble jumps of thought; discarded by reason, they are worked off along channels of least resistance in laughter.

The emotions in question are those of the self-assertive, aggressive-defensive type, which are based on the sympathico-adrenal system and tend to beget bodily activity. Their counter-parts are the participatory or self-transcending emotions—compassion, identification, raptness—which are mediated by physiological processes of a different type, and tend to discharge not in laughter but in tears. As a rule our emotions are a mixture of both; but even in the more subtle or affectionate varieties of humour, an element of aggression—a drop of adrenalin—must be present to trigger off the reaction. Laughter is a luxury reflex which could arise only in a creature whose reason has gained a degree of autonomy from the urges of emotion, and enables him to perceive his own emotions as redundant—to realize that he has been fooled.

After applying the theory to various types of the comic, I discussed the criteria of the humorist's technique: *originality* or unexpectedness; *emphasis* through selection, exaggeration and simplification; and economy or *implicitness* which calls for extrapolation, interpolation and transposition.

The term 'matrix' was introduced to refer to any skill or ability, to any pattern of activity governed by a set of rules—its 'code'. All ordered behaviour, from embryonic development to verbal thinking, is controlled by 'rules of the game', which lend it coherence and stability, but leave it sufficient degrees of freedom for flexible strategies adapted to environmental conditions. The ambiguity of the term 'code' ('code of laws'—'coded message') is deliberate, and reflects a characteristic property of the nervous system: to control all bodily activities by means of coded signals.

The concept of matrices with fixed codes and adaptable strategies, proposed as a unifying formula, appears to be equally applicable to perceptual, cognitive, and motor skills and to the psychological structures variously called 'frames of reference', 'associative contexts', 'universes of discourse', mental 'sets', or 'schemata', etc. The validity of the formula will be tested in the chapters which follow, on various levels from morphogenesis to symbolic thought.

Matrices vary from fully automatized skills to those with a high degree of plasticity; but even the latter are controlled by rules of the game which function below the level of awareness. These silent codes can be regarded as condensations of learning into habit. Habits are the indispensable core of stability and ordered behaviour; they also have a tendency to become mechanized and to reduce man to the status of a conditioned automaton. The creative act, by connecting previously unrelated dimensions of experience, enables him to attain to a higher level of mental evolution. It is an act of liberation—the defeat of habit by originality.*

NOTES

To p. 90. This, of course, equally applies to pictures. The same Rubens nude will call forth different responses from a schoolboy, an art critic, and a nun. In the National Gallery in Vienna there was once to be seen an admirable Leda of the Venetian school, which bore the inscription: *Nackend Weib von böser Gans Gebissen* (Naked Wench Bitten by Angry Goose).

To. p. 96. As this book was nearing completion, Professor Burt kindly brought to my attention a paper he wrote on 'The Psychology of Laughter' for a seminar of his post-graduate students, in which he had come to somewhat similar conclusions:

'Laughter may be regarded as providing a safety-valve for the overflow of emotional energy, instinctively excited by the perception of some specific situation which automatically tends to stimulate the instinct, but which on closer examination is seen not to require energetic action. . . . Every stimulus to laughter thus involves a *double-entendre:* there is first the superficial or manifest meaning which tends to arouse an emotion appropriate to some serious situation (and thus momentarily disturbing equilibrium), and secondly the deeper or latent meaning (which contradicts the first impression); and the outlet of laughter is provided to give immediate relief to the superfluous emotional excitement. . . .' (Burt, 1945).

PART TWO

THE SAGE

PART TWO

CORSAGE

V

MOMENTS OF TRUTH

The Chimpanzee and the Stick

That animals can display originality and inventiveness has been asserted since Aesop, but experimentally demonstrated for the first time by the German psychologist Wolfgang Köhler. In 1918 Köhler published *The Mentality of Apes*, an account of his experiments with chimpanzees on Teneriffe, which has since become a classic. Here is a characteristic description of an animal discovering the use of tools (my italics):

Nueva, a young female chimpanzee, was tested 3 days after her arrival (11th March, 1914). She had not yet made the acquaintance of the other animals but remained isolated in a cage. A little stick is introduced into her cage; she scrapes the ground with it, pushes the banana skins together in a heap, and then carelessly drops the stick at a distance of about three-quarters of a metre from the bars. Ten minutes later, fruit is placed outside the cage beyond her reach. She grasps at it, vainly of course, and then begins the characteristic complaint of the chimpanzee: she thrusts both lips—especially the lower—forward, for a couple of inches, gazes imploringly at the observer, utters whimpering sounds, and finally flings herself on to the ground on her back—a gesture most eloquent of despair, which may be observed on other occasions as well. Thus, between lamentations and entreaties, some time passes, until—about seven minutes after the fruit has been exhibited to her—she suddenly casts a look at the stick, ceases her moaning, seizes the stick, stretches it out of the cage, and succeeds, though somewhat clumsily, in drawing the bananas within arm's length. *Moreover, Nueva at once puts the end of her stick behind and beyond her objective.* The test is repeated after an hour's interval; on this second occasion, the animal has recourse to the stick much sooner, and uses it with more skill; and at a third repetition, the stick is used immediately, as on all subsequent occasions.[1]

It is obvious that Nueva was not led to her discovery by any process of conditioning, or trial and error. Her behaviour from the moment when her eyes fell on the stick was, in Köhler's words, 'unwaveringly purposeful': she seized the stick, carried it without hesitation to the bars, stretched it out of the cage, and placed it behind the banana—a smooth, integrated sequence of actions, quite different from the erratic, hit-and-miss behaviour of rats trying to find their way through a maze, or cats trying to get out of a puzzle-box. It was an original, self-taught accomplishment, which had no precedent in the chimpanzee's past. The process which led to her discovery can be described as a synthesis of two previously unconnected skills, acquired in earlier life. In the first place, Nueva had learned to get at bananas outside her cage by squeezing an arm or foot through the bars; the ensemble of variations of this simple skill constitutes matrix number one. She had also acquired the habit—matrix number two—of scraping the earth with a stick and of pushing objects about with it. But in this playful activity the stick was never used for any utilitarian purpose; to throw, push, or roll things about is a habit common to a variety of young animals. Nueva's discovery consisted in applying this playful habit as an auxiliary matrix to get at the banana. The moment of truth occurred when Nueva's glance fell on the stick while her attention was set on the banana. At that moment the two previously separate matrices fused into one, and the 'stick to play with' became a 'rake to reach with'—an implement for obtaining otherwise unobtainable objects.

Like many other discoveries, Nueva's seems a simple and obvious one—but only after the fact. A dog, for instance, will carry a stick between his teeth, but he will never learn to use it as a rake. Moreover, chimpanzees are not the only species which finds it difficult to apply a 'playful' technique to a utilitarian purpose with which it had not been connected in previous experience; a number of discoveries in the history of human science consisted in just that. Galileo astonished the world when he turned the telescopic toys, invented by Dutch opticians, to astronomic use; the invention of the steam engine as a mechanical toy by Hero of Alexandria in the second century B.C. had to wait two thousand years before it was put to practical use; the geometry of conic sections which Apollonius of Perga had studied in the fourth century

B.C. just for the fun of it, gave Kepler, again two thousand years later, his elliptical orbits of the planets; the passion for dice of the Chevalier de Méré, made him approach Pascal for advice on a safe gambling system, and thus was the theory of probability born, that indispensable tool of modern physics and biology, not to mention the insurance business. 'It is remarkable', wrote Laplace, 'that a science which began with considerations of play has risen to the most important objects of human knowledge.' Thus at the very start of our inquiry we hit on a pattern—the discovery that a playful or *l'art pour l'art* technique provides an unexpected clue to problems in a quite different field— which is one of the leitmotifs in the history of science.

Nueva's discovery was the use of tools; the next one to be described is the making of tools. Its hero is Sultan, the genius among Köhler's chimpanzees:

(17.2.1914) Beyond some bars, out of arm's reach, lies an objective [a banana]; on this side, in the background of the experiment room, is placed a sawn-off castor-oil bush, whose branches can be easily broken off. It is impossible to squeeze the tree through the railings, on account of its awkward shape; besides, only one of the bigger apes could drag it as far as the bars. Sultan is let in, does not immediately see the objective, and, looking about him indifferently, sucks one of the branches of the tree. But, his attention having been drawn to the objective, he approaches the bars, glances outside, the next moment turns round, goes straight to the tree, seizes a thin slender branch, breaks it off with a sharp jerk, runs back to the bars, and attains the objective. From the turning round upon the tree up to the grasping of the fruit with the broken-off branch, is one single quick chain of action, without the least 'hiatus', and without the slightest movement that does not, objectively considered, fit into the solution described.[2]

Had Sultan known Greek he would certainly have shouted Eureka! Köhler comments:

For adult man with his mechanized methods of solution, proof is sometimes needed, as here, that an action was a real achievement, not something self-evident; that the breaking off a branch from a *whole tree*, for instance, is an achievement over and above the simple use of a stick, is shown at once by animals less gifted than Sultan, even when they understand the use of sticks beforehand.[3]

It has been said that discovery consists in seeing an analogy which nobody had seen before. Solomon discovered the analogy between the Shulamite's neck and a tower of ivory. Sultan discovered that a twisted branch on a tree with leaves on it had something in common with a straight, lifeless bamboo-pole lying on the ground. What they had in common was very little: let us say that both looked 'hardish' and 'longish', but that is all. The branch, which previously was part and parcel of the tree, was wrenched out of its visual context—both figuratively and literally speaking—and made into a part of another, functional, context.

The now familiar shift of awareness to the previously unimportant 'pole-like' aspect of the branch was very prettily demonstrated by another of Köhler's chimpanzees, Koko. It took Koko much longer to make the same discovery as Sultan; and when at last he had broken off a branch from the tree to use it as a stick, and marched with it towards the banana outside the cage, he:

> eagerly picked off one leaf after the other, so that only the long, bare stem was left . . . The pulling off of the leaves is both correct and incorrect; *incorrect* because it does not make the stem any longer, *correct* because it makes its length show up better and the stem thus becomes optically more like a stick. . . . There can be no doubt that Koko did not pull off the leaves in play only; his look and his movements prove distinctly that throughout the performance his attention is wholly concentrated on the banana; he is merely concerned now with preparing the implement. Play looks quite different; and I have never seen a chimpanzee play while (like Koko in this case) he was showing himself distinctly intent upon his ultimate purpose.[4]

Before the chimpanzee actually broke off the branch there must have been a moment when he perceived it as a member *of both matrices at the same time*—still a part of the tree but already a detached tool. Thus one could say that Sultan had seen a *visual pun*: a single form (the branch) attached to two different functions.

The act of discovery has a disruptive and a constructive aspect. It must disrupt rigid patterns of mental organization to achieve the new synthesis. Sultan's habitual way of looking at the tree as a coherent, visual whole had to be shattered. Once he had discovered that branches can be made into tools he never again forgot it, and we may assume that a tree never again looked the same to him as before. He had lost the innocence of his vision, but from this loss he derived an immense gain: the perception of 'branches' and the manipulation of 'tools' were now combined into a single, sensory-motor skill; and when two matrices have become integrated they cannot again be torn asunder. This is why the discoveries of yesterday are the commonplaces of today, and why we always marvel how stupid we were not to see what *post factum* appears to be so obvious.

Archimedes

Let me illustrate the last point by a human discovery which has much in common with Sultan's: the Principle of Archimedes. I must tell the story in a somewhat simplified form.

Hiero, tyrant of Syracuse and protector of Archimedes, had been given a beautiful crown, allegedly of pure gold, but he suspected that it was adulterated with silver. He asked Archimedes's opinion. Archimedes knew, of course, the specific weight of gold—that is to say, its weight per volume unit. If he could measure the volume of the crown he would know immediately whether it was pure gold or not; but how on earth is one to determine the volume of a complicated ornament with all its filigree work? Ah, if only he could melt it down and measure the liquid gold by the pint, or hammer it into a brick of honest rectangular shape, or . . . and so on. At this stage he must have felt rather like Nueva, flinging herself on her back and uttering whimpering sounds because the banana was out of her grasp and the road to it blocked.

Blocked situations increase stress. Under its pressure the chimpanzee reverts to erratic and repetitive, random attempts; in Archimedes's case we can imagine his thoughts moving round in circles within the frame of his geometrical knowledge; and finding all approaches to the target blocked, returning again and again to the starting point. This frustrating situation, familiar to everybody trying to solve a difficult problem, may be schematized as in the following diagram, where 'S' represents the starting point, the loops are trains of thought within the blocked matrix, and 'T' represents the target (that is: 'a method of measuring the volume of the crown')—which, unfortunately, is located outside the plane of the matrix.

One day, while getting into his bath, Archimedes watched absent-mindedly the familiar sight of the water-level rising from one smudge

FIGURE 7

on the basin to the next as a result of the immersion of his body, and it occurred to him in a flash that the volume of water displaced was equal to the volume of the immersed parts of his own body—which therefore could simply be measured by the pint. He had melted his body down, as it were, without harming it, and he could do the same with the crown.

Once more, as in the case of the chimpanzee, the matter is childishly simple after the fact—but let us try to put ourselves in Archimedes's place. He was in the habit of taking a daily bath, but the experiences and ideas associated with it moved along habit-beaten tracks: the sensations of hot and cold, of fatigue and relaxation, and a pretty slave-girl to massage his limbs. Neither to Archimedes nor to anybody else before him had it ever occurred to connect the sensuous and trivial occupation of taking a hot bath with the scholarly pursuit of the measurement of solids. No doubt he had observed many times that the level of the water rose whenever he got into it; but this fact, and the distance between the two levels, was totally irrelevant to him—until it suddenly became bisociated with his problem. At that instant he realized that the amount of rise of the water-level was a simple measure of the volume of his own complicated body.

The discovery may now be schematized as follows (Figure 8):

M_1 is the same as in the preceding diagram, governed by the habitual rules of the game, by means of which Archimedes originally tried to solve the problem; M_2 is the matrix of associations related to taking a bath; m_2 represents the actual train of thought which effects the connection. The Link L may have been a *verbal* concept (for instance:

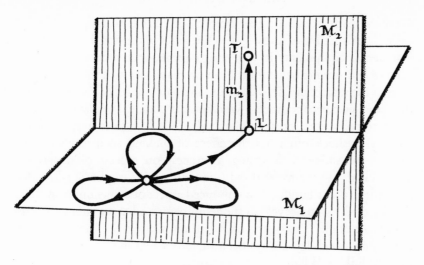

FIGURE 8

'rise of water-level *equals* melting down of my solid body'.); it may equally well have been a *visual* impression in which the water-level was suddenly seen to correspond to the volume of the immersed parts of the body and hence to that of the crown—whose image was constantly lurking on the fringe of his consciousness. The essential point is, that at the critical moment *both* matrices M_1 and M_2 were simultaneously active in Archimedes's mind—though presumably on different levels of awareness. The creative stress resulting from the blocked situation had kept the problem on the agenda even while the beam of consciousness was drifting along quite another plane. Without this constant pressure, the favourable chance-constellation would have passed unnoticed—and joined the legion of man's missed opportunities for a creative departure from the stale habits of thought which numb his mental powers.

The sequel to the discovery is well known; because of its picturesque appeal I shall occasionally refer to discovery in its psychological aspect as the 'Eureka process' or 'Eureka act'.

Let us look at Archimedes's discovery from a different angle. When one climbs into a bath one *knows* that the water-level will rise owing to its displacement by the body, and that there must be as much water displaced as there is body immersed; moreover, one mechanically estimates the amount of water to be let into the bath because of this expectation. Archimedes, too, must have known all this

—but he had probably never before verbalized, that is, consciously formulated that bit of knowledge. Yet *implicitly* it was there as part of his mental equipment; it was, so to speak, included in the code of rules of bath-taking behaviour. Now we have seen that the rules which govern the matrix of a skill function on a lower level of awareness than the actual performance itself—whether it is playing the piano, carrying on a conversation, or taking a bath. We have also seen that the bisociative shock often has the effect of making such implicit rules explicit, of suddenly focussing awareness on aspects of experience which had been unverbalized, unconsciously implied, taken for granted; so that a familiar and unnoticed aspect of a phenomenon—like the rise of the water-level—is suddenly perceived at an unfamiliar and significant angle. Discovery often means simply the uncovering of something which has always been there but was hidden from the eye by the blinkers of habit.

This equally applies to the discoveries of the artist who makes us see familiar objects and events in a strange, new, revealing light—as if piercing the cataract which dims our vision. Newton's apple and Cézanne's apple are discoveries more closely related than they seem.

Chance and Ripeness

Nearly all of Köhler's chimpanzees sooner or later learned the use of implements, and also certain methods of making implements. But a dog, however skilful in carrying a stick or a basket around, will never learn to use the stick to get a piece of meat placed outside its reach. We might say that the chimpanzees were *ripe* to discover the use of tools when a favourable chance-opportunity presented itself—such as a stick lying around just when needed. The factors which (among others) constitute ripeness for this type of discovery are the primates' manual dexterity and advanced oculo-motor co-ordination, which enable them to develop the playful habit of pushing objects about with branches and sticks. Each of the separate skills, whose synthesis constitutes the new discovery, was well established previously and frequently exercised. In a similar way Archimedes's mental skill in manipulating abstract concepts like volume and density, plus his acute powers of observation, even of trivia, made him 'ripe' for his discovery. In more general terms: the statistical probability for a relevant discovery to be made is the greater the more firmly established and well exercised each of the still separate skills, or thought-matrices, are. This explains a puzzling but recurrent phenomenon in the history of science: that the same discovery is made, more or less at the same time, by two or more people; and it may also help to explain the independent development of the same techniques and similar styles of art in different cultures.

Ripeness in this sense is, of course, merely a necessary, not a sufficient, condition of discovery. But it is not quite such an obvious concept as it might seem. The embittered controversies between different schools in experimental psychology about the nature of learning and under-standing can be shown to derive to a large extent from a refusal to take the factor of ripeness seriously. The propounders of Behaviouristic psychology were wont to set their animals tasks for which they were biologically ill-fitted, and thus to prove that new skills could be acquired only through conditioning, chaining of reflexes, learning by rote. Köhler and the Gestalt school, on the other hand, set their chimpanzees tasks for which they were ripe or *almost ripe*, to prove that all learning was based on insight. The contradictory conclusions at which they arrived need surprise us no more than the contrast between the learning achievements of a child of six months and a child of six years. This is a necessarily over-simplified description (for a detailed treatment see Book Two, XII); the only point I wish to make is that the more ripe a situation is for the discovery of a new synthesis, the less need there is for the helping hand of chance.

Archimedes's eyes falling on the smudge in the bath, or the chimpanzee's eyes falling upon the tree, are chance occurrences of such high probability that sooner or later they were bound to occur; chance plays here merely the part of triggering off the fusion between two matrices by hitting on one among many possible appropriate links. We may distinguish between the *biological ripeness* of a species to form a new adaptive habit or acquire a new skill, and the ripeness of a *culture* to make and to exploit a new discovery. Hero's steam engine could obviously be exploited for industrial purposes only at a stage when the technological and social conditions made it both possible and desirable. Lastly (or firstly), there is the personal factor—the role of the creative individual in achieving a synthesis for which the time is more or less ripe.

The emphasis is on the 'more or less'. If ripeness were all—as Shakespeare and the Marxist theory affirm—the role of genius in history would be reduced from hero to midwife, who assists the inevitable birth; and the act of creation would be merely a consumma-tion of the preordained. But the old controversy whether individuals make or are made by history acquires a new twist in the more limited field of the history of science. The twist is provided by the phenomenon of multiple discoveries. Historical research into this curious subject is of fairly recent origin; it came as a surprise when, in 1922, Ogburn and Thomas published some hundred and fifty examples of discoveries and inventions which were made independently by several persons; and, more recently, Merton came to the seemingly paradoxical conclusion that 'the pattern of independent multiple discoveries in science is . . . the dominant pattern rather than a subsidiary one'.[5] He quotes as an example Lord Kelvin, whose published papers contain 'at least thirty-two discoveries of his own which he subsequently found had also been made by others'. The 'others' include some men of genius such as Cavendish and Helmholtz, but also some lesser lights.

The endless priority disputes which have poisoned the supposedly serene atmosphere of scientific research throughout the ages, and the unseemly haste of many scientists to establish priority by rushing into print—or, at least, depositing manuscripts in sealed envelopes with some learned society—point in the same direction. Some—among them Galileo and Hooke—even went to the length of publishing half-completed discoveries in the form of anagrams, to ensure priority without letting rivals in on the idea. Köhler's chimpanzees were of a more generous disposition.

Thus one should not underestimate ripeness as a factor facilitating discoveries which, as the saying goes, are 'in the air'—meaning, that the various components which will go into the new synthesis are all lying around and only waiting for the trigger-action of chance, or the catalysing action of an exceptional brain, to be assembled and welded together. If one opportunity is missed, another will occur.

But, on the other hand, although the infinitesimal calculus was developed independently by Leibniz and by Newton, and a long line of precursors had paved the way for it, it still required a Newton or a Leibniz to accomplish the feat; and the greatness of this accomplishment is hardly diminished by the fact that two among millions, instead of one among millions, had the exceptional genius to do it. We are concerned with the question *how* they did it—the nature of creative originality—and not with the undeniable, but trivial consideration that if they had not lived somebody else would have done it some time; for that leaves the same question to be answered, to wit, *how* that someone else did it. I shall not presume to guess whether outstanding individuals such as Plato and Aristotle, Jesus of Nazareth and Paul of Tarsus,

Aquinas, Bacon, Marx, Freud, and Einstein, were expendable in the above sense, so that the history of ideas in their absence would have taken much the same course—or whether it is the creative genius who determines the course of history. I merely wish to point out that some of the major break-throughs in the history of science represent such dramatic *tours de force*, that 'ripeness' seems a very lame explanation, and 'chance' no explanation at all. Einstein discovered the principle of relativity 'unaided by any observation that had not been available for at least fifty years before';[6] the plum was overripe, yet for half a century nobody came to pluck it. A less obvious example is Everist Galois, one of the most original mathematicians of all times, who was killed in an absurd duel in 1832, at the age of twenty. In the night before the duel he revised a paper to the *Académie des Sciences* (which had previously rejected it as unintelligible); then, in a letter to a friend, he hurriedly put down a number of other mathematical discoveries. 'It was only after fifteen years, that, with admiration, scientists became aware of the memoir which the Academy had rejected. It signifies a total transformation of higher algebra, projecting a full light on what had been only glimpsed thus far by the greatest mathematicians . . .'[7] Furthermore, in the letter to his friend, Galois postulated a theorem which could not have been understood by his contemporaries because it was based on mathematical principles which were discovered only a quarter century after his death. 'It must be admitted,' another great mathematician commented, 'first, that Galois must have conceived these principles in some way; second, that they must have been unconscious in his mind since he makes no allusion to them, though they by themselves represent a significant discovery.'[8]

This leads us to the problem of the part played by unconscious processes in the Eureka act.

Pythagoras, according to tradition, is supposed to have discovered that musical pitch depends on the ratio between the length of vibrating chords—the starting point of mathematical physics—by passing in front of the local blacksmith on his native island of Samos, and noticing that rods of iron of different lengths gave different sounds under the blacksmith's hammer. Instead of ascribing it to chance, we suspect that it was some obscure intuition which made Pythagoras stop at the blacksmith's shop. But how does that kind of intuition work? Here is the core of the problem of discovery—both in science and in art.

I shall briefly describe, for the sake of contrast, two celebrated discoveries of entirely different kinds: the first apparently due to conscious, logical reasoning aided by chance; the second a classic case of the intervention of the unconscious.

Eighteen hundred and seventy-nine was the birth-year of immunology—the prevention of infectious diseases by inoculation. By that time Louis Pasteur had already shown that cattle fever, rabies, silkworm disease, and various other afflictions were caused by micro-organisms, and had firmly established the germ theory of disease. In the spring of 1879—he was fifty-seven at that time—Pasteur was studying chicken cholera. He had prepared cultures of the bacillus, but for some reason this work was interrupted, and the cultures remained during the whole summer unattended in the laboratory. In the early autumn, however, he resumed his experiments. He injected a number of chickens with the bacillus, but unexpectedly they became only slightly ill and recovered. He concluded that the old cultures had been spoilt, and obtained a new culture of virulent bacilli from chickens afflicted by a current outbreak of cholera. He also bought a new batch of chickens from the market and injected both lots, the old and the new, with the fresh culture. The newly bought chicks all died in due time, but, to his great surprise the old chicks, who had been injected once already with the ineffective culture, all survived. An eye-witness in the lab described the scene which took place when Pasteur was informed of this curious development. He 'remained silent for a minute, then exclaimed as if he had seen a vision: "Don't you see that these animals have been *vaccinated!*" '

Now I must explain that the word 'vaccination' was at that time already a century old. It is derived from *vacca*, cow. Some time in the 1760s a young medical student, Edward Jenner, was consulted by a Gloucester dairymaid who felt out of sorts. Jenner thought that she might be suffering from smallpox, but she promptly replied: 'I cannot take the smallpox because I have had the cow-pox.' After nearly twenty years of struggle against the scepticism and indifference of the medical profession, Jenner succeeded in proving the popular belief that people who had once caught the cow-pox were immune against smallpox. Thus originated 'vaccination'—the preventive inoculation of human beings against the dreaded and murderous disease with material taken from the skin sores of afflicted cattle. Although Jenner realized that cow-pox and smallpox were essentially the same disease, which became somehow modified by the organism which carried it, he did not draw any general conclusions from his discovery. 'Vaccination' soon spread to America and became a more or less general practice in a number of other countries, yet it remained limited to smallpox, and the word itself retained its exclusively bovine connotations.

The vision which Pasteur had seen at that historic moment was, once again, the discovery of a hidden analogy: the surviving chicks of the first batch were protected against cholera by their inoculation with the 'spoilt' culture as humans are protected against smallpox by inoculation with pox bacilli in a modified, bovine form.

Now Pasteur was well acquainted with Jenner's work. To quote one of his biographers, Dr. Dubos (himself an eminent biologist): 'Soon after the beginning of his work on infectious diseases, Pasteur became convinced that something similar to "vaccination" was the best approach to their control. It was this conviction that made him perceive immediately the meaning of the accidental experiment with chickens.'

In other words, he was 'ripe' for his discovery, and thus able to pounce on the first favourable chance that offered itself. As he himself said: 'Fortune favours the prepared mind.' Put in this way, there seems to be nothing very awe-inspiring in Pasteur's discovery. Yet for about three-quarters of a century 'vaccination' had been a common practice in Europe and America; why, then, did nobody before Pasteur hit on the 'obvious' idea of extending vaccination from smallpox to other diseases? Why did nobody before him put two and two together? Because, to answer the question literally, the first 'two' and the second 'two' appertained to *different frames of reference*. The first was the technique of vaccination; the second was the hitherto quite separate and independent research into the world of micro-organisms: fowl-parasites, silkworm-bacilli, yeasts fermenting in wine-barrels, invisible viruses in the spittle of rabid dogs. Pasteur succeeded in combining these two separate frames because he had an exceptional grasp of the rules of both, and was thus prepared for the moment when chance provided an appropriate link.

He knew—what Jenner knew not—that the active agent in Jenner's 'vaccine' was the microbe of the same disease against which the subject was to be protected, but a microbe which in its bovine host had undergone some kind of 'attenuation'. And he further realized that the cholera bacilli left to themselves in the test-tubes during the whole summer had undergone the same kind of 'attenuation' or weakening, as the pox bacilli in the cow's body. This led to the surprising, almost poetic, conclusion, that life inside an abandoned glass tube can have the same debilitating effect on a bug as life inside a cow. From here on the implications of the Gloucestershire dairymaid's statement became gloriously obvious: 'As attenuation of the bacillus had occurred spontaneously in some of his cultures [just as it occurred inside the cow], Pasteur became convinced *that it should be possible to produce vaccines at will in the laboratory*. Instead of depending upon the chance of naturally occurring immunizing agents, as cow-pox was for smallpox, vaccination could then become a general technique applicable to all infectious diseases.'[9]

One of the scourges of humanity had been eliminated—to be replaced in due time by another. For the story has a sequel with an ironic symbolism, which, though it does not strictly belong to the subject, I cannot resist telling. The most famous and dramatic application of Pasteur's discovery was his anti-rabies vaccine. It was tried for the first time on a young Alsatian boy by name of Josef Meister, who had been savagely bitten by a rabid dog on his hands, legs, and thighs. Since the incubation period of rabies is a month or more, Pasteur hoped to be able to immunize the boy against the deadly virus which was already in his body. After twelve injections with rabies vaccine of increasing strength the boy returned to his native village without having suffered any ill effects from the bites. The end of the story is told by Dubos: 'Josef Meister later became gatekeeper at the Pasteur Institute in Paris. In 1940, fifty-five years after the accident that gave him a lasting place in medical history, he committed suicide rather than open Pasteur's burial crypt for the German invaders.'[9a] He was evidently predestined to become a victim of one form of rabidness or another.

Now for a discovery of a diametrically opposite kind, where intuition plays the dominant part. The extracts which follow are from a celebrated lecture by Henri Poincaré at the *Societé de Psychologie* in Paris, and concern one of his best-known mathematical discoveries: the theory of the so-called 'Fuchsian functions'. To reassure the reader I hasten to quote from Poincaré's own introductory remarks:

I beg your pardon; I am about to use some technical expressions, but they need not frighten you for you are not obliged to understand them. I shall say, for example, that I have found the demonstration of such a theorem under such circumstances. This theorem will have a barbarous name unfamiliar to many, but that is unimportant; what is of interest for the psychologist is not the theorem but the circumstances. . . .

And now follows one of the most lucid introspective accounts of the Eureka act by a great scientist:

For fifteen days I strove to prove that there could not be any functions like those I have since called Fuchsian functions. I was then very ignorant; every day I seated myself at my work table, stayed an hour or two, tried a great number of combinations, and reached no results. One evening, contrary to my custom, I drank black coffee and could not sleep. Ideas rose in crowds; I felt them collide until pairs interlocked, so to speak, making a stable combination. By the next morning I had established the existence of a class of Fuchsian functions, those which come from the hypergeometric series; I had only to write out the results, which took but a few hours.

Then I wanted to represent these functions by the quotient of two series; this idea was perfectly conscious and deliberate, the analogy with elliptic functions guided me. I asked myself what properties these series must have if they existed, and I succeeded without difficulty in forming the series I have called theta-Fuchsian.

Just at this time I left Caen, where I was then living, to go on a geologic excursion under the auspices of the school of mines. The changes of travel made me forget my mathematical work. Having reached Coutances, we entered an omnibus to go some place or other. At the moment when I put my foot on the step the idea came to me, without anything in my former thoughts seeming to have paved the way for it, that the transformations I had used to define the Fuchsian functions were identical with those of non-Euclidean geometry. I did not verify the idea; I should not have had time, as, upon taking my seat in the omnibus, I went on with a conversation already commenced, but I felt a perfect certainty. On my return to Caen, for conscience' sake I verified the result at my leisure.

Then I turned my attention to the study of some arithmetical questions apparently without much success and without a suspicion of any connection with my preceding researches. Disgusted with my failure, I went to spend a few days at the seaside, and thought of something else. One morning, walking on the bluff, the idea came to me, with just the same characteristics of brevity, suddenness, and immediate certainty, that the arithmetic transformations of indeterminate ternary quadratic forms were identical with those of non-Euclidean geometry.

Returned to Caen, I meditated on this result and deduced the consequences. The example of quadratic forms showed me that there were Fuchsian groups other than those corresponding to the hypergeometric series; I saw that I could apply to them the theory of theta-Fuchsian series and that consequently there existed Fuchsian functions other than those from the hypergeometric series, the ones I then knew. Naturally I set myself to form all these functions. I made a systematic attack upon them and carried all the outworks, one after another. There was one, however, that still held out, whose fall would involve that of the whole place. But all my efforts only served at first the better to show me the difficulty, which indeed was something. All this work was perfectly conscious.

Thereupon I left for Mont-Valérien, where I was to go through my military service; so I was very differently occupied. One day, going along the street, the solution of the difficulty which had stopped me suddenly appeared to me. I did not try to go deep into it immediately, and only after my service did I again take up the question. I had all the elements and had only to arrange them and put them together. So I wrote out my final memoir at a single stroke and without difficulty.

I shall limit myself to this single example; it is useless to multiply them. In regard to my other researches I would have to say analogous things . . .

Most striking at first is this appearance of sudden illumination, a manifest sign of long, unconscious prior work. The role of this unconscious work in mathematical invention appears to me incontestable. . . .[10]

Similar experiences have been reported by other mathematicians. They seem to be the rule rather than the exception. One of them is Jacques Hadamard:[11]

. . . One phenomenon is certain and I can vouch for its absolute certainty: the sudden and immediate appearance of a solution at the very moment of sudden awakening. On being very abruptly awakened by an external noise, a solution long searched for appeared to me at once without the slightest instant of reflection on my part— the fact was remarkable enough to have struck me unforgettably— and in a quite different direction from any of those which I had previously tried to follow.

A few more examples. André Marie Ampère (1775–1836), after whom the unit of electric current is named, a genius of childlike simplicity, recorded in his diary the circumstances of his first mathematical discovery:

> On April 27, 1802, he tells us, I gave a shout of joy . . . It was seven years ago I proposed to myself a problem which I have not been able to solve directly, but for which I had found by chance a solution, and knew that it was correct, without being able to prove it. The matter often returned to my mind and I had sought twenty times unsuccessfully for this solution. For some days I had carried the idea about with me continually. At last, *I do not know how*, I found it, together with a large number of curious and new considerations concerning the theory of probability. As I think there are very few mathematicians in France who could solve this problem in less time, I have no doubt that its publication in a pamphlet of twenty pages is a good method for obtaining a chair of mathematics in a college.[12]

The memoir did in fact get him a professorship at the Lycée in Lyon. It was called *Considerations of the Mathematical Theory of Games of Chance*, and demonstrated, among other things, that habitual gamblers are, in the long run, bound to lose.

Another great mathematician, Karl Friedrich Gauss, described in a letter to a friend how he finally proved a theorem on which he had worked unsuccessfully for four years:

> At last two days ago I succeeded, not by dint of painful effort but so to speak by the grace of God. As a sudden flash of light, the enigma was solved. . . . For my part I am unable to name the nature of the thread which connected what I previously knew with that which made my success possible.[13]

On another occasion Gauss is reported to have said: 'I have had my solutions for a long time, but I do not yet know how I am to arrive at them.' Paraphrasing him, Polya—a contemporary mathematician—remarks: 'When you have satisfied yourself that the theorem is true, you start proving it.'[14]

We have seen quite a few cats being let out of the bag—the mathematical mind, which is supposed to have such a dry, logical, rational texture. As a last example in this chapter I shall quote the dramatic case of Friedrich August von Kekulé, Professor of Chemistry in Ghent, who, one afternoon in 1865, fell asleep and dreamt what was probably the most important dream in history since Joseph's seven fat and seven lean cows:

> I turned my chair to the fire and dozed, he relates. Again the atoms were gambolling before my eyes. This time the smaller groups kept modestly in the background. My mental eye, rendered more acute by repeated visions of this kind, could now distinguish larger structures, of manifold conformation; long rows, sometimes more closely fitted together; all twining and twisting in snakelike motion. But look! What was that? One of the snakes had seized hold of its own tail, and the form whirled mockingly before my eyes. As if by a flash of lightning I awoke . . . Let us learn to dream, gentlemen.[15]

The serpent biting its own tail gave Kekulé the clue to a discovery which has been called 'the most brilliant piece of prediction to be found in the whole range of organic chemistry' and which, in fact, is one of the cornerstones of modern science. Put in a somewhat simplified manner, it consisted in the revolutionary proposal that the molecules of certain important organic compounds are not open structures but closed chains or 'rings'—like the snake swallowing its tail.

Summary

When life presents us with a problem it will be attacked in accordance with the code of rules which enabled us to deal with similar problems in the past. These rules of the game range from manipulating sticks to operating with ideas, verbal concepts, visual forms, mathematical entities. When the same task is encountered under relatively unchanging conditions in a monotonous environment, the responses will become stereotyped, flexible skills will degenerate into rigid patterns, and the person will more and more resemble an automaton, governed by fixed habits, whose actions and ideas move in narrow grooves. He may be compared to an engine-driver who must drive his train along fixed rails according to a fixed timetable.

Vice versa, a changing, variable environment will tend to create flexible behaviour-patterns with a high degree of adaptability to circumstances—the driver of a motor-car has more degrees of freedom than the engine-driver. But novelty can be carried to a point—by life or in the laboratory—where the situation still resembles *in some respects* other situations encountered in the past, yet contains new features or complexities which make it impossible to solve the problem by the same rules of the game which were applied to those past situations. When this happens we say that the situation is *blocked*—though the subject may realize this fact only after a series of hopeless tries, or never at all. To squeeze the last drop out of the metaphor: the motorist is heading for a frontier to which all approaches are barred, and all his skill as a driver will not help him—short of turning his car into a helicopter, that is, playing a different kind of game.

A blocked situation increases the stress of the frustrated drive. What happens next is much the same in the chimpanzee's as in Archimedes's case. When all hopeful attempts at solving the problem by traditional methods have been exhausted, thought runs around in circles in the blocked matrix like rats in a cage. Next, the matrix of organized, purposeful behaviour itself seems to go to pieces, and random trials make their appearance, accompanied by tantrums and attacks of despair—or by the distracted absent-mindedness of the creative obsession. That absent-mindedness is, of course, in fact single-mindedness; for at this stage—the 'period of incubation'—the whole personality, down to the unverbalized and unconscious layers, has become saturated with the problem, so that on some level of the mind it remains active, even while attention is occupied in a quite different field—such as looking at a tree in the chimpanzee's case, or watching the rise of the water-level; until either chance or intuition provides a link to a quite different matrix, which bears down vertically, so to speak, on the problem blocked in its old horizontal context, and the two previously separate matrices fuse. But for that fusion to take place a condition must be fulfilled which I called 'ripeness'.

Concerning the psychology of the creative act itself, I have mentioned the following, interrelated aspects of it: the displacement of attention to something not previously noted, which was irrelevant in the old and is relevant in the new context; the discovery of hidden analogies as a result of the former; the bringing into consciousness of tacit axioms and habits of thought which were implied in the code and taken for granted; the un-covering of what has always been there.

This leads to the paradox that the more original a discovery the more obvious it seems afterwards. The creative act is not an act of creation in the sense of the Old Testament. It does not create something out of nothing; it uncovers, selects, re-shuffles, combines, synthesizes already existing facts, ideas, faculties, skills. The more familiar the parts, the more striking the new whole. Man's knowledge of the changes of the tides and the phases of the moon is as old as his observation that apples fall to earth in the ripeness of time. Yet the combination of these and other equally familiar data in Newton's theory of gravity changed mankind's outlook on the world.

'It is obvious', says Hadamard, 'that invention or discovery, be it in mathematics or anywhere else, takes place by combining ideas. . . . The Latin verb *cogito* for "to think" etymologically means "to shake together". St. Augustine had already noticed that and also observed that *intelligo* means "to select among".'

The 'ripeness' of a culture for a new synthesis is reflected in the recurrent phenomenon of multiple discovery, and in the emergence of similar forms of art, handicrafts, and social institutions in diverse cultures. But when the situation is ripe for a given type of discovery it still needs the intuitive power of an exceptional mind, and sometimes a favourable chance event, to bring it from potential into actual existence. On the other hand, some discoveries represent striking *tours de force* by individuals who seem to be so far ahead of their time that their contemporaries are unable to understand them.

Thus at one end of the scale we have discoveries which seem to be due to more or less conscious, logical reasoning, and at the other end sudden insights which seem to emerge spontaneously from the depth of the unconscious. The same polarity of logic and intuition will be found to prevail in the methods and techniques of artistic creation. It is summed up by two opposite pronouncements: Bernard Shaw's 'Ninety per cent perspiration, ten per cent inspiration', on the one hand, Picasso's 'I do not seek—I find' (*je ne cherche pas, je trouve*), on the other.

VI

THREE ILLUSTRATIONS

Before proceeding further, let me return for a moment to the basic, bisociative pattern of the creative synthesis: the sudden interlocking of two previously unrelated skills, or matrices of thought. I shall give three somewhat more detailed examples which display this pattern from various angles: Gutenberg's invention of printing with movable types; Kepler's synthesis of astronomy and physics; Darwin's theory of evolution by natural selection.

1. *The Printing Press*

At the dawn of the fifteenth century printing was no longer a novelty in Europe. Printing from wooden blocks on vellum, silk, and cloth apparently started in the twelfth century, and printing on paper was widely practised in the second half of the fourteenth. The blocks were engraved in relief with pictures or text or both, then thoroughly wetted with a brown distemper-like substance; a sheet of damp paper was laid on the block and the back of the paper was rubbed with a so-called *frotton*—a dabber or burnisher—until an impression of the carved relief was transferred to it. Each sheet could be printed on only one side by this method, but the blank backs of the sheets could be pasted together and then gathered into quires and bound in the same manner as manuscript-books. These 'block books' or *xylographs* circulated already in considerable numbers during Gutenberg's youth.

He was born in 1398 at Mainz and was really called Gensfleisch, meaning gooseflesh, but preferred to adopt the name of his mother's birthplace. The story of his life is obscure, highlighted by a succession of lawsuits against money-lenders and other printers; his claim to priority is the subject of a century-old controversy. But there exists a series of letters to a correspondent, Frère Cordelier, which has an authentic ring and gives a graphic description of the manner in which Gutenberg arrived at his invention.[1] Whether others, such as Costa of Haarlem, made the same invention at the same time or before Gutenberg is, from our point of view, irrelevant.

Oddly enough, the starting point of Gutenberg's invention was not the block-books—he does not seem to have been acquainted with them —but playing-cards. In his first letter to Cordelier he wrote:

> For a month my head has been working; a Minerva, fully armed, must issue from my brain. . . . You have seen, as I have, playing-cards and pictures of saints. . . . These cards and pictures are engraved on small pieces of wood, and below the pictures there are words and entire lines also engraved. . . . A thick ink is applied to the engraving; and upon this a leaf of paper, slightly damp, is placed; then this wood, this ink, this paper is rubbed and rubbed until the back of the paper is polished. This paper is then taken off and you see on it the picture just as if the design had been traced upon it, and the words as if they had been written; the ink applied to the engraving has become attached to the paper, attracted by its softness and by its moisture. . . .
>
> Well, what has been done for a few words, for a few lines, I must succeed in doing for large pages of writing, for large leaves covered entirely on both sides, for whole books, for the first of all books, the Bible. . . .
>
> How? It is useless to think of engraving on pieces of wood the whole thirteen hundred pages. . . .
>
> What am I to do? I do not know: but I know what I want to do: I wish to manifold the Bible, I wish to have the copies ready for the pilgrimage to Aix la Chapelle.

Here, then, we have matrix or skill No. 1: the printing from wood-blocks by means of rubbing.

In the letters which follow we see him desperately searching for a simpler method to replace the laborious carving of letters in wood:

> Every coin begins with a punch. The punch is a little rod of steel, one end of which is engraved with the shape of one letter, several letters, all the signs which are seen in relief on a coin. The punch is moistened and driven into a piece of steel, which becomes the

'hollow' or 'stamp'. It is into these coin-stamps, moistened in their turn, that are placed the little discs of gold, to be converted into coins, by a powerful blow.

This is the first intimation of the method of type-casting. It leads Gutenberg, by way of analogy, to the *seal*: 'When you apply to the vellum or paper the seal of your community, everything has been said, everything is done, everything is there. Do you not see that you can repeat as many times as necessary the seal covered with signs and characters?'

Yet all this is insufficient. He may cast letters in the form of coins, or seals, instead of engraving the wood, yet they will never make a clear print by the clumsy rubbing method; so long as his search remains confined to this one and only traditional method of making an 'imprint', the problem remains blocked. To solve it, an entirely different kind of skill must be brought in. He tries this and that; he thinks of everything under the sun: it is the period of incubation. When the favourable opportunity at last offers itself he is ready for it:

> I took part in the wine harvest. I watched the wine flowing, and going back from the effect to the cause, I studied the power of this press which nothing can resist. . . .

At this moment it occurs to him that the same, steady pressure might be applied by a seal or coin—preferably of lead, which is easy to cast—on paper, and that owing to the pressure, the lead would leave a trace on the paper—Eureka!

> . . . A simple substitution which is a ray of light. . . . To work then! God has revealed to me the secret that I demanded of Him. . . . I have had a large quantity of lead brought to my house and that is the pen with which I shall write.

'The ray of light' was the bisociation of wine-press and seal—which, added together, become the letter-press. The wine-press has been lifted out of its context, the mushy pulp, the flowing red liquid, the jolly revelry—as Sultan's branch was wrenched out of the context of the tree—and connected with the stamping of vellum with a seal. From now onward these separate skills, which previously had been as different as the butcher's, the baker's, and the candlestick-maker's, will appear integrated in a single, complex matrix:

> One must strike, cast, make a form like the seal of your community; a mould such as that used for casting your pewter cups; letters in relief like those on your coins, and the punch for producing them like your foot when it multiplies its print. There is the Bible!

2. Gravity and the Holy Ghost

'If I have been able to see farther than others,' said Newton, 'it was because I stood on the shoulders of giants.' One of the giants was Johannes Kepler (1571–1630) whose three laws of planetary motion provided the foundation on which the Newtonian universe was built. They were the first 'natural laws' in the modern sense: precise, verifiable statements expressed in mathematical terms; at the same time, they represent the first attempt at a synthesis of astronomy and physics which, during the preceding two thousand years, had developed on separate lines.

Astronomy before Kepler had been a purely descriptive geometry of the skies. The motion of stars and planets had been represented by the device of epicycles and eccentrics—an imaginary clockwork of circles turning on circles turning on circles. Copernicus, for instance, had used forty-eight wheels to represent the motion of the five known planets around the sun. These wheels were purely fictitious, and meant as such—they enabled astronomers to make more or less precise predictions, but, above all, they satisfied the dogma that all heavenly motion must be uniform and in perfect circles. Though the planets moved neither uniformly nor in perfect circles, the imaginary cogwheels did, and thereby 'saved the appearances'.

Kepler's discoveries put an end to this state of affairs. He reconciled astronomy with physics, and substituted for the fictitious clockwork a universe of material bodies not unlike the earth, freely floating and turning in space, moved by forces acting on them. His most important book bears the provocative title: *A New Astronomy Based on Causation Or Physics of the Sky* (1609). It contains the first and second of Kepler's three laws. The first says that the planets move around the sun not in circles but in elliptic orbits; the second says that a planet moves in its orbit not at uniform speed but at a speed that varies according to its

position, and is defined by a simple and beautiful law: the line connecting planet and sun sweeps over equal areas in equal times. The
third law establishes an equally elegant mathematical correlation
between the length of a planet's year and its mean distance from the
sun.

Kepler did not start his career as an astronomer, but as a student of
theology (at the Lutheran University of Thuebingen); yet already as a
student he was attracted by the Copernican idea of a sun-centred
universe. Now Canon Copernicus's book, *On the Revolutions of the
Heavenly Spheres*, had been published in the year of his death, 1543;
that is, fifty years before Kepler first heard of him; and during that half
century it had attracted very little attention. One of the reasons was its
supreme unreadability, which made it into an all-time worst-seller:
its first edition of a thousand copies was never sold out. Kepler was the
first Continental astronomer to embrace the Copernican theory. His
Mysterium Cosmographicum, published in 1597 (fifty-four years after
Copernicus's death), started the great controversy—Galileo entered the
scene fifteen years later.

The reason why the idea of a sun-centred universe appealed to Kepler
was repeatedly stated by himself: 'I often defended the opinions of
Copernicus in the disputations of the candidates and I composed a
careful disputation on the first motion which consists in the rotation of
the earth; then I was adding to this the motion of the earth around the
sun *for physical or, if you prefer, metaphysical reasons.*'[2] I have emphasized
the last words because they contain the leitmotif of Kepler's quest, and
because he used the same expression in various passages in his works.
Now what were those 'physical or, if you prefer, metaphysical
reasons' which made Kepler prefer to put the sun into the centre of the
universe instead of the earth?

My ceaseless search concerned primarily three problems, namely,
the number, size, and motion of the planets—why they are just as
they are and not otherwise arranged. I was encouraged in my daring
inquiry by that beautiful analogy between the stationary objects,
namely, the sun, the fixed stars, and the space between them, with
God the Father, the Son, and the Holy Ghost. I shall pursue this
analogy in my future cosmographical work.[3]

Twenty-five years later, when he was over fifty, Kepler repeated his
credo: 'It is by no means permissible to treat this analogy as an empty

comparison; it must be considered by its Platonic form and archetypal quality as one of the primary causes.'

He believed in this to the end of his life. Yet gradually the analogy underwent a significant change:

> The sun in the middle of the *moving* stars, himself at rest and yet the source of motion, carries the image of God the Father and Creator. He distributes his motive force through a medium which contains the moving bodies, even as the Father creates through the Holy Ghost.[4]

Thus the 'moving bodies'—that is, the planets—are now brought into the analogy. The Holy Ghost no longer merely fills the space between the motionless sun and the motionless fixed stars. It has become an active force, a *vis motrix*, which *drives* the planets. Nobody before Kepler had postulated, or even suspected, the existence of a physical force acting between the sun and the planets. Astronomy was not concerned with physical forces, nor with the causes of the heavenly motions, merely with their description. The passages which I have just quoted are the first intimation of the forthcoming marriage between physics and astronomy—the act of betrothal, as it were. By looking at the sky, not through the eyes of the geometrician only, but of the physicist concerned with natural causes, he hit upon a question which nobody had asked before, The question was: 'Why do the planets closer to the sun move faster than those which are far away? What is the mathematical relation between a planet's distance from the sun and the length of its year?'

These questions could only occur to one who had conceived the revolutionary hypothesis that the motion of the planet—and therefore its velocity and the duration of its year—was governed by a physical force emanating from the sun. Every astronomer knew, of course, that the greater their distance from the sun the slower the planets moved. But this phenomenon was taken for granted, just as it was taken for granted that boys will be boys and girls will be girls, as an irreducible fact of creation. Nobody asked the cause of it because physical causes were not assumed to enter into the motion of heavenly bodies. The greatness of the philosophers of the scientific revolution consisted not so much in finding the right answers but in asking the right questions; in seeing a problem where nobody saw one before; in substituting a 'why' for a 'how'.

Kepler's answer to the question why the outer planets move slower than the inner ones, and how the speed of their motion is related to their distance from the sun, was as follows:

> There exists only one moving soul in the centre of all the orbits; that is the sun which drives the planets the more vigorously the closer the planet is, but whose force is quasi-exhausted when acting on the outer planets because of the long distance and the weakening of the force which it entails.[5]

Later on he commented: 'If we substitute for the word "soul" the word "force", then we get just the principle which underlies my "Physics of the Skies". As I reflected that this cause of motion *diminishes in proportion to distance* just as the light of the sun diminishes in proportion to distance from the sun, I came to the conclusion that this force must be substantial—"substantial" not in the literal sense but . . . in the same manner as we say that light is something substantial, meaning by this an unsubstantial entity emanating from a substantial body.'[6]

We notice that Kepler's answer came *before* the question—that it was the answer that begot the question. The answer, the starting point, was the analogy between God the Father and the sun—the former acting through the Holy Ghost, the latter through a physical force. The planets must obey the law of the sun—the law of God—the mathematical law of nature; and the Holy Ghost's action through empty space diminishes, as the light emanating from the sun does, with distance. The degenerate, purely descriptive astronomy which originated in the period of the Greek decline, and continued through the Dark and Middle Ages until Kepler, did not ask for meaning and causes. But Kepler was convinced that physical causes operate between heavenly, just as between earthly, bodies, and more specifically that the sun exerts a physical force on the planets. It was this conviction which enabled him to formulate his laws. Physics became the auxiliary matrix which secured his escape from the blocked situation into which astronomy had manœuvred itself.

The blockage—to cut a very long story short—was due to the fact that Tycho de Brahe had improved the instruments and methods of star-gazing, and produced observational data of a hitherto unequalled abundance and precision; and the new data did not fit into the traditional schemes. Kepler, who served his apprenticeship under

Tycho, was given the task of working out the orbit of Mars. He spent six years on the task and covered nine thousand folio-sheets with calculations in his small handwriting without getting anywhere. When at last he believed he had succeeded he found to his dismay that certain observed positions of Mars differed from those which his theory demanded by magnitudes up to eight minutes arc. Eight minutes arc is approximately one-quarter of the apparent diameter of the moon.

This was a catastrophe. Ptolemy, and even Copernicus, could afford to neglect a difference of eight minutes, because their observations were accurate only within a margin of ten minutes, anyway. 'But,' Kepler wrote in the *New Astronomy*, 'but for us, who by divine kindness were given an accurate observer such as Tycho Brahe, for us it is fitting that we should acknowledge this divine gift and put it to use. . . . Henceforth I shall lead the way towards that goal according to my ideas. For if I had believed that we could ignore these eight minutes, I would have patched up my hypothesis accordingly. But since it was not permissible to ignore them, those eight minutes point the road to a complete reformation of astronomy. . . .'[7]

Thus a theory, built on years of labour and torment, was instantly thrown away because of a discord of eight miserable minutes arc. Instead of cursing those eight minutes as a stumbling block, he transformed them into the cornerstone of a new science. For those eight minutes arc had at last made him realize that the field of astronomy in its traditional framework was well and truly blocked.

One of the recurrent frustrations and tragedies in the history of thought is caused by the uncertainty whether it is possible to solve a given problem by traditional methods previously applied to problems which seem to be of the same nature. Who can say how many lives were wasted and good minds destroyed in futile attempts to square the circle, or to construct a *perpetuum mobile*? The proof that these problems *are* insoluble was in each case an original discovery in itself (such as Maxwell's second law of thermodynamics); and such proofs could only be found by looking at the problem from a point of view outside its traditional matrix. On the other hand, the mere knowledge that a problem is soluble means that half the game is already won.

The episode of the eight minutes arc had convinced Kepler that his problem—the orbit of Mars—was insoluble so long as he felt bound by the traditional rules of sky-geometry. Implied in those rules was the dogma of 'uniform motion in perfect circles'. *Uniform* motion he had already discarded before the crisis; now he felt that the even more sacred one of *circular* motion must also go. The impossibility of constructing a circular orbit which would satisfy all existing observations suggested to him that the circle must be replaced by some other curve.

> The conclusion is quite simply that the planet's path is not a circle —it curves inward on both sides and outward again at opposite ends. Such a curve is called an oval. The orbit is not a circle but an oval figure.[8]

This oval orbit was a wild, frightening new departure for him. To be fed up with cycles and epicycles, to mock the slavish imitators of Aristotle was one thing; to assign an entirely new, lopsided, implausible path for the heavenly bodies was quite another. Why indeed an oval? There is something in the perfect symmetry of spheres and circles which has a deep, reassuring appeal to the unconscious mind—otherwise it could not have survived two millennia. The oval lacks that archetypal appeal. It has an arbitrary, distorted form. It destroyed the dream of the 'harmony of the spheres', which lay at the origin of the whole quest. At times he felt like a criminal, or worse: a fool. All he had to say in his own defence was: 'I have cleared the Augean stables of astronomy of cycles and spirals, and left behind me only a single cartful of dung.'[9]

That cartful of dung—non-uniform motion in non-circular orbits —could only be justified and explained by arguments derived not from geometry, but from physics. A phrase kept humming in his ear like a catchy tune, and crops up in his writings over and again: there is a force in the sun which moves the planets, there is a force in the sun. ... And since there is a force in the sun, there must exist some simple relationship between the planet's distance from the sun, and its speed. A light shines the brighter the nearer one is to its source, and the same must apply to the force of the sun: the closer the planet to it, the quicker it will move. This had been his instinctive conviction; but now he thought that he had found the proof for it. 'Ye physicists, prick your ears, for now we are going to invade your territory.' The next six chapters in the *Astronomia Nova* are a report on that invasion into celestial physics, which had been out of bounds for astronomy since Plato. He had found the second matrix which would unblock his problem.

That excursion was something of a comedy of errors—which

nevertheless ended with finding the truth. Since he had no notion of the principle of inertia, which makes a planet persist in its tangential motion under its own momentum, and had only a vague intuition of gravity, he had to invent a force which, emanating from the sun, sweeps the planet round its path like a broom. In the second place, to account for the eccentricity of the orbits he had to postulate that the planets were 'huge round magnets' whose poles pointed always in the same direction so that they would alternately be drawn closer to and be repelled by the sun. But although today the whole thing seems cockeyed, his intuition that there are *two antagonistic forces* acting on the planets, guided him in the right direction. A single force, as previously assumed—the divine Prime Mover and its allied hierarchy of angels—would never produce elliptic orbits and periodic changes of speed. These could only be the result of some dynamic tug of war going on in the sky—as indeed there is. The concept of two antagonistic forces provided rules for a new game in which elliptic orbits and velocities depending on solar distance had their legitimate place.

He made many mistakes during that wild flight of thought; but 'as if by miracle'—as he himself remarked—the mistakes cancelled out. It looks as if at times his conscious critical faculties had been anaesthetized by the creative impulse, by the impatience to get to grips with the physical forces in the solar system. The problem of the planetary orbits had been hopelessly bogged down in its purely geometrical frame of reference, and when he realized that he could not get it unstuck he tore it out of that frame and removed it into the field of physics. That there were inconsistencies and impurities in his method did not matter to him in the heat of the moment, hoping that somehow they would right themselves later on—as they did. This inspired cheating—or, rather, borrowing on credit—is a characteristic and recurrent feature in the history of science. The latest example is sub-atomic physics, which may be said to live on credit—in the pious hope that one day its inner contradictions and paradoxes will somehow resolve themselves.

Kepler's determination of the orbit of Mars became the unifying link between the two formerly separate realms of physics and astronomy. His was the first serious attempt at explaining the mechanism of the solar system in terms of physical forces; and once the example was set, physics and cosmology could never again be divorced.

3. Darwin and Natural Selection

Charles Darwin is perhaps the most outstanding illustration of the thesis that 'creative originality' does not mean creating or originating a system of ideas out of nothing but rather out of the combination of well-established patterns of thought—by a process of cross-fertilization, as it were. With a pinch of salt it could be said that Darwin's essential achievement was to combine the evolutionary philosophy of Anaximander, who taught that man's ancestor was an aquatic animal and that the earth and its inhabitants were descended from the same Prime Material, with the philosophy of Empedokles who taught the survival of the fittest among the random aggregations of organic forms. Aristotle the naturalist believed that nature fashions organs in the order of their necessity, whereas Aristotle the Platonist asserted that the species are immutable and denied the continuity between *homo sapiens* and the animal kingdom.

From this point onward two basic metaphysical doctrines of opposite nature can be more or less clearly discerned throughout the history of European thought; one might call them—provided the words are not taken too literally—the 'descending' and 'ascending' views of the universe. The former is represented by Plato, the Neoplatonists, and by the fundamentalist trend in Christianity from the Fathers to the Victorians; it postulates an absolute act of creation, followed by a *descent* (Plato's cave, the Fall), followed by a static, immutable, deep-freeze state of affairs, a marking of time until the Last Judgement. The *ascending* or evolutionary doctrine, which had flourished during the heroic age of Greek science and was still partially upheld by Epicureans such as Lucretius, went into a long period of hibernation, but awoke with renewed vigour at the dawn of the Scientific Revolution. Tycho, Kepler, Galileo, destroyed the dogma of immutability; Newton in his *Optics* declared that nature was 'delighted with transmutations'; and from there onward through Leibniz, de Maillet, Locke to Kant (to mention only a few), the idea of a growing 'Tree of Nature', on which the species branched out from a common root, gained increasing support among the leading spirits.

The conflict between the two doctrines came to a head a century before the Darwin scandal—in the great controversy between Linnaeus and Buffon, who were both born in the same year, 1707. Carl von Linné's published works amount to a hundred and eighty volumes; the Comte de Buffon's *Histoire Naturelle* had forty-four quarto volumes, and took fifty years to publish. Linné, who laid down the laws for defining genera and species, and whose system of classification survives to this day, started as a believer in immutability; but later in life he admitted that new species may arise as 'daughters of Time'. Buffon attacked not only Linnaeus's classification, but the principles underlying it; he denied the existence of rigid boundaries between one species and another, between vegetable and animal, between animal and man: species arose, transformed themselves, and became extinct according to climatic and other changes in nature. Judged by the form and organization of its body, he wrote, 'the orangutang would approach nearer to man than to any other animal'. A century later Darwin admitted that 'whole pages [in Buffon] are laughably like mine'.

By the end of the eighteenth century the cumulative evidence from 'the general facts in the affinities, embryology, rudimentary organs, geological history, and geographical distribution of organic beings' (Darwin to Asa Gray)[10] led to the simultaneous appearance of evolutionary theories in a number of European countries. 'It is a rather singular instance,' he remarked elsewhere, 'of the manner in which similar views arise at about the same time, that Goethe in Germany, Dr. [Erasmus] Darwin in England and Geoffroy Saint-Hilaire in France . . . came to the same conclusion on the origin of the species, in the years 1794-95'[11]—that is, fifteen years before Charles Darwin was born.

The second great public controversy between evolutionists and anti-evolutionists originated in the fateful years 2 and 3—according to the calendar of the French Revolution—when the three main protagonists in the drama were all given chairs at the University of Paris by the Revolutionary Government. They were Lamarck, Cuvier, Geoffroy Saint-Hilaire. The climax came in 1830, when Geoffroy, the evolutionist, and Cuvier, who denied evolution, confronted each other in public debate before the French Academy of Sciences. Cuvier won the debate—and rightly so because Geoffroy had tried to demonstrate a good cause by a badly chosen example—but the outcome mattered less than the debate itself, which Goethe declared to be an event far more memorable than the French Revolution. This was a quarter of a century before Darwin submitted his first paper on evolution to the Royal Society.

A further scandal broke in 1844—still fifteen years before the publication of The Origin of Species—when Robert Chambers published anonymously his Vestiges of Creation, an impassionate if dilettantic plea for the evolutionary doctrine. Its impact may be gathered from a scene in Disraeli's *Tancred*, in which the heroine sings the book's praises: 'You know, all is development. The principle is perpetually going on. First, there was nothing, then there was something; then—I forget the next—I think there were shells, then fishes; then we came—let me see—did we come next? Never mind that; we came at last. And at the next change there will be something very superior to us—something with wings. Ah! that's it: we were fishes, and I believe we shall be crows. But you must read it . . . it is all proved. . . . You understand, it is all science; it is not like those books in which one says one thing and another the contrary, and both may be wrong. Everything is proved . . .'

The passage has that particular flavour which we have come to associate with the Darwinian controversy. Even Tancred's rejoinder to the enthusiastic lady: 'I do not believe I ever was a fish,' has the familiar ring of music-hall jokes about 'my grandpa was an ape'. And yet, I repeat, all this excitement pre-dates the publication of Darwin's first paper by more than ten years.

Thus Darwin originated neither the idea nor the controversy about evolution, and in his early years was fully aware of this. When he decided to write a book on the subject, he jotted down several versions of an apologetic disclaimer of originality for the preface of the future work:

> State broadly [that there is] scarcely any novelty in my theory . . . The whole object of the book is its proof, its extension, its adaptation to classification and affinities between species.
> Seeing what von Buch (Humboldt), G. H. Hilaire [*sic*] and Lamarck have written I pretend to no originality of idea (though I arrived at them quite independently and have read them since). The line of proof and reducing facts to law [is the] only merit, if merit there be, in following work.[12]

The remark that he had arrived at his ideas independently from his predecessors should not perhaps be taken at face value, for Darwin's own notebooks are conclusive proof that he had certainly read Lamarck, the greatest among his precursors, and a number of other works on evolution, before he arrived at formulating his own theory. Even so, the intended apology never found its way into the book which it was meant to preface. In his early notebooks, not intended for publication, Darwin paid grateful tribute to Lamarck as a source of inspiration, 'endowed with the prophetic spirit in science, the highest endowment of lofty genius'. Later on he called Lamarck's work 'veritable rubbish' which did the cause 'great harm'—and insisted that he had got 'not a fact or idea' from Lamarck.[13] In this respect he resembled Copernicus and Galileo who also excelled in denying credit where credit was due, and other great men who, at the beginning of their career, gratefully acknowledged indebtedness to their spiritual forbears, but later on quietly forgot or denied them. In some cases, of which Galileo is a striking example, the motive was an overwhelming vanity; in others, a subtler form of self-deception seemed to operate. Once one embraces an idea and lives with it day and night, one can no longer bear the thought that she, the idea, has formerly belonged to someone else; to possess her completely and be possessed by her, one must extinguish her past. That seems to have been Darwin's case; for, throughout the decisive ten years in which the battle was fought, he behaved like a jealous husband about his theory; but once the battle was won he relented and gave others their due—including Lamarck, whose ghost was never to be exorcized from the edifice that Darwin built.

On his own account, Darwin became an evolutionist after his voyage on the *Beagle*, which ended in 1836, when he was twenty-seven; but *The Origin of Species* was only published twenty-three years later. It opens with the statement:

> When on board H.M.S. *Beagle* as naturalist, I was much struck with certain facts in the distribution of the organic beings inhabiting South America, and in the geological relations of the present to the past inhabitants of that continent. These facts, as will be seen in the latter chapters of this volume, seemed to throw some light on the origin of species—that mystery of mysteries, as it has been called by one of our great philosophers.
>
> After my return to England it appeared to me that . . . by collecting all facts which bore in any way on the variation of animals and plants under domestication and nature, some light might perhaps be thrown on the whole subject. My first notebook was opened in July 1837. I worked on true Baconian principles and without any theory, collected facts on a wholesale scale . . . After five years' work I allowed myself to speculate on the subject and drew up some short notes.

As Darwin's own notebooks show, the last two sentences in this account again should not be taken at face value—they are pious lip-service to the fashionable image of the scientist collecting facts 'with an unprejudiced mind', without permitting himself, God forbid, to speculate on them. In reality, as the notebooks show, shortly after his return from the voyage (and not 'five years later'), Darwin became committed to the evolutionary theory—and then set out to collect facts to prove it. A month after publication of *The Origin*, in December 1859, he admitted this—apparently forgetting what he had said in the Preface—in a letter eloquently defending the procedure of 'inventing a theory and seeing how many classes of facts the theory would explain'.[14] In another letter he remarks that 'no one could be a good observer unless he was an active theorizer'; and again: 'How odd it is that anyone should not see that all observation must be for or against some view if it is to be of any service.'[15] I am stressing this point because scientists adhering to the positivist tradition take a perverse pride in seeing themselves in the role of rag-pickers in the dustbin of 'empirical data'—unaware that even the art of rag-picking is guided by intuition.

How, then, did Darwin become an evolutionist? The answer is in the notebooks for 1837–8, written after his return. The five years spent on the *Beagle* had taught him a wealth of lessons about living and extinct species, and about the gradual shading of one species into another. While the voyage lasted he did not draw any conscious conclusions from this; much later he wrote that although 'vague doubts occasionally flitted' across his mind, he still believed, while on the voyage, in the doctrine of the immutability of all species.[16] Yet the rich experiences of those five years must have sunk in, together with the 'vague doubts'. When, on his return, he read Lamarck and other standard works on evolution, the seeds began to germinate, the accumulated facts began to whirl through his head, then arrange themselves into a meaningful pattern. The notebooks start with the drawing of analogies between individuals and whole species:

If [the] individual cannot propagate he has no issue—so with species.

If *species* generate other *species*, their race is not utterly cut off—otherwise all die.

Absolute knowledge that species die and others replace them.

... The permanent variations produced by confined breeding and changing circumstances are continued and produced according to the adaptation [to] such circumstances and therefore ... death of species is a consequence ... of non-adaptation [to] circumstances.

If we choose to let conjecture run wild, then animals, our fellow brethren in pain, disease, death, suffering and famine—our slaves in the most laborious works, our companions in our amusements—they may partake our origin in one common ancestor—we may be all melted away.

... Organized beings represent [a] tree irregularly branched ... [This is probably an echo of Lamarck's 'branching series irregularly graded'.]

Species according to Lamarck disappear as collections made perfect.

If all men were dead, then monkeys may make men, men make angels.

Let man visit orang-outang in domestication, hear expressive whine, see its intelligence when spoken, as if it understood every word ... see its affection to those it knows, see its passion and rage, sulkiness and ... despair; let him look at savage, roasting his parent, naked, artless, not improving yet improvable; and then let him dare to boast of his proud pre-eminence.

Man in his arrogance thinks himself a great work, worthy the interposition of a deity. More humble and I believe true to consider him created from animals.

By now he is fully committed. Moreover (after all, he is only twenty-eight) he sees himself in the future role of a hero and possible martyr:

Mention persecution of early astronomers. Then add chief good of individual scientific men is to push their science a few years in advance of their age (differently from literary men). Must remember that if they *believe* and do not openly avow their belief, they do as much to retard.

That was easily said, but in fact Darwin did retard the publication of his theory by twenty years, until his hand was forced. The reasons were chronic illness, other pressing work, and, in his own words: 'I was so anxious to avoid prejudice, that I determined not for some time to write even the briefest sketch of it.' To counteract 'prejudice' he had to assemble and build massive pillars of fact in support of the slender bridge of his theory. For, contrary to the pious assertions in the preface, the bridge had come first and the pillars afterwards—as was nearly always the case in the history of scientific thought. The result proved that this caution was justified. Without those pillars, assembled with heroic patience and effort, the bridge would have collapsed in the ensuing storm. Here is one of the cases where the process of elaboration, verification, and confirmation—the long donkey-work following the brief flash of insight—is more decisive than the discovery itself. That is why Darwin is remembered, whereas Wallace, who made the same discovery, is all but forgotten.

Given the long line of evolutionists, from Anaximander to Charles's own grandfather Erasmus, wherein lies Darwin's greatness, the originality of his contribution? In picking up, one might say, the disjointed threads, plaiting them into a braid, and then weaving an enormous carpet around it. The main thread was the evolutionist's credo that the various species in the animal and vegetable kingdom 'had not been independently created, but had descended, like varieties, from other species'.[17] Now this doctrine disposed of the idea of the Creator putting down separately the first serpent, giraffe and walrus as ready-made products on the earth; but it gave no explanation of the *reasons* which caused the common ancestor to transform itself gradually into serpents, walruses, and giraffes. Only Lamarck had attempted to provide a comprehensive reason for evolution in his four 'laws'. They said, in essence, that an animal's physical characteristics and particularities of behaviour are shaped by its *needs*, that is, by adaptation to its natural environment; that specialized organs grow and decline in proportion to their use or disuse; and that these adaptive changes which the animal acquires in its lifetime are *inherited* by its offspring.

Contrary to popular belief, Darwin had no objection against the last point, the 'inheritance of acquired characteristics'—decried as a mortal heresy by neo-Darwinians. On the contrary, in his *Variations of Animals and Plants under Domestication*, and in the later editions of the *Origin*, he gave a series of examples of what he believed to be inherited characteristics in the offspring, due to adaptive changes in their ancestors. But he refused to accept such direct adaptations as the only, or even the main cause of evolution, because the evidence seemed to speak against it. Evidence showed that a great variety of species lived under identical environmental conditions; and vice versa, that the same species could be found under widely varying conditions. If species evolved, as Lamarck's theory proposed, by direct adaptations to the environment, then their variety remained unexplained. Evolution was a fact; but what caused it? What was the nature of the force which transformed animals and plants into new shapes?

The second thread that he picked up was of almost as trivial a nature for a country-bred English gentleman as Archimedes's daily bath: domestic breeding. The improvement of domestic breeds is achieved by the selective mating of favourable variations:

> It seemed to me probable that a careful study of domesticated animals and of cultivated plants would offer the best chance of making out this complicated problem. Nor have I been disappointed; in this and in all other perplexing cases I have invariably found that our knowledge, imperfect though it be, of variation under domestication, afforded the best and safest clue. I may venture to express my conviction of the high value of such studies, *although they have been very commonly neglected by naturalists*.[18] (my italics)

We might say that Darwin had discovered 'evolution through artificial selection'. Incidentally the discovery is again not quite as original as the last sentence might suggest. Darwin's notebooks of that period show that he had been reading and pondering Lamarck; and twenty years earlier, in his *Philosophie Zoologique*, Lamarck had written:

> What nature does in the course of long periods we do every day when we suddenly change the environment in which some species of living plants is situated ... Where in nature do we find our cabbages, lettuces, etc., in the same state as in our kitchen gardens? And is not the case the same with regard to many animals which have been altered or greatly modified by domestication?[19]

Whether Darwin read this passage from Lamarck, or similar passages, we do not know. But the question is irrelevant except for historians who specialize in priority claims. At any rate, Darwin now set out to collect facts about domestic breeding 'patiently and indiscriminately', not only from technical journals but from 'skilful breeders and gardeners'. A great number of the 'facts' were spurious, and some of his theorizings were as wild and fantastic as Kepler's speculations on the broom-like sweeping force emanating from the sun:

The cat had its tail cut off at Shrewsbury and its kittens had all short tails; but one a little longer than the rest; they all died. She had kittens before and afterwards with tails.

My father says on authority of Mr. Wynne, the bitch's offspring is affected by previous marriages with impure breed . . .

Dr. Smith says he is certain that when white men and Hottentots or Negroes cross at Cape of Good Hope, the children cannot be made intermediate. The first children partake more of the mother, the later ones of the father.

In his book on *Variations of Animals and Plants under Domestication* we are further informed that a cow having lost its horn owing to an infected wound, gave birth 'to three calves, each with a small bony lump in place of a horn'.

A contemporary biologist has commented on Darwin's 'amiable credulity'.[20] It is a character trait which he shared with Tycho, Kepler, Freud, Pasteur, and a large number of other great scientists. Ernest Jones[21] remarked in an essay about Freud that creative genius seems to be a mixture of scepticism and naïveté: scepticism regarding the dogmas implied in traditional modes of thought, combined with the willingness of a wide-open mind to consider far-fetched theories. Darwin himself, as one of his biographers remarked, 'was able to give ultimate answers because he asked ultimate questions. His colleagues, the systematizers, knew more than he about particular species and varieties, comparative anatomy and morphology. But they had deliberately eschewed such ultimate questions as the pattern of creation, or the reasons for any particular form, on the grounds that these were not the proper subjects of science. Darwin, uninhibited by these restrictions, could range more widely and deeply into the mysteries of Nature. . . . It was with the sharp eyes of the primitive, the open mind of the innocent, that he looked at his subject, daring to ask questions that his more learned and sophisticated colleagues could not have thought to ask' (Himmelfarb).[22]

However, the study of domestic breeding led into another cul-de-sac; for, in the case of domestic animals, *man* acts as the agent of selection; but who or what selects the favourable variations for breeding in the case of undomesticated animals or plants? 'How selection could be applied to organisms living in a state of nature remained for some time a mystery to me.'

The deadlock lasted a year and three months. He tried a number of hypotheses, but none of them worked. He toyed with the idea of some universal law, according to which species were born, matured, and died, just as individuals do. 'There is nothing stranger in the death of a species than in the death of individuals.' Then he assumed, by a perverse analogy, that since nothing is preserved of an individual who dies without leaving offspring, so a species too will die out unless it gives rise to another species. But they were wrong guesses, and his thoughts kept running in circles in the blocked matrix—as Sultan's did until his eyes fell on the stick.

In Darwin's case the stick was Malthus's *An Essay on the Principle of Population*. It had been published in 1797—more than forty years earlier. When Darwin read the essay—among other books which he read 'for amusement', as he said—he saw in a flash the 'natural selector', the causative agent of evolution, for which he had been searching:

> As many more individuals of each species are born than can possibly survive; and as consequently there is a frequently recurring struggle for existence, it follows that any being, if it vary ever so slightly in a manner profitable to itself . . . will have a better chance of survival, and thus be *naturally selected* (Darwin's italics). Thus favourable variations would tend to be preserved, and unfavourable ones to be destroyed. Here, then, I had at last got a theory by which to work.[23]

He had found the third thread. Now the pattern of the theory was complete: what remained to be done was its elaboration—the weaving of the huge carpet which took him most of the rest of his life.

The odd thing about the story is—as others have pointed out—that Darwin had completely misunderstood Malthus. The struggle for existence, in which Darwin discovered the causative mechanism of evolutionary *improvement*, Malthus himself had regarded as a cause of misery, frustration, and *decline*. The increase of population was for Malthus an unmitigated evil and an obstacle to progress. The essay had actually been written as a polemic against Condorcet and Godwin, who had argued the perfectability of the human species. Domestic breeding,

Malthus retorted, could improve animals and plants only to a very limited degree; but a carnation could never be made to reach the size of a cabbage, and similar limits were set to human progress. Thus the struggle for existence was for Malthus not the whiphand of evolution, but a scourge. What Darwin found in Malthus's essay he had read into it himself—as Kepler had read his brooms and planetary lodestones into the skies.

Even odder is the fact that Wallace arrived at the same discovery also by way of Malthus. Alfred Russell Wallace was even more gullible, and at the beginning of his career even more of a dilettante than the young Darwin. He was fourteen years younger than Darwin; he had been educated at an indifferent grammar school and learned the trade of land-surveying. Before he took up that occupation, he had shown no interest in nature, and 'it took another four years for him to advance beyond the recognition of rose and buttercup, and to learn, from a shilling booklet published by the Society for the Diffusion of Useful Knowledge, the elementary classifications of botany'.[24]

At twenty-one he became a schoolteacher of sorts. In that year he read, among other books, Darwin's *Journal of a Naturalist's Voyage on the Beagle* and Malthus's *Essay on Population*. But his mind did not click. He struck up a friendship with the entymologist Henry Walter Bates and became an expert collector of beetles. This led him to speculate about 'the almost infinite number of specific forms [among beetles], the endless modifications of structure, shape, colour, and surface-markings . . . and their innumerable adaptations to diverse environments'; he was 'bitten by the passion for species',[25] and the secret of their origin. Like Darwin he became an evolutionist by an act of faith; like Darwin he was searching for its cause; like Darwin he embarked—with his friend Bates—on a naturalist expedition to collect insects, shells, birds, and animals; like Darwin he wrote a book about it (*Travels on the Amazon and Rio Negro*).

The expedition lasted four years; two years later, in 1854, he published an article in a scientific journal in which he postulated that 'every species has come into existence coincident both in space and time with a pre-existing, closely allied species'; all species together thus formed a 'branching tree'. But, like Darwin earlier on, he did not know what made the tree grow: 'the question of *how* changes of species could have been brought about was rarely out of my mind'. Darwin read the paper and wrote to Wallace that he agreed with 'almost every word' in it; he added that he himself had been working for twenty years on the problem and had a 'distinct and tangible idea of its solution'.

One year later the same 'distinct and tangible idea' came to Wallace. In his autobiography Wallace described how he was 'lying muffled in blankets in the cold fit of a severe attack of intermittent fever at Ternate' (an island near New Guinea) when he suddenly remembered Malthus's essay on population which he had read 'twelve or more years earlier'.[26]

The effect was analogous to that of friction upon the specially prepared match, producing that flash of insight which led immediately to the simple but universal law of the 'survival of the fittest' . . . 'It suddenly flashed upon me that this self-action process [i.e. the struggle for existence] *would necessarily improve the race*, because in every generation the inferior would inevitably be killed off and the superior would remain—that is, *the fittest would survive*. The more I thought over it the more I became convinced that I had at length found the long-sought-for law of nature that solved the problem of the origin of the species.'[27] In the course of the next two evenings, 'in a few feverish hours', he put his theory into a paper of four thousand words and sent it off to Darwin, in the pleasant belief that it would be a surprise to him—since Darwin had not yet published his own theory, although he had put it on paper years earlier in several versions and shown it to his friends.

'I never saw a more striking coincidence', Darwin wrote. 'If Wallace had my manuscript sketch written out in 1842, he could not have made a better short abstract.'

Luckily, both Wallace and Darwin acted with a generosity and reasonableness rare in the annals of science; the result was the presentation on 1 July 1858 of a joint memoir by Darwin and Wallace to the Linnean Society, under the title 'On the Tendency of Species to form Varieties; and on the Perpetuation of Varieties and Species by Natural Means of Selection'. Neither author was present; Wallace was overseas, Darwin ill in bed. When the paper was read out there was no discussion and no sign of interest. At the end of the year the President of the Society said in his annual report: 'The year which has passed . . . has not, indeed, been marked by any of those striking discoveries which at once revolutionize, so to speak, the department of science on which they bear.'[28] In November next year *The Origin of Species* was published, and only then did the storm break.

Though both men were constantly ailing from real and perhaps also from imaginary diseases, Darwin lived to be seventy-three, and

Wallace ninety. Though they differed on some points of theory and though their opponents tried to play them out against each other, they managed to remain life-long friends; towards the end of his life Darwin obtained a pension for Wallace from Mr. Gladstone, and Wallace was one of Darwin's pall-bearers. At the fiftieth anniversary, in 1909, commemorating the joint publication of the Darwin-Wallace papers, Wallace modestly declared that their relative contributions 'could be justly estimated as the proportion of twenty years to one week'[29]— which was an exaggeration, as Wallace's later works, particularly the 'Contributions' and 'Darwinism' were of considerable importance.

The psychologically fascinating aspect of the story is that the same bisociative process was triggered off in Darwin's case by reading Malthus, in Wallace's by the buried memory of Malthus, whom he had read many years earlier, popping into consciousness at a feverish moment. Thus Darwin's discovery strikes one as more rational, Wallace's as more dramatic and bizarre, and this is in keeping with the character of the two men. If Darwin had more patience and clarity of mind, Wallace had more fantasy and perhaps even more depth. His remark that selection through survival of the fittest was a 'self-acting process' anticipated the concept of negative feed-back. His conviction that the rise of organic life, the rise of consciousness, and the rise of man represent 'jumps' in the evolutionary series, due to some 'unknown reality' which has to be added to the mechanical operation of natural selection, had a religious flavour; yet his conclusion that the quick evolution of man had an explosive character has been confirmed by contemporary anthropology. If Darwin had an 'amiable credulity', Wallace believed, among other things, in phrenology and in the cruder forms of mesmerism and spiritualism. No wonder he had to dive into the depths of his unconscious mind to bring up the same trophy which Darwin spied drifting on the surface, and secured with a boat-hook.

That both read Malthus is not much of a coincidence as his essay was well known and discussed at the time; and had it not been Malthus, they could have extracted the same idea from other sources— from Erasmus Darwin, for instance, or from certain passages in Lamarck. The time was ripe; 'it was not the coincidence of discovery that is surprising but rather the fact that the coincidence was so long delayed'.[30] This remark by one of Darwin's biographer's is not based on hind-sight, but on the opinion of Darwin's friends and contemporaries:

'How extremely stupid not to have thought of that,' was Huxley's first reaction, reflecting that 'Columbus' companions had probably felt the same way when he made the egg stand on end'. The same thought suggested itself to the ornithologist Alfred Newton, who did not know whether to be 'more vexed at the solution not having occurred to me, than pleased that it had been found at all', partic-ularly since it was 'a perfectly simple solution' of the problem that had been plaguing him for months. . . . Many of Darwin's friends must have felt as Huxley did . . . and many of his enemies must have agreed with Samuel Butler: 'Buffon planted, Erasmus Darwin and Lamarck watered, but it was Mr. Darwin who said "that fruit is ripe", and shook it into his lap.'[31]

VII

THINKING ASIDE

Limits of Logic

In an old *Alchemist's Rosarium*, whose author I have forgotten, I once saw two pieces of advice for finding the Philosopher's Stone printed side by side:

> The Stone can only be found when the search lies heavily on the searcher.—Thou seekest hard and findest not. Seek not and thou wilst find.

The introspective reports of artists and scientists on their sources of inspiration and methods of work often display the same contradiction. 'Saturate yourself through and through with your subject . . . and wait' was Lloyd Morgan's advice. 'Chance only favours invention for minds which are prepared for discoveries by patient study and persevering efforts.' This was said by Pasteur, and his meaning goes here beyond what I have called the factor of 'ripeness': he seems to regard chance as a kind of legitimate reward, causally related to the effort—an almost mystic conception. Souriau's famous 'to invent you must think aside'— '*pour inventer il faut penser à côté*' quoted with approval by Poincaré, points in the same direction. The consensus, at least among mathematicians, seems to be that if you strive hard enough to get to India you are bound to get to some America or other. 'One sometimes finds,' Fleming once said, 'what one is not looking for. For instance, the technician who set out to find a way to synchronize the rate of fire of a machine-gun with the revolutions of an air-screw discovered an excellent way of imitating the lowing of a cow.'

The history of discovery is full of such arrivals at unexpected destinations, and arrivals at the right destination by the wrong boat. Kepler set out to prove that the universe is built on simple geometrical or musical principles—and found that it was built 'on a cartload of dung': the elliptic orbits. He celebrated his discovery with a quotation from Virgil's *Eclogues* where Truth appears as a teasing hussy: you chase after her until you almost collapse; then when you have given up she smilingly surrenders.

At times one almost suspects that all these references to mysterious inspirations and sudden flashes of insight, all these protestations about 'I have no idea how I did it' and *'je ne cherche pas, je trouve'*, may stem from an unconscious desire to appear as the privileged master of some Socratic demon. Yet the evidence for large chunks of irrationality embedded in the creative process, not only in art (where we are ready to accept it) but in the exact sciences as well, cannot be disputed; and it is particularly conspicuous in the most rational of all sciences: mathematics and mathematical physics. From Kepler and Descartes to Planck and de Broglie, the working methods of the great pioneers seem to have been inspired by Einstein's jingle, improvised for the benefit of an unknown lady who asked him for a dedication on a photograph:

> A thought that sometimes makes me hazy:
> Am I—or are the others crazy?

In the popular imagination these men of science appear as sober ice-cold logicians, electronic brains mounted on dry sticks. But if one were shown an anthology of typical extracts from their letters and autobiographies with no names mentioned, and then asked to guess their profession, the likeliest answer would be: a bunch of poets or musicians of a rather romantically naïve kind. The themes that reverberate through their intimate writings are: the belittling of logic and deductive reasoning (except for verification after the act); horror of the one-track mind; distrust of too much consistency ('One should carry one's theories lightly', wrote Titchener); scepticism regarding all-too-conscious thinking ('It seems to me that what you call full consciousness is a limit case which can never be fully accomplished. This seems to me connected with the fact called the narrowness of consciousness *Enge des Bewusstseins*,'—Einstein). This sceptical reserve is compensated by trust in intuition and in unconscious guidance by quasi-religious or by aesthetic sensibilities. 'I cannot believe that God plays dice with the world,' Einstein repeated on several occasions, rejecting the tendency in modern physics to replace causality by statistical probabilities. 'There is a scientific taste just as there is a literary or artistic one', wrote Renan. Hadamard emphasized that the mathematician is in most cases unable to foresee whether a tentative line of attack will be successful; but he has a 'sense of beauty that can inform us, and I cannot see anything else allowing us to foresee. This is undoubtedly the way the Greek geometers thought when they investigated the ellipse, because there is no other conceivable way.' Poincaré was equally specific: 'It may be surprising to see emotional sensibility invoked *à propos* of mathematical demonstrations which, it would seem, can interest only the intellect. This would be to forget the feeling of mathematical beauty, of the harmony of numbers and forms, of geometric elegance. This is a true aesthetic feeling that all real mathematicians know. The useful combinations [of ideas] are precisely the most beautiful, I mean those best able to charm this special sensibility.' Max Planck, the father of quantum theory, wrote in his autobiography that the pioneer scientist must have 'a vivid intuitive imagination for new ideas not generated by deduction, but by *artistically* creative imagination'. The quotations could be continued indefinitely, yet I cannot recall any explicit statement to the contrary by any eminent mathematician or physicist.

Here, then, is the apparent paradox. A branch of knowledge which operates predominantly with abstract symbols, whose entire rationale and credo are objectivity, verifiability, logicality, turns out to be dependent on mental processes which are subjective, irrational, and verifiable only after the event.

The Unconscious before Freud

The apparent paradox arises out of certain misconceptions about the process of thinking and about the methods of science. Both originated in the Age of Enlightenment, and hardened into a dogmatic creed during the nineteenth century; the rapid expansion of the area of knowledge exacted its price in a temporary loss of depth. The depth-psychologies of men like Nietzsche, Freud, and Jung bored through the shallow crust, but each drove its shafts into one particular direction inhabited by demons of a particular breed. The concept of the unconscious acquired a mystical halo and a clinical odour; it became a kind of Pandora's box, which sceptical psychologists asserted to be empty, while to others it served as a stage-magician's trunk, equipped with a trapdoor underneath and secret drawers. A good many of these violent reactions originated in the mistaken belief that 'the unconscious mind' was, like the Relativity Theory and sub-atomic physics, an invention of the twentieth century.

In fact, however, the unconscious was no more invented by Freud than evolution was invented by Darwin, and has an equally impressive pedigree, reaching back to antiquity; a brief historic retrospect may help to see it in a broader perspective and a more balanced context. The larger part of the quotations which follow are taken from L. L. Whyte's book on *The Unconscious Before Freud* (1962)—a remarkable contribution to that neglected branch of historiography, the History of Ideas.

I shall not bore the reader with obscure quotations from the Upanishads, or ancient Egypt and Greece. At the dawn of Christian Europe the dominant influence were the Neoplatonists; foremost among them Plotinus, who took it for granted that 'feelings can be present without awareness of them', that 'the absence of a conscious perception is no proof of the absence of mental activity', and who talked confidently of a 'mirror' in the mind which, when correctly aimed, reflects the processes going on inside it, when aimed in another direction, fails to do so—but the process goes on all the same. Augustine marvelled at man's immense store of unconscious memories—'a spreading, limitless room within me—who can reach its limitless depth?'

The knowledge of unconscious mentation had always been there, as can be shown by quotations from theologians like St. Thomas Aquinas, mystics like Jacob Boehme, physicians like Paracelsus, astronomers like Kepler, writers and poets as far apart as Dante, Cervantes, Shakespeare, and Montaigne. This in itself is in no way remarkable; what is remarkable is that this knowledge was lost during the scientific revolution, more particularly under the impact of its most influential philosopher, René Descartes, who flourished in the first half of the seventeenth century.

As modern physics started with the Newtonian revolution, so modern philosophy starts with what one might call the Cartesian Catastrophe. The catastrophe consisted in the splitting up of the world into the realms of matter and mind, *and* the identification of 'mind' with conscious thinking. The result of this identification was the shallow rationalism of *l'esprit Cartesien*, and an impoverishment of psychology which it took three centuries to remedy even in part. But it also had a further, unexpected consequence. To quote Whyte:

Prior to Descartes and his sharp definition of the dualism there was no cause to contemplate the possible existence of unconscious mentality as part of a separate realm of mind. Many religious and speculative thinkers had taken for granted factors lying outside but influencing immediate awareness. . . . Until an attempt had been made (with apparent success) to choose *awareness* as the defining characteristic of mind, there was no occasion to invent the idea of *unconscious* mind . . . It is only after Descartes that we find, first the idea and then the term 'unconscious mind' entering European thought.[1]

Only gradually did the reaction set in—the realization that 'if there are two realms, physical and mental, awareness cannot be taken as the criterion of mentality [because] the springs of human nature lie in the unconscious . . . as the realm which links the moments of human awareness with the background of organic processes within which they emerge'.[2]

Among the first to take up the cudgels against Descartes's '*Cogito ergo sum*' was the Cambridge philosopher Cudworth:

. . . Those philosophers themselves who made the essence of the soul to consist in cogitation, and again, the essence of cogitation in clear and express consciousness, cannot render it in any way probable, that the souls of men in all profound sleeps, lethargies, and apoplexies . . . are never so much as one moment without expressly conscious cogitations; which, if they were, according to the principles of their philosophy, they must, *ipso facto*, cease to have any being. . . . It is certain, that our human souls themselves are not always conscious of whatever they have in them; for even the sleeping geometrician hath, at that time, all his geometrical theorems some way in him; as also the sleeping musician, all his musical skills and songs. . . . We have all experience of our doing many animal actions non-attendingly, which we reflect upon afterwards; as, also, that we often continue a long series of bodily motions, by a mere virtual intention of our minds, and as it were by half a cogitation. . . .[3]

John Locke sided with Descartes, declaring boldly: 'It is impossible to perceive without perceiving that he does perceive.' John Norris (1657–1711) retorted with equal boldness:

We may have ideas of which we are not conscious. . . . There are infinitely more ideas impressed on our minds than we can possibly attend to or perceive. . . . There may be an impression of ideas without any actual perception of them.[4]

This was written in 1690.
At about the same time the Earl of Shaftesbury wrote:
One would think, there was nothing easier for us, than to know our own minds. . . . But our thoughts have generally such an obscure implicit language, that it is the hardest thing in the world to make them speak out distinctly.[5]

Leibniz—Newton's rival as a mathematician, and Descartes's opponent as a philosopher—tried to determine quantitative thresholds of awareness. He came to the conclusion:
Our clear concepts are like islands which arise above the ocean of obscure ones.[6]

We now enter the eighteenth century. Leibniz's concept of the unconscious found many followers in Germany, among them Christian Wolff:
Let no-one imagine that I would join the Cartesians in asserting that nothing can be in the mind of which it is not aware. That is a prejudice which impedes the understanding of the mind.[7]

Lichtenberg, a hunch-backed genius, satirical writer, and professor of physics at Goettingen, regarded dreams as a means to self-knowledge, and thoughts as products of the *Id*:
It thinks, one ought to say. We become aware of certain representations which do not depend on us; others depend on us, or at least so we believe; where is the boundary? One should say, it thinks, just as one says, it rains. To say *cogito* is already too much if one translates it by '*I* think'.
The same protest is echoed by Lamartine: 'I never think—my thoughts think for me.'

Kant is probably the driest among the great philosophers—who would have suspected him among the forerunners of Freud?—:
The field of our sense-perceptions and sensations, of which we are not conscious, though we undoubtedly can infer that we possess them, that is, the dark ideas in man, is immeasurable. The clear ones

in contrast cover infinitely few points which lie open to consciousness; so that in fact on the great map of our spirit only a few points
are illuminated.[8]

The German physician and philosopher E. Platner—of whom I
confess never to have heard before—was, according to Whyte, the first
to use the term *Unbewusstsein*, unconsciousness, and to assert that
thinking is a constant oscillation between conscious and unconscious
processes:

> Consciousness is no essential part of an idea. Ideas with conscious-
> ness I call apperceptions following Leibniz; ideas without conscious-
> ness perceptions, or dark images. The life of the mind is an unbroken
> series of actions, a continuous series of ideas of both kinds. For
> apperceptions alternate with perceptions throughout life. Ideas with
> consciousness are often the psychological results of ideas without
> consciousness.[9]

As we approach the nineteenth century, the single voices grow into
a chorus in praise of the creative faculties of the unconscious mind. It is
perhaps most audible in Germany; among those who join in are, to
mention only a few, Herder, Schelling, Hegel, Goethe, Fichte. Here,
for instance, is Goethe:

> Man cannot persist long in a conscious state, he must throw himself
> back into the Unconscious, for his root lives there. . . . Take for
> example a talented musician, composing an important score:
> consciousness and unconsciousness will be like warp and weft.[10]

Jean-Paul Richter, an outstanding novelist (unfortunately little
known in England):

> The unconscious is really the largest realm in our minds, and just
> on account of this unconsciousness it is an inner Africa, whose
> unknown boundaries may extend far away. Why should everything
> come to consciousness that lies in the mind since, for example, that
> of which it has already been aware, the whole great realm of
> memory, only appears to it illuminated in small areas while the
> entire remaining world stays invisible in the shadows? And may
> there not be a second half world of our mental moon which never
> turns towards consciousness?
>
> The most powerful thing in the poet, which blows the good and
> the evil spirit into his works, is precisely the unconscious. . . .[11]

I. H. Fichte (a psychologist, son of the philosopher) postulated the existence of *pre-conscious* states:

> Beneath *active* consciousness there must lie consciousness in a merely potential state, that is a middle condition of the mind, which though not yet conscious, none the less positively carries the specific character of Intelligence; from those conditions of preconscious existence the true consciousness must be explained and developed step by step.[12]

In France the Cartesian spirit survived longest—until the second half of the nineteenth century in fact, when Charcot and his colleagues revolutionized psychiatry (Freud, at one time, had studied under Charcot). But in England the concept of the unconscious had a long and distinguished line of ancestors, some of whom I have already quoted. Here is Abraham Tucker, an influential philosopher, writing around 1750:

> . . . our mental organs do not stand idle the moment we cease to employ them, but continue the motions we put into them after they have gone out of our sight, thereby working themselves to a glibness and smoothness and falling into a more regular and orderly posture than we could have placed them with all our skill and industry.[13]

The term 'unconscious cerebration' was coined by W. B. Carpenter, a nineteenth-century physician and naturalist:

> . . . That action of the brain which, through unconscious cerebration, produces results which might never have been produced by thought.[14]

Other characteristic English coinages are Wordsworth's 'caverns in the mind which sun can never penetrate', Coleridge's 'twilight realm of consciousness', William James's 'fringe consciousness', and Myers's 'subliminal self'. In 1860 Sir Thomas Laycock wrote that—

> no general fact is so well established by the experience of mankind or so universally accepted as a guide in the affairs of life, as that of unconscious life and action.[15]

And Maudsley, writing a few years later:

> The most important part of mental action, the essential process on which thinking depends, is unconscious mental activity.[16]

For the climax of this story we must return to Germany in the second half of the nineteenth century. The pioneers of German experimental psychology were Fechner ('Fechner's law') and Wilhelm Wundt. Fechner's attitude is summed up in his famous metaphor of the mind as an iceberg, with only a fraction of it above the surface of consciousness, moved by the winds of awareness, but mostly by hidden under-water currents. Wundt continued where Fechner had left off:

> Our mind is so fortunately equipped, that it brings us the most important bases for our thoughts without our having the least knowledge of this work of elaboration. Only the results of it become conscious. This unconscious mind is for us like an unknown being who creates and produces for us, and finally throws the ripe fruits in our lap.[17]

At about the same time, in 1868, Erich von Hartmann published his *Philosophy of the Unconscious*, which became a best-seller. From a period novel by the popular Spielhagen we learn that in 1870 two main topics dominated conversation in the intellectual salons of Berlin: Wagner and the Unconscious. We are reminded of the scene in the London salon of Disraeli's play, where the fashionable topic of Evolution is discussed—fifteen years before anybody had heard the name of Darwin. Whyte lists six philosophical works published within ten years after von Hartmann's which carry the word 'unconscious' in their titles. In the literature of the period Nietzsche was the towering giant. He took over the unconscious *Id* from Lichtenberg (which Groddeck then took over from Nietzsche, and Freud from Groddeck); it is one of the leitmotifs in Nietzsche's work:

> Where are the new doctors of the soul?... Consciousness is the last and latest development of the organic, and is consequently the most unfinished and least powerful of these developments. Every extension of knowledge arises from making conscious the unconsciousness. The great basic activity is unconscious. For it is *narrow*, this room of human consciousness.

Whyte concludes: 'The general conception of unconscious mental process was *conceivable* (in post-Cartesian Europe) around 1700, *topical* around 1800, and *fashionable* around 1870–1880. . . . It cannot be disputed that by 1870–1880 the general conception of the unconscious mind was a European commonplace and that many special applications of this general idea had been vigorously discussed for several decades.'[18]

I have confined this digest to unconscious *thinking*; there is an equal abundance in relevant quotations which refer to the motivational, affective, and pathological aspects of the unconscious, and of the dream. My intent was not to belittle either the greatness or the originality of Freud—that would be as stupid as trying to run down Newton because he had 'stood on the shoulders of giants'. But while Newton was aware of this—the expression is his own—Freud, curiously, was not. He never realized how respectable the idea was on which he built his edifice.

The Mechanization of Habits

The feeling of mystery—or of wary scepticism—which mention of 'the unconscious' evokes is part of our mental heritage, derived from the Cartesian tradition. The tenacity of that tradition, deeply engrained in our thinking habits, makes us constantly forget the obvious fact—rubbed in by everyday experience—that *awareness is a matter of degrees*. Conscious and unconscious experiences do not belong to different compartments of the mind; they form a continuous scale of gradations, of degrees of awareness. We may call, as Leibniz did, conscious events 'light', unconscious ones 'dark'—provided that we remember the infinite shadings from lighter to darker grey between them. The dark end of the scale extends well below the human level to an unknown limit—which may possibly be some form of 'proto-plasmic consciousness'; Bergson even asserted that 'the unconscious-ness of a falling stone is something different from the unconsciousness of a growing cabbage'.

In human beings we find at the bottom of the scale the self-regulating activities which control the viscera and glands, the circula-tion of the blood and other physiological processes of which we are normally unaware; yet in their ensemble they may supply that vegetative or bovine consciousness of being warmly alive and kicking. From here on the scale of awareness ascends to the more or less mechanical—i.e. less or more conscious—exercise of practised skills: from walking along a road to picking one's way through puddles in the rain, to climbing an exposed rock-face; from tying one's shoe-strings to knotting a broken shoe-string; humming a tune absent-mindedly—singing it to an audience; adding up a column of figures mechanically—checking it, after a mistake has been discovered, with great attention. At the top of the scale we find the quasi-hypnotic state

of utter concentration on a problem, or absorption in a thriller, blind
and deaf to one's surroundings.

Equally continuous gradients of awareness are found in the exercise
of perceptual and cognitive skills, the working of memory, the ebbs
and tides of emotion. We are conscious only of a fraction of the input
into our eyes, ears, and skin; yet the intake is registered nevertheless.
We are unaware of the ticking of the clock, but aware that it has
stopped. While reading we are unaware of the shape of the letters
because the skill of transforming them into words is fully automatized,
and awareness is focussed on the meaning behind the shapes—a phenomenon known as the 'transparency' of language. We summon
memories asleep in the dormitory of the mind, while others barge in
uninvited. Oddest of all, we hold ourselves and others responsible for
forgetting something which ought to have been remembered. The
schoolboy who has left his gym-shoes at home, the maid who has
forgotten to put sugar on the breakfast tray, are held responsible for
unconscious acts of omission.

The greater mastery and ease we gain in the exercise of a skill, the
more automatized it will tend to become, because the code of rules
which controls it now operates below the threshold of awareness. But
the degree of conscious attention which accompanies the performance
depends also on a second factor: the prevailing environmental conditions, the lie of the land—whether it is familiar, or contains unusual
features. The inexperienced driver must concentrate even on an empty
road. The experienced driver functions automatically; but he must
concentrate in heavy traffic.

We may then, somewhat paradoxically, describe awareness as that
experience which decreases and fades away with our increasing mastery
of a skill exercised under monotonous conditions. Mastery of the code
and stability of environment are the two factors which lead to the
formation of habit; and habit-formation is accompanied by a gradual
dimming and darkening of the lights of awareness. On the other hand,
we may regard this tendency towards the progressive automatization
of skills as an act of mental parsimony, as a handing-down of the
controls to lower levels in the hierarchy of nervous functions, enabling
the higher levels to turn to more challenging tasks. Thus the typist can
go on transcribing letters while thinking of her boy friend; and the boy
friend can drive the car while discussing with her their weekend plans
—thanks to the benevolent workings of the principle of parsimony,
which seems to be an essential factor in mental progress.

To revert to an earlier example: the beginner, hopefully facing a chessboard, feels uncertain about the manner in which bishops and rooks are permitted to move, and has to consult his textbook or his teacher. After some practice it becomes impossible for him to move a rook diagonally without a feeling of aesthetic and moral revulsion, of having committed an obscenity or violated a sacred taboo: the rules have become automatized, encoded in the circuitry of his nervous system. At a still later stage he learns to apply certain stratagems just as automatically: to avoid 'pins' and 'forks', not to expose the king, to seek open rook files, etc. In games simpler than chess the same type of situation will recur over and again, and the appropriate stratagems will be codified in their turn. Computer engineers have actually built electronic brains in which both the rules *and* the stratagems of simple board games, such as noughts and crosses, are built into the 'memory' of the machine. They can beat any opponent if he blunders, and draw if he plays a correct game. The machine illustrates the process of relegating familiar tasks to lower levels of the mental hierarchy which function as unawares—or nearly—as involuntary reflexes.

But how does all this relate to mental creativity? Only indirectly. The intervention of unconscious processes in the creative act is a phenomenon quite different from the automatization of skills; and our unawareness of the sources of inspiration is of a quite different order from the unawareness of what we are doing while we tie our shoe-strings or copy a letter on the typewriter. In the creative act there is an *upward* surge from some unknown, fertile, underground layers of the mind; whereas the process I have described is a *downward* relegation of the controls of skilled techniques.

In fact I have so far discussed only one aspect or dimension of consciousness: let us call it the linear scale, or *linear gradient* of awareness. At one end of the scale we found routines performed without awareness; at the opposite end the single-minded, hyper-awake concentration on a problem, where consciousness is focussed into a narrow beam with darkness all round. But such a one-dimensional interpretation of the varieties of consciousness, as a line running from automatism to obsession, seems highly unsatisfactory. Consciousness is a multi-dimensional affair, as I hope to show in the pages that follow. The 'linear' gradient of awareness which I have discussed is only one of these dimensions—though nevertheless an important one. It is along that gradient that learning is transformed into habit, that the control of new skills, once mastered, slides down under its own gravity as it were, into the basement, making room upstairs for new acquisitions.

A pianist, after practising a piece for some time, can reel it off 'in his sleep', as the saying goes. The exact opposite of this process is illustrated by the famous case of Tartini composing the Devil's Trill Sonata while asleep. The first example shows the unconscious as a repository of habits which no longer need being 'attended to'; the second, as a breeding ground of novelties.

It is essential to bear both processes in mind—and not to confuse them. Most Behaviourists accept only the first: they regard habit-formation as the essence of mental progress; original ideas, on this view, are lucky hits among random tries, retained because of their utility value—just as biological evolution is held to be the outcome of random mutations retained because of their survival value.

Among those prepared to accept the positive role of the unconscious, there is a frequent tendency to confuse 'downward' and 'upward' traffic—to equate automatism with intuition. Some highly developed, semi-automatized skills have a great amount of flexibility—the result of years of hard training; but their practitioners are devoid of originality. Tightrope walkers, acrobats, night-club pianists, and calculating prodigies display virtuosity; a virtuoso is defined by the *Oxford Dictionary* as 'a person skilled in the mechanical part of a fine art'. Needless to say, virtuosity may combine in the same person with creativity; but in itself it is no more than the highest elaboration of a routine with fixed, automatized rules of the game and a malleable strategy.

Such mechanical virtuosity has probably reached its highest development in the Japanese arts inspired by Zen Buddhism: swordsmanship, archery, Judo, calligraphic painting. The method to reach perfection has been authoritatively described as 'practice, repetition, and repetition of the repeated with ever-increasing intensity',[19] until the adept 'becomes a kind of automaton, so to speak, as far as his own consciousness is concerned'.[20]* That is the method by which Professor Skinner of Harvard University, a leader of the Behaviourist school, trained pigeons to perform circus acts, intended as an explanation of mental development in man.

We have heard conscious thoughts being compared to icebergs, or islands in the ocean of unconscious mentation; we have heard Einstein affirm that 'full consciousness is a limit case which can never be fully accomplished'. Let me proceed from these metaphors to a closer analogy, which may help to dispel common illusions about the clarity of conscious thought.

Most people with normal eyesight tend to the flattering belief that they see the world around them at any time in sharp focus; in fact, however, they see a blur. Only a minute fraction of the visual field—about one-thousandth of it—is seen distinctly; outside of this centre vision becomes increasingly vague and hazy. If you gaze fixedly at a single word in the centre of the page you are reading, and try to prevent your gaze from straying along the line (which is not easy because reading is an automatized skill), you will see only about a couple of words sharp in focus, the rest of the line on both sides trails off into a haze. And how about the whole page, and the rest of the room around you?

Focal vision subtends an angle of only about four degrees, less than the angle at the point of a pin, out of a total field of a hundred and eighty degrees. Yet we are unaware of this, because we constantly scan the field with, mostly unconscious, movements of the eye, to bring the blurred periphery into the narrow beam of focal vision—pinpointed at the fovea, the tiny spot at the centre of the retina which alone conveys true and distinct sight.

This much every schoolboy learns (and forgets); but in 1960 experiments at McGill University led to the rather surprising discovery that the unconscious movements of the eye are not merely *aids* to clearer vision, but a *sine qua non* of vision. When the subject's gaze remained really fixed on a stationary object (by means of a mechanical device, see Book Two, X), his vision went haywire, the image of the object disintegrated and disappeared—then reappeared after a while but in distorted shape or in fragments. Static vision does not exist; there is no seeing without exploring.

With due caution we can draw a limited analogy between visual scanning and mental scanning—between the blurred, peripheral vision outside the focal beam, and the hazy, half-formed notions which accompany thinking on the fringes of consciousness. 'Every definite image in the mind', wrote William James, 'is steeped and dyed in the free water that flows round it. With it goes the sense of its relations, near and remote, the dying echo of whence it came to us, the dawning sense of whither it is to lead. The significance, the value of the image, is all in this halo or penumbra that surrounds and escorts it'.[21]

If one attempts to hold fast to a mental image or concept—to hold it, immobile and isolated, in the focus of awareness, it will disintegrate, like the static, visual image on the fovea: a word, constantly repeated, becomes meaningless; an idea, stripped of its hazy penumbra, vanishes like the Cheshire Cat. Thinking is never a sharp, neat, linear process; it could rather be compared to the progress of a boat on a lake. When you day-dream you drift before the wind; when you read or listen to a narrative you travel like a barge towed by a tug. But in each case the progress of the boat causes ripples on the lake, spreading in all directions —memories, images, associations; some of these move quicker than the boat itself and create anticipations; others penetrate into the deep. The boat symbolizes focal awareness, the ripples on the surface are the fringes of consciousness, and you can furnish the deeps, according to taste, with the nasty eddies of repressed complexes, the deep-water currents of the collective unconscious, or with archetypal coral-reefs. When thinking is in the tow of a narrative, focal awareness must stick to its course and cannot follow the ripples on their journey across the lake; but it is their presence all round the horizon, on the peripheries of awareness, which provides resonance, colour, and depth, the atmosphere and feel of the story. When it comes to productive thinking, however, the metaphor breaks down—unless we equip it with an outboard motor, a gyro-compass, servo-steering, and other paraphernalia.

The existence of an intermediary region between the 'limit case' of sharp, narrow focal awareness and the vast unconscious regions of the mind has been recognized for a long time. Fichte (and later Freud) called it the pre-conscious (*das Vorbewusstsein*), James called it the fringe; Polànyi 'subsidiary awareness'; the analogy with vision yielded 'peripheral awareness'; but since awareness is a matter of degrees, it would be mistaken to draw a sharp line between pre- and unconscious processes, between the shallows and the deep. What matters is the distinction between the single event (the percept, or concept, or word, or muscle-action) which for a fleeting moment occupies the focus of attention—and the processes on the periphery which define the context, the purpose and meaning of the former.

But how do they interact? How do pre- or unconscious processes influence the direction of thought; how do some enter focal awareness

and sink back again into twilight and darkness; how do they assist
mental creativity? The answers we have heard up to now were of
a general nature; they all asserted that such assistance was indispensable
and did in fact occur; but they had little to say regarding the concrete
mechanism or procedure through which it was rendered. Perhaps the
most lucid attempt in this direction was made by that versatile genius
Francis Galton in a famous analogy:

> When I am engaged in trying to think anything out, the process
> of doing so appears to me to be this: the ideas that lie at any
> moment within my full consciousness seem to attract of their own
> accord the most appropriate out of a number of other ideas that are
> lying close at hand, but imperfectly within the range of my
> consciousness. There seems to be a presence-chamber in my mind
> where full consciousness holds court, and where two or three ideas
> are at the same time in audience, and an ante-chamber full of more
> or less allied ideas, which is situated just beyond the full ken of
> consciousness. Out of this ante-chamber the ideas *most nearly allied*
> to those in the presence-chamber appear to be summoned *in a*
> *mechanically logical way*, and to have their turn of audience.[22]

The italics are mine, and are meant to register protest. Assuming the
idea in the presence-chamber of my mind is, as it happens to be, Mr.
Galton himself, I can recall six distinct occasions in the last few months
when I thought of him. He helped to ease the gloom of my last birthday—because Galton lived to the age of eighty-nine; and the idea
'most nearly allied', which was summoned from the ante-chamber
'in a mechanically logical way', was 'Methuselah'. On another occasion
I read about the acquittal of a woman who had been tried for the
mercy-killing of her malformed baby; Galton was summoned because
he had invented the word 'eugenics'; next came, logically, the 'most
nearly allied' idea of Adolf Hitler, whose S.S. men practised eugenics
after their own fashion. On yet another occasion the closest association
was 'colour-blindness'—first studied by Dalton which rhymes with
Galton; and so forth. Each summons into the presence-chamber had
its own 'mechanical logic', if you wish to call it that; and the choice of
the 'most nearly allied idea', the order of precedence in the ante-
chamber, depended on what sort of logic, or rule of the game, was at
the time in control of the mind. Galton was a pioneer of the experimental method in word-association tests; but as a follower of the English

associationist school, he failed to realize that association is always controlled by a code of rules, whether the subject is aware of it or not; and that different codes are active at different times.

Thus the famous analogy of the ante-chamber of the mind does not get us much further; but it helps us to clarify the problem by showing the pitfalls of the mechanistic approach, and leading us back, as it were, to our starting point. It was the comparison between the blurred periphery of the visual field and the vague intimations which pass through the twilight of the pre-conscious. We can now venture a step further, and draw a parallel between the part-automatic visual scanning of a landscape, and the mental scanning of a kind of inner landscape in purposive thinking. In both cases, the scanning process is controlled by a specific, selective code that determines which features in the landscape are relevant and which are not. Scanning a panorama through my window purely for pleasure corresponds to the aimless drift of thought along the most gratifying features—memories, images, pleasurable anticipations—of the inner landscape. But if I explore with my eyes the mountain before me for the safest route to the summit, or the amount of timber it will yield; for a sign of *edelweiss*, or a strategic gun-site safe from air attack, the whole visual field will in each case become organized and patterned in different ways; and the scanning motions of my eyes, guiding the beam of focal vision, will automatically be governed by certain rules which I am unable to name, and by a purposeful strategy determined by the lie of the land.

In this example visual exploration and mental exploration are actually indistinguishable; the observational data derived from looking at the rock face, and the lessons derived from previous experience combine into one. In other situations, the exploratory process may be confined to the inner landscape, to the exclusion of all stimuli from the world outside. The poet's or the mathematician's trance-like condition while he concentrates on a problem, the vivid fantasies of the day-dreamer, the delusions of the insane, the dreams of the sleeper, are products of widely different games of the mind; but they all have this in common, that the beam of focal awareness is exploring the inner environment, and ignoring the input from the senses. The features on which the beam alights are images of a pictorial or verbal nature, memories in abstracted, conceptualized, or distorted shape; in a word, they are past experiences internalized. The inner landscape may be regarded as a kind of private, miniature model—or caricature—of the world in the subject's brain-mind (see Book Two).

Thus the *objects* of the scanning process are ultimately the individual's past experiences (including his pre-natal past) incorporated in one form or another into his mental landscape. And the *rules* which control the scanning process (the pattern of 'mental eye motions', as it were) are also derived from past experiences by abstraction and generalization; they are the results of learning compressed into the operational codes of thinking skills.

As an example, take the parlour game 'Towns with M' (see page 38). The moment I start playing it a fixed code takes control of my mental processes, and their freedom is whittled down to strategic choices. These may be based on exploring an imagined geographical map, or on the 'tuning-fork' method. The mental map is a blurred, hazy, and distorted replica of what I learned in school and on travels; but as I proceed to scan it, from west to east with the mind's eye, name after name emerges from the misty twilight: Manchester, Munich, Moscow, Murmansk, Michigan, etc. If, on the other hand, I apply the tuning-fork method, Manchester will call out Mannheim, Madrid, Madras, and so forth. All of these names were learned in the past; all of them were members of the 'M' matrix (otherwise they could not have been summoned on the 'wavelength' of that particular code); all of them were unconscious or pre-conscious the moment before the beam of focal awareness alighted on them. The beam was guided firstly by the *rule* of the game ('find *towns* with *M*, not *rivers* with *S*'), and secondly by *strategy* ('move from west to east'). The rule was fixed, the strategy variable. A further point to note is (though it does not concern us yet) that strategy operates by a kind of *feed-back* from the lie of the land: I was searching for towns with 'M' between Munich and Moscow, but found none: so I moved on. Other factors enter: I might have remembered Mannheim, but did not because of an unpleasant experience there: *emotional disturbances* interfering with 'mechanical logic'. Incidentally, the forming of a sentence in ordinary conversation follows a similar pattern. Instead of scanning a map for towns with 'M', you must scan your vocabulary for words which will fit a given meaning.

Take an even simpler practical example. I live in London and have to spend a day in Paris some time next week to see my French publisher. If this were a pleasure-trip the fringes of my consciousness would at once be crowded with half-remembered, floating images of bistros, streets, galleries, métro stations; but, as it is a business trip, a different code enters into action and the matrix is cluttered with timetables, appointment books, galley proofs, and dustcovers, which strategic planning must co-ordinate into the proper sequence.

Purposive thinking, even of this ordinary, humdrum kind, proceeds in several steps. First, the code of rules appropriate to the task is 'tuned in'—by dint of analogy with similar tasks encountered in the past. As a result, a matrix will emerge, a kind of patterned mental grid or chessboard, which provides a preliminary selection of permissible moves, a first guidance for the exploratory process. Next comes strategy, dependent upon the particulars of the situation.

Each step involves processes more or less removed from focal awareness. The code which guides the focal beam of consciousness functions more or less unconsciously. (It could not be otherwise, for if the beam were guided by the beam, we would be landed in the paradox of a little man inside the brain with a little man inside his brain, and so forth.) The codes of grammar and syntax function unconsciously; the meaning you wish to express provides the strategy for selecting the proper word. The words—just like the towns with 'M'—were lying in darkness before the beam searched them out and lit them up for a fleeting moment; then they sink back into darkness again.

Thus all reasoning, even of a trivial order, is steeped in unconscious processes. But when the task is of a more complex order, thinking may run into difficulty at each of the steps which I have outlined. A situation may share certain features with other situations encountered in the past, yet the code of rules which enabled us to cope with them proves mysteriously inadequate in the new situation. Bleeding and purging the patient proved beneficial in a number of cases, so it came to be regarded as an all-cure; why did it not work? We can bisect an angle with compass and ruler, so it was assumed that we can trisect angles by the same method; but it did not work. Sound waves are propagated in thin air, so it was assumed that light waves are propagated in a thin ether; but the analogy provided the wrong matrix. Circles turning upon circles yielded an adequate description of heavenly motions, until Tycho perfected the methods of observation; the new data disrupted the pattern, and the matrix was blocked.

When a situation is blocked, straight thinking must be superseded by 'thinking aside'—the search for a new, auxiliary matrix which will unblock it, without having ever before been called to perform such a task. The essence of discovery is to hit upon such a matrix—as Gutenberg hit on the wine-press and Kepler on the sun-force.

In the trivial routines of thinking, we are exploring the shallows on the twilight periphery of awareness, guided by a more or less automatized scanning procedure. In creative thinking we are exploring the deeps, without any obvious guidance. Yet some guidance there must be—unless all novelty is due to random hits produced by the patient monkey on the typewriter.

The 'Hooked Atoms of Thought'

Let me return once more to Henri Poincaré, who proposed a theory concerning the nature of this unconscious guidance. We have heard him describe how, on three different occasions, the solution of a problem popped up spontaneously and ready-made, as it were, from the depths of the unconscious. Further on in that famous lecture from which I have quoted (pp. 114–16) he tried to give an explanation of this phenomenon. His starting point was that mathematical discovery consists in a 'combination of ideas'; and his description of this process stresses the characteristic features of what I have called the bisociative act:

> Among chosen combinations the most fertile will often be those formed of elements drawn from domains which are far apart. . . . Most combinations so formed would be entirely sterile; but certain among them, very rare, are the most fruitful of all.

Now these combinations are engineered by the unconscious or, as he calls it, the 'subliminal self'; but how? There are, he says, two possibilities. The first is that the unconscious 'is capable of discernment; it has tact, delicacy; it knows how to choose, to divine. What do I say? It knows better how to divine than the conscious self since it succeeds where that has failed. In a word, is not the subliminal self superior to the conscious self? I confess that, for my part, I should hate to accept this. . . .' So he rejects this first hypothesis in favour of the second: the unconscious is an automaton which mechanically runs through all possible combinations:

> Figure the future elements of our combinations as something like the hooked atoms of Epicurus. During the complete repose of the mind, these atoms are motionless, they are, so to speak, hooked to the

wall. During a period of apparent rest and unconscious work, certain of them are detached from the wall and put in motion. They flash in every direction through the space . . . as would, for example, a swarm of gnats, or if you prefer a more learned comparison, like the molecules of gas in the kinematic theory of gases. Then their mutual impacts may produce new combinations.

But two objections come to his mind. Firstly, is not the number of possible combinations infinite, and the chance of hitting on a favourable one infinitesimal? No, he answers, because during the conscious preparatory work which preceded the period of unconscious incubation, a first selection was already made of those atoms which are to be unhooked from the wall; and although no satisfactory combination of them was found, 'after this shaking up imposed upon them by our will, these atoms do not return to their previous rest. They freely continue to dance'—until the one favourable collision in a million occurs. (This is rather like saying that the chances of the monkey on the typewriter hitting on a Shakespeare sonnet would be considerably improved by building a typewriter which uses whole words as keys instead of letters.)

The second objection which occurred to Poincaré is as follows: although countless combinations are formed 'in consequence of the automatism of the subliminal self, only the interesting ones . . . break into the domain of consciousness'. But, if so, what is the nature of the mysterious sieve which rejects the useless combinations and allows only the lucky hits to pass into consciousness? Poincaré's answer is that the selection is done by 'the aesthetic sensibility of the real creator. The useful combinations are precisely the most beautiful, I mean those best able to charm this special sensibility'.

This is certainly a more attractive answer than Galton's, who summons ideas from the ante-chamber 'in a mechanically logical way'; yet Poincaré himself felt its unsatisfactoriness. For it combines a mechanistic theory about the random collision of atomic ideas in the unconscious, with an aesthetic sensibility which resides in the conscious, and plays the part of a *deus ex machina*. We do not doubt that this kind of sensibility is present in the creative mind, and to inquire into its nature is precisely what we are after; but Poincaré lets the matter rest just where the problem starts.

Particularly fascinating in this lecture, delivered in 1908, is the fact that Poincaré, after acknowledging his debt to the 'subliminal self' and singing its praises, confesses that he would 'hate to accept' that it might in some respects be superior to the conscious self, and relegates it to the role of an automatic mixing machine in the basement. He worked by intuition, but for all his modesty and open-mindedness he was unable to shake off the rationalist *hubris* of the nineteenth century.*

Exploring the Deeps

All we have gleaned from these excursions into the history of our subject, from Plotinus to Poincaré, is firstly, a negative insight into the narrow limitations of conscious thinking; and, on the positive side, affirmations of the superiority of unconscious mentation at certain stages of creative work. But regarding the reasons for this superiority, and the process by which it manifests itself, we got merely a few vague intimations, or else unsatisfactory mechanistic hypotheses such as Galton's and Poincaré's. Nor, I may add here, had Freud or Jung much to say about the specific problem how unconscious processes lead to new discoveries.

Let us at this stage follow the advice we have so often heard repeated, and 'think aside'—by turning, for a moment, from scientists to poets. If we were to apply Poincaré's hypothesis we would come to the conclusion that the poet has a conscious mind endowed with aesthetic sensibility, and an unconscious mind equipped with an automatic rhyme-computer (built on the principle of rhyming lexicons), and also with an image computer (a kind of magic lantern with an automatic slide-changer). Out of the hundreds of rhymes and similes produced per minute the vast majority would, of course, be valueless, and the aesthetic censor in the conscious mind would have a full-time job rejecting them—until he went out of his mind.

It seems neither an economical nor an inspired procedure. Now let us listen to Coleridge's celebrated description of the genesis of Kubla Khan. He is speaking of himself in the third person singular:

> In the summer of the year 1797, the Author, then in ill health, had retired to a lonely farm-house between Porlock and Linton. . . . In consequence of a slight indisposition, an anodyne had been prescribed, from the effects of which he fell asleep in his chair at the moment that he was reading the following sentence, or words of the same substance, in *Purchas's Pilgrimage*:

'Here the Khan Kubla commanded a palace to be built, and a stately garden thereunto. And thus ten miles of fertile ground were enclosed with a wall.'

The Author continued for about three hours in a profound sleep, at least of the external senses [sic] during which time he has the most vivid confidence, that he could not have composed less than from two to three hundred lines; if that indeed can be called composition in which all the images rose up before him as *things* with a parallel production of the correspondent expressions, without any sensation or consciousness of effort. On awakening he appeared to himself to have a distinct recollection of the whole, and taking his pen, ink, and paper, instantly and eagerly wrote down the lines that are here preserved.

This, of course, is an extreme case of unconscious production—even if, in all likelihood, it did not originate in a dream, but in an intense day-dream or hypnogogic state. (In another, and probably earlier, statement Coleridge gives a different version: 'This fragment with a good deal more, not recoverable, composed in a sort of Reverie brought on by two grains of Opium, taken to check a dysentery.' The 'reverie' version is strengthened by the words 'in a profound sleep, *at least of the external senses*'—which point towards some intermediary kind of 'waking dream'.)

But whether he was asleep or half asleep is unimportant; the point to note is the emphasis he puts on visual images 'which rose up as *things*'. Unfortunately, no sooner had he started on the actual writing down of the poem than he was interrupted 'by a person on business from Porlock, and detained by him above an hour, and on his return to his room, found, to his no small surprise and mortification . . . that with the exception of some eight or ten scattered lines and images, all the rest had passed away *like the images on the surface of a stream into which a stone has been cast*'. This incidental metaphor suddenly sets off in its author another chain of visual imagery which illustrates how the dream version of 'Kubla Khan' was lost, thanks to the gentleman from Porlock, but reconstructed later on out of the remaining fragments. After the 'stone had been cast':

> . . . all the charm
> Is broken—all that phantom-world so fair
> Vanishes, and a thousand circlets spread,

And each mis-shape the other. Stay awhile,
Poor youth! . . .
The stream will soon renew its smoothness, soon
The visions will return! And lo, he stays,
And soon the fragments dim of lovely forms
Come trembling back, unite, and now once more
The pool becomes a mirror.

The whole poem, with its rather striking allegory, grew out of a hackneyed metaphor, which was meant to serve only as a visual illustration to a verbal narrative. But all at once the servant becomes master, the illustration takes over from the text; visual association, the logic of the eye are in command, and the words must follow their lead. . . .

We further note that the whole sequence of 'not less than from two to three hundred lines' of the Kubla Khan dream itself was triggered off by a passage read in *Purchas's Pilgrimage*, as indifferent as the simile of the stone cast into the stream: 'Here the Khan Kubla commanded a palace to be built', etc. But at that point his imagination caught on, the opium took effect, visual thinking took over, and images 'rose up as things'.

Thinking in pictures dominates the manifestations of the unconscious —the dream, the hypnogogic half-dream, the psychotic's hallucinations, the artist's 'vision'. (The 'visionary' prophet seems to have been a visualizer, and not a verbalizer; the highest compliment we pay to those who trade in verbal currency is to call them 'visionary thinkers'.)

But, on the other hand, pictorial thinking is a more *primitive* form of mentation than conceptual thinking, which it precedes in the mental evolution of the individual and of the species. The language of the primitive (and of the child) is, to borrow Kretschmer's simile, 'like the unfolding of a picture-strip: each word expresses a picture, a pictorial image, regardless of whether it signifies an object or an action'. In Golding's novel *The Inheritors* the Neanderthal men always say 'I had a picture' when they mean 'I thought of something'; and anthropologists agree that for once a novelist got the picture right.

Thus the poet who reverts to the pictorial mode of thought is *regressing* to an older and lower level of the mental hierarchy—as we do every night when we dream, as mental patients do when they regress to infantile fantasies. But the poet, unlike the dreamer in his sleep, alternates between two different levels of the mental hierarchy; the dreamer's awareness functions on one only. The poet thinks both in images and verbal concepts, at the same time or in quick alternation; each *trouvaille*, each original find, bisociates two matrices. The dreamer floats among the phantom shapes of the hoary deep; the poet is a skin-diver with a breathing tube.

Similar considerations apply—and will be discussed in Part III —to rhythm, metre, alliteration, assonance, rhyme. The rhythmic beat, echoing the shaman's tom-tom, awakens archaic resonances and 'lulls the mind into a waking trance' (Yeats). The rhyme appeals to the tendency to vocal repetition in the language of primitives and children (kala-kala, ma-ma), and to the equally deep-rooted tendency to associate by sound—punning. To conclude this anticipatory excursion: the creative activity of the artist involves *momentary regressions* to earlier stages in mental evolution, bringing forms of mentation into play which otherwise manifest themselves only in the dream or dream-like states.

The Word and the Vision

Let us return from poets to scientists, and to the question what guidance the latter could possibly derive from the intervention of unconscious processes. The answer which, by analogy, now suggests itself is that *the temporary relinquishing of conscious controls liberates the mind from certain constraints which are necessary to maintain the disciplined routines of thoughts but may become an impediment to the creative leap; at the same time other types of ideation on more primitive levels of mental organization are brought into activity.* The first part of this sentence indicates an act of abdication, the second an act of promotion. It will be useful to remember this dual aspect of the Eureka act; it will be seen, later on, to correspond to the destructive-constructive character of all great revolution in the history of thought.

The scientific counterpart of the Coleridge episode is the Kekulé episode (p. 118). But the vision of the serpent biting its tail was only the last one in a series, which extended over a period of seven or eight years. This is how Kekulé described one of the early but decisive quasi-hallucinations, which led to his theory of molecular constitution—he was then living in London:

'One fine summer evening,' he relates, 'I was returning by the last omnibus, "outside" as usual, through the deserted streets of the metropolis, which are at other times so full of life. I fell into a reverie, and lo! the atoms were gambolling before my eyes. Whenever, hitherto, these diminutive beings had appeared to me, they had always been in motion; but up to that time, I had never been able to discern the nature of their motion. Now, however, I saw how, frequently, two smaller atoms united to form a pair; how a larger one embraced two smaller ones; how still larger ones kept hold of three or even four of the smaller; whilst the whole kept whirling in a giddy dance. I saw how the larger ones formed a chain . . . I spent part of the night putting on paper at least sketches of these dream forms.'[23]

The whirling, giddy vision reminds one of the hallucinations of schizophrenics, as painted or described by them. Kekulé's case is rather exceptional, but nevertheless characteristic in one respect: the sudden abdication of conceptual thought in favour of semi-conscious visual conceits.

Another example is Michael Faraday, one of the greatest physicists of all time, who also was a 'visionary' not only in the metaphorical but in the literal sense. He saw the stresses surrounding magnets and electric currents as curves in space, for which he coined the name 'lines of forces', and which, in his imagination, were as real as if they consisted of solid matter. He visualized the universe patterned by these lines—or rather by narrow tubes through which all forms of 'ray-vibrations' or energy-radiations are propagated. This vision of curved tubes which 'rose up before him like things' proved of almost incredible fertility: it gave birth to the dynamo and the electric motor; it led Faraday to discard the ether, and to postulate that light was electro-magnetic radiation. Perhaps the most remarkable fact about Faraday is that he lacked any mathematical education or gift, and was 'ignorant of all but the merest elements of arithmetic'; and mathematics is of course regarded as an indispensable tool of the physicist. In his Faraday memorial lecture in 1881, von Helmholtz—himself one of the greatest mathematical physicists of the century—remarked:

It is in the highest degree astonishing to see what a large number of general theorems, the methodical deduction of which requires the highest powers of mathematical analysis, he found by a kind of intuition, with the security of instinct, without the help of a single mathematical formula.[24]

Kekulé's visions resemble hallucinatory flights; Faraday's, the stable delusional systems of paranoia. Kekulé's serpent reminds one of paintings by Blake; the curves of force which crowd Faraday's universe recall the vortices in Van Gogh's skies.

Around fifty—like Newton, and at the same age—Faraday had a nervous breakdown. He had always hated writing letters and had stopped lecturing; now he seemed to have developed an abhorrence of language itself: 'This is to declare in the present instance, when I say I am not able to bear much talking, it means really, and without any mistake, or equivocation or oblique meaning, or implication, or subterfuge, or omission, that I am not able, being at present rather weak in the head and able to work no more.'[25] Distrust of words is a trait often found among those who create with their eyes.

Let us leave the borderlands of pathology. Nobody could have been further removed from it than the mild, sober, and saintly Einstein. Yet we find in him the same distrust of conscious conceptual thought, and the same reliance on visual imagery. In 1945 an inquiry was organized among eminent mathematicians in America to find out their working methods. In reply to the questionnaire which was sent to him, Einstein wrote:

> The words or the language, as they are written or spoken, do not seem to play any role in my mechanism of thought. The physical entities which seem to serve as elements in thought are certain signs and more or less clear images which can be 'voluntarily' reproduced and combined. . . .
> . . . Taken from a psychological viewpoint, this combinatory play seems to be the essential feature in productive thought—before there is any connection with logical construction in words or other kinds of signs which can be communicated to others.
> The above-mentioned elements are, in any case, of visual and some of muscular type. Conventional words or other signs have to be sought for laboriously only in a secondary stage, when the mentioned associative play is sufficiently established and can be reproduced at will.
> According to what has been said, the play with the mentioned elements is aimed to be analogous to certain logical connections one is searching for.
> In a stage when words intervene at all, they are, in my case, purely

auditive, but they interfere only in a secondary stage as already mentioned.[26]

The inquiry was organized by Jacques Hadamard, whom I have repeatedly quoted, since he is to my knowledge the only mathematician who has made a systematic research into the psychology of mathematical creation. Of himself he said:

I distinctly belong to the auditory type; and precisely on that account my mental pictures are exclusively visual. The reason for that is quite clear to me: such visual pictures are more naturally vague, as we have seen it to be necessary in order to lead me without misleading me.

He summed up the results of the inquiry as follows:

Among the mathematicians born or resident in America . . . phenomena are mostly analogous to those which I have noticed in my own case. Practically all of them . . . avoid not only the use of mental words but also, just as I do, the mental use of algebraic or any other precise signs; also as in my case, they use vague images. . . .* The mental pictures . . . are most frequently visual, but they may also be of another kind for instance, kinetic. There can also be auditive ones, but even these . . . quite generally keep their vague character.[27]

It rather sounds as if mathematical discoveries were born out of the airy nothings of *A Midsummer Night's Dream*:

> . . . as imagination bodies forth
> The forms of things unknown, the poet's pen
> Turns them to shapes, and gives to airy nothing
> A local habitation and a name.

The inquiry brought conclusive proof that among mathematicians, verbal thinking plays only a subordinate part in the decisive phase of the creative act; and there is a mass of evidence to show that this is also the rule among original thinkers in other branches of science.

This is a rather startling discovery in view of the fact that language is the proudest possession of *homo sapiens*, and the very foundation on which mental evolution could build. 'Logic' derives from *logos*, which originally meant 'language', 'thought', and 'reason', all in one. Thinking in concepts emerged out of thinking in images through the slow development of the powers of abstraction and symbolization, as the phonetic script emerged by similar processes out of pictorial symbols and hieroglyphs. Most of us were brought up in the belief that 'thinking' is synonymous with verbal thinking, and philosophers from Athens to Oxford have kept reasserting this belief. The early Behaviourists went even further, asserting not only that words are indispensable to thought, but also that thinking is nothing more than the subliminal movements of the vocal chords, an inaudible whispering to oneself. Yet if all thinking were verbal thinking Einstein would not qualify as a thinker. In fact, the whole evidence points in the opposite direction, summed up in a single sentence in Woodworth's classic textbook of experimental psychology: 'Often we have to get away from speech in order to think clearly.' And we heard one testimony after another from great scientists, which show that in order to create they had to regress at times from the word to the picture-strip, from verbal symbolism to visual symbolism—some, like Einstein, even to the kinesthetic sensation of muscle-motions. The word 'regression' is appropriate, because the high *aesthetic* value which we put on visual imagery should not obscure the fact that *as vehicles of thought*, pictorial and other non-verbal representations are indeed earlier, both phylogenetically and ontogenetically older forms of ideation, than verbal thinking. Kekulé's 'Let us dream, gentlemen', is an invitation to regression and retreat—but a regression which prepares the forward leap, a *reculer pour mieux sauter*.

The Snares of Language

The necessity for this retreat derives from the fact that words are a blessing which can turn into a curse. They crystallize thought; they give articulation and precision to vague images and hazy intuitions. But a crystal is no longer a fluid. 'Language is not only the foundation for the whole faculty of thinking, but the central point also from which proceed the misunderstandings of reason by herself.'[28] This was written by Hamman, a German philosopher of the eighteenth century, who had a great influence on Goethe. Roman Jakobson, a contemporary linguist—to quote one among many—voices the same ancient doubt:

Signs are a necessary support of thought. For socialized thought (stage of communication) and for the thought which is being socialized (stage of formulation), the most usual system of signs is language properly called; but internal thought especially when creative, willingly uses other systems of signs which are more flexible, less standardized than language and leave more liberty, more dynamism to creative thought.[29]

The vital importance of language as a thought-crystallizer was perfectly described by little Alice who, on being admonished to think carefully before she spoke, indignantly exclaimed: 'How can I know what I think till I see what I say?' For it is, of course, undeniable that in *some* forms of intellectual activity language is not only an indispensable tool, but that the stream of language actually carries the thought, so that the processes of ideation and verbal formulation become indistinguishable. The same applies to certain phases in the poet's and writer's work; but only to certain phases. The counterpart to the little girl's predicament is the little boy's who said: 'I see what I mean but I don't know how to say it.'

Not only scientists, painters, and musicians find it often difficult to convert their ideas into verbal currency, but writers too. Even H. G. Wells lamented: 'The forceps of our minds are clumsy things and crush the truth a little in the course of taking hold of it.' The novelist suffers—among other things—from the poverty of his vocabulary when he tries to describe what his characters *feel* (as distinct from what they think or do). He can write streams of what goes on in the cranial cavity, but if it is a pain in the abdominal cavity, all he can say is, 'it hurts'—or use some equally insipid synonym. Suffering is 'dumb'; the glandular and visceral processes which colour emotion do not lend themselves to verbal articulation.

The scientist's trouble with language is of a different nature. He suffers not from the poverty of his verbal tools but rather from their over-precision, and the hidden snares in them.

Take, for example, the deceptively simple words 'Space' and 'Time'. Before the dawn of the scientific revolution, medieval man lived in a closed universe with firm boundaries in space and time—a few million miles in diameter, and a few thousand years of duration. Space taken in itself, as an abstract concept, did not exist; it was merely an *attribute* of material bodies—their length, width, and depth; empty space was unthinkable, a contradiction in terms; and infinite space even more so.

Time, similarly, was simply the duration of an event. Nobody in his senses would have said that things move *through* space or *in* time—how can a thing move in or through an attribute of itself?

The over-precise meaning which these words carried had ensnared scientific thought from Aristotle to the Renaissance. Even Galileo still believed that a heavenly body, left to itself, would for ever continue to move in a *circular* path, because a straight line would carry it towards infinity—which was unthinkable. And when he noticed that two polished marble slabs stuck to each other with astonishing strength, he ascribed this to nature's horror of empty space which would be created at the moment of their separation—and thus failed to discover the phenomenon of surface-adherence.

The first thaw of these frozen word-crystals occurred in 1277, when a council of theologians in Paris condemned the Aristotelian doctrine that even God could not create empty or infinite space. Thus both empty space and infinite space became at least *thinkable*—which previously they had not been. A few unorthodox thinkers did in fact speculate about them; yet it took another four centuries until Space and Time acquired a new meaning in the Newtonian universe.

For the next two hundred years after Newton Space meant the rigid three-dimensional frame of the universe, which remained at rest; so that the motion of a boat sailing up a river was *relative* measured against the water or coast, but *absolute* motion measured against the frame of Space. Time had an equally absolute nature; and that is what to most of us the words Space and Time still mean—except in our dreams, when the rigid, Newtonian framework breaks down.

Einstein could never have transformed man's view of the universe, had he accepted those two words as ready-made tools. 'When I asked myself', he confided to a friend, 'how it happened that I in particular discovered the Relativity Theory, it seemed to lie in the following circumstance. The normal adult never bothers his head about space-time problems. Everything there is to be thought about, in his opinion, has already been done in early childhood. I, on the contrary, developed so slowly that I only began to wonder about space and time when I was already grown up. In consequence I probed deeper into the problem than an ordinary child would have done.'[30] Modesty can hardly be carried further; nor insight put into simpler terms.

'For me [the Relativity Theory] came as a tremendous surprise', said Minkovsky, who had been one of Einstein's teachers, 'for in his student days Einstein had been a lazy dog. He never bothered about mathematics at all. . . . From now on "space in itself" and "time in itself" must sink into the shade and only a union of the two will preserve independence.'[31]

The spelling of the two words had remained the same, but they now signified something quite different from what they had signified before.

Words are essential tools for formulating and communicating thoughts, and also for putting them into the storage of memory; but words can also become snares, decoys, or strait-jackets. A great number of the basic verbal concepts of science have turned out at various times to be both tools and traps: for instance, 'time', 'space', 'mass', 'force', 'weight', 'ether', 'corpuscle', 'wave', in the physical sciences; 'purpose', 'will', 'sensation', 'consciousness', 'conditioning', in psychology; 'limit', 'continuity', 'countability', 'divisibility', in mathematics. For these were not simple verbal tags, as names attached to particular persons or objects are; they were artificial constructs which behind an innocent façade hid the traces of the particular kind of logic which went into their making. As Sidney Hook has put it: 'When Aristotle drew up his table of categories which to him represented the grammar of existence, he was really projecting the grammar of the Greek language on the cosmos.'[32] That grammar has kept us to this day ensnared in its paradoxes: it made the grandeur and misery of two millennia of European thought. If Western philosophy, to quote Popper, consisted in a series of footnotes to Plato, Western science took a full two thousand years to liberate itself from the hypnotic effect of Aristotle, whose encyclopaedic philosophy penetrated the very structure of our language. It determined not only what was 'science' but also what was 'common sense'. Each of the major break-throughs in scientific thought had to be achieved not only in the teeth of Aristotelian, Platonic, and Christian dogma, but also in the teeth of what appeared to be self-evident and commonsensical—the implied rules of the code. Each revolution had to make a hole in the established fabric of conceptual thought. Kepler destroyed the 'self-evident' doctrine of uniform circular motion; Galileo the equally commonsense notion that any moving body must have a 'mover' which pulls or pushes it along. Newton, to his horror, had to go against the obvious experience that action is only possible by contact; Rutherford had to commit the contradiction in terms of asserting the divisibility of the atom, which in Greek means 'indivisible'. Einstein destroyed our belief that clocks move at the same rate anywhere in the universe; quantum physics has made the traditional meaning of words like matter, energy, cause and effect, evaporate into thin air.

'The awkward fact', said L. L. Whyte, 'that reason, as we know it, is never aware of its hidden assumptions—has been too much for some philosophers, and even many scientists to admit.'[33] One of the philosophers who saw this clearly was Wittgenstein: 'Propositions cannot represent the logical form: this mirrors itself in the propositions. That which mirrors itself in language, language cannot represent. That which expresses *itself* in language, *we* cannot represent.'[34]

The prejudices and impurities which have become incorporated into the verbal concepts of a given 'universe of discourse' cannot be undone by any amount of discourse within the frame of reference of that universe. The rules of the game, however absurd, cannot be altered by playing that game. Among all forms of mentation, verbal thinking is the most articulate, the most complex, and the most vulnerable to infectious diseases. It is liable to absorb whispered suggestions, and to incorporate them as hidden persuaders into the code. Language can become a screen which stands between the thinker and reality. This is the reason why true creativity often starts where language ends.

NOTES

To p. 157. Zen philosophy, in the form in which it is taught by its contemporary propounders (foremost among them Prof. D. T. Suzuki and his Western disciples), is a welter of confusions, derived from the failure to discriminate between automatized skills and creative originality—between the 'downward' and the 'upward' traffic to and from the unconscious. The former results in getting the 'knack' of a skill; the latter in the sudden flash of a new insight (the 'It'). The practitioner of the various applied Zen arts was trained to act 'spontaneously, unthinkingly'—and this led to the added confusion between the pseudo-spontaneity displayed by the responses of a well-oiled automaton, and the genuine spontaneity of original inspiration. (Cf. 'The "It" and the Knack', pp. 260 seq., in my *The Lotus and the Robot*, 1960).

To p. 166. Less understandable is the case of Spearman, who wrote a book on the *Creative Mind* (1930) with only passing mention of unconscious processes, the main reference being a sneer at Freud's preoccupation with 'subconscious bestiality'. This was written when Spearman was Professor of Psychology at the University of London.

To p. 172. The exceptions were G. D. Birkhoff, Norbert Wiener (who said that 'he happens to think with or without words'), and G. Polya.

VIII

UNDERGROUND GAMES

The Importance of Dreaming

To recapitulate: ordered, disciplined thought is a skill governed by set rules of the game, some of which are explicitly stated, others implied and hidden in the code. The creative act, in so far as it depends on unconscious resources, presupposes a relaxing of the controls and a regression to modes of ideation which are indifferent to the rules of verbal logic, unperturbed by contradiction, untouched by the dogmas and taboos of so-called common sense. At the decisive stage of discovery the codes of disciplined reasoning are suspended—as they are in the dream, the reverie, the manic flight of thought, when the stream of ideation is free to drift, by its own emotional gravity, as it were, in an apparently 'lawless' fashion.

The laws of disciplined thinking demand that we should stick to a given frame of reference and not shift from one universe of discourse to another. When I am arguing about *Richard III* and somebody quotes 'my kingdom for a horse' I am not supposed to shift my attention to my chances of drawing a winner in the Grand National, however tempting it may be. The strain of concentrating on an abstract subject derives mainly from the effort to inhibit emotionally more tempting associations outside of its field. But when concentration flags and primitive motivations take over, thought will shift from one matrix to another, like a ball bouncing down a mountain stream, each time an idea (like 'horse' in the above example) provides a link to a more attractive context.

We might say that while dreaming *we constantly bisociate in a passive way*—by drift as it were; but we are, of course, unaware of it because the coherence of the logical matrices is weakened, and the codes which govern them are dormant. Hence, while dreaming, we do not realize their incompatability; there is no simultaneous juxtaposition of matrices, no awareness of conflict and incongruity; that comes only on awakening. To put it in another way: the dream associates by methods which are impermissible in the waking state—such as affinities of sound detached from meaning, and similarities of form regardless of function. It makes use of 'links' which, while awake we 'would not dream' of using—except where dream-logic intrudes into humour, discovery, and art.

It is not surprising, then, that we find all the bisociative patterns that I have discussed prominently displayed in the dream: the *pun*: two strings of thought tied together by a purely accoustic knot; the *optical pun*: one visual form bisociated with two functional contexts; the *phenomenon of displacement* or shift of attention to a previously unnoticed feature; the *concretization* of abstract and general ideas in a particular image; and vice versa, the use of concrete images as *symbols* for nascent, unverbalized concepts; the *condensation* in the same linkidea of several associative contexts; the unearthing of *hidden analogies*; *impersonation* and double identity—being oneself and something else at the same time, where the 'something else' might belong to the animal, vegetable, or mineral kingdom. The ensemble of these and related operations constitutes the grammar and logic of dream-cognition. To go on with the list would be tedious, the more so as the categories overlap; but one more trick ought to be added to the repertory: the occasional *reversal* of causal sequences. This, however, is putting the phenomenon into over-concrete terms, since 'causality' (together with space, time, matter, identity, etc.) appear in the dream in a semi-fluid shape like a half-melted snowman; yet even a snowman may be standing on his head. Lastly, I must mention the obvious fact of the dreamer's extreme gullibility. Hamlet's cloud merely *resembles* a camel, weasel, or whale; to the dreamer the cloud actually *becomes* a camel, a weasel, or whale—without his turning a hair.

A child, watching a television thriller with flushed face and palpitating heart, praying that the hero should realize in time the deadly trap set for him, is at the same time aware that the hero is a shadow on the screen. A day-dreamer—like Thurber's Walter Mitty—is aware of the fantasies which he creates for his own benefit; but also aware, though less intensely so, of the fact that he is creating them. He lives, like the spectator in front of the screen, on two different levels, simultaneously or in quick alternations—by mental quantum-jumps, as it were. If he settles for a single level then either the illusion ceases to function—or it grows into hallucinatory delusion.

The dream occupies a privileged position among these ambiguous mental states; privileged, in that it is included in the normal daily cycle in spite of—or because of—its pronounced hallucinatory, 'abnormal' character. Dreaming is distinguished from other delusionary states by being transitory, easily interrupted, and by being confined to the 'inner landscape', by a more or less complete shuttering of the senses (whereas in pathological states the senses may continue to function, but perception may be perverted). On the other hand, dreaming is distinguished from day-dreaming in that the dreamer is aware of the fantasies which he creates, but unaware of the fact that he is creating them. He is the spectator passively watching the sequence of images on one level, which he actively produces on another; he is the cinema operator who works the projection machine, and the audience at the same time. But while the spectacle on the screen is visible, the operator is not. He operates in complete darkness, and there is a good reason for it: the production is frequently childish, obscene, confusing, an affront to logic and common sense.

There is no need to emphasize, in this century of Freud and Jung, that the logic of the dream is not the logic of Aristotle; that it derives from the magic type of causation found in primitive societies and the fantasies of childhood; that it is indifferent to the laws of identity and contradiction; that the dream's reasoning is guided by emotion, its morality blush-making, its symbolism pre-verbal and archaic. If these ancient codes which govern the games of the dreamer were allowed to operate in the waking state they would play havoc with civilized adult behaviour; they must be kept underground.

But these underground, in normal states subconscious, *levels* or planes in the hierarchy of mental functions must not be confused with the *linear scale* of awareness (pp. 154–7). The latter forms a continuous gradient from focal awareness, through peripheral awareness to unawareness of a given event; whereas the *levels* of the mental hierarchy form quasi-parallel (or concentric) layers, which are discontinuous, and are under normal conditions kept separate, as waking is from dreaming. The codes which govern organic activities, automatized habits, and routine skills, function unawares because they are either inborn or have been mastered by practice; the 'underground' codes function underground because they have been superseded by the codes of rational thinking. In the first case we see the working of mental economy; in the second, of mental evolution. Automatized codes serve the maintenance of normal functioning; underground codes disrupt routine in a creative or destructive sense. We are concerned with the creative aspect only; but I should mention in passing that the underground layers of the mental hierarchy must not be confused with 'repressed complexes'. The latter form a special category within the much broader realm of subconscious phenomena. Complexes originate in traumatic experiences; the underground games of the mind reflect the facts of mental evolution.

The levels of mental organization have been compared to the archaeological strata of ancient and prehistoric civilizations, buried, but not irretrievably, under our contemporary towns. The analogy is Freud's[1] but I would like to carry it one step further. Imagine for a moment that all important written records and monuments pre-dating the Industrial Revolution have been destroyed by some catastrophe like the burning down of the library in Alexandria; and that knowledge of the past could be obtained only by archaeological excavations. Without digging into the undergound strata, modern society, ignorant of the culture of the Renaissance, of Antiquity, Prehistory, and the Age of the Dinosaurs, would be reduced to an unimaginably superficial, two-dimensional existence: a species without a past and probably —for lack of comparative values—without much future. An individual deprived of his dreams, of irrational impulses, of any form of ideation except articulate verbal thought, would be in much the same position. Dreaming, in the literal and metaphorical sense, seems to be an essential part of psychic metabolism—as essential as its counterpart, the formation and automatization of habits. Without this daily dip into the ancient sources of mental life we would probably all become desiccated automata. And without the more spectacular exploratory dives of the creative individual, there would be no science and no art.

To sum up, there is a two-way traffic between conscious and unconscious. One traffic stream continually moves in a downward direction: we concentrate on new experiences, arrange them into patterns, develop new observational skills, muscular dexterities, verbal aptitudes; and when these have been mastered by continued practice, the controls are handed over to a kind of automation, and the whole assembly is dispatched, along the gradients of awareness, out of sight. The upward traffic stream moves in the small fluctuating pulses from the unconscious which sustain the dynamic balance of the mind—and in the rare, sudden surges of creativity, which may lead to a re-structuring of the whole mental landscape.

I have illustrated this upward traffic by a number of examples. In each case the creative act consisted in a new synthesis of previously un-connected matrices of thought; a synthesis arrived at by 'thinking aside', a temporary relinquishing of the rational controls in favour of the codes which govern the underground games of the mind. We have seen that the dream operates with a type of logic which is in-admissible in the waking state, and which, for precisely that reason, proved useful in critical situations where the matrices of conscious thought are blocked. Thus the illogicality and apparent naïveté of visual associations, or the indifference of the dreaming mind to con-vention and common sense, turned out to be of great value in forging new combinations out of seemingly incompatible contexts. All the bisociative mechanisms of the comic we found in the dream free-wheeling as it were, without being harnessed to any obvious rational purpose. But when the whole personality, on all its levels, becomes saturated with the problem in hand during the period of incubation, then the freewheeling machinery too is 'engaged' in its service and goes into action—not necessarily in the dream, but mostly on some intermediary, part-conscious level.

The examples in previous chapters had been meant to illustrate various aspects of unconscious discovery. In the sections which follow I shall try to show, a little more systematically, how the peculiarities of subconscious ideation, reflected in the dream, facilitate the bisociative click.

Concretization and Symbolization

The sleeper producing a Freudian dream, in which a broomstick represents a phallus, has made an *optical pun:* he has connected a single visual form with two different functional contexts. The same technique is employed by the caricaturist who equates a nose with a cucumber, the discoverer who sees a molecule as a snake, the poet who compares a lip to a coral. When Jean Cocteau underwent a drug-withdrawal cure, he drew human figures constructed out of the long, thin stalks of opium pipes. William Harvey, watching the exposed heart-valve at work in a living fish, suddenly visualized it as a pump—but the analogy between the gory mess he actually saw and the neat metallic gadget existed in his mind's eye only.

These, however, are rather dramatic examples. As a rule, visual imagery does not work in such precise fashion. The visualizer rather feels his way around a problem and strokes it with his eye, as it were,

trying to fit it into some convincing or elegant shape; he plays around
with his vague forms like the couturier with his fabrics, draping and
undraping them on the model. Let me call on Einstein once more. We
remember that he described the 'physcical entities which seem to serve
as elements in thoughts' in terms of 'signs and more or less clear images
of visual, and some of muscular type'. On another occasion, he described how the basic insight into the relativity of Time, to wit, 'the
knowledge that the events which are simultaneous for one observer
are not necessarily simultaneous for another', came to him early one
morning just as he got out of bed. But that sudden moment of truth
had been preceded 'by ten years of contemplation, of considering a
paradox which had struck me at the age of sixteen: if I pursue a ray of
light with the speed c—the speed of light in a vacuum—I must accept
such a ray of light as a stationary, spatially oscillating electro-magnetic
field'.[2] In other words, if you travel with the speed of light, you will
see no light—you will be, roughly speaking, in the position of the
surf-rider in whose eyes the waves around him form a stationary pattern.
Yet—'intuitively it seemed clear to me that, judged by such an observer, everything should follow the same laws as for a stationary
observer'.[3] In other words, the traveller ought to see the world just
as the person sees it who remained at home on earth.

It is of course, not enough to visualize oneself as a passenger riding
on a ray of light; and the ride lasted ten years, even for Einstein. But
visual thinking enabled him to escape the snares of verbal thought, and
to brave the apparent logical contradiction that 'at the same time' for
A may mean 'at different times' for B. This apparent contradiction
derived from the axiom of absolute time, which had been built into
the codes of 'rational'—meaning post-Newtonian—thinking about
the physical world. In the pre-rational codes of the dream time is discontinuous, and the sequence of events can be reversed—as in a film.
Needless to say, the relativity of psychological time has nothing to do
with the relativity of time in physics. I merely wished to point out
that to the visual thinker 'time' loses the awesome, cast-iron character
which it automatically assumes in verbal thought. The Theory of
Relativity was an affront to conceptualized thinking, but not to
visualized thinking.

Let me take a more trivial example: a famous brain-teaser:

One morning, exactly at sunrise, a Buddhist monk began to
climb a tall mountain. The narrow path, no more than a foot or

two wide, spiralled around the mountain to a glittering temple at the summit.

The monk ascended the path at varying rates of speed, stopping many times along the way to rest and to eat the dried fruit he carried with him. He reached the temple shortly before sunset. After several days of fasting and meditation he began his journey back along the same path, starting at sunrise and again walking at variable speeds with many pauses along the way. His average speed descending was, of course, greater than his average climbing speed.

Prove that there is a spot along the path that the monk will occupy on both trips at precisely the same time of day.[4]

I used to amuse myself putting this to various friends—scientists and others. Some chose a mathematical approach; others tried to 'reason it out'—and came to the conclusion that it would be a most unlikely coincidence for the monk to find himself at the same time of day, on the same spot on the two different occasions. But others—who evidently belonged to the category of visualizers—*saw* the solution in a manner for which the following description of a young woman without any scientific training is typical:

> I tried this and that, until I got fed up with the whole thing, but the image of that monk in his saffron robe walking up the hill kept persisting in my mind. Then a moment came when, super-imposed on this image, I saw another, more transparent one, of the monk walking *down* the hill, and I realized in a flash that the two figures *must* meet at some point some time—regardless at what speed they walk and how often each of them stops. Then I reasoned out what I already knew: whether the monk descends two days or three days later comes to the same; so I was quite justified in letting him descend on the same day, in duplicate so to speak.

Now it is, of course, quite impossible for the monk to duplicate himself, and to be walking up the mountain and down the mountain at one and the same time. But in the visual image he does; and it is precisely this indifference to logical contradiction, the irrational, dream-like telescoping of the two images into one, which leads to the solution.

We could call the double image of the monk, or Einstein's traveller riding on a ray of light, a *concretization* of abstract problems as it sometimes occurs in dreams; and we could equally well call Kekulé's serpent which seizes its own tail 'to whirl mockingly before his eyes', the *symbolization* of a nascent, unformulated theory; these categories overlap. The following example illustrates both; it refers to an incident which has recently come to my knowledge:

Dr. X, a biologist, dreamed that as he was walking home from his laboratory he was joined by the wife and two children of his colleague Dr. Y—, one a boy, the other an enchanting little girl. The little girl seemed to take an immediate liking to X; she insisted on his picking her up, and gave him a kiss, or rather a peck, on the cheek. They all walked on with a feeling of friendly elation, but on arriving at the house where X lived—it had, unaccountably, become a big railway-station hotel—the girl declared peremptorily that she would be staying with him; and as he looked at her he discovered that she was no longer a child but an adolescent, 'almost fully developed', with a provocative glint in her eye. Dr. Y's wife gave him a glance which showed irony but no surprise; and the girl said to him mockingly: 'Don't worry, *I am all brains.*' He felt both tempted and terribly embarrassed; at which he woke up.

The first thought that flashed through his mind was: 'She is Y's *brain-child*'; and immediately the message of the dream was clear to him. Some time earlier on Y had, in conversation, thrown out an idea, which had taken root in X's mind, and had eventually set him off on a line of research. The peck on his cheek had been 'the kiss of the muse'; but by now the idea was 'almost fully developed'—in fact, the day before the dream, he had started drafting a paper on the preliminary results of his research. But he had postponed telling Y about it until he had something positive to show; and now he could neither face owning up to Y that he had taken up his brain-child, nor could he face stealing it (by omitting to give Y due credit in the paper). The conversion of X's house into a railway hotel indicated that this state of mind could not be a lasting one.

The dream solved his dilemma by producing a biological analogy for the growth of a 'brain-child' from infancy to 'full development'. The seminal idea had been Y's; but it was X who had done the work and brought it to maturation; every scientist knows that it is quite a different matter to throw out a casual suggestion which might or might not lead somewhere—and to follow it up by months of hard work in the laboratory. The dream made him see the situation in its proper perspective; now all he had to do was to tell Y the simple facts of the matter, and to give due credit in his paper to Y's paternity.

On one level of his mind X had, of course, known all this; discovery in this case, as in many others, consisted in uncovering what had always been there. But his knowledge had been buried under the rigid crust of a conventional matrix, which made his conscious thoughts turn in a vicious circle.

Punning for Profit

Charles Lamb once remarked in a letter that he wished 'to draw his last breath through a pipe and exhale it in a pun'.

The benefits which the humorist and the poet derive from two meanings linked together by one sound are evident; in the natural sciences they are non-existent, for the simple reason that verbal formulation, the choice of the particular words in which a theory is expressed, is to a large extent irrelevant to its content. But in the sciences concerned with language and meaning, the relations between sense and sound play an important part. Homonyms and homophones, sound affinities and transformations, are essential pointers in etymology and comparative philology, in the study of the structure and development of language. I have mentioned the 'divine pun' by which *adām*, man, was created out of *adamāh*, earth. Eve's Hebrew name is *Havvāh*, life; while *ahavvah* is love; *esh*, a synonym for man, has the same root as *ish*, fire; and *milkhamāh*, war, is derived from *lekhēm*, bread; so is the village of Beth-lehem: the House of Bread.

Affinities of sound provide the threads which lead from contemporary words and concepts back to the Greek and Sanskrit womb. The deciphering of the scripts of ancient languages is often aided by clues such as the frequency with which a certain sign occurs, and other 'links' between sign, symbol, sound, and sense. Thus the links which, in 1821, enabled Champollion to break into the secret of hieroglyphics, were the proper names Ptolemy, Cleopatra, and Alexander, which appeared on the Rosetta Stone (and on various other documents) bearing parallel inscriptions in Greek and in two different Egyptian scripts. The three names, inscribed in conspicuous cartouches, provided Champollion with altogether fourteen alphabetic signs of ascertained value—certainly the greatest service which any Cleopatra has rendered to history.

In the infantile and primitive imagination, the ties between sound and meaning are still very intimate; name and object form an almost indivisible unity, shown in the universal practices of word magic, incantations, and verbal spells. Related to this is the belief that the letters contained in a word form secret connections according to certain hermeneutical rules—a belief, shared by Judaism, several other Oriental religions, and adopted by the Christian Fathers. It was thought, for instance, that to extract their hidden meaning, certain texts in Hebrew Scriptures should be arranged in vertical columns and read downwards; or that the first and last letter in each word should be used to form new words; or that the letters should be reduced to their numerical value, and the sums so obtained should then be manipulated according to the rules of mystic numberlore. Here we have the archaic origins of the pun, the crossword puzzle, the acrostic, anagram, and cryptogram, which have always exerted such a curious fascination in the most varied cultures—from Pythagoras and Lao-Tse to Champollion and Freud. The humorist's joke, the linguist's discovery, the poet's euphony, all derive from that source.

The Benefits of Impersonation

'As far as my observations go', wrote C. G. Jung, 'I have not discovered in the unconscious anything like a personality comparable to the conscious ego. But . . . there are at least *traces of personalities* in the manifestations of the unconscious. A simple example is the dream, in which a variety of real and imaginery people enact the dream thoughts. . . . The unconscious *personates*.'[5]

The boundaries of the self are fluid or blurred in the dream. I may watch an execution, and the next moment become the person to be executed. The actors on the stage are interchangeable; their cards of identity are often reshuffled.

To be oneself and somebody else at the same time is an experience shared by the dreamer, the Shaman impersonating the rain-god, the patient possessed by demons. The same projective faculty is made use of by the actor, to create the illusion in the audience that he is both himself and Prince Hamlet; by the priest offering the eucharist in Holy Communion; by the healer, who projects himself into the patient's place, and at the same time acts as a father-figure.

The fluid boundaries of the self as represented in the unconscious mind, confer on it the gift of empathy—*Einfuehlung*—of entering into a kind of mental symbiosis with other selves. Empathy is a nicely sober, noncommittal term for designating the rather mysterious processes which enable one to transcend his boundaries, to step out of his skin as it were, and put himself into the place of another. One reads the mood of the other from such scant and crude pointers as the lifting or lowering of the corners of the lips, or almost imperceptible changes in the muscles which control the eyes; but the interpretation of these signs is not a conscious act. It belongs to the repertory of underground games.

Empathy is at the source of our understanding how others think and feel; it is the starting point of the art of medical diagnosis and of the science of psychology. The medicine man, ancient and modern, has a twofold relationship with the patient: he is trying to feel what the patient feels, and he is, at the same time, acting a part: the exorcizer of evil spirits himself endowed with divine powers; magician, witch, saint, sage, hypnotist, faith-healer, confessor, father. The roles have changed, but the principle has remained the same: to induce the patient to an act of faith, to submission, worship, transference, catharsis. Psychotherapy in its modern form expresses in explicit terms the principle of ab-reaction, of the mental purge, which has always been implied in the ancient cathartic techniques from the Dionysian and Orphic mystery-cults to the rites of baptism and the confessional. The psycho-analyst induces his patients to relive their conflicts in an illusionary drama, where he himself impersonates the central figure—halfway between comedian and tragedian. The tragedian creates illusion, the comedian debunks illusion; the therapist does both. In the dreams of patients under Jungian therapy, supposed aspects of their underground-personality—*anima*, *animus* and 'shadow'—keep appearing under various disguises, like actors on a stage. Finally, the technique of impersonation is used deliberately and explicitly in the form of group-therapy known as 'psycho-drama'.

Some eminent psychiatrists—among them Charcot, Freud, Jung, and Theodor Reik—have expressed, or hinted at their belief that not only empathy, but something akin to telepathy operates between doctor and patient in the hothouse atmosphere of the analytical session. But there is no need to go that far in order to realize that some of the basic insights of medicine and psychology are derived from the underground games which permit us to transcend the limits of personal identity while we dream—or stare into the footlights of the stage.

We have seen that the sudden shift of attention to a seemingly irrelevant aspect of a phenomenon—which was previously ignored or taken
for granted—plays a vital part in humour, art, and discovery. In the
comic story, the abrupt displacement of emphasis ('What am I supposed to do at 4 a.m. in *Grimsby*?') has the same effect as the matador's
nonchalant side-stepping while the bull charges at his muleta. In discovery, it makes a familiar thing or idea appear under a new angle, in
an unexpected light. In the art of photography a shift in the direction
and focus of the lens may turn a trivial object into a thing of wonder.

In the waking state 'side-stepping', 'shift of emphasis', and related
expressions signify a change-over from one frame of reference to
another. But while we dream, the coherence of these frames is so
much loosened that the change is not experienced as such, and side-
stepping becomes almost the normal way of the dream's progress.
It is by virtue of its freedom from restraint that the 'dreamy' way
of thinking can benefit the creative person—whether he is Archimedes
relaxing in his bath, or the chimpanzee gazing absent-mindedly at a
tree.

In one of his experiments, Carl Duncker—the psychologist who
fathered the Buddhist monk problem—set his experimental subjects
the task of making a pendulum. The subject was led to a table on which
had been placed, among some miscellaneous objects, a cord with a
pendulum-weight attached to its end, and a nail. All he had to do was
to drive the nail into the wall and hang the cord with the pendulum-
weight on the nail. But there was no hammer. Only fifty per cent of
the experimental subjects (all students) found the solution: to use the
pendulum-weight as a hammer.

Next, another series of students, of the same average age and intelligence, were given the same task under slightly altered conditions.
In the first series the weight on the table was attached to the cord, and
was expressly described to the students as a 'pendulum-weight'. In
the second series, weight and cord were lying separately on the table,
and the word 'pendulum-weight' was *not* used. Result: *all* students in
the second group found the solution without difficulty. They took in
the situation with an unprejudiced mind, saw a nail and a weight, and
hammered the nail in, then tied the cord to the nail and the weight
to the cord. But in the minds of the first group the weight was firmly
'embedded' into its role as a 'pendulum-weight' and nothing else,

because it had been verbally described as such *and* because visually it formed a unit with the cord to which it was attached. Thus only half of the subjects were able to wrench it out of that context—to perform the shift of emphasis which transformed a 'pendulum-weight' into a 'hammer'—as Sultan transformed a 'branch' into a 'stick.'

I have quoted only one among many experiments on similar lines. The fact that fifty per cent of Duncker's presumably bright students failed at this simple task is an illustration of the stubborn coherence of the perceptual frames and matrices of thought in our minds. The visual gestalt of weight-attached-to-cord, plus the verbal suggestion of their venerated teacher, made that pendulum-weight stick to its matrix like an insect caught in amber.

To undo wrong connections, faulty integrations, is half the game. To acquire a new habit is easy, because one main function of the nervous system is to act as a habit-forming machine; to break out of a habit is an almost heroic feat of mind or character. The prerequisite of originality is the art of forgetting, at the proper moment, what we know. Hence, once more, the importance of the Unconscious—as an anaesthetist, who puts reason to sleep, and restores, for a transient moment, the innocence of vision. Without the art of forgetting, the mind remains cluttered up with ready-made answers, and never finds occasion to ask the proper questions.

If forgetting can be an art, ignorance can be bliss—in the limited sense, of course, of procuring for a certain type of mind freedom from certain types of constraint. To Faraday, his ignorance of mathematics was an asset; Edison benefited from his shocking ignorance of science. As a child, 'his demands for explanations of what seemed obvious to his elders created the belief that he was less than normally intelligent. As his head was abnormally large, it was thought that he might have a brain disease'.[6] At a time when his inventions were transforming the pattern of our civilization, 'his ignorance of scientific theory raised criticism and opposition, especially among highly trained scientists and engineers without inventive talent'.[7] He was said to have carried the art of forgetting to such extremes, that on one occasion, when he had to queue at New York City Hall to pay his taxes, and an official suddenly asked him his name, Edison could not at the moment remember it, and lost his place in the queue.

Let me return from the laboratory of the Sorcerer at Menlo Park to that blacksmith's workshop in Samos which, according to tradition, was the birthplace of the first quantitative law in physics. One would expect that Pythagoras, as an acute and scientifically minded observer, would concentrate on the techniques the men employed in the exercise of their craft. Instead of this, his attention shifted to a phenomenon that was totally irrelevant and adventitious to that craft—the fact that under the strokes of the hammer, iron bars of different size gave out different sounds. The ear-splitting crashes and bangs in the workshop, which, since the Bronze Age had yielded to the Iron Age, had been regarded by ordinary mortals as a mere nuisance, were suddenly lifted out of their habitual context: the 'bangs' became 'clangs' of music. In the technical language of the communication engineer, Pythagoras had turned 'noise' into 'information'.

'The great field for new discoveries', wrote William James, 'is always the unclassified residuum. Round about the accredited and orderly facts of every science there ever flows a sort of dust-cloud of exceptional observations, of occurrences minute and irregular and seldom met with, which it always proves more easy to ignore than to attend to.'[8] The genius of Sherlock Holmes manifested itself in shifting his attention to minute clues which poor Watson found too obvious to be relevant, and so easy to ignore. The psychiatrist obtains his clues from the casual remark, the seemingly irrelevant drift of associations; and he has learned to shift the emphasis from the patient's meaningful statements to his meaningless slips of the tongue, from his rational experiences to his irrational dreams. The Lord Almighty seems to be fond of the trick which Poe's character employed when he let the secret document lie open on his desk—where it was too obvious to be seen.

Standing on One's Head

A drastic form of displacement is the sudden shift of emphasis from one aspect of a situation to its opposite, accompanied by a kind of 'reversal of logic' (p. 65).

'The dream', wrote Freud, 'neglects in a most conspicuous manner the logical category of opposition and contradiction. The concept "No" does not seem to exist in the dream. It likes to compress opposites into a unity, or to represent them as one. It takes the further liberty of representing any given entity by its emotional opposite, so that *a priori* one never knows whether a reversible entity is thought of in the dream with a plus or a minus sign.'[9] When a patient says to the doctor: 'You think that I am now going to say something offensive, but I really have no intention of doing so,' then, says Freud, 'you can take it for granted that he did have that intention. Or, the patient will say: "You are asking me who that person in my dream could be. It is *not* my mother." We then correct him: "In other words, it's your mother." ... At times one can obtain information about unconscious repressed processes by a very easy method. One asks: "What do you consider to be the most unlikely aspect of that situation? What was it that you least intended to do?" If the patient swallows the bait, and tells one what he can believe least, then he has almost invariably conceded the true answer.'[10]

Freud seemed to believe (following Bain and others) that the reason for the unconscious tendency to unify opposites is the relativity of all scales by which attributes are measured: a 'hot' summer-day in London is 'cold' to the visitor from the Sudan, and Gulliver is a 'giant' or a 'dwarf' according to the country he visits. He further refers to the fact that in some ancient languages pairs of opposites are designated by the same word: thus *altus* means both 'high' and 'deep', and *sacer* both 'holy' and 'accursed'.

For once, however, Freud did not seem to have probed deep enough; he did not mention the rites of the Saturnalia and other ancient festivals, in which the roles of slaves and masters are reversed; nor the constant affirmation of the unity of opposites in most Oriental religions and philosophies. It seems indeed that the tendency to stand things, from time to time, on their head, has its deep, unconscious roots, which probably reach down into the physiological peculiarities of the nervous system.* One of its striking manifestations is the reversibility of 'figure' and 'background' in visual perception—about which below.

I am not at all sure how far these considerations are relevant to a certain pattern of discovery which recurs with curious insistence in the biological sciences: we find, over and again, mishaps and minor laboratory disasters which turn out to be blessings in disguise, and spoilt experiments which perversely yield the solution—by brutally shifting the experimenter's attention from a 'plus' to a 'minus' aspect of the problem, as it were. One might call this pattern 'discovery by misadventure'. A classic case is that of the Abbé Haüy (1743–1822), a humble teacher at the college at Lemoine, whose leisure hours were devoted to collecting specimens of plants and minerals—until a small, embarrassing accident suddenly changed the direction of his interests and his whole life:

One day, when examining some minerals at the house of a friend, he was clumsy enough to allow a beautiful cluster of prismatic crystals of calcareous spar to fall on the ground. One of the prisms broke in such a way as to show at the fracture faces which were no less smooth than those elsewhere, but presented the appearance of a new crystal altogether different in form from the prism. Haüy picked up this fragment and examined the faces with their inclinations and angles. To his great surprise, he discovered that they are the same in rhomboidal spar as in Iceland spar.

He wished to be able to generalize: he broke his own little collection into pieces; crystals lent by his friends were broken; everywhere he found a structure which depended upon the same laws.[11]

The result was Haüy's *Traité de Mineralogie* which made him a member of the French Academy and a pioneer of the science of crystallography.

Haüy had a favourite pupil, Delafosse, who later became Pasteur's teacher at the École Normale in Paris. Under his influence Pasteur took up the study of crystallography; it was in this field that he made his first important discoveries, which contained the germs of all his later achievements. The decisive incident was again a laboratory mishap.

Pasteur was studying his favourite mineral, Para-Tartrate, derived from the red Tartar deposit in the vats of fermented wine. One day one of his Tartrate solutions became affected by a mould, and spoiled. This kind of thing frequently happens in warm weather; the normal reaction of chemists is to pour, with a gentle oath, the turbid liquid down the drain. Pasteur reversed the logic of the situation: he shifted his attention to the accidental and irrelevant mould, and turned 'accident' into 'experiment' by studying the mould's action on the Tartrate. The result was 'the first link in the chain of arguments which led him into the study of fermentation, to the recognition that micro-organisms play an essential role in the economy of nature, and eventually to his epoch-making discoveries in the field of infectious diseases'.

In his later life Pasteur performed the same kind of mental head-stand on at least two more momentous occasions. One I have already mentioned: the discovery of immunization by vaccines, which grew out of a spoilt culture of chicken cholera. The other was the 'domestication' of micro-organizms, their transformation from enemies into allies of man, which led to industrial micro-biology and, eventually, to the anti-biotics: microbes destroying microbes. 'In the inferior organisms,' he wrote, 'still more than in the big animal and vegetable species, life hinders life.' It sounds simple. But what a long way it was from the enunciation of the principle to the discovery of penicillin! It took more than half a century; and it was again due to an almost ludicrous series of misadventures. They started in 1922, when Alexander Fleming caught a cold. A drip from his nose fell into a dish in his laboratory at St. Mary's Hospital; the nasal slime killed off the bacilli in the culture; Fleming isolated the active agent in the mucus, which was also present in tears, and called it lysozyme. That was the first step; but lysozyme was not powerful enough as a germ-killer, and another seven years had to pass until a gust of wind blew through the lab window a spore of the mould *penicillium notatum*, which happened to settle in a culture dish of staphylococci. But Fleming had been waiting for that stroke of luck for fifteen years; and when it came, he was ready for it. As Lenin has said somewhere: 'If you think of Revolution, dream of Revolution, sleep with Revolution for thirty years, you are bound to achieve a Revolution one day.'

I shall have to return to Fleming in a different context. The examples of 'discovery by misadventure', which I have just given, were taken from biology; but the same kind of perverse- or reverse-logic can also be found operating in other branches of science and art.

In 1821 Faraday invented the electric motor, and constructed a crude model of it. For more than fifty years no attention was paid to his invention. In 1831 he also invented (independently from, and roughly simultaneously with Joseph Henry) the electrical dynamo. A motor converts electric current into mechanical motion; a dynamo converts mechanical motion into electricity. But, curiously, the reciprocal nature of the two machines was not realized until 1873. By that time huge dynamo machines, driven by steam power, were in use to generate electrical current; but Faraday's earlier invention had been forgotten, and electric *motors* did not exist.

In 1873, at an exhibition in Vienna, several dynamo machines of an improved type were displayed. In the happy-go-lucky manner of the Austrians, one of the technicians mistakenly connected a dynamo, driven by a steam-engine, with a second dynamo which was at rest. The current fed into the resting dynamo promptly set it into motion—and thus the electrical motor came into existence. Electric trains, the electrical transmission of power, one of the foundations of modern technology, originates in the accidental reversal of the function of a single machine.

The history of photography and the early history of radiography seem to hinge on fluorescent screens and photographic plates which showed effects they were not supposed to show, and vice versa. Daguerre put an exposed plate into an untidy cupboard full of various bottles of chemicals—including some mercury. The next morning he found to his surprise that a perfect image had developed on the plate. He repeated the experiment, systematically eliminating one chemical after another in the cupboard—until he knew that it was mercury vapour which had done the trick. Prior to the discovery of mercury as an ideal developer of latent images, Daguerre had written: 'The time required to procure a photographic copy of a landscape is from seven to eight hours; but single monuments, when strongly lighted by the sun, or which are themselves very bright, can be taken in about three hours.'[12] After the discovery the time of exposure was shortened to between three and thirty minutes.

In 1895 Wilhelm Konrad Röntgen, Professor of Physics at the University of Würzburg, noticed by accident that a paper-screen covered with barium platinocyanide became fluorescent without any apparent cause. He had at the time a cathode-ray tube going—an apparatus used to study the conduction of electricity through gases—which was enclosed in a box of black cardboard. But in those days there was no radiation known hard enough to penetrate black cardboard, and such a thing was in fact considered to be impossible. Röntgen immediately accepted the impossible as true: the fluorescent glow which he saw on the screen must be caused by rays of an unknown kind, emitted by the tube, and capable of traversing the black cardboard. Within a few weeks he had demonstrated that the rays were equally capable of traversing human flesh and showing the outline of the bones as shadows cast upon the luminous screen. He called them X-rays.

Some few weeks later, Henri Becquerel saw a demonstration of Röntgen's X-rays at a meeting of the French Academy of Sciences. Becquerel's father and grandfather had also been professors of physics and members of the Academy; they had taken a special interest in the fluorescent glow which certain substances—among them uranium compounds—emit, when exposed to light. He therefore immediately formed the—wrong—theory that X-rays were a normal accompaniment of the fluorescent glow, and he set out to prove this theory by experiment. He wrapped a photographic plate into heavy black paper to screen it from ordinary light. On top of the paper-wrapping he laid some crystals of the uranium compound; between the crystals and the wrapping he placed a bit of metal with holes in it. Then he placed this whole arrangement outside his window so that the sun's rays should set the uranium aglow with fluorescence, and thereby set the X-rays going across the wrapper. This worked admirably: when he developed his plates the rays had penetrated the wrapping and produced a photograph of the holes in the metal. It was a wonderful example of an experiment confirming a prediction based on a false hypothesis.

No sooner had he communicated his results to the Academy, when the sky clouded over, and Becquerel put his plates and the uranium into a dark drawer. Here the crystals were shut off from the sunlight; hence there was no fluorescent glow; hence there could be no X-rays to blacken the photographic plate. But when he took them out of the drawer, the plates were blackened nevertheless. Once more the impossible had happened; and once more a reversal of logic brought the solution. The fluorescent glow had been caused by the X-rays—and not the other way round. Becquerel now tried non-fluorescent uranium compounds and found that they, too, produced rays. He tried other fluorescent materials which did not contain uranium, and found that they did not produce the rays. That clinched the matter: the source of the rays, the radio-active agent, was the uranium itself. It was from here that the Curies took over.

Perhaps the prettiest example of reasoning in reverse gear is the invention of the phonograph.

As a young man Edison worked as a telegraphist. His main job was the taking of messages from the Morse-ticker by ear; if the line was bad, the ticking became blurred, and he had to rely on guessing. This annoyed him all the more as, owing to an earlier accident, Edison was partially deaf. So the young telegraphist invented a simple Morse-signal-recording apparatus. It consisted mainly of a paper disc, which was made to rotate like the gramophone disc of the future; on the disc the incoming dots and dashes were recorded as indentations. But from the telegraph company's point of view transcribing from the record instead of doing it directly by ear from the ticker was a sheer waste of time; Edison, then seventeen, lost his job.

Eleven years later, in the first laboratory of his own, he was working on about fifty inventions simultaneously—among them the typewriter and an improved telegraph-recorder, on which the incoming dots and dashes were embossed by a needle. When the message was to be sent on to another station, the paper disc was placed on a transmitting machine with a contact lever which moved up and down according to the indentations on the disc. It was a gadget with the sole purpose of recording and transmitting electrical impulses, and had nothing what-soever to do with the production of sounds. Yet it *did* produce purely accidental sounds—because the lever, while tracing the embossed dots and dashes, was apt to rattle; and when the disc was rotated very quickly this rattle became a hum, then something like a musical sound. A sudden reversal of logic and the phonograph was born.

The rest was a matter of elaboration. Instead of a paper disc, Edison proposed to use a cylinder covered with soft tin-foil; instead of attach-ing the needle to a Morse-telegraph, he attached it to a membrane set into vibration by the waves of sound. He made a sketch of the machine, and gave it to one of his workmen, a certain John Kruesi. It cost altogether eighteen dollars to build it, but Kruesi had no idea what the contraption was for. When it was finished Edison shouted at it: 'Mary had a little lamb.' Then he turned the handle of the recording cylinder:

'The machine reproduced perfectly. Everybody was astonished. . . .' And that was that. To quote once more the jargon of communication engineering: the background 'noise' of the vibrating lever had been turned into 'information'.

We have met the same kind of logical mirror-writing in humour—'a sadist is a person who is kind to a masochist', 'operation successful, patient dead'. All jokes based on a turning-the-tables technique show the same pattern (for instance, the Prince and the Retainer story on p. 84).

In the classical tragedy, on the other hand, it is the gods, or the stars, who turn the tables on the mortal hero, or lure him into appointments in Samara. They particularly like to use seemingly harmless coinci-dences—the blind gaps in the meaningful order of events—as levers of destiny. In later forms of literature, it is characters which are made to stand on their heads, or are turned inside out like a glove. Prince Mishkin, the 'Idiot', is revealed as a sage in reverse; saints are sinners, sinners are saints, heroes are cowards, adults are children, and every Jekyll has something to Hyde.

In visual perception we find a parallel phenomenon in the reversible figure-background relation. If one stares at the mosaic on the bathroom floor, unconscious and often uncontrollable shifts in perception make the pattern of black tiles stand out at one moment, and the pattern of white tiles at the next. A more dramatic illustration is the following, found in many psychological textbooks:

FIGURE 9

Urn or profiles—whichever is master for a while, will become slave in turn, 'figure' will change into 'ground', 'noise' into 'information', in a kind of visual saturnalia. The two perceptual matrices are reciprocal, and their alternation seems to be determined by unconscious physiological processes.

Some of the great revolutions in the history of painting entailed almost equally brutal reversals of vision. Up to the late Venetians, the landscape on the canvas was primarily perceived as a conventional background against which human figures were displayed; roughly from Giorgione onward it became possible to paint landscapes in which the human figure played an accidental part. At different stages one finds similar reversals in the logic of the eye: from ornate drapery to personal expression, from contours to surfaces, from naturalism to other isms of perception. At each of these upheavals the cat without a grin was superseded by the grin without a cat.

In the realm of music the relativity and reversibility of 'figure' and 'background' (accompaniment, counterpoint, fugue) is self-evident. It is less obvious in modern theoretical physics, although it is implied in one of its basic postulates: according to Niels Bohr's *Principle of Complementarity* the ultimate constituents of the universe—electrons, protons, photons, etc.—behave on some occasions as if they were particles, that is, hard lumps of matter, on other occasions as if they were ripples of energy without definite location. Although the two descriptions are mutually exclusive in terms of traditional physics and philosophy, the theory works remarkably well. As a matter of fact, most physicists are not much bothered by the inherent contradiction, and are quite content to believe that the 'wavicles', the actual stuff the world is made of, are at one moment like the solid urn, and the next like the empty space between the two profiles.

That the most brilliant scientists of this century should be capable of accepting this paradox is a rather striking indication of the susceptibility of the human mind for reversals of logic, and the unification of opposites. The complementarity of energy and matter in quantum-physics is not so far removed as it would seem from the dualism of Yang and Yin, the feminine and masculine principles in Taoist philo-sophy. I do not mean that Lao-Tse, in the sixth century B.C., foresaw the behaviour of alpha-particles in a Wilson chamber; I mean that it is a timeless characteristic of the unconscious mind to work in that way.

Analogy and Intuition

The great biologist Elie Mechnikoff felt rather lonely one afternoon in 1890 'when the whole family had gone to the circus to see some extraordinary performing apes, and I remained alone with my micro-scope'.[13] The microscope was in a laboratory of the École Normale which Pasteur had given him; Mechnikoff was observing the life of the mobile cells in the transparent larvae of starfish, and idly threw a few rose-thorns among them. The thorns were promptly surrounded by the larvae and dissolved inside their transparent bodies—they had been gobbled up and digested. This reminded him of what happens when a human finger is infected by a splinter: it will be surrounded by pus which, like the starfish larvae, will attack and try to digest the intruder. By this analogy Mechnikoff discovered the organisms' main defence mechanism against invading microbes: the 'phagocytes', cell-eaters, a population of mobile cells among the white blood corpuscles.

The starting point of Kepler's discoveries was a supposed analogy between the role of the Father in the Trinity and the role of the Sun in the Universe. Lord Kelvin hit on the idea of the mirror galvanometer when he noticed a reflection of light on his monocle. Sultan saw that a branch was like a stick; Newton saw that the moon behaved like an apple. Pasteur saw the analogy between a spoilt culture and a cow-pox vaccine; Fleming saw the analogy between the action of a mould and the action of a drip from his nose. Freud, on his own account, conceived the idea of the sublimation of instincts by looking at a funny cartoon in the *Fliegende Blätter*—the one-time German equivalent of *Punch*. In the first picture a little girl was herding a flock of goslings with a stick. In the second she had grown into a governess herding a flock of young ladies with a parasol.[14]

Some writers identify the creative act in its entirety with the unearthing of hidden analogies. 'The discoveries of science, the works of art are explorations—more, are explosions, of a hidden likeness', Bronowski wrote.[15] But where does the hidden likeness hide, and how is it found? Sultan's branch could literally be *seen* as a stick—though even in this case, a change of the perceptual frame was required to discover the likeness. But in most truly original acts of discovery the 'seeing' is in fact imagining; it is done in the mind's, and mostly the unconscious mind's, eye. The analogy between the life of one kind of microbe inside a cow and another kind of microbe in a forgotten culture tube was not 'hidden' anywhere; it was 'created' by the imagination; and once an analogy has been created, it is of course there for all to see—just as a poetic metaphor, once created, soon fades into a cliché.

Analogy, in logic, means a process of 'reasoning from parallel causes'; in common parlance it means that two situations or events are similar in some respects, but not in all respects. The rub is in the words 'parallel' and 'similar'; the latter, in particular, has bedevilled psychology ever since the term 'association by similarity' was invented (by Bain, I believe) as an explanation of how the mind works. A Chinaman who collects stamps is 'similar' to a Negro in that both are males; he is similar to a Chinese girl in that both are Chinese; and he is similar to other stamp-collectors of any nationality. Mathematics began, wrote Bertrand Russell, when it was discovered that a brace of pheasants and a couple of days have something in common: the number two. 'Similarity' is not a thing offered on a plate (or hidden in a cupboard); it is a relation established in the mind by a process of selective emphasis on those features which overlap in a certain respect—along one dimensional gradient—and ignoring other features. Even such a seemingly simple process as recognizing the similarity between two letters 'a' written by different hands, involves processes of abstraction and generalization in the nervous system which are largely unexplained.

Thus the real achievement in discoveries of the type mentioned in this section is 'seeing an analogy where no one saw one before'. The scientist who sets out to solve a problem looks at it from various angles, through glasses of different colours, as it were—in the jargon of the present theory, he experiments with various matrices, hoping that one will fit. If it is a routine problem of a familiar type, he will soon discover some aspect of it which is similar in some respect to other problems encountered in the past, and thus allows him to come to grips with it. Some of the mental operations involved in such routine cases we have already encountered in discussing the solving of witty riddles (pp. 84–6): extrapolation, interpolation, transposition. These are 'rules of the game' which enter as sub-codes into any complex mental skill. To put it in a different way: solving a problem means bridging a gap; and for routine problems there usually exist matrices—various types of prefabricated bridges—which will do the job; though it may require a certain amount of sweat to adjust them to the terrain.

But in original discoveries, no single pre-fabricated matrix is adequate to bridge the gap. There may be some similarities with past situations, but these may be more misleading than helpful, and lure the victim into fruitless experimentation based on traditional rules of the game. Here the only salvation lies in hitting on an auxiliary matrix in a previously unrelated field—the larvae of starfish or the Holy Ghost. One may call the process which follows *after* the hit 'reasoning from a parallel case'— but the real achievement was to 'appoint', as it were, the larva as a parallel case to the pus, and the action of the Holy Ghost as 'similar' to the action of gravity. It is an achievement much closer to the birth of a poetic simile than to a logical production. After all, the Walrus too was arguing by analogy when he talked 'Of shoes—and ships—and sealing wax/Of cabbages—and kings.'

The essence of discovery is that unlikely marriage of cabbages and kings—of previously unrelated frames of reference or universes of discourse—whose union will solve the previously insoluble problem. The search for the improbable partner involves long and arduous striving— but the ultimate matchmaker is the unconscious. I have discussed several tricks which qualify it for that role: the greater fluency and freedom of unconscious ideation; its 'intellectual libertinage'—as one might call the dream's indifference towards logical niceties and mental prejudices consecrated by tradition; its non-verbal, 'visionary' powers. To these must be added, in our present context, the dream's tendency towards creating unusual analogies. These may be verbal puns, or 'optic puns' or visual symbols; but there is another type of vague and cloudy analogy generated in the dream and half-dream, which disintegrates on awakening and cannot be put into words—except by muttering 'something reminded me of something, but I don't know what reminded me of what, and why'. Some dreams have a way of dissolving in the wakening mind like solid crystals melting in a liquid; and if we reverse the process we get at least a speculative pointer to the manner in which those 'somethings' vaguely reminding me of other 'somethings' condense into a nascent analogy. This may be a hazy, tentative affair—the dance of Poincaré's unhooked atoms; and its shape may be changing from camel to weasel, as Hamlet's cloud. The unconscious regions of fertile minds must be pullulating with such nascent analogies, hidden likenesses, and the cloudy forms of things unknown. But most clouds form and dissolve again; only a few intuitions reach the stage of 'seeding the cloud' which results in the formation of verbal drops; and cloud-bursts are a rarity.

Two final examples may serve to illustrate the actual process of discovering hidden analogies. The first is related to clouds in a literal sense—Franklin's invention of the lightning conductor.

Benjamin Franklin became interested in electricity in 1746 when he was forty, and began playing about with Leyden jars—a kind of electrified bottle which gave one fearful shocks. Within the next three years he rediscovered by himself virtually everything that was known about electricity to that date, and added several fundamental discoveries of his own.

In 1749 he noted in his diary that he thought lightning and thunder to be electrical phenomena.* He also found that when brought near to an electrified body, a pointed object, like a finger, will draw a much stronger spark than a blunt one. 'To know this power of points', he musingly wrote, 'may possibly be of some use to mankind, though we should never be able to explain it.' He then drew an analogy between a cloud and an electrified body, and concluded that lightning was an electrical discharge phenomenon. But if that was the case, mankind could protect itself against this cosmic scourge:

> I say, if these things are so, may not the knowledge of this power of points be of use to mankind, in preserving houses, churches, ships & cont. from the stroke of lightning, by directing us to fix on the highest parts of those edifices, upright rods of iron made sharp as a needle, and gilt to prevent rusting, and from the foot of those rods a

wire down one of the shrouds of a ship, and down her side till it reaches the water? Would not these pointed rods probably draw the electrical fire silently out of a cloud before it came nigh enough to strike, and thereby secure us from that most sudden and terrible mischief?[16]

However, before he could convince mankind to put 'Franklin rods' on their houses he had to prove his fantastically sounding notion that thunderclouds were in fact giant Leyden jars floating in the air. He waited for some time hopefully for the erection of a tall spire at Philadelphia, intending to fix a pointed rod on top of it, and so to bring down the electricity from a passing thundercloud. But the difficulties of the project proved insurmountable; it was during this period of impatient waiting and restless searching for a simpler method to prove his theory that he hit on the fantastic yet at the same time astonishingly simple idea of the kite.

How did it happen? Franklin was an expert swimmer. On his first sojourn in London, at the age of nineteen, he swam from Chelsea to Blackfriars, a distance of three miles, 'performing on the way many feats of activity both upon and under the water'—and was advised by some English gentlemen, who watched him, to open a swimming school. He did not do that, but he devised a new method of learning to swim: 'Choosing a place where the water deepens gradually, walk coolly into it till it is up to your breast, then turn around, your face to the shore, and throw an egg into the water between you and the shore.' The learner then must 'boldly retrieve the egg'—and in the act of retrieving acquires the art of swimming.

Even earlier on he had devised another aquatic sport: as a boy he used to drift for hours on a lake, floating on his back, and towed by the string of a kite. He suggested that this method might be utilized by swimmers to cross the Channel from Dover to Calais—with the judicious addendum: 'The packet-boat, however, is still preferable.'

It is easy to imagine how, in a moment of weariness and 'thinking aside' from that wretched spire in Philadelphia, a pleasant childhood memory rose like a bubble to the surface of his consciousness: drifting on the lake attached to the kite in the sky. Eureka! With the enthusiastic assistance of his young son, Franklin fabricated a kite out of a cross of cedar wood and a silk handkerchief. All he needed now were a few good thunderclouds—which conveniently appeared in June 1752. Father and son sent up the kite and, with due precaution, drained the clouds' electric charge into a Leyden jar; 'by the electric fire thus obtained spirits were inflamed and other experiments performed'.

Such was the excitement caused all over the world that one of Franklin's imitators, a certain Monsieur Riehmann, was killed in St. Petersburg by the lightning discharge he drew from a cloud. He was worshipped as a hero and found many would-be imitators; among them the German inventor Herr Boze. Even Joseph Priestley, one of the great British scientists of the century, rhapsodized about 'the sentiments of the magnanimous Mr. Boze, who with a truly philosophic heroism, worthy of the renowned Empedocles, said he wished he might die by the electric shock, that the account of his death might furnish an article for the memoirs of the French Academy of Sciences. But it is not given to every electrician to die the death of the justly envied Riehmann.'[17]

There are two successive Eureka processes involved in this story. In the first, the bisociative link was what Franklin called 'the power of points'; it gave rise to the analogy: pointed finger discharges Leyden jar, pointed rod discharges cloud. It may have been attained by ideation on a relatively conscious level, probably with the aid of visual imagination. The second stroke of genius was the use of the kite to reach the thunderbolt. It illustrates the argument I have put forward earlier in this chapter: one can hardly say that a hidden analogy was pre-existent in the universe between a kite used as a sail by a boy floating on a lake, and a lightning conductor. What actually happened was that Franklin was desperately searching for a means to make contact with a thundercloud, thinking in habitual terms of tall spires, long iron rods, and perhaps the Tower of Babel. But all these approaches proved impracticable, and the matrix was blocked—until in a moment of lassitude and day-dreaming the previously unrelated memory-train of swimming, egg-retrieving, and kite-sailing was brought to bear on it.

The last example that I shall quote in this section is a particularly impressive illustration of the unconscious in the role of matchmaker. I am referring to the discovery, in 1920, of the chemical transmission of nerve-impulses by Otto Loewi. Since the matter is somewhat technical, I shall give a simplified account of it.

Before Loewi's discovery it was generally believed that nervous control of bodily functions was exercised by a direct transmission of electrical impulses from nerve-terminal to muscle or gland. But this theory failed to account for the fact that the same type of electric impulse travelling down a nerve had an excitatory effect on some organs, an inhibitory effect on others. Now certain drugs were known to have precisely the same effect. In a discussion with a friend in 1903, it occurred to Loewi that the chemical agents which were contained in these drugs may also be present at the nerve-terminals; the electric impulse would initiate chemical action, which in its turn would act on the muscle or gland. But Loewi could not think of an experimental method to test the idea—and forgot it for the next seventeen years.

Fifteen years later, for quite different purposes, he designed an experiment. He made preparations of two frogs' hearts which were kept beating in salt solutions to see whether their activities gave out any chemical substance. In the sequel he forgot all about the experiment.

Another two years passed until the critical event:

> The night before Easter Sunday of that year [1920] I awoke, turned on the light, and jotted down a few notes on a tiny slip of thin paper. Then I fell asleep again. It occurred to me at six o'clock in the morning that during the night I had written down something most important, but I was unable to decipher the scrawl. The next night, at three o'clock, the idea returned. It was the design of an experiment to determine whether or not the hypothesis of chemical trans- mission that I had uttered seventeen years ago was correct. I got up immediately, went to the laboratory, and performed a simple experiment on a frog heart according to the nocturnal design. . . .

No lesser person that Walter B. Cannon, the discoverer of adrenalin, has described this noctural design as 'one of the neatest, simplest, and most definite experiments in the history of biology'. Loewi again isolated two frog hearts, the first with its nerves, the second without. He stimulated the vagus nerve of the first heart for a few minutes. The vagus has an inhibitory effect on the heart, and its beats slowed down. Loewi now removed the salt solution from the first heart and applied it to the second. It slowed down just as if its own (no longer existent) vagus had been stimulated. . . . He repeated the experiment, this time stimulating the accelerator nerve of the first heart. When the liquid was transferred to the second heart it accelerated. . . . He concludes:

> These results unequivocally proved that the nerves do not influence the heart directly but liberate from their terminals specific chemical substances which, in their turn, cause the well-known modifications of the function of the heart characteristic of the stimulation of its nerves.

The story of this discovery shows that an idea may sleep for decades in the unconscious mind and then suddenly return. Further, it indicates that we should sometimes trust a sudden intuition without too much scepticism. If carefully considered in the daytime, I would undoubtedly have rejected the kind of experiment I performed. It would have seemed likely that any transmitting agent released by a nervous impulse would be in an amount just sufficient to influence the effector organ. It would seem improbable that an excess that could be detected would escape into the fluid which filled the heart. It was good fortune that at that moment of the hunch I did not think but acted immediately.

For many years this nocturnal emergence of the design of the crucial experiment to check the validity of a hypothesis uttered seventeen years earlier was a complete mystery.[18]

In 1955—twenty-five years after the discovery, which earned him the Nobel Prize—Loewi had to compile a bibliography:

I glanced over all the papers published from my laboratory. I came across two studies made about two years before the arrival of the nocturnal design in which, also in search of a substance given off from the heart, I had applied the technique used in 1920. This experience, in my opinion, was an essential preparation for the idea of the finished design. In fact, the nocturnal concept represented a sudden association of the hypothesis of 1903 with the method tested not long before in other experiments. Most so-called 'intuitive' discoveries are such associations suddenly made in the unconscious mind.[19]

Let me briefly recapitulate the three stages of this drama. The first is the sudden emergence, during a conversation in 1903, of the hunch that his problem could be solved by switching from a 'spark theory' to a 'soup theory' (in neurological jargon, 'spark' refers to electrical, 'soup' to chemical transmission of nerve impulses). But a hunch of this kind as often as not turns out to be a fallacious over-simplification; so the idea went into the incubator for the next seventeen years, till 1920.

Act Two. In 1918, fifteen years after the hunch, Loewi performs certain experiments for which purpose he has to design a technique for the detection of fluids secreted by the frog's heart. He then forgets all about it.

On the night before Easter Sunday the two previously unrelated memories meet; but their meeting place is so deep underground that the next morning he can remember nothing, and cannot even decipher his own scribbled note. He has to wait until the next night for another underground excursion—which takes place at 3 a.m., followed by the rush to the laboratory.

After the event one wonders, of course, why one idea had to wait for seventeen years, the second for two years, and then choose such a secret place for their final rendezvous that the identity of the second was only revealed another twenty-five years later. The first was a theory of the transmission of nerve impulses to organs by a fluid; the second was a technique for tracing fluids in an organ; what could be more logical than that the twain should meet? Yet they did not meet through all those years because mortal minds, even those of genius, are not governed by logic but by habit, and the two ideas were embedded each in its own habitual context. Wallace, too, had been thinking of evolution for two years, and had read Malthus many years before the two fused—during an attack of tropical fever. It seems that encounters of this kind can occur only when the normal rules of the game are suspended and the unconscious match-maker enters into action. Loewi's inability to read his own note, and other cases of 'snowblindness' which I shall mention, indicate the stubborn resistance of habit against such breaches of the rules and illicit liaisons.

'We are somewhat more than ourselves in sleep and the Slumber of the Body seems to be but the Waking of the Soul', Sir Thomas Browne wrote three centuries ago. Yet it is difficult and frustrating to write consciously on the unconscious, rationally on the irrational. It is rather like praising the beauties and expounding the grammar of the Sanskrit language—but a Sanskrit which you speak only in your sleep and the command of which you lose when awake. Only fragments of it emerge to the surface—disjointed memories and the testimonies of creative minds. When these fragments are pieced together, as best we can, they do not form a coherent pattern—but they do provide evidence that such a pattern exists.

Summary

The interlocking of two previously unrelated skills or matrices of thought was again seen to constitute the basic pattern of discovery in the illustrative cases of Gutenberg, Kepler, and Darwin-Wallace

(Chapter VI). Gutenberg combined the techniques of the wine-press and the seal; Kepler married physics to astronomy; Darwin connected biological evolution with the struggle for survival.

On the question how the new synthesis comes into being, the evidence indicates that verbal thinking, and conscious thinking in general, plays only a subordinate part in the decisive phase of the creative act. Hadamard's inquiry among leading mathematicians in America revealed that 'practically all of them . . . avoid not only the use of mental words but also . . . the mental use of algebraic or any other signs'. On the testimony of those original thinkers who have taken the trouble to record their methods of work, this also seems to be the rule in other branches of science. Their virtually unanimous emphasis on spontaneous intuitions, unconscious guidance, and sudden leaps of imagination which they are at a loss to explain, suggests that the role of strictly rational thought-processes in scientific discovery has been vastly overestimated since the Age of Enlightenment; and that, contrary to the Cartesian bias in our beliefs, 'full consciousness', in the words of Einstein, 'is a limit case'.

'Full consciousness' must indeed be regarded as the upper limit of a continuous gradient from focal awareness through peripheral awareness to total unawareness of an event. Awareness is a matter of degrees; and only a fraction of our multi-levelled activities at any moment enters the beam of focal consciousness. But this realization in itself provides no answer to the question how unconscious guidance works.

We have approached that question in several cautious steps. First, I have tried to show that unconscious automatisms must not be confused, as they often are, with unconscious intuitions. To be able to recite the lines of Kubla Khan 'in one's sleep' is not the same thing as conceiving them in a dream; it is, in fact, the result of the opposite process. The formation and gradual automatization of habits of all kinds, of muscular, perceptual, thinking skills, follows the principle of economy. Once a new skill has been mastered, the controls begin to function automatically and can be dispatched underground, out of sight; and under stable conditions strategy too will tend to become stereotyped. I called this the 'downward' stream of mental traffic.

The next step led us to inquire how in ordinary, routine thinking we explore the 'shallows' of our minds—operating on the twilight peripheries of awareness, as it were. Galton's oft-quoted metaphor of the ante-chamber, from which the 'most closely allied' idea is summoned to the presence-chamber of the mind in a 'mechanically logical way', proved to be inadequate, because the order of precedence was seen to depend firstly, on the specific rules of the game in which the mind is engaged at the time, and secondly, on strategic considerations dependent on the lie of the land. Purposive thinking, then, may be compared to the scanning of a landscape with the narrow beam of focal vision—whether it is a panorama, a chessboard, or an 'inner landscape'. Those features which are relevant to the purpose of the operation will stand out as 'members' of the matrix, while the rest sinks into the background. Thus the first act in skilled routine-thinking and problem-solving is the 'tuning-in' of the code appropriate to the task, guided by some obvious similarity with situations encountered in the past. This leads to the emergence of a matrix which provides a preliminary selection of *possible* moves; the *actual* moves depend on strategy, guided by feedback, and distorted by emotional interferences.

However, the problems which lead to original discoveries are precisely those which cannot be solved by any familiar rule of the game, because the matrices applied in the past to problems of similar nature have been rendered inadequte by new features or complexities in the situation, by new observational data, or a new type of question. The search for a clue, for Poincaré's 'good combination' which will unlock the blocked problem, proceeds on several planes, involving unconscious processes at various levels of depth.

In a general way this simultaneous activity on various levels, during the period of incubation, in itself creates a state of receptivity, a readiness of the 'prepared mind' to pounce on favourable chance-constellations, and to profit from any casual hint (Gutenberg and the winepress, Archimedes, Pasteur, Darwin, Fleming). In discoveries of this type, where both rational thinking and the trigger-action of chance play a noticeable part, the function of the unconscious seems to be mainly to keep the problem constantly on the agenda, even while conscious attention is occupied elsewhere. In this context the word 'unconscious' refers primarily to processes (such as perceptions and memories) which occur fairly low down on the gradient of awareness.

But in other types of discovery the unconscious plays a more specific, guiding role by bringing forms of ideation into play which otherwise manifest themselves only in dreaming and related states. Their codes function more or less permanently 'underground', because they govern the type of thinking prevalent in childhood and in primitive societies, which has been superseded in the normal adult by techniques of thought which are more rational and realistic—or are considered as such. These ancient, quasi-archaeological layers in the mental hierarchy form a world apart, as it were, glimpses of which we get in the dream; their existence is a kind of historic record, which testifies to the facts of mental evolution; and they must not be confused with automatized skills which, once mastered, function unawares, for reasons of mental economy. (It would perhaps be preferable to call these 'archeological' strata of the mind the '*sub*-conscious', to distinguish them from processes of which we are merely *un*-conscious because they happen to rank low on the linear scale of awareness. But the Freudian connotations of the word subconscious would probably lead to confusion of a different kind.)

The period of incubation represents a *reculer pour mieux sauter*. Just as in the dream the codes of logical reasoning are suspended, so 'thinking aside' is a temporary liberation from the tyranny of over-precise verbal concepts, of the axioms and prejudices engrained in the very texture of specialized ways of thought. It allows the mind to discard the straitjacket of habit, to shrug off apparent contradictions, to un-learn and forget—and to acquire, in exchange, a greater fluidity, versatility, and gullibility. This rebellion against constraints which are necessary to maintain the order and discipline of conventional thought, but an impediment to the creative leap, is symptomatic both of the genius and the crank; what distinguishes them is the intuitive guidance which only the former enjoys.

Though Poincaré was doubtless one of its beneficiaries, I have quoted his hypothesis regarding the nature of that guidance—the automatic mixing machine in the basement—as an example of a mechanistic explanation. In fact, however, the underground games of the mind were seen to be of a highly sophisticated, visionary and witty nature, although its rules are not those of formal logic. The dreamer constantly bisociates—innocently as it were—frames of reference which are regarded as incompatible in the waking state; he drifts effortlessly from matrix to matrix, without being aware of it; in his inner landscape, the bisociative techniques of humour and discovery are reflected upside down, like trees in a pond. The most fertile region seems to be the marshy shore, the borderland between sleep and full awakening—where the matrices of disciplined thought are already operating but have not yet sufficiently hardened to obstruct the dreamlike fluidity of imagination.*

I have discussed various bisociative devices in which the matchmaking activities of the unconscious manifest themselves: the substitution of vague visual images for precise verbal formulations; symbolization, concretization, and impersonation; mergers of sound and sense, of form and function; shifts of emphasis, and reasoning in reverse gear; guidance by nascent analogies. In day-dreaming, and in most dreams of ordinary mortals, these activities are free-wheeling or serving intimately personal ends; in the inspired moments of artists and scientists they are harnessed to the creative purpose.

The moment of truth, the sudden emergence of a new insight, is an act of intuition. Such intuitions give the appearance of miraculous flashes, or short-circuits of reasoning. In fact they may be likened to an immersed chain, of which only the beginning and the end are visible above the surface of consciousness. The diver vanishes at one end of the chain and comes up at the other end, guided by invisible links.

Habit and originality, then, point in opposite directions in the two-way traffic between conscious and unconscious processes. The condensation of learning into habit, and the automatization of skills constitute the downward stream; while the upward traffic consists in the minor, vitalizing pulses from the underground, and the rare major surges of creation.

NOTES

To p. 192. Jung's emphasis on the mandala as the symbol of the *coincidencia oppositorum* concerns the reconciliation of opposites in the fully integrated person—which is an altogether different question.

To p. 202. Half a century earlier, the cracklings and sparks produced by rubbing a piece of amber had been compared to lightning and thunder by Wall, a friend of Boyle's; but as the context shows, the comparison was meant in a purely metaphorical way.

To p. 210. '. . . Einstein has reported that his profound generalization connecting space and time occurred to him while he was sick in bed. Descartes is said to have made his discoveries while lying in bed in the morning and both Cannon and Poincaré report having got bright ideas when lying in bed unable to sleep—the only good thing to be said for insomnia! It is said that James Brindley, the great engineer, when up against a difficult problem, would go to bed for several days till it was solved. Walter Scott wrote to a friend:
' "The half-hour between waking and rising has all my life proved propitious to any task which was exercising my invention. . . . It was always when I first opened my eyes that the desired ideas thronged upon me." ' (Beveridge, W. I. B., 1950, pp. 73-4).

IX

THE SPARK AND THE FLAME

False Inspirations

I have discussed the genesis of the Eureka act—the sudden shaking together of two previously unconnected matrices; let us now turn to the aftermath of it.

If all goes well that single, explosive contact will lead to a lasting fusion of the two matrices—a new synthesis will emerge, a further advance in mental evolution will have been achieved. On the other hand, the inspiration may have been a mirage; or premature; or not sufficiently impressive to be believed in.

A stimulating inquiry by the American chemists Platt and Barker showed that among those scientists who answered their questionnaire eighty-three per cent claimed frequent or occasional assistance from unconscious intuitions. But at the same time only seven per cent among them asserted that their intuitions were always correct; the remainder estimated the percentage of their 'false intuitions' variously at ten to ninety per cent.

A false inspiration is not an ordinary error committed in the course of a routine operation, such as making a mistake in counting. It is a kind of inspired blunder which presents itself in the guise of an original synthesis, and carries the same subjective conviction as Archimedes's cry did. Let me quote Poincaré once more:

> I have spoken of the feeling of absolute certitude accompanying the inspiration; often this feeling deceives us without it being any the less vivid. . . . When a sudden illumination seizes upon the mind of the mathematician, it usually happens that it does not deceive him, but it also sometimes happens, that it does not stand the test of verification; well, we almost always notice that this false idea, had it been true, would have gratified our natural feeling for mathematical elegance.[1]

The previous chapters may have given the mistaken impression that the genius need only listen to his Socratian demon and all will be well. But the demon is a great hoaxer—precisely because he is not bound by the codes of disciplined thought; and every original thinker who relies, as he must, on his unconscious hunches, incurs much greater risks to his career and sanity than his more pedestrian colleagues. 'The world little knows', wrote Faraday, 'how many of the thoughts and theories which have passed through the mind of a scientific investigator have been crushed in silence and secrecy; that in the most successful instances not a tenth of the suggestions, the hopes, the wishes, the preliminary conclusions have been realized.'[2] Darwin, Huxley, and Planck, among many others, made similar confessions; Einstein lost 'two years of hard work' owing to a false inspiration. 'The imagination', wrote Beveridge, 'merely enables us to wander into the darkness of the unknown where, by the dim light of the knowledge that we carry, we may glimpse something that seems of interest. But when we bring it out and examine it more closely it usually proves to be only trash whose glitter had caught our attention. Imagination is at once the source of all hope and inspiration but also of frustration. To forget this is to court despair.'[3]

All through his life Kepler hoped to prove that the motions of the planets round the sun obeyed certain musical laws, the harmonies of the spheres. When he was approaching fifty, he thought he had succeeded. The following is one of the rare instances on record of a genius describing the heady effect of a false inspiration—Kepler never discovered that he was the victim of a delusion:

The thing which dawned on me twenty-five years ago before I had yet discovered the five perfect bodies between the heavenly orbits; which sixteen years ago I proclaimed as the ultimate aim of all research; which caused me to devote the best years of my life to astronomical studies, to join Tycho Brahe and to choose Prague as my residence—that I have, with the aid of God, who set my enthusiasm on fire and stirred in me an irrepressible desire, who kept my life and intelligence alert—that I have now at long last brought to light. Having perceived the first glimmer of dawn eighteen months ago, the light of day three months ago, but only a few days ago the plain sun of a most wonderful vision—nothing shall now hold me back. Yes, I give myself up to holy raving. If you forgive me, I shall rejoice. If you are angry, I shall bear it. Behold, I have cast the dice, and I am writing a book either for my contemporaries, or for posterity. It is all the same to me. It may wait a hundred years for a reader, since God has also waited six thousand years for a witness.[4]

T. H. Huxley has said that the tragedies of science are the slayings of beautiful hypotheses by ugly facts. Against this tragedy, at least, the artist seems to be immune. On the other hand, it is generally believed that the scientist can at least rely on the verification of his intuitions by experiment, whereas the artist has no such objective tests to decide whether or not he should burn his manuscript, or slash his canvas to pieces.

In fact, however, 'verification by experiment' can never yield absolute certainty, and when it comes to controversial issues the data can usually be interpreted in more than one way. The history of medicine is full of obvious and distressing examples of this. In physics and chemistry too, the best we can do by so-called 'crucial experiments' is to confirm a prediction—but not the theory on which the prediction is based (see below, pp 270–6); and scientific controversies about the interpretation of experimental results have been just as passionate and subjective as controversies between theologians or art critics. If a hunch is drastically contradicted by experiment, it will of course be abandoned. But, by and large, scientists are inclined to trust their intuitions; and if confronted with experiments which give ambiguous or divergent results, either to declare—as Einstein once did—that 'the facts are wrong'; or—as Hobbes did—that 'the instance is so particular and singular, that 'tis scarce worth our observing'; or to resort to the standard phrase that the unfavourable experimental result is due 'to unknown sources of error'—hoping that some day, somehow, it will all work out. Modern theoretical physics lives to a large extent on that hope. Thus verifiability is a matter of degrees, and neither the artist, nor the scientist who tries to break new ground, can hope ever to achieve absolute certainty.

Premature Linkages

I have mentioned discoveries which were the happy outcome of a comedy of errors. No less frequent are those tragedies in the history of thought, where the right kind of intuition begets wrong results—faulty integrations, premature births.

The first attempt to describe physical reality by mathematical relations was made in the sixth century B.C. by the Pythagorean Brotherhood—a religious, scientific, and political Order which wielded great power in the south of Italy. They succeeded in explaining musical quality by quantitative laws, and believed that ultimately 'all things are numbers'.

But they translated this prophetic intuition into a premature synthesis between 'things' and 'numbers', based on the assumption that a line consisted of a definable number of tiny dots, a plane of a definable number of these lines, and so on. They soon discovered, however, that the length of a line such as the diagonal of a square cannot be defined by any countable number of dots; one can draw the diagonal in a jiffy, but to write down the number defining its length one would have to use an infinite series of decimals. To make the scandal worse, numbers of this kind could be shown to be neither even nor odd—or both. Pythagoreans called these numbers *arrhetos*, unspeakable (we call them, more politely, irrational numbers), and tried to keep their existence secret, because they were convinced that their assertion of a harmonious mathematical order behind the untidy world of appearances was true and correct; when a member of the Brotherhood, Hippasos, let the secret leak out, he was reportedly put to death. The failure of this premature attempt at a synthesis brought the quantitative approach to nature into discredit. The physics of Aristotle, which ruled Europe for two thousand years, paid no attention to quantity or measurement; physics remained divorced from mathematics until the scientific revolution in the seventeenth century A.D. brought them together again.

Another premature synthesis, which I have already mentioned, was the Keplerian cosmology, in which the sun sweeps the lazy planets round their orbits with invisible heavenly brooms. But, in this case, the error was a fertile one: physics and astronomy, once 'shaken together' even though in the wrong way, could never again be separated. Equally fertile was the alchemists' right intuition, supported by wrong arguments, of the transmutability of chemical elements. On the other hand, the phrenology of Franz Josef Gall had the opposite effect. Gall thought that every mental faculty is seated in a definite region on the surface of the brain, and that a person's abilities and character could be assessed by the bumps on his skull. It was the first, premature, and naïve attempt to correlate psychology with brain-physiology. Though phrenology was highly fashionable around A.D. 1800, it brought such discredit in its wake that for a century or more psychologists would have nothing to do with speculations about the structure and function of the brain.

Thus the premature integration of matrices which are not yet sufficiently consolidated has in some cases a wholesome effect, by stimulating more mature attempts in the same direction; while in other cases it acts as a deterrent and carries the stigma of superstition or 'un-scientific thinking'. Taken in a wider sense, the category of premature intuitions accommodates the whole body of folk-wisdom—herbal knowledge, weather-lore, psychosomatic healing by hypnosis, suggestion, shock, and abreaction—down to Jenner's diarymaid who 'would not take the pox'. We have learned to recognize in these intuitive insights and techniques the forerunners of our more mature discoveries and re-discoveries; and we thus arrive at a progression in several stages. In the first stage the two matrices which will participate in the ultimate synthesis are tentatively and inadequately joined together by the logic of the unconscious. In the second the haphazard connection is severed again, and a reaction may set in which keeps them apart for a consider-able time. In the final stage, after the definite merger, the previously separate matrices become mentally inseparable, and we marvel at our former blindness.

Snowblindness

'The mind', wrote Wilfred Trotter, 'likes a strange idea as little as the body likes a strange protein and resists it with similar energy. It would not perhaps be too fanciful to say that a new idea is the most quickly acting antigen known to science. If we watch ourselves honestly we shall often find that we have begun to argue against a new idea even before it has been completely stated.'[5]

I shall not dwell on the martyrology of genius; the title of this section refers to that remarkable form of blindness which often prevents the original thinker from perceiving the meaning and significance of *his own* discovery. Jealousy apart, the anti-body reaction directed against new ideas seems to be much the same whether the idea was let loose by others—or oneself. The defence mechanisms which protect habits against the instrusion of novelty accounts both for our mental inertia—and mental stability.

Copernicus was an orthodox believer in the physics of Aristotle, and stubbornly clung to the dogma that all heavenly bodies must move in perfect circles at uniform velocities. In the fourth chapter of the Third

Book of the *Revolutions of the Heavenly Spheres*, the original manuscript of the book contains the following lines:

> It should be noticed, by the way, that if the two circles have different diameters, other conditions remaining unchanged, then the resulting movement will not be a straight line but . . . what mathematicians call an *ellipse*. (my italics)

This is actually not true, for the resulting curve will be a cycloid resembling an ellipse—but the odd fact is that Copernicus had hit on the ellipse which is the form of all planetary orbits—had arrived at it for the wrong reasons and by faulty deduction—and having done so, promptly dropped it: the passage is crossed out in the manuscript, and is not contained in the printed edition of the *Revolutions*. The history of human thought is full of triumphant eurekas; but only rarely do we hear of the anti-climaxes, the missed opportunities, which leave no trace.

Kepler, too, nearly threw away the elliptic orbits; for almost three years he held the solution in his hands—without seeing it. His conscious mind refused to accept the 'cartload of dung' which the underground had cast up. When the battle was over, he confessed: 'Why should I mince my words? The truth of Nature, which I had rejected and chased away, returned by stealth through the backdoor, disguising itself to be accepted. Ah, what a foolish bird I have been!'[6]

Poor Kepler, he was even more foolish than he thought: he actually discovered universal gravity—then rejected it. In the Preface to the *New Astronomy* he explains that the tides are due to the attraction of the moon, and describes the working of gravity—even that the attracting force is proportionate to mass; but in the *text* of that book, and of all subsequent works, he has—incredible as it sounds—completely forgotten all about it. I have given elsewhere a detailed account of this remarkable case of snowblindness.[7]

Galileo revolutionized astronomy by the use of the telescope; but he refused to believe in the reality of comets and declared them to be optical illusions. For he too believed that heavenly bodies must move in perfect circles; and since comets moved in very elongated elliptical orbits, they could not be heavenly bodies.

Freud's revered master, Professor Brucke at the Vienna Medicine Faculty, discovered, in 1849, a technique to illuminate the retina of the eye; but the idea of *observing* the illuminated retina through a lens did not occur to him! It was his friend Helmholtz who hit on the idea—

while preparing a lecture on Brucke's work—and thus became the inventor of the ophthalmoscope.

Freud himself had two narrow escapes, as it were, from achieving world fame in his twenties. In the course of his physiological researches at Brucke's Institute 'he was trembling on the very brink of the important neurone theory, the basis of modern neurology'; but, as Ernest Jones said, 'in the endeavour to acquire "discipline" he had not yet perceived that in original scientific work there is an equally important place for imagination'.[8] It is strange indeed to hear the founder of psychoanalysis being accused by his pupil and biographer of having in his early years suffered from lack of imagination; but there it is—and worse to come.

The fantastic character of the 'Cocaine Episode' in Freud's life can be appreciated only by comparing the silences in Freud's autobiography with the revelations in Jones's biography. In the spring of 1884 Freud —then twenty-eight—read in a German medical paper that an Army doctor had been experimenting 'with cocaine, the essential constituent of coca leaves which some Indian tribes chew to enable them to resist privations and hardships'. He ordered a small quantity of the stuff from a pharmaceutical firm, tried it on himself, his sisters, fiancée, and patients, decided that cocaine was a 'magical drug', which procured 'the most gorgeous excitement', left no harmful after-effect, and was not habit-forming! In several publications he unreservedly recommended the use of cocaine against depression, indigestion, 'in those functional states comprised under the name of neurasthenia', and during the withdrawal-therapy of morphine addicts; he even tried to cure diabetes with it. 'I am busy', he wrote to his future wife, 'collecting the literature for a song of praise to this magical substance.' One is irresistibly reminded of Aldous Huxley's songs of praise to mescaline; but Huxley was neither a member of the medical profession nor the founder of a new school in psychotherapy.

Two years after the publication of his first paper on the wonder-drug Knapp, the great American ophthalmologist, greeted Freud 'as the man who had introduced cocaine to the world, and congratulated him on the achievement. In the same year, 1886, however, cases of cocaine addiction and intoxication were being reported from all over the world, and in Germany there was a general alarm. . . .[9] The man who had tried to benefit humanity or at all events to create a reputation by curing "neurasthenia" was now accused of unleashing evil on the world.' Among Freud's personal patients one died as a result of a large dose of the drug; another—his close friend Fleischl—whom he tried to cure from morphine addiction, became cocaine-addicted instead, and developed 'a delirium tremens with white snakes creeping over his skin'.[10] A leading neurologist, Erlenmeyer, described cocaine as 'the third scourge of humanity'—the other two being alcohol and morphine.[11]

I have said enough about the disasters of this episode. And yet Freud's dabbling with cocaine became a blessing to humanity—but not in the way in which he had thought of it. Two of his colleagues at the Medical Faculty, Koller and Koenigstein, both ophthalmologists, both of incomparably smaller stature than Freud, read his 1884 paper, experimented with cocaine, and saw almost at once what Freud's snowblindness prevented him from seeing. Freud was not interested in surgery; it did not enter into his habits of thought. He was fascinated by the possible *internal* uses of cocaine, and, above all, its effects on nervous disorders. Only in the final paragraph of his paper did he casually mention some possible 'additional uses' of cocaine as a pain-deadener in local infections; its uses as an anaesthetic in minor surgery never occurred to him. He and Koller both noticed that after swallowing cocaine their mouths and lips went numb—the familiar sensation after the dentist's injection. Koller took the hint—Freud did not. Freud suggested to Koenigstein that cocaine could be used to alleviate the pain in certain eye-diseases; but it was Koenigstein who thought of using it as an anaesthetic in eye-operations. Among the first of these, incidentally, was an operation on Freud's father for glaucoma—carried out by Koenigstein, with Koller administering the cocaine, and Freud assisting. . . .

But even at that stage Freud still considered the tremendous benefits of local anaesthetics as merely 'one more of the outlying applications of which his beloved drug was capable. It took a long time before he could assimilate the bitter truth that Koller's use of it was to prove practically the only one of value and all the rest dust and ashes.'[12]

Copernicus, Kepler, Galileo, Freud—I have quoted only a few outstanding examples of mental eye-cataract. How often did Archimedes get into his bath and watch the rising water-level which gave a perfect measure of the volume of his gnarled body? We must resign ourselves to the fact that snowblindness is inherent in the human condition; if it were not so, then everything we know today about the theory of numbers, or analytical geometry, would have been discovered within a few generations after Euclid.

In some of the discoveries which I discussed earlier on a sudden intuition sparked off the instant fusion of previously unrelated matrices. In the cases described in the previous section the spark failed to ignite. In yet other cases it initiates the fusion without completing it. Loewi could not decipher the note relating to his dream, and had to dream a second time before he accepted its message. Kepler rejected the 'truth of Nature', and only admitted it when it returned 'by the backdoor'. Some of Köhler's less gifted chimpanzees discovered, unaided, various new techniques for making and using tools—then seemed to forget them again; but on the next test they rediscovered them after a much shorter period of trying than the first time (See Book Two, XIII). The human equivalent of this situation is a cry of distress: 'Blast it, I *had* the solution, but now I have forgotten it again.'

Cases of this kind make one think of a lighter whose wick has started to glow, without properly burning. The struggle will have to go on, and more sparks will have to be produced, before it bursts into flame. In other words, intuition has established some tentative link between the two distant frames of reference, but that link is insufficient to overcome resistances and effect their fusion. It will have to be strengthened by repetition (as in the case of Loewi) or else additional links will have to be discovered to precipitate the integration.

The Dawn of Language

The most common example for this type of gradual process is the way in which the child discovers that 'all things have names'. During the first year of its life, the average baby progresses from spontaneous babbling to the imitative repetition of syllables and words spoken by adults—with some vague intimations that these words are somehow connected with the situation in which they are regularly used. It seems that eager parents frequently teach their offspring its first words by a process of repetitive 'stamping in', at an age when the baby is not yet ripe to grasp the principles involved. Thus Watson conditioned an infant to say 'da' whenever it was given the bottle, starting at five months, twenty days—that is, six months earlier than the first words normally appear. The process took more than three weeks, at the end of which the word 'da' became the first, mechanically established link between the two otherwise still unrelated matrices of 'sounds' and 'things'.

With each month that passes, the acquisition of new word-links becomes quicker and easier; the child is 'learning to learn'; until, usually in the second half of the second year, it 'makes the most important discovery of its whole life—*that everything has a name*'.[13] As far as one can generalize from the scant statistics, the vocabulary of the average child at the close of the first year is three words; at eighteen months twenty-two words. This seems to be the approximate age when the 'naming discovery' is made, for three months later the average vocabulary has jumped to a hundred and eighteen:

SMITH'S TEST[14]
Average size of vocabularies

Age	Number of cases reported	Number of words
—8	13	0
—10	17	1
1—0	52	3
1—3	19	19
1—6	14	22
1—9	14	118
2—0	25	272
2—6	14	446
3—0	20	896
3—6	26	1222
4—0	26	1540
4—6	32	1870
5—0	20	2072
5—6	27	2289
6—0	9	2562

The integration of the matrices is indicated not only by the steep rise of the learning curve after the eighteenth month, but by the fact that from now on the child, of its own initiative, will point at a thing and ask to be told its name. Delighted with its discovery, it sometimes develops a veritable 'naming mania': it indicates an object, calls out its name, or, if it has forgotten it, invents a name of its own; for henceforth a person or thing is felt to be incomplete if it has no name attached to it.

Thus the dawn of symbol-consciousness is a gradual, cumulative event; a kind of diluted Eureka process, spread out in time, because the final integration can take place only when the child's mental organization has attained sufficient maturity. But the same process may occur in a telescoped, highly dramatized form in rare cases such as Helen Keller's. The blind, deaf, and mute little girl was nearly seven when Miss Sullivan took charge of her and taught her the first few words, c-a-k-e, d-o-l-l, etc., by means of the manual alphabet, a kind of morse spelt by finger-play. Since Helen was 'overripe' for learning a language, she covered, within less than a month, the same ground which takes a normal child about two years, from the imitative acquisition of the first word ('I did not know that I was spelling a word or even that words existed; I was simply making my fingers go in monkey-like imitation')—to the final discovery:

> We walked down the path to the well-house, attracted by the fragrance of the honeysuckle with which it was covered. Some one was drawing water and my teacher placed my hand under the spout. As the cool stream gushed over one hand she spelled into the other the word *water*, first slowly, then rapidly. I stood still, my whole attention fixed upon the motions of her fingers. Suddenly I felt a misty consciousness as of something forgotten—a thrill of returning thought; and somehow the mystery of language was revealed to me. I knew then that 'w-a-t-e-r' meant the wonderful cool something that was flowing over my hand. That living word awakened my soul, gave it light, joy, set it free! . . .
>
> I left the well-house eager to learn. Everything had a name, and each name gave birth to a new thought. As we returned to the house each object that I touched seemed to quiver with life. That was because I saw everything with the strange new sight that had come to me.[15]

Here we have the undiluted bisociative act, the sudden synthesis of the universe of signs and the universe of things. In its sequel each matrix imparts a new significance, a new dimension to the other: the words begin to 'live', to 'give birth to new thoughts'; and the objects begin to 'quiver' under the touch of the magic wand of language.

Helen Keller's dramatic moment of truth is quite unlike the gradual dawn of the name-relation in normal children, and much closer to the sudden insight in discoveries of the type of Pasteur's. The normal child's naming discovery could be likened to the process known in logic as *empirical induction*: 'some things have names *ergo* I assume that all things have names'. (Needless to say, I do not mean to impute any conscious reasoning of this kind to the babe in its cradle.) The chick episode, on the other hand, which made Pasteur jump to his conclusion and establish the general principle of immunization, could be called 'induction from a single case'—a procedure usually illustrated in primers on logic by the example 'all French waiters have red hair'. For a detailed discussion of the relations of gradual learning to sudden discovery I must refer the reader to Book Two.

Summary

New integrations arise by various processes which can be arranged in a series. It ranges from faulty or premature integrations, through partial blindness towards the meaning and significance of one's own discoveries, to the gradual blending of matrices by dint of repetitive experiences, which increase the number of links between them. Finally, there is the sudden illumination of 'spontaneous' discoveries, sparked off by an unconscious intuition, or a chance observation, or a combination of both.

X

THE EVOLUTION OF IDEAS

There is a theory, put forward by George Sarton, and held to be self-evident by many scientists, which says, broadly speaking, that the history of science is the only history which displays a cumulative progress of knowledge; that, accordingly, the progress of science is the only yardstick by which we can measure the progress of mankind; and moreover, that the word 'progress' itself has no clearly defined meaning in any field of activity—except the field of science.

This is the kind of pronouncement where it is advisable to hold one's breath and count to ten before expressing indignant protest or smug agreement, according to one's allegiance to eggheads or engineers. Personally I believe that there is a grain of truth in Sarton's proposition —but no more than that.

Separations and Reintegrations

There are certain analogies between the characteristic stages in the history of an individual discovery, and the historical development of a branch of science as a whole. Thus a 'blocked matrix' in the individual mind reflects some kind of impasse into which a science has manœuvred itself. The 'period of incubation', with its frustrations, tensions, random tries, and false inspirations, corresponds to the critical periods of 'fertile anarchy' which recur, from time to time, in the history of every science. These crises have, as we saw, a destructive and a constructive aspect. In the case of the individual scientist, they involve a temporary retreat to some more primitive form of ideation—innocence regained through the sacrifice of hard-won intellectual positions and established beliefs; in the case of a branch of science taken as a whole, the crisis manifests itself in a relaxation of the rigid rules of the game, a thawing of the collective matrix, the breakdown of mental habits and absolute frontiers—a process of *reculer pour mieux sauter* on an historic scale. The Eureka act proper, the moment of truth experienced by the creative individual, is paralleled on the collective plane by the emergence, out of the scattered fragments, of a new synthesis, brought about by a quick succession of individual discoveries—where, characteristically, the same discovery is often made by several individuals at the same time (cf. p. 110 f).

The last stage—verification, elaboration, consolidation—is by far the least spectacular, the most exacting, and occupies the longest periods of time both in the life of the individual and in the historical evolution of science. Copernicus picked up the ancient Pythagorean teaching of the sun as the centre of all planetary motions when he was a student in Renaissance Italy (where the idea was much discussed at the time), and spent the rest of his life elaborating it into a system. Darwin hit on the idea of evolution by natural selection at the age of twenty-nine; the remaining forty-four years of his life were devoted to its corroboration and exposition. Pasteur's life reads like a story divided into several chapters. Each chapter represents a period which he devoted to one field of research; at the beginning of each period stands the publication of a short preliminary note which contained the basic discovery in a nut-shell; then followed ten or fifteen years of elaboration, consolidation, clarification.

The collective advances of science as a whole, and of each of its specialized branches, show the same alternation between relatively brief eruptions which lead to the conquest of new frontiers, and long periods of consolidation. In the case of the individual, this protracted chore has its natural limits at three score years and ten, or thereabouts; but on the historical stage, the assimilation, consolidation, interpretation, and elaboration of a once revolutionary discovery may go on for generations, and even centuries. The new territory opened up by the impetuous advance of a few geniuses, acting as a spearhead, is subsequently occupied by the solid phalanxes of mediocrity; and soon the revolution turns into a new orthodoxy, with its unavoidable symptoms of one-sidedness, over-specialization, loss of contact with other provinces of knowledge, and ultimately, estrangement from reality. We see this happening—unavoidably, it seems—at various times in the history of various sciences. The emergent orthodoxy hardens into a 'closed system' of thought, unwilling or unable to assimilate new empirical data or to adjust itself to significant changes in other fields of knowledge; sooner or later the matrix is blocked, a new crisis arises, leading to a new synthesis, and the cycle starts again.

This does not mean, of course, that science does not advance; only that it advances in a jerky, unpredictable, 'unscientific' way. Although 'in the year 1500 Europe knew less than Archimedes who died in the year 212 B.C.',[1] it would nevertheless be foolish to deny that today we know considerably more than Archimedes. And I mean by that not only the fantastic and threatening achievements of applied science which have transformed this planet to a point where it is becoming increasingly uninhabitable; but that we also know more than Archimedes in other, more worthwhile ways, by having gained deeper insights into the structure of the universe, from the spiral nebulae to the acid molecules which govern heredity.

But these insights were not gained by the steady advance of science along a straight line. Mental evolution is a continuation of biological evolution, and in various respects resembles its crooked ways. 'Evolution is known to be a wasteful, fumbling process characterized by sudden mutations of unknown cause, by the slow grinding of selection, and by the dead-ends of over-specialization and loss of adaptability. "Progress" can by definition never go wrong; evolution constantly does; and so does the evolution of ideas, including those of "exact science". New ideas are thrown up spontaneously like mutations; the vast majority of them are useless, the equivalent of biological freaks without survival-value. There is a constant struggle for survival between competing theories in every branch of the history of thought. When we call ideas "fertile" or "sterile", we are unconsciously guided by biological analogy. . .

'Moreover, there occur in biological evolution periods of crisis and transition when there is a rapid, almost explosive, branching out in all directions, often resulting in a radical change in the dominant trend of development. After these stages of "adaptative radiations", when the species is plastic and malleable, there usually follow periods of stabilization and specialization along the new lines—which again often lead into dead ends of rigid over-specialization.'[2]

But there the analogy ends. The branching of the evolutionist's tree of life is a one-way process; giraffes and whales do not bisociate to give rise to a new synthesis. The evolution of ideas, on the other hand, is a tale of ever-repeated differentiation, specialization and reintegrations on a higher level; a progression from primordial unity through variety to more complex patterns of unity-in-variety.

If we could take a kind of grandstand view of the history of scientific thought we would at once be struck by its discontinuity, its abrupt changes of tempo and rhythm. The record starts in the sixth century B.C. when we find suddenly, as if sprung from nowhere, a galaxy of Philosophers of Nature in Miletus and Elea and Samos, discussing the origins and evolution of the universe, its form and substance, its structure and laws, in terms which have become forever incorporated into our vocabulary and our matrices of thought. They were searching for some simple, ultimate principles and primeval substances underlying all diversity: four elements, four humours, atoms of a single kind, moving according to fixed laws. The Pythagoreans attempted the first grand synthesis: they tried to weave the separate threads of religion, medicine, astronomy, and music into a single carpet with an austere geometrical design. That carpet is still in the making, but its basic pattern was laid down in the three centuries of the heroic age of Greek science between Thales and Aristotle.

After the Macedonian conquest of Greece there followed a period of consolidation, orthodoxy, and decline. Aristotle's categories became the grammar of existence, his animal spirits ruled the world of physics, everything worth knowing was already known, and everything inventable already invented. The Heroic Age was guided by the example of Prometheus stealing the fire of the gods; the philosophers of the Hellenistic period dwelt in Plato's cave, drawing epicycles on the wall, their backs turned to the daylight of reality.

After that there came a period of hibernation lasting for fifteen centuries. During that time the march of science was not only halted, but its direction reversed. M. Pyke, a contemporary philosopher of science, wrote about 'the inability of science to go backwards—once the neutron has been discovered it remains discovered'.[3] Does it? In the fifth century B.C. the educated classes knew that the earth was a spherical body floating in space and spinning round its axis; a thousand years later they thought that it was a flat disc, or a rectangle perhaps. Similar, though less drastic examples of forgetfulness can also be shown to have occurred in modern science.

In the twelfth century A.D. we observe the first signs of a thaw, and during the next hundred years there are hopeful stirrings: it is the century of Roger Bacon and Peter Peregrine, of the budding universities at Oxford and Cambridge, Salerno, Bologna, and Paris. But it is also the century of the fatal *mésalliance* between Aristotelian physics and the theology of St. Thomas Aquinas. Within a few generations this 'faulty synthesis' was to create a new orthodoxy, which led to another three centuries of sterility and stagnation.

Then comes A.D. 1600—a landmark second in importance only to 600 B.C.—which inaugurates the second heroic age of science: the century of Dr. Gilbert, Kepler, Galileo, Pascal, Descartes, Leibniz, Huyghens, Harvey, and Newton. In the next century, the eighteenth, the speed of the advance is considerably reduced: it is a period of assimilation, consolidation, and stock-taking, the age of the popularizers, classifiers, and systematizers; of Fontanelle, Linnaeus, and Buffon, of the *Philosophes* and *Encyclopédistes*. As Pledge has remarked: 'An observer born early in the century, and making the Grand Tour, would have been an old man before he came across, in the Paris of Lavoisier, anyone worthy of Newton.'[4]

Finally, in the nineteenth century and in the first half of the twentieth, we have an explosive development of ever-increasing momentum. The nineteenth century was the age of the most spectacular syntheses in the history of thought—of royal marriages between previously unrelated and often hostile dynasties. The science of electricity merged with that of magnetism.* Then electro-magnetic radiations were discovered to account for light, colour, radiant heat, Hertzian waves. Chemistry was swallowed up by atomic physics. The control of the body by nerves and glands was seen to rely on electro-chemical processes. The previously independent 'effluvia' or 'powers of nature' which had been known as 'heat', 'light', 'electric fire', 'mechanical motion', 'magnetic flux' were recognized to be all convertible one into another, and to be merely different forms of 'energy', whose total amount contained in the universe always remained the same. Soon afterwards, the various forms of matter, the 'elements' of chemistry, suffered the same fate, as they were all found to be constructed out of the same building blocks in different combinations. And lastly, these building blocks themselves seemed to be nothing but parcels of compressed energy, packed and patterned according to certain mathematical formulae.

The Pythagorean aspiration, to reduce 'all things to numbers', seemed to be at last on the point of fulfilment. The advance of science in the last century offers the panorama of a majestic river-delta, where the various branches first separate and diverge, then follow more or less parallel courses, in a complex pattern of cross-connections and re-unifications, as they approach their ultimate confluence in the sea.

Even this short and breathless gallop through the twenty-six centuries since the dawn of scientific thought, ought to be sufficient to show that the progress of science is neither gradual nor continuous. Each basic advance was effected by a more or less abrupt and dramatic change: the breaking down of frontiers between related territories, the amalgamation of previously separate frames of reference or experimental techniques; the sudden falling into pattern of previously disjointed data. Let me illustrate this process by a few further examples—no longer of individual discoveries, but of episodes in the evolution of the collective matrices of science.

In the recurrent cycle described in the previous section I mentioned periods of crisis and creative anarchy (corresponding to the individual's 'period of incubation'), which precede the new synthesis. The first such crisis occurred at the very beginning of our story when the ritualized worship of the Olympian gods and demi-gods could no longer provide answers to the ultimate questions after the meaning of existence. Mythology had become a 'blocked matrix'; from the whims of Vulcan and Poseidon man's interest turned to the nature of fire and water; from the chariot of Helios to the motions of the sun along the ecliptic; from the antics of Zeus and Athena to the natural causes of physical events. The result was intoxicating. To quote Burnet: 'No sooner did an Ionian philosopher learn half a dozen geometrical propositions and hear that the phenomena of the heavens recur in cycles than he set to work to look for law everywhere in nature and with an audacity amounting to *hubris* to construct a system of the universe.'[5]

The same audacity and *hubris* characterized the early seventeenth century, when the stranglehold of the Aristotelian Schoolmen was broken, and the solid, walled-in universe of the Middle Ages lay in shambles, exposed to the speculative depradations of hosts of Paracelsians, Gilbertians, Copernicans, and Galileans. ' 'Tis all in pieces, all coherence gone', lamented John Donne; it must have been an intoxicating age to live in.

Lastly, since the discoveries of the 1920s, theoretical physics, and with it our picture of sub-atomic and extra-galactic reality, of substance and causality, have again reverted to a state of creative anarchy. And so the cycle keeps repeating itself:

> Nature and Nature's laws lay hid in night:
> God said let Newton be, and all was light . . .

But alas:

> It did not last: the Devil howling 'Ho!
> Let Einstein be!' restored the *status quo*.[5a]

'*Connect, Always Connect . . .*'

Out of the creative anarchy emerges the new synthesis.

I have given in previous chapters a series of examples to show how new syntheses arise in the brains of original thinkers through the bisociation of previously unconnected matrices. The parallel process on the collective plane—on the map of history—is the confluence of two branches of science which had developed independently, and did not seem to have anything in common. 'The progress of science', Bronowski wrote, 'is the discovery at each step of a new order which gives unity to what had long seemed unlike.'*

The new synthesis in the mind of the thinker may emerge suddenly, triggered by a single 'link'; or gradually, by an accumulation of linkages. On the map of history the 'links' are the discoveries of individuals; and here again the process of integration may be sudden, or the result of a series of discoveries by several people. The unification of arithmetic and geometry—analytical geometry—was a one-man show, accomplished by the formidable Descartes. The unification of electricity and magnetism, on the other hand, took a hundred years— from 1820, when Hans Christian Oersted discovered by chance that an electric current flowing through a wire deflected a compass needle which happened to lie on the table, to 1921, when O. W. Richardson explained ferro-magnetism in terms of electron-spin; and it needed a whole series of original discoveries by Ampère, Faraday, Maxwell, and others to act as links and bring the crowning synthesis about (see Appendix I).

All decisive advances in the history of scientific thought can be described in terms of mental cross-fertilization between different disciplines. Some of these historic bisociations appear, even in retrospect, as surprising and far-fetched as the combination of cabbages and kings. What lesson, for instance, could one expect neurophysiology to derive from astronomy? And yet, here it is. In 1796 a minor scandal occurred at the Greenwich Observatory: Maskelyne, the Astronomer Royal, dismissed one of his assistants because the latter's observations differed from his own by half a second to a whole second. Ten years later the German astronomer Bessel read about this incident in a history of the Greenwich Observatory. Bessel, who combined a highly original mind with meticulous precision in his observations, was puzzled by the frequent occurrence of similar timing mistakes by astronomers. It was a typical case of a 'shift of attention' from the nuisance aspect of a trivial phenomenon to the investigation of its causes.

After ten years of comparing his own records with those of several other astronomers, Bessel was able to prove that there existed systematic and consistent differences between the speed with which each of them reacted to observed events; and he also succeeded in establishing the characteristic reaction-time—called 'the personal equation'—of several of his colleagues.

These studies were continued by other astronomers over the next thirty years, in the course of which the development of more precise, automatic recording instruments made it possible to arrive at 'absolute personal equations'. Finally, fifty years after Bessel's discovery, von Helmholtz published a paper showing that the rate of conduction of impulses in nerves was of a definite, measurable order—and not, as had previously been assumed, practically instantaneous. Helmholtz was well acquainted with the work that astronomers had done on personal equations, and his experiments on the propagation of impulses in motor and sensory nerves followed their procedure and techniques. Helmholtz's discovery inaugurated the era of 'mental chronometry', and was a decisive step in the progress of neurophysiology and experimental psychology.

In a similar manner the basic advances in our knowledge of infectious diseases were mostly due to the importation of experimental techniques which had been developed for quite different purposes—such as the use of filtering procedures, microscopic techniques, tissue-cultures and the statistical methods employed in genetics.

Bartlett, in *Thinking—An Experimental and Social Study* (1958), gave a series of similar illustrations. The conclusions at which he arrived seem to paraphrase the thesis of the present theory that bisociation is the essence of creative activity:

As experimental science has gained wider and wider fields, and won increasing recognition, it has often happened that critical stages for advance are reached when what has been called one body of knowledge can be brought into close and effective relationship with what has been treated as a different, and a largely or wholly independent, scientific discipline.

... The alert experimenter is always on the lookout for points and areas of overlap, between things and processes which natural and unaided observations has tended to treat merely, or chiefly, as different. . . .

One of the most important features of these turning points in experimental development is that they very often introduce methods and instrumentation new to the field of research involved, but already developed in some other region of investigation. . . .

The winding progress of any branch of experimental science is made up essentially by a relatively small number of original inquiries, which may be widely separated, followed, as a rule, by a very large number of routine inquiries. The most important feature of original experimental thinking is the discovery of overlap and agreement where formerly only isolation and difference were recognized. This usually means that when any experimental science is ripe for marked advance, a mass of routine thinking belonging to an immediately preceding phase has come near to wearing itself out by exploiting a limited range of techniques to establish more and more minute and specialized detail. A stage has been reached in which finding out further details adds little or nothing to what is known already. . . .

However, at the same time, perhaps in some other branch of science, and perhaps in some hitherto disconnected part of what is treated as the same branch, there are other techniques generating their own problems, opening up their own gaps. An original mind, never wholly contained in any one conventionally enclosed field of interest, now seizes upon the possibility that there may be some unsuspected overlap, takes the risk whether there is or not, and gives the old subject-matter a new look. Routine starts again. . . .

The conditions for original thinking are when two or more streams of research begin to offer evidence that they may converge and so in some manner be combined. It is the combination which can generate new directions of research, and through these it may be found that basic units and activities may have properties not before suspected which open up a lot of new questions for experimental study.[6]

But I must add to this a word of warning. Except when it is merely a matter of borrowing, so to speak, an existing technique or laboratory equipment from a neighbouring science (as in most of Bartlett's examples), the integration of matrices is not a simple operation of adding together. It is a process of mutual interference and cross-fertilization, in the course of which both matrices are transformed in various ways and degrees. Hidden axioms, implied in the old codes, suddenly stand revealed and are subsequently dropped; the rules of the game are revised before they enter as sub-rules into the composite game. When Einstein bisociated energy and matter, both acquired a new look in the process.

The Thinking Cap

I have repeatedly mentioned 'shifts of attention' to previously neglected aspects of experience which make familiar phenomena appear in a new, revealing light, seen through spectacles of a different colour. At the decisive turning points in the history of science, all the data in the field, unchanged in themselves, may fall into a new pattern, and be given a new interpretation, a new theoretical frame.

By stressing the importance of the *interpretation* (or reinterpretation) of facts, I may have given the impression of underestimating the importance of *collecting* facts, of having emphasized the value of theory-making at the expense of the empirical aspect of science—an unforgivable heresy in the eyes of Positivists, Behaviourists, and other theorists of the anti-theory school. Needless to say, only a fool could belittle the importance of observation and experiment—or wish to revert to Aristotelian physics which was all speculation and no experiment. But the collecting of data is a discriminating activity, like the picking of flowers, and unlike the action of a lawn-mower; and the selection of flowers considered worth picking, as well as their arrangement into a bouquet, are ultimately matters of personal taste. As T. H. Huxley has said in an oft-quoted passage:

> Those who refuse to go beyond fact rarely get as far as fact; and anyone who has studied the history of science knows that almost every step therein has been made by . . . the invention of a hypothesis which, though verifiable, often had little foundation to start with. . . .

Sir Lawrence Bragg is the only physicist who shared a Nobel Prize with his own father—for their joint work on analysing crystal structures by means of X-rays, doubtless an eminently factual pre-occupation, which took two lifetimes. Yet in his book on *The History of Science* he too concluded that the essence of science 'lies not in dis-covering facts, but in discovering new ways of thinking about them'.[7]

New facts do emerge constantly; but they are found as the result of a search in a definite direction, based on theoretical considerations—as Galle discovered the planet Neptune, which nobody had seen before, by directing his telescope at the celestial region which Leverrier's calcula-tions had indicated.* This is admittedly an extreme case of observation guided by theory; but it remains nevertheless true that it is not enough for the scientist to keep his eyes open unless he has an idea of what he is looking for.

The telescope is, of course, the supreme eye-opener and fact-finder in astronomy; but it is rarely appreciated that the Copernican revolu-tion came *before* the invention of the telescope—and so did Kepler's *New Astronomy*. The instruments which Copernicus used for observing the stars were less precise than those of the Alexandrian astronomers Hipparchus and Ptolemy, on whose data Copernicus built his theory; and he knew no more about the actual motions of stars and planets than they had known:

> Insofar as actual knowledge is concerned, Copernicus was no better off, and in some respects worse off, than the Greek astronomers of Alexandria who lived in the time of Jesus Christ. They had the same data, the same instruments, the same know-how in geometry, as he did. They were giants of 'exact science'; yet they failed to see what Copernicus saw after, and Aristarchus had seen before them: that the planets' motions were obviously governed by the sun.[8]

Similarly, Harvey's revolutionary discoveries were made before the microscope was developed into a serviceable tool; and Einstein formulated his 'Special Theory of Relativity' in 1905 based on data which, as I have already said, were by no means new. Poincaré, for instance, Einstein's senior by twenty-five years, had held all the loose threads in his hands, and the reasons for his failure to tie them together are still a matter of speculation among scientists. To quote Taton:

> Poincaré, who had so much wider a mathematical background than Einstein, then a young assistant in the Federal Patents Office of Berne, knew all the elements required for such a synthesis, of which

he had felt the urgent need and for which he had laid the first foundations. Nevertheless, he did not dare to explain his thoughts, and to derive all the consequences, thus missing the decisive step separating him from the real discovery of the principle of relativity.[9]

Without the hard little bits of marble which are called 'facts' or 'data' one cannot compose a mosaic; what matters, however, are not so much the individual bits, but the successive patterns into which you arrange them, then break them up and rearrange them. 'We shall find', wrote Butterfield on the opening page of his history of the Scientific Revolution, 'that in both celestial and terrestrial physics—which hold the strategic place in the whole movement—change is brought about, not by new observations or additional evidence in the first instance, but by transpositions that were taking place inside the minds of the scientists themselves. . . . Of all forms of mental activity, the most difficult to induce even in the minds of the young, who may be presumed not to have lost their flexibility, is the art of handling the same bundle of data as before, but placing them in a new system of relations with one another by giving them a different framework, all of which virtually means putting on a different kind of thinking-cap for the moment. It is easy to teach anybody a new fact about Richelieu, but it needs light from heaven to enable a teacher to break the old framework in which the student has been accustomed to seeing his Richelieu.'[10]

Once more we are facing the stubborn powers of habit, and the antithesis of habit and originality. New facts alone do not make a new theory; and new facts alone do not destroy an outlived theory. In both cases it requires creative originality to achieve the task. The facts which proved that the planetary motions depended on the sun have been staring into the face of astronomers throughout the ages—but they preferred to look away.

The Pathology of Thought

I have discussed 'snowblindness' and faulty integrations on the individual level. In the evolution of the collective matrices of science, similar aberrations occur on an historic scale, and are transmitted from one generation to the next—sometimes over a number of centuries. Indeed, some of the most important discoveries consisted in the elimination of psychological road-blocks—in uncovering what had always been there.

The classic example of a mental road-block, extending over two millennia, is one to which I have repeatedly alluded before. If one had to sum up the history of scientific ideas about the universe in a single sentence, one could only say that up to the seventeenth century our vision was Aristotelian, after that Newtonian. It would, of course, be naïve to blame the giant figure of the Stagyrite for crystallizing trends in Greek thought which were originated by others, and reflected the intellectual mood of Greece at the disastrous period before and immediately after the Macedonian conquest. The reasons why his absurd theory of physics acquired such a firm hold over medieval Europe I have discussed elsewhere;[10a] they do not enter into our present context.

The central postulate of the theory was that a moving body will immediately revert to immobility when it ceases to be pushed or pulled along by a second body, its 'mover'. Now an ox-cart on a muddy road will indeed come to a halt when its movers, the oxen, are unyoked. But an arrow will fly through the air once the initial impulse has been imparted to it—whereas, according to Aristotelian physics, it should have dropped to earth the very instant it parted from the bow, its mover. The answer to this objection was that the initial motion of the arrow, while still on the bow, created a disturbance in the air, a kind of vortex, which now became the arrow's 'mover', and pulled it along its course. Not before the fourteenth century was the further objection raised that if the arrow (or spear, or catapulted stone) was pulled by an air-current, it could never fly against the wind.

This inability to perceive that a moving body tends to persist in its course was the psychological road-block which prevented the emergence of a true science of physics from the fourth century B.C. to the seventeenth century A.D. Yet every soldier who threw a spear *felt* that the thing had a momentum of its own—and so, of course, did the victim whom it hit; and every traveller in a post-coach which came to an abrupt halt, had experienced to his sorrow that his motion continued after the mover's had stopped. The experience, the bodily 'feel' of inertial momentum is as old as mankind—but it was prevented from becoming conscious and explicit knowledge by the mental block built into the collective matrix. Even Galileo saw only part of the truth: he thought that a moving body, left to itself in empty space, would persist not in straight, but in circular motion. Such are the difficulties of clearing away the man-made heaps of rubble under which some simple truth lies buried.

The necessity for every moving body to be constantly accompanied and pushed along by a 'mover' also applied to the stars; it created a 'universe in which unseen hands had to be in constant operation'.[11] The planets had to be rolled along their orbits, like beer-barrels, by a host of angels; even Kepler needed a heavenly broomstick, wielded by the sun, to sweep them round their path. Yet here again, the knowledge of centrifugal force has always existed, ever since children swung stones round at the end of a string; and this knowledge had even been explicitly formulated in antiquity. In his treatise *On the Face in the Disc of the Moon* Plutarch, who took a great interest in science and particularly in astronomy, wrote that the moon was of solid stuff, like the earth; and that the reason why it did not fall down on the earth, in spite of its weight, was as follows:

> ... The moon has a security against falling in her very motion and the swing of her revolutions, just as objects put in slings are prevented from falling by the circular whirl; *for everything is carried along by the motion natural to it if it is not deflected by anything else.* Thus the moon is not carried down by her weight because her natural tendency is frustrated by her revolution.[12] (my italics)

The translation is by Heath, who remarks: 'This is practically Newton's first Law of Motion.' It is curious that this passage has aroused so little comment.

Perhaps the most disastrous feature of the Aristotelian system was its denial that the whole universe was made out of the same basic stuff (as Parmenides and the Atomists had asserted before him) and to split the world into two parts, divided by a kind of metaphysical iron curtain. The 'sublunary' region (the earth and its vicinity) was made of four unstable elements, the skies of a fifth, permanent ether; the sublunary region was infected with the vice of change—an abominable slum where generation, corruption, and decay never stopped, whereas on the other side of the curtain fifty-five celestial intelligences were spinning round as many pure, crystalline spheres, carrying the planets and stars in their unchanging circular orbits.

It was the most dramatic splitting operation the world had seen since Lucifer was expelled from heaven; and it was unavoidably followed by a series of divorces and remarriages between incompatible partners.

Celestial mechanics became dissociated from sublunary physics and married to theology when Aristotle's 'first mover' became identified with God, and his star-spinning spirits with the hierarchy of angels. Terrestrial physics, in its turn, was divorced from mathematics, and married to animism. The most striking fact about pre-Renaissance science is indeed its complete indifference to quantitative measurements and numerical relations—not to mention experiment and observation; and its obsession with ascribing animate powers to inanimate objects. Stones fell to earth because it was their natural home, as flames rose upward because their home was in the sky; and the stone accelerated its fall because it was hurrying home as horses hurry to their stable. All motion, all change, was due to a purposeful striving of objects to realize what was potentially inherent in their nature, to move 'from potency to act'—a principle derived by specious analogy from embryonic development. It took about three centuries (from Occam to Newton) to undo the tangled mess which these divorces and *mésalliances* had brought about.

In the healthy evolution of a science, we observe a branching out of specialized, relatively autonomous lines of research; and a parallel process of confluences and integrations mediated by the discovery of universal principles underlying variety. But we also find pathological developments of a rather drastic and persistent kind in the history of scientific thought—collective mental blockages which keep apart what belongs together, and lead to the segregation of 'closed systems'. The healthy periods in the growth of a science remind one of the differentiation of structure and integration of function in organic development. In the unhealthy periods, on the other hand, we find dissociation instead of differentiation, and faulty integrations.

Some of the latter were the result of shotgun-marriages, as it were—imposed from outside, by religious or political pressures. Medieval astronomy had to embrace theology, Soviet biology was wedded to a crude form of Lamarckism. The development of science cannot be isolated from its historic context, from the climate of a given age or civilization; it influences and is influenced by its philosophy, religion, art, social organization, economic needs. But scientific thinking nevertheless enjoys a considerable amount of autonomy; its tortuous progress is unpredictable, its victories and defeats are of its own making. The reason why Copernicus postponed the publication of his theory till the end of his life was not fear of the Catholic Church (which encouraged and protected him) but the fear of ridicule from his fellow astronomers. Galileo's conflict with the Church could have probably been avoided if he had been endowed with less passion and more diplomacy; but long before that conflict started, he had incurred the implacable hostility of the orthodox Aristotelians who held key-positions at the Italian universities. Religious and political oppression play only an incidental part in the history of science; its erratic course and recurrent crises are caused by internal factors.[13]

One of the conspicuous handicaps is the conservatism of the scientific mind in its corporate aspect. The collective matrix of a science at a given time is determined by a kind of establishment, which includes universities, learned societies, and, more recently, the editorial offices of technical journals. Like other establishments, they are consciously or unconsciously bent on preserving the *status quo*—partly because unorthodox innovations are a threat to their authority, but also because of the deeper fear that their laboriously erected intellectual edifice might collapse under the impact. Corporate orthodoxy has been the curse of genius from Aristarchus to Galileo, to Harvey, Darwin, and Freud; throughout the centuries its phalanxes have sturdily defended habit against originality. The uses of hypnotism in dental surgery, child-birth, etc., are regarded as a modern discovery. In fact, Esdaile, who lived from 1808 to 1859, carried out three hundred major operations under 'Mesmeric trance'; but since Mesmer had been declared an impostor, medical journals refused to print Esdaile's papers. In 1842 Ward amputated a leg painlessly under hypnotic trance and made a Report to the Royal Medical and Chirurgical Society. The Society refused to believe him. One of its most eminent members argued that the patient had merely pretended not to feel the pain, and the note of the paper having been read was struck from the minutes of the Society.

The martyrology of science mentions only a few conspicuous cases which ended in public tragedies. Robert Mayer, co-discoverer of the Principle of the Conservation of Energy, went insane because of lack of recognition for his work. So did Ignaz Semmelweiss, who discovered, in 1847, that the cause of childbed fever was infection of the patient with the 'cadaveric material' which surgeons and students carried on their hands. As an assistant at the General Hospital in Vienna, Semmelweiss introduced the strict rule of washing hands in chlorinated lime water before entering the ward. Before this innovation, one out of every eight women in the ward had died of puerperal fever; immediately afterwards mortality fell to one in thirty, and the next year to one in a hundred. Semmelweiss's reward was to be hounded out of Vienna by the medical profession—which was moved, apart from stupidity, by resentment of the suggestion that they might be carrying death on their hands. He went to Budapest, but made little headway with his doctrine, denounced his opponents as murderers, became raving mad, was put into a restraining jacket, and died in a mental hospital.

Apart from a few lurid cases of this kind we have no record of the countless lesser tragedies, no statistics on the numbers of lives wasted in frustration and despair, of discoveries which passed unnoticed. The history of science has its Pantheon of celebrated revolutionaries—and its catacombs, where the unsuccessful rebels lie, anonymous and forgotten.

Limits of Confirmation

From the days of Greece to the present that history echoes with the sound and fury of passionate controversies. This fact in itself is sufficient proof that the same 'bundle of data', and even the same 'crucial experiment', can be interpreted in more than one way.

To mention only a few of the more recent among these historic controversies: the cosmology of Tycho de Brahe explained the facts, as they were known at the time, just as well as the system of Copernicus. In the dispute between Galileo and the Jesuit Father Sarsi on the nature of comets we now know that both were wrong, and that Galileo was more wrong than his forgotten opponent. Newton upheld a corpuscular, Huyghens a wave-theory of light. In certain types of experiment the evidence favoured Newton, in other types Huyghens; at present we tend to believe that both are true. Leibniz derided gravity and accused Newton of introducing 'occult qualities and miracles' into science. The theories of Kekulé and Van't Hoff on the structure of organic molecules were denounced by leading authorities of the period as a 'tissue of fancies.'[14] Liebig and Wöhler—who had synthesized urea from anorganic materials—were among the greatest chemists of the nineteenth century; but they poured scorn on those of their colleagues who maintained that the yeast which caused alcoholic fermentation consisted of living cellular organisms. They even went so far as to publish, in 1839, an elaborate skit in the *Annalen der Chemie*, in which yeast was described 'with a considerable degree of anatomical realism, as consisting of eggs which developed into minute animals shaped like distilling apparatus. These creatures took in sugar as food and digested it into carbonic acid and alcohol, which were separately excreted.'[15] The great controversy on fermentation lasted nearly forty years, and overlapped with the even more passionate dispute on 'spontaneous generation'—the question whether living organisms could be created out of dead matter. In both Pasteur figured prominently; and in both controversies the philosophical preconceptions of 'vitalists' opposed to 'mechanists' played a decisive part in designing and interpreting the experiments—most of which were inconclusive and could be interpreted either way.

I have compared the nineteenth century to a majestic river-delta, the great confluence of. previously separate branches of knowledge. This was the reason for its optimism—and its *hubris*; the general convergence of the various sciences created the conviction that within the foreseeable future the whole world, including the mind of man, would be 'reducible' to a few basic mechanical laws. Yet as we enter our present century, we find that in spite of this great process of unification, virtually every main province of science is torn by even deeper controversies than before.

Thus, for instance, the most exact of the exact sciences has been split, for the last twenty years, into two camps: those who assert (with Bohr, Heisenberg, von Neumann) that strict physical causality must be replaced by statistical probability because subatomic events are indeterminate and unpredictable; and those who assert (with Einstein, Planck, Bohm, and Vigier) that there is order hidden beneath the apparent disorder, governed by as yet undiscovered laws, because they 'cannot believe that God plays with dice'. Another controversy opposes the upholders of the 'big-bang theory', according to which the universe originated in the explosion of a single, densely packed mass some thirty thousand million years ago and has been expanding ever since—and the upholders of the 'steady-state theory', according to which matter is continually being created in a stable cosmos. In genetics, the neo-Darwinian orthodoxy maintains that evolution is the result of chance mutations, against the neo-Lamarckian heretics, who maintain that evolution is not a dice-game either—that some of the improvements due to adaptive effort can be transmitted by heredity to successive generations. In neuro-physiology, one school maintains that there is rigid localization of functions in the brain, another, that the brain works in a more flexible manner. In mathematics, 'intuitionists' are aligned against 'formalists'; in the medical profession, opinions are divided regarding the psychological or somatological origin of a great number of diseases; therapeutic methods vary accordingly, and each school is subdivided into factions.

Some of these controversies were decided by cumulative evidence in favour of one of the competing theories. In other cases the contradiction between thesis and antithesis was resolved in a synthesis of a higher order. But what we call 'scientific evidence' can never confirm that a theory is *true*; it can only confirm that it is *more true* than another.

I have repeatedly emphasized this point—not in order to run down science, but to run down the imaginary barrier which separates 'science' from 'art' in the contemporary mind. The main obstacle which prevents us from seeing that the two domains form a single continuum is the belief that the scientist, unlike the artist, is in a position to attain to 'objective truth' by submitting theories to experimental tests. In fact, as I have said before, experimental evidence can confirm certain expectations based on a theory, but it cannot confirm the theory itself. The astronomers of Babylon were able to make astonishingly precise predictions: they calculated the length of the year with a deviation of only 0·001 per cent from the correct value; their figures relating to the motions of sun and moon, which form a continuous record starting with the reign of Nabonasser 747 B.C., were the foundation on which the Ptolemaic, and later the Copernican, systems were built. Theirs was certainly an exact science, and it 'worked'; but that does not prove the truth of their theories, which asserted that the planets were gods whose motions had a direct influence on the health of men and the fortunes of states. Columbus put his theories to a rather remarkable experimental test; what did the evidence prove? He and his contemporaries navigated with the aid of planetary tables, computed by astronomers who thought the planets ran on circles, knew nothing of gravity and elliptic orbits, yet the theory worked—though they had the wrong idea *why* it worked. Time and again new drugs against various diseases were tried in hospital wards, and improvement in the patients' condition was considered experimental evidence for the efficacity of the drug; until the use of dummy pills indicated that other explanations were equally valid. Eysenck has questioned the value of psychotherapy in general, by suggesting that the statistical evidence for successful cures should be reinterpreted in the light of the corresponding numbers of spontaneous recoveries of untreated patients. His conclusions may be quite wrong; but his method of argument has many honourable precedents in the history of science. To quote Polànyi:

For many prehistoric centuries the theories embodied in magic and witchcraft appeared to be strikingly confirmed by events in the eyes of those who believed in magic and witchcraft. . . . The destruction of belief in witchcraft during the sixteenth and seventeenth centuries was achieved in the face of an overwhelming, and still rapidly growing body of evidence for its reality. Those who denied that witches existed did not attempt to explain this evidence at all, but successfully urged that it be disregarded. Glanvill, who was one of the founders of the Royal Society, not unreasonably denounced this proposal as unscientific, on the ground of the professed empiricism of contemporary science. Some of the unexplained evidence for witchcraft was indeed buried for good, and only struggled painfully to light two centuries later when it was eventually recognized as the manifestation of hypnotic powers.[16]

It is generally thought that physical theories are less ambiguous than medical and psychological theories, and can be confirmed or refuted by harder and cleaner experimental tests. Speaking in relative terms, this is, of course, true; physics is much closer to the 'ultra-violet' than to the 'infra-red' end of the continuous spectrum of the sciences and arts. But a last example will show on what shaky 'empirical evidence' a generally accepted theory can rest; and in this case I am talking of the cornerstone of modern physics, Einstein's Theory of Relativity.

According to the story told in the textbooks, the initial impulse which set Einstein's mind working was a famous experiment carried out by Michelson and Morley in 1887. They measured the speed of light and found, so we are told, that it was the same whether the light travelled in the direction of the earth or in the opposite direction; although in the first case it ought to have appeared slower, in the second faster, because in the first case the earth was 'catching up' with the light-ray, in the second was racing away from it. This unexpected result, so the story goes, convinced Einstein that it was nonsense to talk of the earth moving through space which was at rest, as a body moves through a stationary liquid (the ether); the constancy of the speed of light proved that Newton's concept of an absolute frame of space, which allowed us to distinguish between 'motion' and 'rest', had to be dropped.

Now this official account of the genesis of Relativity is not fact but fiction. In the first place, on Einstein's own testimony the Michelson-Morley experiment 'had no role in the foundation of the theory'. That foundation was laid on theoretical, indeed speculative, considerations.

And in the second place, the famous experiment did not in fact confirm, but contradicted Einstein's theory. The speed of light was not at all the same in all directions. Light-signals sent 'ahead' along the earth's orbit travelled slower than signals 'left behind'. It is true that the difference amounted to only about one-fourth of the magnitude to be expected on the assumption that the earth was drifting through a stationary ether. But the 'ether-drift' still amounted to the respectable velocity of about five miles per second. The same results were obtained by D. C. Miller and his collaborators, who repeated the Michelson-Morley experiments, with more precise instruments, in a series of experiments extending over twenty-five years (1902 to 1926). The rest of the story is best told by quoting Polànyi again:

> The layman, taught to revere scientists for their absolute respect for the observed facts, and for the judiciously detached and purely provisional manner in which they hold scientific theories (always ready to abandon a theory at the sight of any contradictory evidence) might well have thought that, at Miller's announcement of this overwhelming evidence of a 'positive effect' in his presidential address to the American Physical Society on December 29th, 1925, his audience would have instantly abandoned the theory of relativity. Or, at the very least, that scientists—wont to look down from the pinnacle of their intellectual humility upon the rest of dogmatic mankind—might suspend judgement in this matter until Miller's results could be accounted for without impairing the theory of relativity. But no: by that time they had so well closed their minds to any suggestion which threatened the new rationality achieved by Einstein's world-picture, that it was almost impossible for them to think again in different terms. Little attention was paid to the experiments, the evidence being set aside in the hope that it would one day turn out to be wrong.[17]

So it may. Or it may not. Miller devoted his life to disproving Relativity—and *on face value*, so far as experimental data are concerned, he succeeded.* A whole generation later, W. Kantor of the U.S. Navy Electronics Laboratory repeated once more the 'crucial experiment'. Again his instruments were far more accurate than Miller's, and again they *seemed* to confirm that the speed of light was *not* independent from the motion of the observer—as Einstein's theory demands. And yet the vast majority of physicists are convinced—and I think rightly so—that

Einstein's universe is superior to Newton's. Partly this trust is based on evidence less controversial than the 'crucial' experiments that I have mentioned; but mainly on the intuitive feeling that the whole picture 'looks right', regardless of some ugly spots that will, with God's help, vanish some day. One of the most prominent among them, Max Born, who inclines to a positivistic philosophy, betrayed his true feelings, when he hailed the advent of Relativity because it made the universe of science 'more beautiful and grander'.

Paul Dirac, undoubtedly the greatest living British physicist, was even more outspoken on the subject. He and my late friend Erwin Schrödinger shared the Nobel Prize in 1933 as founding fathers of quantum mechanics. In an article[17a] on the development of modern physics, Dirac related how Schrödinger discovered his famous wave equation of the electron. 'Schrödinger got his equation by pure thought, looking for some beautiful generalization . . . and not by keeping close to the experimental developments of the subject', Dirac remarks approvingly. He then continues to describe how Schrödinger, when he tried to apply his equation, 'got results that did not agree with experiment. The disagreement arose because at that time it was not known that the electron has a spin.' This was a great disappointment to Schrödinger, and induced him to publish, instead of his original formula, an imperfect (non-relativistic) approximation. Only later on, by taking the electron's spin into account, did he revert to his original equation. Dirac concludes:

> I think there is a moral to this story, namely that it is more important to have beauty in one's equations than to have them fit experiment. If Schrödinger had been more confident of his work, he could have published it some months earlier, and he could have published a more accurate equation . . . It seems that if one is working from the point of view of getting beauty in one's equations, and if one has really a sound insight, one is on a sure line of progress. If there is not complete agreement between the results of one's work and experiment, one should not allow oneself to be too discouraged, because the discrepancy may well be due to minor features that are not properly taken into account and that will get cleared up with further developments of the theory . . .

In other words, a physicist should not allow his subjective conviction that he is on the right track to be shaken by contrary experimental data. And *vice versa*, its apparent confirmation by experimental data does not necessarily prove a theory to be right. There is a rather hideous trick used in modern quantum mechanics called the 'renormalization method'. Dirac's comment on it is:

> I am inclined to suspect that the renormalization theory is something that will not survive in the future, and that the remarkable agreement between its results and experiment should be looked on as a fluke . . .

I think I have said enough to show that 'scientific evidence' is a rather elastic term, and that 'verification' is always a relative affair. The criteria of truth differ from the criteria of beauty in that the former refer to cognitive, the latter to emotive processes; but neither of them are absolute. 'The evidence proves' is a statement which is supposed to confer on Science a privileged intimacy with truth which art can never hope to attain. But 'the evidence proves' that the statement in quotes is always based on an act of faith. To quote K. R. Popper:

> The old scientific ideal of *epistēmē*—of absolutely certain, demonstrable knowledge—has proved to be an idol. The demand for scientific objectivity makes it inevitable that every scientific statement must remain *tentative for ever*. It may indeed be corroborated, but every corroboration is relative to other statements which, again, are tentative. Only in our subjective experiences of conviction, in our subjective faith, can we be 'absolutely certain'.[18]

Fashions in Science

Controversy is the yeast which keeps science in lively fermentation. But its progress is also beset with pseudo-controversies which appear to reflect differences of opinion, whereas in reality they only reflect differences of emphasis on single aspects of a complex process at the expense of others. Nature and nurture are evidently complementary factors in shaping an individual's appearance and character; yet a whole library could be filled with the disputes between proponents of 'heredity is all' and 'environment is all'. Quantitative measurements were virtually ignored in pre-Newtonian physics; today even psychology is obsessed with quantity, and presumes to measure human minds by

I.Q. ratings and character-parameters. Often a branch of science assumes a 'new look' because its pundits have put on, not a new type of thinking cap but a fashionable hat. We find in the history of science as many fashions, crazes, and 'schools' as in the history of literature or interior decoration. The Ionians loved discussing whether the basic stuff of the universe was water, air, or fire; the alchemists were hypnotized by the properties of sulphur, salt, and mercury; the invention of the Leyden jar threw scientists all over the world into such excitement that to die by electric stroke appeared an enviable fate. In medicine, fads, fashions, and fancies chase one another tirelessly, from the barber's horror-shop to the serene citadels in Harley Street. They have always been an easy target ·for satire; the difficulty in this disturbed border-province is to distinguish between the quack who consciously deludes the patient, and the sincere fanatic who deludes himself into believing that one particular aspect, organ, or function represents the whole, and that a partial remedy is an all-cure.

A more positive aspect of the changes of fashion is that its pendular motions from one extreme to another occasionally result in establishing a more balanced view. One of the remarkable achievements of Pasteur was that, having established against considerable opposition the germ-theory of disease and made the medical profession 'microbe-conscious', he changed the emphasis in his writings from 'figure' to 'background', from the microbe itself to the environment in which the microbe operates. As Dubos puts it:

> Far from being hypnotized with the idea that micro-organisms are the only factors of importance in medicine, Pasteur knew that men as well as animals, in health or in disease, must always be considered as a whole and in relation to their environment. . . . In all his publications . . . he repeatedly stated the thesis—almost as an obsession— that the activities of micro-organisms can be controlled, not only by acting on them directly, but also by modifying the environment in which they operate.[19]

'Environment' to Pasteur meant the whole range of conditions from proper sanitation, through aseptic surgery, to the patient's bodily and mental state. Much of this has become a fashionable truism today, but it was not in the days of Victorian medicine; and even today the lesson has not sunk in sufficiently, otherwise the mass-production of 'super-hygienic' food in sterilized wrappings would be recognized as detrimental to man's internal environment—by depriving it of the immunizing effect of ingesting a healthy amount of muck and bugs.

I have talked more about physics than the other sciences, because it is regarded—both by its practitioners and the awe-stricken lay public, as the paragon of objectivity. In the sciences of life the subjective, and indeed emotive factor, is of course much more in evidence. When it comes to psychology, fashion seems to be almost the dominant factor which determines into which channels the research efforts of thousands of hopeful graduates in the universities of the world will be directed. It seems doubtful whether the doctrines of the hostile schools of analytical psychotherapy differ as fundamentally as their practitioners believe, or mainly by accent and emphasis; and it is becoming increasingly obvious that the therapist's personality is a more decisive factor than the school to which he belongs. But even on the apparently firmer ground of Experimental Psychology and Learning Theory, the history of the last fifty years shows a bewildering succession of changing fashions in experimental design, technical jargon, and field of interest. English associanism; the Würzburg school with its emphasis on introspection; Watsonian Behaviourism which declared introspection a heresy; Gestalt-theory stressing holism and insight; Neo-Behaviourism in its more sophisticated guise—none of them can claim to represent a comprehensive theory of the phenomenon Man—or the phenomenon Rat, Cat, Ape, for that matter. Rather it looks as if each school had focussed its gaze, or collective squint, on a single aspect or slice of human nature, designed its experiments and formulated its questions in such a way that other aspects never had a chance to enter the picture. If one goes on sowing cabbage seeds, one cannot expect them to grow into mimosas—but that hardly gives one a right to denounce belief in the existence of mimosas as a superstition; and if one puts a creature into a Skinner Box, it will behave as one expects a creature in a Skinner Box to behave—with certain quantitative variations which are gratifyingly measurable, but still refer to behaviour in a Skinner Box.

Boundaries of Science

I have emphasized, at the risk of repetitiveness, the irrational factors in scientific thought, first in their positive aspect: the intuitive leap, the *reculer pour mieux sauter*, then in their negative aspects: snowblindness, closed systems, faulty integrations.

These features are reflected, on a magnified scale, in the evolution of every science as a corporate body. Their histories refute the naïve belief that progress in science is an orderly, rational affair, represented by a continuous curve which approaches the ultimate truth by ever closer approximations; or—as we are often told—that our wisdom increases in a cumulative manner, like the steady rise of the water-level in a reservoir.

In reality progress is neither continuous nor cumulative in the strict sense. If it were continuous, there would be no 'revolutionary' discoveries, no discarding of discredited theories and sudden changes of direction—a continuous curve has no abrupt brakes, it is not a zig-zag line.

Nor is progress cumulative in a simple and direct way. The walls of the reservoir—the frame of reference into which new data are poured— are periodically changing their shape: narrowing, expanding, curving this way or that; pipes are built to connect with other reservoirs of knowledge, while rusty connections are sealed off. Moreover, the reservoir is leaky and wasteful: gallons of knowledge are forgotten, discoveries 'stillborn or smothered at birth'.*

It is also asserted that science moves in progressively closer approximations to truth, like a curve approaching its asymptote, even though it will reach it only in infinity. But this statement is rather ambiguous and leads to the frequent confusion between progress in *exactitude* of observations and measurements, with progress in the *explanatory power* of theories—which is an altogether different affair. Tycho de Brahe's observations of the motions of the planets represent a definite advance in so far as precision is concerned. Yet his theory of the solar system was not an advance, but a retreat from Copernicus. Einstein's formula of gravity looks like a small adjustment to Newton's approximation, but it implies a radically different conception of the universe.

The bubble chamber is a kind of aquarium window into the sub-atomic world. It provides us with photographs of the condensation trails, like jet trails in the sky, of what we take to be the elementary particles of matter: electrons, neutrons, mesons, muons, etc., of some forty different varieties. But the particles themselves can of course never be seen, their inferred lifespan often amounts to no more than a millionth of a millionth second, they ceaselessly transform themselves into different kinds of particles, and the physicists ask us to renounce thinking of them in terms of identity, causality, tangibility, or shape—in a word, to renounce thinking in intelligible terms, and to confine it to mathematical symbols. The rapid, continuous increase in the precision and power of our methods for exploring and exploiting nature is so impressive that we are apt to forget the discontinuity and periodic upheavals in the formation of explanatory theories.

No doubt the modern scientist knows more than Archimedes; and no doubt the modern novelist has a wider range of experience than Homer, and more precise tools to analyse human thoughts and emotions. But neither of them arrived at their present station by the shortest way; and though both of them have solved many riddles and attained to important part-truths, neither of them is sure whether the present direction of his zig-zag course leads him towards a 'closer approximation'. Nor is the scientist in a much better position to ascertain the correctness of his course. He, too, must ultimately rely on his intuitions, and the interpretation which he puts on his bundle of data will remain open to controversy.

In the symbolic year 1899 the foremost German biologist Ernst Haeckel published a best-selling book *The Riddles of the Universe*, which became the bible of my youth. Haeckel was the first propagandist of Darwin in Germany, and the first to draw up a geneological tree of the various orders of animals. Like Spencer and Huxley in England, he was a typical representative of the buoyant and arrogant optimism of the nineteenth century. His book enumerated seven Great Riddles of the Universe, of which six were 'definitely solved'— including the Structure of Matter and the Origin of Life; the seventh was man's experience of freedom of choice. However, this was not really a riddle but 'a pure dogma, based on an illusion and having no real existence'—so there were no more riddles left. Science was 'dizzy with success'—as Stalin has said in a famous speech celebrating the triumphs of rural collectivization on the eve of the great famine of 1932.

Other ages have been similarly dizzy with success, convinced that they stood on the doorstep of the Temple of Truth. The Pythagoreans believed it, before they stumbled into the 'Unspeakable Numbers' and the Temple vanished in the mist. Again, in the seventeenth century, intoxicated by the vista which the Scientific Revolution had opened up, most of its pioneers thought that it would take only one or possibly two generations until they wrested its last secret from nature. 'Give me matter and motion, and I will construct the world', wrote Descartes. 'The particular phenomena of the arts and sciences are

really but a handful,' wrote Francis Bacon, 'the invention of all causes
and all sciences would be a labour of but a few years.'

Within a generation after Haeckel had proclaimed that the Riddles
of the Universe had been solved, nearly all the solutions turned out
to be spurious. In 1925 Whitehead wrote that the physical theory of
matter 'got into a state which is strongly suggestive of the epicycles
of astronomy before Copernicus'; in the lifetime of the next generation it became a welter of paradoxa, compared to which the universe
of rotating crystal spheres had been a model of sanity.

I have written elsewhere about the great vanishing act which accompanied the process of unification in science. It started when Galileo
discarded colour, sound, smell, and taste as illusions of the senses which
could all be reduced to the 'primary qualities' of physics, to matter
and motion. But one after another these 'ultimate and irreducible'
entities vanished to the tune of the 'Ten Little Nigger Boys'. First the
indivisible atom went up in fireworks, then the atomic nucleus, then
the 'elementary particles' in the nucleus; matter evaporated in the
physicists' hands, and its ultimate constituents joined electricity, magnetism, and gravity as manifestations of excited states of 'fields' which
could be described only in mathematical terms. Theoretical physics is
no longer concerned with things, but with the mathematical relations
between abstractions which are the residue of the vanished things. To
quote Russell: 'Physics is mathematical not because we know so much
about the physical world, but because we know so little; it is only its
mathematical properties that we can discover.'

For three centuries the reduction of qualities to quantities has been
spectacularly successful, and it was reasonable to hope that within a
generation or two the supreme synthesis which would enable us to
reduce all phenomena in the physical world to a few basic mathematical formulae—something of the nature of the Unified Field
Theory on which Einstein worked, unsuccessfully, throughout the
second half of his life. It is still not unlikely that this hope was well
founded, that in the foreseeable future subatomic physics will strike
rock bottom as it were, and obtain the answers to the questions it has
asked. But it is becoming increasingly evident that both the questions
and the answers of contemporary physics are couched in an elusive
symbol-language which has only a very indirect bearing on reality,
and has little to offer to satisfy man's craving for glimpses of the ultimate truth. Eddington realized long ago that these symbols 'have as
much resemblance to the real qualities of the material world . . . as

a telephone number has to a subscriber'. And two centuries before him, in the jubilant days which followed the unveiling of Newton's universe, Swift, the passionate sceptic, had this prophetic intuition:

> He said, that new Systems of Nature were but new Fashions, which would vary in every Age; and even those who pretend to demonstrate them from Mathematical Principles, would flourish but a short Period of Time, and be out of Vogue when that was determined.[20]

Perhaps that saturation point is not far away, and perhaps science will then start asking a new type of question. One branch after another of chemistry, physics, and cosmology has merged in the majestic river as it approaches the estuary—to be swallowed up by the ocean, lose its identity, and evaporate into the clouds; the final act of the great vanishing process, and the beginning, one hopes, of a new cycle. It has been said that we know more and more about less and less. It seems that the more universal the 'laws' which we discover, the more elusive they become, and that the ultimate consummation of all rivers of knowledge is in the cloud of unknowing.

Thus, contrary to appearances and beliefs, science, like poetry or architecture or painting, has its genres, 'movements', schools, theories which it pursues with increasing perfection until the level of saturation is reached where all is done and said—and then embarks on a new approach, based on a different type of curiosity, a different scale of values. Not only Newton, but Leonardo, Mozart, and Flaubert saw further because they too stood on the shoulders of giants; and Einstein's space is no closer to reality than Van Gogh's sky. The glory of science is not in a truth 'more absolute' than the truth of Bach or Tolstoy, but in the act of creation itself. The scientist's discoveries impose his own order on chaos, as the composer or painter imposes his; an order that always refers to limited aspects of reality, and is biassed by the observer's frame of reference, which differs from period to period, as a Rembrandt nude differs from a nude by Manet.

Summary

The history of science shows recurrent cycles of differentiation and specialization followed by reintegrations on a higher level; from unity to variety to more generalized patterns of unity-in-variety. The process also has certain analogies with biological evolution—such as wastefulness, sudden mutations, the struggle for survival between competing theories.

The various phases in the historic cycle correspond to the characteristic stages of individual discovery: the periods of creative anarchy to the period of incubation; the emergence of the new synthesis to the bisociative act. It may emerge suddenly, sparked off by a single individual discovery; or gradually, as in the history of electromagnetism, where a series of individual discoveries acted as 'links'. Each revolutionary historic advance has a constructive and a destructive aspect: the thaw of orthodox doctrines and the resulting fertile chaos correspond to the regressive phase of the individual *reculer-pour-mieux-sauter* phenomenon. Lastly, the process of verification and elaboration of individual discoveries is reflected on the map of history as the consolidation of the new frontier—followed by the development of a new orthodoxy, a hardening of the collective matrix—until it gets blocked and the cycle starts again.

The decisive phase in the historic cycle, the dawn of the new synthesis, appears as the confluence of previously separate branches of science, or a cross-fertilization between different mental disciplines or experimental techniques. The collection of new empirical data is of essential importance, but both the collection and interpretation of the data are selective processes guided by theoretical considerations. The history of every science proves that observations and experiments which *prima facie* seem to contradict a theory do not necessarily lead to its abandonment; and vice versa, successful theories (such as the heliocentric system or Special Relativity) have been built on data which had been available for a long time by rearranging the mosaic of hard facts into a different pattern.

'Snowblindness', faulty integrations, and other forms of the individual pathology of thought, are reflected on a vastly magnified scale in the history of science; and the power of habit over the individual mind is reflected in the conservatism of scientific bodies and schools—which has impeded progress for periods ranging from years to centuries.

Thus the progress of science is neither continuous, nor cumulative in the strict sense. Its discoveries are often forgotten or ignored, and rediscovered later on. Its history echoes with controversies which prove that the same bundle of 'objective data' and even the same 'crucial experiment' can be interpreted in more than one way. No experimental test can provide the scientist with absolute certainty; and the difference in the 'verifiability' between various types of scientific and artistic statements is a matter of degree (see also below, Chap. XVII). Some scientific controversies are decided by cumulative weight of evidence; others are resolved by a synthesis embracing both competing theories; but still others are pseudo-controversies reflecting differences in emphasis and fashions of thought—and the latter are often as subjective and emotional as fashions in art.

Lastly, a distinction should be made between progress in the precision of scientific statements and their explanatory power. The latter depends on the type of question the statement is meant to answer; and history shows that the questions change with the changing values in different periods and cultures.

NOTES

To p. 228. See Appendix I.

To p. 230. Bronowski (1961), p.27. Cf. also: 'The most fortunate moments in the history of knowledge occur when facts which have been as yet no more than special data are suddenly referred to other apparently distant facts, and thus appear in a new light' (Wolfgang Köhler, 1940, p.89).

To p. 234. The French theoretical astronomer, Leverrier, had predicted the existence of an eighth planet from disturbances in the motion of the seventh planet, Uranus. The planet was discovered by the German astronomer Galle on 24 September 1846.

To p. 244. In his Presidential Address to Section 1 of the British Association, Cambridge, 1938, C. G. Darwin said of D. C. Miller's experiments: 'We cannot see any reason to think that this work would be inferior to Michelson's work, as he had at his disposal not only all the experience of Michelson's work, but also the very great technical development of the intervening period, but in fact he failed to verify the exact vanishing of the aether drift. What happened? Nobody doubted relativity. There must therefore be some unknown source of error which had upset Miller's work.'

To p. 249). It took two thousand years until Archimedes and Euclid were rediscovered. It took four hundred years until the Occamites' work on impetus was appreciated. In the hectic nineteenth century, it took thirty-five years until the significance of Mendel's work was recognized. In 1845 J. J. Waterston wrote a paper on the molecular theory of gases which partly anticipated Maxwell: 'The referee of the Royal Society to whom the paper was submitted said: "The paper is nothing but nonsense," and the work lay in utter oblivion until exhumed forty-five years later. Waterston lived on disappointed and obscure for many years and then mysteriously disappeared leaving no sign. As Trotter remarks, this story must strike a chill upon anyone impatient for the advancement of knowledge. Many discoveries must have thus been stillborn or smothered at birth. We know only those that survived' (Beveridge, op. cit., p. 108).

There may be thousands of relevant bits of information lying dormant in hundreds of technical journals on dusty library shelves which, if remembered, would act as Open Sesames.

XI

SCIENCE AND EMOTION

Three Character-Types

Let me revert for a moment to our starting point, the triptych of
creative activities.

In folklore and popular literature the Artist is traditionally represented as an inspired dreamer—a solitary figure, eccentric, im-
practical, unselfish, and quixotic.

His opposite number is the earthy and cynical Jester—Falstaff or
Sancho Panza; he spurns the dreamer, refuses to be taken in by any
romantic nonsense, is wide-awake, quick to see his advantage and to
get the better of his fellows. His weapons range from the bludgeon of
peasant cunning to the rapier of irony; he always exercises his wits at
the expense of others; he is aggressive and self-asserting.

In between these antagonistic types once stood the Sage who combined the qualities of both: a sagacious dreamer, with his head in the
clouds and his feet on the solid earth. But his modern incarnation, the
Scientist, is no longer represented by a single figure in the waxworks
of popular imagination; instead of one prototype, we had better
compose three.

The first is the Benevolent Magician, whose ancestry derives from
the rain-making Shamans and the calendar-making Priest-Astronomers
of Babylon. At the dawn of Greek science we find him assuming the
semi-mythical figure of Pythagoras, the only mortal who could hear
with ears of flesh the music made by the orbiting stars; and from there
onward, every century created its own savant-shamans whom it could
venerate—even throughout the Dark Ages of science. The first millen-
nium was seen in by Sylvester II, the 'Magician Pope', who reinstated
the belief that the earth was round. The Jews had their Maimonides,
the Arabs their Alkhazen, Christendom the Venerable Bede, before
St. Thomas Aquinas and Albert the Great revived the study of nature.

255

From the Renaissance on there is an uninterrupted procession of magicians whose names were legends, admired and worshipped by a public which had only the vaguest notion of their achievements: Paracelsus, Tycho on his Sorcerer's Island, Galileo with his telescope, Newton who brought the Light, Franklin who tamed the thunderbolt, Mesmer who cured by magnetism; Edison, Pasteur, Einstein, Freud. The popular image of the Magician has certain features in common with that of the Artist: both are unselfishly devoted to lofty tasks—which frequently overlapped in the *uomo universale* of the Renaissance.

The second archetype is the 'Mad Professor' who, in contrast to the former, practises black instead of white magic for the sake of his own aggrandizement and power. Empedokles jumped into the crater of Etna to gain immortality; Paracelsus's rival, Agrippa, was allied to the devil in the shape of an enormous black poodle; the Anatomists were allied to body-snatchers for their sinister purposes. The alchemists distilled witches' brews; electric rays became a favourite delusion in persecution manias; vivisection, and even compulsory vaccination, became symbols of the scientist's blasphemous presumption and cruelty. The Mad Professor—either a sadist or obsessed with power—looms large in popular fiction from Jules Verne's Captain Nemo and H. G. Wells' Dr. Moreau to Caligari, Frankenstein, and the monsters of the horror-comics. He is a Mephistophelian character, endowed with caustic wit; he spouts sarcasm, a sinister jester plotting to commit some monstrous practical joke on humanity. His place in the waxworks is next to the malicious satirist's, as the Benevolent Magician's is next to the imaginative Artist's.

The last of the three figures into which the popular image of the scientist has split occupies the centre space and is of relatively recent origin: the dry, dull, diligent, pedantic, uninspired, scholarly bookworm or laboratory worker. He is aloof and detached, not because he has outgrown passion but because he is devoid of temperament, desiccated, and hard of hearing—yet peevish and petulant and jealous of anybody who dares to interfere with his crabbed little world. This imaginary type probably originates with the Schoolmen of the period of decline, whom Erasmus lampooned: 'They smother me beneath six hundred dogmas; they are surrounded with a bodyguard of definitions, conclusions, corrolaries, propositions explicit and propositions implicit; they are looking in utter darkness for that which has no existence whatsoever.'

Swift satirized the type in *Gulliver in Laputa;* then Goethe in his *Famulus* Wagner: *Mit Eifer hab' ich mich der Studien beflissen—Zwar weiss ich viel, doch möcht' ich alles wissen.* 'Thanks to my diligence, my wisdom is growing—If I but persevere I shall be all-knowing.' His modern incarnations are the Herr Professor of German comedy, and the mummified dons of Anglo-Saxon fiction. At his worst, he incarnates the pathological aspects in the development of science: rigidity, orthodoxy, snowblindness, divorce from reality. But the patience and dogged endurance of the infantrymen of science are as indispensable as the geniuses who form its spearhead. 'The progress of science', Schiller wrote, 'takes place through a few master-architects, or in any case through a number of guiding brains which constantly set all the industrious labourers at work for decades.'[1] That the industrious labourers tend to form trade unions with a closed-shop policy and restrictive practices, is an apparently unavoidable development. It is no less conspicuous in the history of the arts: the uninspired versifiers, the craftsmen of the novel and the stage, the mediocrities of academic painting and sculpture, they all hang on for dear life to the prevailing school and style which some genius initiated, and defend it with stubbornness and venom against heretic innovators.

Thus we now have five figures facing us at our allegorical Madame Tussaud's. They are from left to right: the malicious Jester; the Mad Professor with his delusions of grandeur; the uninspired Pedant; the Benevolent Magician; and the Artist.

At the moment only the three figures in the centre concern us. If we strip them of the gaudy adornments which folklore and fiction bestowed upon them, the figure of the Black Magician will turn out to be an archetypal symbol of the *self-assertive element* in the scientist's aspirations. In mythology, this element is represented by the Promethean quest for omnipotence and immortality; in science-fiction it is caricatured as a monstrous lusting for power; in actual life, it appears as the unavoidable component of competitiveness, jealousy, and self-righteousness in the scientist's complex motivational drive. 'Without ambition and without vanity', wrote the biologist Charles Nicolle, 'no one would enter a profession so contrary to our natural appetites.'[2] Freud was even more outspoken: 'I am not really a man of science, not an observer, not an experimenter, and not a thinker. I am by temperament nothing but a conquistador . . . with the curiosity, the boldness, and the tenacity that belong to that type of person.'[3]

The unassuming figure of the Pedant in the centre of the waxworks is an indispensable stabilizing element; he acts as a restraining influence on the self-asserting, vainglorious conquistadorial urges, but also as a sceptical critic of the inspired dreamer on his other side.

This last figure, the White Magician, symbolizes the *self-transcending element* in the scientist's motivational drive and emotional make-up; his humble immersion into the mysteries of nature, his quest for the harmony of the spheres, the origins of life, the equations of a unified field theory. The conquistadorial urge is derived from a sense of power, the participatory urge from a sense of oceanic wonder. 'Men were first led to the study of natural philosophy', wrote Aristotle, 'as indeed they are today, by wonder.'[4] Maxwell's earliest memory was 'lying on the grass, looking at the sun, and *wondering*'. Einstein struck the same chord when he wrote that whoever is devoid of the capacity to wonder, 'whoever remains unmoved, whoever cannot contemplate or know the deep shudder of the soul in enchantment, might just as well be dead for he has already closed his eyes upon life'.[5]

This oceanic feeling of wonder is the common source of religious mysticism, of pure science and art for art's sake; it is their common denominator and emotional bond.

Magic and Sublimation

The creative scientist in actual life hardly resembles any of these single wax-figures—the Conquistador, the Pedant, or the inspired Dreamer; he contains ingredients of all of them in varying proportions, melted down as it were, and recast according to a personal formula. I have said already (p. 87 f.) that by calling science the 'neutral art' I did not mean that the scientist operates 'dispassionately'—as the cliché goes; but on the contrary, that he is motivated by a particular blend of passions into which both the self-asserting and participatory drives enter, but in a highly sublimated state, complementing each other. A modicum of ambition or vanity or financial need, or even aggression, is indispensable to the most 'disinterested' scientist or explorer—but the conquistadorial appetite must have undergone a great amount of refinement if it is to find its satisfaction in the publication of a paper, representing years of labour, in the columns of a technical journal. Except for the chosen few who attain popular fame, the vast majority of scientists spend their lifetime working in obscurity, and for paltry rewards. In his private life, the scientist can indulge his ego; but in his work, ambition and vanity are denied all but the most indirect and tortuous outlets, in conformity with the complex rules of the game. The compensation for this sacrifice is in the game itself—in that 'enchantment of the soul' which makes interest disinterested, as it were.

The sublimation of the self-assertive, aggressive-defensive impulses is easily understood, since we all have to go through this painful process, abdicating the tyrannic powers of infancy—including the primitive fantasies of omnipotence, from which the figure of the Black Magician is derived—and accepting the rules of the game of civilized society. But the self-transcending, participatory emotions are also subject to the process of sublimation, both in the history of the individual and in the evolution of cultures. One aspect of the latter is the sublimation of magic into art; another, of magic into science.

I have explained earlier on (p. 54 f.) that the term 'self-transcending' or 'participatory' tendencies is meant to refer to those emotional states where the need is felt to behave *as a part* of some real or imaginary entity which transcends the boundaries of the individual self (whereas when governed by the self-assertive class of emotion, the ego is experienced as a self-contained whole and the ultimate value). Now obviously a person's character and pattern of behaviour is to a large extent dependent on the nature of that higher entity of which he feels himself to be a part. There is of course often a multitude of such entities, some forming a hierarchy (family, tribe, nation), others causing rival identifications; some are of the nature of social, others of spiritual or mystical bonds. It is with the latter that we are concerned; more precisely with the transition from one type of mystic participation in a universe governed by sympathetic magic, to another type of mystic communion with a universe governed by a divine or natural order. That transformation was never completed; but even the partial transition which the Greeks achieved had a decisive influence on the pattern of Western culture. At the risk of repetitiveness I must once more mention here the Pythagoreans, the chief engineers of that epoch-making change. I have spoken in more detail elsewhere of the inspired methods by which, in their religious order, they transformed the Orphic mystery cult into a religion which considered mathematical and astronomical studies as the main forms of divine worship and prayer. The physical intoxication which had accompanied the Bacchic rites was superseded by the mental intoxication derived from *philo-sophia*, the love of knowledge. It was one of the many key concepts they coined and which are still basic units in our verbal currency. The cliché about the '*mysteries* of nature' originates in the revolutionary innovation of applying the word referring to the secret rites of the worshippers of Orpheus, to the devotions of stargazing. '*Pure* science' is another of their coinages; it signified not merely a contrast to the 'applied' sciences, but also that the contemplation of the new mysteria was regarded as a means of purifying the soul by its immersion in the eternal. Finally, 'theorizing' comes from *Theoria*, again a word of Orphic origin, meaning a state of fervent contemplation and participation in the sacred rites (*thea* spectacle, *theoris* spectator, audience). Contemplation of the 'divine dance of numbers' which held both the secrets of music and of the celestial motions became the link in the mystic union between human thought and the *anima mundi*. Its perfect symbol was the Harmony of the Spheres—the Pythagorean Scale, whose musical intervals corresponded to the intervals between the planetary orbits; it went on reverberating through 'soft stillness and the night' right into the poetry of the Elizabethans, and into the astronomy of Kepler.

It was indeed this sublimated form of Orphic mysticism which, through the Pythagorean revival in Renaissance Italy, inspired the Scientific Revolution. Galileo, Descartes, and Newton all regarded God as a kind of 'chief mathematician' of the Universe. 'Geometry existed before the Creation, is co-eternal with the mind of God, is God himself',[6] wrote Kepler; and the other giants echoed his conviction. The 'oceanic feeling' of religious mysticism had been distilled intc differential equations; the mind of the *anima mundi* was reflected in the rainbow colours of the spectroscope, the ghostly spirals of distant galaxies, the harmonious patterns of iron-filings around a magnet. In all the 'great and generous minds', from Nicolas of Cusa down to Einstein, we find this feeling of awe and wonder, an intellectual ecstasy of distinctly religious flavour. Even those who professed to be devoid of it based their labours on an act of faith: the belief that there *is* a harmony of the spheres—that the universe is not a tale told by an idiot, but governed by hidden laws waiting to be discovered and uttered. 'The mystic believes in an unknown God, the thinker and scientist in an unknown order; it is hard to say which surpasses the other in nonrational devotion' (L. L. Whyte)[7] In a similar vein, Butterfield wrote on the pioneers of the scientific revolution: 'The aspiration to demonstrate that the universe ran like a piece of clockwork . . . was itself initially a religious aspiration. It was felt that there would be something defective in Creation itself—something not quite worthy of God—unless the whole system of the universe could be shown to be interlocking, so that it carried the patttern of reasonableness and orderliness. Kepler, inaugurating the scientist's quest for a mechanistic universe in the seventeenth century, is significant here—his mysticism, his music of the spheres, his rational deity demand a system which has the beauty of a piece of mathematics.'[8]

It is the axiomatic belief that the pointers on his dials do not move at random, which makes the readings of his instruments meaningful to the scientist. Though Eddington may have been justified in saying that the dials, in the present state of physics, have no more bearing on reality than telephone numbers, this takes nothing away from the excitement of watching their motions. After all, to the worshipful lover even her telephone number acquires some of the magic attraction of the beloved.

The sublimation of the self-transcending emotions has transformed 'magic' into 'science'; but there is no hard-and-fast boundary between the two. Unconscious, pre-rational, 'magical' thinking enters both into the creative act and into the beliefs or superstitions of the scientist. As Dubos said, 'the alchemist never entirely ceased to live and function within the academician'. Not only Kepler's astronomy was derived from belief in the Holy Trinity and the Harmony of the Spheres; most of the giants of science were similarly inspired by religious, mystical or transcendental beliefs.

In Appendix II the reader will find this generalization exemplified by a series of short character-sketches, from Copernicus and Galileo to Franklin, Faraday, Maxwell, Darwin, and Pasteur. I shall close this section with three quotations by men who played decisive parts in shaping the scientific outlook of the twentieth century. The first is Louis Pasteur, who was born a Roman Catholic and remained one throughout his life. At the age of sixty he was elected a member of the Académie Française; the welcoming speech on that ceremonial occasion was made, ironically, by that great and wise agnostic, Ernest Renan. In his reply Pasteur explained that although an inescapable conclusion of thinking, the notion of infinity is incomprehensible to human reason—indeed more incomprehensible than all the miracles of religion: 'I see everywhere in the world the inevitable expression of the concept of infinity. It establishes in the depths of our hearts a belief in the supernatural. The idea of God is nothing more than one form of the idea of infinity. So long as the mystery of the infinite weighs on the human mind, so long will temples be raised to the cult of the infinite, whether God be called Brahmah, Allah, Jehovah or Jesus. . . . The Greeks understood the mysterious power of the hidden side of things. They bequeathed to us one of the most beautiful words in our language—the word 'enthusiasm'—*en theos*—a god within. The grandeur of human actions is measured by the inspiration from which they spring. Happy is he who bears a god within—an ideal of beauty and who obeys it, an ideal of art, of science. All are lighted by reflection from the infinite.'

The second quotation is from Einstein who, when questioned about his own religious views, described them as 'what in ordinary terms one would call pantheistic'. On another occasion he talked of 'cosmic religiousness':

> . . . I maintain that cosmic religiousness is the strongest and most noble driving force of scientific research. Only the man who can conceive the gigantic effort and above all the devotion, without which original scientific thought cannot succeed, can measure the strength of the feeling from which alone such work . . . can grow. What a deep belief in the intelligence of Creation and what longing for understanding, even if only of a meagre reflection in the revealed intelligence of this world, must have flourished in Kepler and Newton, enabling them as lonely men to unravel over years of work the mechanism of celestial mechanics. . . . Only the man who devotes his life to such goals has a living conception of what inspired these men and gave them strength to remain steadfast in their aims in spite of countless failures. It is cosmic religiousness that bestows such strength. A contemporary has said, not unrightly, that the serious research scholar in our generally materialistic age is the only deeply religious human being.[9]

And lastly here is Bertrand Russell, writing at the age of eighty-nine:

> I must, before I die, find some means of saying the essential thing which is in me, which I have not yet said, a thing which is neither love nor hate nor pity nor scorn but the very breath of life, shining and coming from afar, which will link into human life the immensity, the frightening, wondrous and implacable forces of the non-human.[10]

From the Pythagoreans onward, through the Renaissance to our times, the oceanic feeling, the sense of participation in the mystery of the infinite, was the principal inspiration of that wingèd and flat-footed creature, the scientist.

The Boredom of Science

We have seen earlier on (pp. 87–89) that the emotional reaction which follows the act of discovery is a complex one, reflecting the complexity of the motivational drive. There is the sudden explosion of tension, which has become redundant and must somehow be worked off in gestures or shouts of jubilation—an overflow-reaction continuous with laughter, but of a more individual character because derived from a more sublimated kind of emotion. Concurrent with it, there is pure intellectual delight, the peaceful catharsis of the self-transcending emotions. The first is derived from the fact that 'I' made a discovery—the second from the fact that a discovery has been made, another glimpse of the truth revealed.

Let me now turn from the creative person's emotional reactions to those of the audience, to the 'consumer's' point of view. Whether he listens to a joke, or reads a scientific work, or visits an art gallery, he is supposed to participate in the intellectual and emotional experiences of the 'producer'—to relive or re-create them. The bond between them is the need for social communication. The consumer hopes that by being allowed to share the creator's vision he will gain a deeper and broader view of reality. The producer has an urge to share his own experience with others—to win accomplices to his malice, partners in understanding, resonance for his emotions. In order to succeed, however, he must use appropriate techniques. In Chapter III (pp. 82–86) I have discussed certain criteria by which to judge the impact of comic inventions—originality, emphasis, and economy. Are these criteria of any value when applied to scientific discovery?

The importance of *originality* is self-evident. Selective *emphasis* on one particular aspect of reality, with its concomitant exaggerations and simplifications is, as we saw, the essence of model-making, and plays almost as great a part in the changing fashions and 'schools' in science as in art. *Economy* enters in various ways—from Occam's razor and the satisfaction derived from an 'elegant' solution to various techniques of enticing the audience in the lecture-room into an imaginative, re-creative effort.

It is generally supposed that in this respect the creative scientist and his audience are at a disadvantage. In contrast to the artist, the scientist is not supposed to appeal to emotions, and the student of science not to be guided by them. But we have seen that the equation of science with logic and reason, of art with intuition and emotion, is a blatant popular fallacy. No discovery has ever been made by logical deduction; no work of art produced without calculating craftsmanship; the emotive games of the unconscious enter into both.

The aesthetic satisfaction derived from an elegant mathematical demonstration, a cosmological theory, a map of the human brain, or an ingenious chess problem, may equal that of any artistic experience—given a certain connoisseurship. But connoisseurship is equally required for the true appreciation of any but the most vulgar forms of art; and particularly for ancient, alien, and 'modern' art. However, the absurd division of our society into 'two cultures' produced the paradoxical phenomenon that the average educated person will be reluctant to admit that a work of art is beyond the level of his comprehension; but he will in the same breath and with a certain pride confess his complete ignorance of the principles which make his radio work, the forces which make the stars go round, the factors which determine the heredity of his children, and the location of his own viscera and glands.

One of the consequences of this attitude is that he utilizes the products of science and technology in a purely possessive, exploitive manner without comprehension or feeling. His relationship to the objects of his daily use, the tap which supplies his bath, the pipes which keep him warm, the switch which turns on the light—in a word, to the environment in which he lives, is impersonal and possessive—like the capitalist's attitude to his bank account, not the art collector's to his treasures which he cherishes because he 'understands' them, because he has a participatory relationship to them. Modern man lives isolated in his artificial environment, not because the artificial is evil as such, but because of his lack of comprehension of the forces which make it work—of the principles which relate his gadgets to the forces of nature, to the universal order. It is not central heating which makes his existence 'unnatural', but his refusal to take an interest in the principles behind it. By being entirely dependent on science, yet closing his mind to it, he leads the life of an urban barbarian.

The historical causes which led to the split between the two cultures are outside the scope of this book; but I must mention one specific factor which is largely responsible for turning science into a bore, and providing the humanist with an excuse for turning his back on it. It is the academic cant, of relatively recent origin, that a self-respecting scientist *must* be a bore, that the more dehydrated the style of his writing, and the more technical the jargon he uses, the more respect he will command. I repeat, this is a recent fashion, less than a century old, but its effect is devastating. The pre-Socratics frequently wrote their treatises in verse; the ancient Peruvian language had a single word—*hamavec*—for both poet and inventor. Galileo's *Dialogues* and polemical writings were literary masterpieces which had a lasting influence on the development of Italian didactic prose; Kepler's *New Astronomy* is a baroque tale of suspense; Vesalius' *Anatomy* was illustrated by a pupil of Titian. Even the abstract symbol language of the mathematicians lent itself to works of art. As the great Boltzmann wrote: 'A mathematician will recognize Cauchy, Gauss, Jacobi, or Helmholtz, after reading a few pages, just as musicians recognize, from the first few bars, Mozart, Beethoven, or Schubert.' And Jeans compared Maxwell's physics with an enchanted fairyland where no one knew what was coming next.

I have given samples of Pasteur's and Poincaré's style; Franklin was an accomplished stylist; Maxwell wrote commendably funny,* and Erasmus Darwin unintentionally funny verse; as for William James, I must confess that I find his style far more enjoyable than his brother Henry's. In our present century Eddington, Jeans, Freud, Kretschmer, Whitehead, Russell, Schrödinger, to mention only a few, gave convincing proof that works on science can at the same time be works of literary art. (One could also quote works by literary and art critics as pedantic and desiccated as papers in a technical journal for applied chemistry.) Needless to say, technical communications addressed to specialists must employ technical language; but even here the overloading with jargon, the tortuous and cramped style, are largely a matter of conforming to fashion.

The same inhuman—in fact anti-humanistic—trend pervades the climate in which science is taught, the classrooms and the textbooks. To derive pleasure from the art of discovery, as from the other arts, the consumer—in this case the student—must be made to re-live, to some extent, the creative process. In other words, he must be induced, with proper aid and guidance, to make some of the fundamental discoveries of science by himself, to experience in his own mind some of those flashes of insight which have lightened its path. This means that the history of science ought to be made an essential part of the curriculum, that science should be represented in its evolutionary context—and not as a Minerva born fully armed. It further means that the paradoxes, the 'blocked matrices' which confronted Archimedes, Copernicus, Galileo, Newton, Harvey, Darwin, Einstein should be reconstructed in their historical setting and presented in the form of riddles—with appropriate hints—to eager young minds. The most productive form of learning is problem-solving (Book Two, XIII–XIX). The traditional method of confronting the student not with the problem but with the finished solution, means depriving him of all excitement, to shut off the creative impulse, to reduce the adventure of mankind to a dusty heap of theorems.

Art is a form of communication which aims at eliciting a re-creative echo. Education should be regarded as an art, and use the appropriate techniques of art to call forth that echo. The novice, who has gone through some of the main stages in the evolution of the race during his pre-natal development, and of the evolution from savage to civilized society by the time he reaches adolescence, should then be made to continue his curriculum by re-capitulating some of the decisive episodes, impasses, and turning points on the road to the conquest of knowledge. Our textbooks and methods of teaching reflect a static, pre-evolutionary concept of the world. For man cannot inherit the past; he has to re-create it.

Summary

The scientist's motivational drive is a blend of passions in which both the self-asserting and self-transcending tendencies participate—symbolized by the Mad Professor and the Benevolent Magician of folklore. It is, however, a blend in which both tendencies are sublimated and balance each other. This development is already foreshadowed in the exploratory behaviour of clever animals. When Köhler's chimpanzee Sultan discovered, after many unsuccessful efforts, that he could rake the banana into the cage by fitting two short hollow sticks into each other, his motivation was obviously to get at the banana. But his new discovery 'pleased him so immensely' that he kept repeating the trick and forgot to eat the banana (for similar observations, see Book Two, VIII). If Archimedes was originally motivated by the desire to obtain money or favours from the tyrant of Syracuse, his jubilant shout was certainly not due to anticipation of the reward.

Ambition, greed, vanity can enter the service of creativity only through indirect channels; and the self-transcending emotions must undergo a similar process of sublimation from mystic immersion in the harmony of the spheres to the scrupulous attention paid to eight minutes arc. The process is reflected in the gradual transformation of magic into science.

The creative achievements of the scientist lack the 'audience appeal' of the artist's for several reasons briefly mentioned—technical jargon, antiquated teaching methods, cultural prejudice. The boredom created by these factors has accentuated the artificial frontiers between continuous domains of creativity.

NOTE

To page 265: See Appendix II, p, 691.

PART THREE

THE ARTIST

XII

THE LOGIC OF THE MOIST EYE

Laughter and Weeping

The classic responses to comedy and tragedy are laughter and weeping. Both are overflow channels for the disposal of emotions; luxury reflexes without apparent utility. This much they have in common; in other respects they are direct opposites.

There is a vast literature on the psychology of laughter, but hardly any on the psychology of weeping.* The theory of the comic which I have proposed, however controversial, can at least be judged in the light of earlier theories on similar or opposite lines; where weeping is concerned we are on virgin territory. This indifference towards the manifestation of emotions in weeping (which is after all neither an uncommon nor a trivial phenomenon) is in itself symptomatic of the contemporary trend in psychology—about which later.

Weeping and crying confront us with an even more confusing variety of expressions than laughter. There are variations in intensity; in mood; in spontaneity. The bawling of a spoilt child, the contrived sobs of public or private stagecraft are secondary derivatives which distort the original pattern; cultural restraints and social infection are further superimpositions on it. We must disregard these adventitious elements and concentrate on spontaneous weeping in its pure form, as an automatic 'reflex' (see pp. 28–29).

The first step is to distinguish between weeping and crying—it is a peculiarity of the English language to treat them as synonyms. *Weeping* has two basic reflex-characteristics which are found in all its varieties: the overflow of the tear-glands and a specific form of breathing. These vary in intensity from a mere moistening of the eye and 'catching one's breath' (or feeling 'a lump in the throat') to a profusion of tears accompanied by convulsive sobbing; just as laughter varies in intensity from smiling to convulsions. *Crying*, on the other hand, is the emitting of sounds signalling distress, protest, or some other emotion. It may be combined with, or alternate with, weeping. Frequently when a child, or a depressed patient, is said to be 'crying his head off' his eyes are in fact dry: he is *not* weeping. On the other hand, when your char-lady has a 'good cry' at the movies, she isn't crying at all but weeping. Crying is a form of communication (even if the audience is only imagined); weeping is not.

Let me now compare the external manifestations—bodily changes—in weeping and in laughter. In weeping, the eyes are 'blinded' by tears: they lose their focus and lustre. The laugher's eyes sparkle, the corners are wrinkled, but brow and cheeks are taut and smooth, which lends the face an expression of radiance; the lips are parted, the corners lifted. In weeping, the features crinkle and crumple; even when weeping for joy or in aesthetic rapture, the transfigured face reflects a serene languidness.

The breathing pattern in weeping is a series of short, deep, gasping inspirations, i.e. sobs, followed by long, sighing expirations, with the glottis partially closed—the lump in the throat. This is the exact opposite of the breathing pattern of laughter with its bursts of *expiratory* puffs—sobs in reverse, followed by long, deep *intakes*—reversed sighs. A prolonged, violent fit of laughter, however, may produce the sobbing type of respiration as an after-effect—a phenomenon which strengthens the hypothesis (see below) that laughter and crying are mediated by rival branches of the autonomous nervous system—the first being sympathicotonic, the second vagotonic.

The third contrast is between bodily postures and motions. The person who laughs tends to throw his head back by a vigorous contraction of the elevators in the neck; the person who weeps 'lets the head droop' (into the hands, on the table, or on somebody's shoulder). Laughter contracts the muscles and throws the body into violent motion—banging the table or slapping one's knees; in weeping, the muscles go flabby, the shoulders slump forward, the whole posture reflects a 'breaking down', a 'letting go'.

In the fourth place, vocalization in laughter—roaring, giggling, chuckling, etc.—is expressive of *joie de vivre* with aggressive overtones; but if weeping is accompanied by crying, the sounds express lament, appeals for sympathy.

Finally, in laughter tension is suddenly exploded, emotion debunked; in weeping it is drained away in a gradual process *which does not break the continuity of mood*; there is no dis-owning of emotion, thought and sentiment remain united to the end. Moreover, the gradual relief in weeping does not prevent the simultaneous generation of more emotion of the same type, so that the influx may balance the overflow, and relief is incomplete, or not even experienced as such.

Why do we Weep?

Let me discuss a few typical situations which may cause the shedding of tears.

A. *Raptness*. Listening to the organ in a cathedral, looking at a majestic landscape from the top of a mountain, observing an infant hesitantly returning a smile, being in love—any of these experiences may cause a welling-up of emotions, a moistening or overflowing of the eyes, while the body is becalmed and drained of its tensions. A few steps higher on the intensity-scale, and the 'I' seems no longer to exist, to dissolve in the experience like a grain of salt in water; awareness becomes de-personalized and expands into 'the oceanic feeling of limitless extension and oneness with the universe'.*

Here, then, we see the self-transcending emotions displayed in their purest form. Once you start fondling the smiling baby and making a fuss of it, an active, possessive element enters into the situation and the spell is broken. The purely *self-transcending emotions do not tend towards action, but towards quiescence, tranquillity, and catharsis*. Respiration and pulse-rate are slowed down, muscle-tone is lowered; 'entrancement' is a step towards the trance-like states induced by the contemplative techniques of Eastern mysticism and by certain drugs. The experience of 'the blending of the finite with the infinite' can become so intense that it evokes Faust's prayer: *O Augenblick verweile*—let this moment last for eternity, let me die. But there is nothing morbid in this; it is a yearning for an even more complete communion, the ultimate catharsis or *samadhi*.

The reason for their passive, quietistic nature is that the self-transcending emotions *cannot be consummated by any specific voluntary action*. You cannot take the mountain panorama home with you; the surest method to break the charm is clicking your camera. You cannot merge with the infinite or dissolve in the universe by any exertion of the body; and even in the most selfless forms of love and communion each individual remains an island. To be 'overwhelmed' by love, wonder, devotion, 'enraptured' by a smile, 'entranced' by beauty—each verb expresses a passive state, a surrender; the surplus of emotion cannot be worked off in action—it can be consummated only in *internal*, visceral and glandular, processes.

These observations are again in keeping with the character of the two divisions of the autonomous nervous system. We have seen that the self-assertive emotions operate through the powerful adrenal-sympathico system which galvanizes the body into action under the stress of hunger, pain, rage, and fear. The parasympathetic division, on the other hand, never goes into action as a compact unit; it does not dispose of a powerful pep-hormone like adrenalin, acting directly on the body as a whole. The sympathetic division has been compared to the pedals of a piano, which affect all the notes sounded; the parasympathetic to the separate keys which act locally on various organs. In the main, its function is to counteract and to complement sympathico-adrenal excitation: to lower blood-pressure and pulse-rate, neutralize excesses of blood-sugar and acidity, to facilitate digestion and the disposal of body-wastes, to activate the flow of tears, etc. In other words, the general action of the para-sympathetic system is *inward-directed, calming, and cathartic*. All this, and other arguments of a more technical nature, point to the correlation of the participatory emotions with the parasympathetic system.*

B. Mourning. A woman is notified of the sudden death of her husband. At first she is stunned, unable to believe the news; then she finds some relief in tears.

Again, it is a situation in which nothing purposeful can be done, which does not beget action, but passive surrender—'giving in to grief'. And, again, the emotion originates in the experience of 'belonging to', 'belonging together', of a communion which transcends the boundaries of the self. Resentment, guilt, unconscious gratification, may, of course, enter into the widow's mixed feelings, but we are concerned at the moment only with her experience of identification and belonging. That experience, and the emotions generated by it, have not come to an end with the husband's death; on the contrary, they have at the same time become more intense and frustrated. The overflow of tears is insufficient to relieve her from this surplus of emotions; she weeps 'in grief', whereas the euphoric experiences of the previous section caused 'weeping in joy'.

But the difference is in fact a matter of degrees. The moist eyes in the transfigured face of the young mother also reflect an emotion which cannot be completely consummated, lived out; the urge to transcend the self's boundaries, to break out of its insulation always carries a certain amount of frustration. Saints and mystics spend their lives trying to escape the prison of the flesh; Hemingway, who was not a saint, wrote of the 'heart-breaking profile' of his young Venetian contessa; and to be overwhelmed by beauty may indeed be as 'heart-breaking' as a widow's tears sweetened by self-pity. A long, enforced separation may be as painful as a final one; and there are cases of mourning where worship of the dead partner, with or without hope for a reunion in after-life, creates a more harmonious, if imaginary, communion than the actual partnership ever did.

These continuous transitions between 'weeping in joy' and 'weeping in sorrow' reflect the relative nature of 'pleasure' and 'unpleasure' (*Unlust*, disphoria, as distinct from physical pain). Emotions have been called 'overheated drives'. A drive becomes 'overheated' when it has no immediate outlet; or when its intensity is so increased that the normal outlets are insufficient; or for both reasons. A moderate amount of overheating may be experienced as a pleasurable arousal, thrill, excitement, or appetite—while anticipating (or imagining) the consummatory act. Even physical discomfort and pain are readily tolerated (for instance, in mountain-climbing or trout-fishing on an icy morning) in the pleasurable anticipation of the reward. But when the 'overheating' exceeds a critical level it is experienced as tension, stress, frustration, suffering. However, the pleasure-unpleasure tone is determined not only by the *intensity* of emotive pressure; it also depends on whether the pressure is *increasing or decreasing*. Intense frustration changes into incipient relief the moment the consummatory action has started—or has merely come into sight. Decrease of tension is pleasurable—up to a point. If the water-level, so to speak, falls *below* a critical point, there is a sensation of drying-up, of boredom and restlessness. At this stage increases of emotion are induced by various methods of seeking out thrills—from wild-game hunting to horror comics and other forms of what one might call 'emotional window-shopping': the vicarious satisfactions derived from reading the social gossip columns or watching a strip-tease. In these cases the pleasurable experience is derived not from anticipating, but from *imagining* the reward; and the satisfaction obtained—such as it is—consists in the 'internal consummation' of those components in the complex drive which can be lived out in fantasy.

Thus pleasure-unpleasure form a continuous scale of 'feeling-tones' which accompany emotion: the former indicating the progress (real, anticipated, or imagined) of a drive towards its consummation, the latter indicating its frustration.

This leads us to a quasi three-dimensional theory of emotions (which sounds involved, but is probably still a woeful over-simplification). In the first place, we must obviously differentiate between the various emotions according to the *nature of the drive*, originating in various physiological, social, or 'psychogenic'[1] needs and urges— hunger, sex, protection of offspring, curiosity (the 'exploratory drive'), conviviality, etc. To use a coarse but comfortable analogy, let each of these be represented by a different tap in a saloon-bar, which is turned on as the demand arises, each serving a beverage with a different flavour. In the second place, we have the *pleasure-unpleasure* scale, corresponding to the pressure in the tap—whether the liquid flows smoothly, or gurgles and splutters because of air-locks or excess pressure. In the third place, we have the polarity between the *self-assertive and participatory* tendencies which enter into each emotion (for instance, possessiveness versus identification in maternal love); this could be represented by the relative proportion of alcohol and water in the liquid. We can thus distinguish between three variables or 'parameters' in every emotional experience: 'flavour' (hunger, love, curiosity); 'pressure', pleasant or unpleasant; and 'alcohol-content': toxic, i.e. aggressive-defensive, or soothing and cathartic.

C. Relief. A woman whose son has been reported by the War Office as missing suddenly sees him walking into her room, safe and sound. Again the first reaction is shock and rigidity; then she flings herself into his arms, *alternately laughing and weeping*.

Obviously there are two processes involved here. The first is the sudden, dramatic relief from anxiety; the other an overwhelming joy, love, tenderness. Some writers on the subject are apt to confuse these two reactions—to regard *all* joyous emotion as due to relief from anxious tension. But clearly a tender reaction would be expected in any case from the mother on her son's return—even if he were merely returning from a day at school, and there had been no previous anxiety. Vice versa, relief from anxiety in itself, though always pleasant, does not create tender feelings overflowing in tears. What happened in the present case is that the agony the woman endured had increased the intensity of her yearning and love; and that relief from anxiety had increased out of all proportion the gratification she would have felt on his return after an absence under normal circumstances.

Let me be a little more explicit—for the situation has, as we shall see, a direct bearing on the emotional reactions induced by works of dramatic art. The mother's sudden relief from anxiety could be verbalized as 'thank God you are not dead'. Up to that moment she had tried to control her fears, to banish from consciousness the terrible images of what may have been happening to her boy. Now she can let herself go, allow her emotions a free outlet. Hence the manic display of hugging, bustling, laughing, calling in the neighbours, and upsetting the tea kettle: she is working off the adrenalin of all that pent-up and suddenly released anxiety. But in the middle of these hectic activities there are moments when she glances at the embarrassed prodigal with a kind of incredulous, rapt expression and her eyes again overflow with soothing, peaceful tears. The alternation and overlapping of the two patterns—one eruptive and agitated, the other gradual and cathartic—indicate the now familiar two processes and the nature of the emotions acted out.

These become even more evident in exclamations such as 'How silly of me to cry', followed by more bustling and merriment. The unexpected return of the boy was like a the 'bolt out of the blue' which cut short the tense narrative of her anxious fantasies; the tension has suddenly become redundant, and is disowned by reason. At other moments she is still unable 'to believe her eyes' and emotion wells up again. This may even include some unconscious resentment against the cause of so much needless worry, who stands in her room, sunburnt and grinning, unaware of the suffering he has caused: 'What a fool I have been to worry so much' may be translated as 'What a fool you have made of me'.

'Laughing through one's tears' is caused by quickly oscillating mental states, where reason and emotion are alternately united and dissociated. A sudden shock which demands a major emotional readjustment is often followed by such oscilatory phases in which the subject alternately believes and disbelieves her eyes, until a full grasp of reality is reached on all levels. If instead of the happy ending, there had been a tragic one—a telegram informing the woman of her boy's death—then, instead of disbelieving her eyes, she would have been tempted to disbelieve the news; and while the happy mother behaves at moments as if the boy were still in danger, the bereaved mother may behave at times as if he were still alive. In the former case, the successive flashes of reality which disrupt the web of illusion bring happy relief; in the latter, each flash brings renewed despair. A person with psychotic dispositions may, however, cling to the illusion, and it will be the matrix of reality which disintegrates instead. The 'hollow' laughter in certain forms of insanity seems to echo the effort of reversing the process of adjustment—the effort of going mad in the teeth of a world that is sane.

In the milder forms of paranoia induced by the stage and screen, the oscillations between illusion and reality are deliberately created and prolonged. The cathartic effect of the antique mysteries and of the modern drama alike are derived from man's unique faculty of believing and disbelieving his eyes in the same blink.

D. When a woman weeps *in sympathy* with another person's sorrow (or joy), she partially identifies herself with that person by an act of projection, introjection, or empathy—whatever you like to call it. The same is true when the 'other person' is a heroine on the screen or in the pages of a novel. But it is essential to distinguish here between two emotional processes—although they are experienced simultaneously and mixed together.

The first is the act of identification itself—the fact that the subject has for the moment more or less forgotten her own existence and participates in the existence of another, at another place and time. This in itself is a self-transcending, gratifying and 'ennobling' experience for the simple reason that while it lasts, the subject, Mrs. Smith, is prevented from thinking of her own anxieties, ambitions, and grudges against Mr. Smith. In other words, the act of identification temporarily *inhibits* the self-asserting tendencies.

The second process is mediated by the first: the act of identification leads to the experiencing of vicarious emotions. When Mrs. Smith is 'sharing Mrs. Brown's sorrow' there is in the first place the *sharing*, and in the second, the *sorrow*. The first is an unselfish participatory experience which makes her feel 'good'—in the literal, not in the cheap sense (when self-congratulatory or gloating sentiments are present, there is no true identification). The second is the sorrow—a vicarious experience, but genuinely felt. It may of course be joy or anxiety instead. The tears of Mrs. Smith at the happy ending when the lovers on the screen are reunited or the baby's life is saved in the nick of time, are released by the same process as the tears of the woman whose son has suddenly returned: relief from anxiety, and a hot surge of joy.

The anxiety which grips the spectator of a thriller-film, though vicarious, is nevertheless real; it is reflected in the familiar physical symptoms—palpitations, tensed muscles, sudden 'jumps' of alarm. The same applies to the anger felt at the machinations of the perfidious villain on the screen, whom Mexican audiences have been known to riddle with bullets. This leads us to an apparent paradox which is basic to the understanding of all dramatic art forms. We have seen that on the one hand the self-transcending emotions—participation, projection, identification—*inhibit* the self-asserting tendencies: they soothe, calm, eliminate worry and desire, purge body and mind of its tensions. On the other hand, the act of self-transcending identification may *stimulate* the surge of anger, fear, cruelty, which, although experienced on behalf of somebody else, nevertheless belong to the self-assertive, aggressive-defensive class and display all their bodily symptoms. The mother's bustling, laughter, agitation on her son's return, shows the classic 'adreno-toxic' pattern, characteristic of the self-assertive emotions—although her anxiety was centred not on herself, but experienced on behalf of her son. Anger, fear, and the related 'emergency-reactions' use the same physiological mechanism whether the threat is directed at one's own person, or the person with whom one has identified oneself. They are always 'self-assertive'—although the 'self' has momentarily changed its address—by being, for instance, projected into the handsome and guileless heroine on the screen. Righteous indignation about injustices inflicted on others can generate behaviour just as fanatical as the sting of a personal insult. Self-sacrificing devotion to a creed bred ruthless inquisitors—'the worst of madmen is a saint run mad'.

The glory and the tragedy of the human condition are closely related to the fact that under certain circumstances the participatory tendencies may serve as mediators or vehicles for emotions belonging to the opposite class; whereas under different circumstances the two tendencies counteract and harmoniously balance each other. We shall return to this subject, from a different angle, in the next section; but let me note in passing that the preceding remarks on the various ways in which the two tendencies interact on the psychological level are again in keeping with the facts (as far as known) about the different modes of interaction between the two divisions of the autonomous nervous system, which may be antagonistic, compensatory, cathartic, or catalytic, according to conditions.[2]

E. Self-Pity. A littly boy is beaten up by a gang of bullies. For a while he tries to fight back, to hit, scratch, and kick, but his tormentors immobilize him, and at last he begins to cry in 'impotent rage'.

But the expression is misleading. Anybody who has watched children fight knows that weeping will start only after the victim has given up struggling and wriggling and accepted defeat. After a while new outbursts of rage may renew the struggle, but, each time this happens, weeping is interrupted. It is not an expression of rage (although the two may overlap) but an expression of helplessness after rage has been exhausted and a feeling of being abandoned has set in—a yearning for love, sympathy, consolation. In other words, the tears once more signify a frustration of the participatory emotions; and if no sympathy is forthcoming, self-pity will provide a substitute—a mild dissociation of the personality, in which the self is experienced almost as an alien object of loving commiseration.

Similar considerations apply to so-called 'crying in pain'. In states of violent physical pain, as in acute states of rage, the organism is fully occupied coping with the emergency and has no time for tears.

> 'Great pain', wrote Darwin, 'urges all animals, and has urged them during endless generations, to make the most violent and diversified efforts to escape from the cause of sufferings. Even when a limb or other separate part of the body is hurt, we often see a tendency to shake it as if to shake off the cause, though this obviously be impossible. Thus a habit of exerting with the utmost force all the muscles will have been established whenever great suffering is experienced.'[3]

Cannon has shown that the *Bodily Changes in Pain, Hunger, Fear, and Rage* (the title of his classic work) all follow the same basic pattern, that they are emergency responses of the sympathico-adrenal system. Violent pain seems to be experienced by the unconscious mind as an aggression, whether it is inflicted by an outside agent or not. When the aggressor is a tooth or a cramp in the stomach we are apt to say '*it hurts*', as if the offending organ were not part of oneself, and we try to shake the aggressor off, as animals do, by writhing, or pressing against it. Only when the pain has abated to a tolerably steady, 'dull' level do we accept it as part of ourselves—we 'have' a headache or 'are' under the weather—at the same time admitting that nothing can be done about it; writhing and struggling cease in the admission of defeat, as in the case of the child in the grip of its tormentors. 'Weeping in pain' starts only when the specific pain-behaviour stops, as 'weeping with rage' starts when rage-behaviour stops, and for precisely the same reasons: it is an abandoning of defences, an expression of help-lessness, a craving for sympathy, and—if accompanied by vocal cries—an appeal for help.

Another misconception is that children 'cry with fear', if 'crying' is used as a synonym for weeping. A child may cry out, in the literal sense, when suddenly frightened; it may run away, and if it cannot, strain away from the threatening apparition, lift his hands in protec-tion, and distort his face into a mask of terror. Once more, the tears will come only after the acute fright and the specific strained fright-reactions have ceased; they do not mean 'I *am* frightened' but 'I *was* so frightened, and maybe still am a little, and now I want to be comforted.'

Consider what happens when a little boy, running along a gravel path, suddenly stumbles and falls. The fright-reaction consists in the protective outstretching of hands, and related muscle-reflexes. Once the contact with the earth is made and the first shock overcome, the acute scare ebbs away, the muscles relax in surrender, the facial expression changes from fear to the sympathy-begging grimace of incipient weeping. If there is no witness to the drama, self-pity will again pro-vide the overflow. If it is witnessed by the mother, who makes a fuss and betrays her anxiety, this will increase the child's craving for tender-ness and its tears will ask for more. If, on the other hand, she gently but firmly debunks the drama, then, after a moment of puzzlement, the child may break into rather hesitant laughter—the residue of the scare, and even the slight pain, are denied by reason and worked off, while at the same time the sympathy-craving emotions are nipped in the bud by the mother's matter-of-fact attitude.

Lastly, 'crying in hunger'. A baby never weeps from hunger—it cries to signal hunger. The proof is that crying instantaneously stops when the bottle or breast is offered, before hunger can have ceased; furthermore, once the child is weaned from breast and bottle, hunger ceases to be expressed by crying or weeping.[4]

Needless to say, when a baby cries to attract attention, to signal that it is hungry or in distress, if often breaks into tears at the same time. Yet in such situations we say 'the baby is crying', not 'the baby is weeping', because the essence of the performance is the vocal protest or appeal for help; the shedding of tears is merely an accompaniment.

The baby's bawling, kicking, and tossing is a typical and impressive emergency-reaction in 'pain, hunger, fear, and rage' of a dramatically self-asserting kind. The simultaneous overflow of the tear-glands may be 'genuine' weeping—longing for affection and tenderness—as an accompaniment to the bawling; it may also be due to physiological causes. Watering of the eyes can be induced as a purely physiological defence reflex against the intrusion of a foreign body—a piece of grit or the molecules which carry the smell of onions. (Lachrymation caused by such local irritation is, by the way, unilateral—it occurs initially in the affected eye only).[5] It can also be caused by coughing, sneezing, vomiting, and after prolonged fits of laughter. The physiological mechanism is still somewhat obscure, except that all these violent exertions affect the mucous membranes of the nose and throat, and tend to dry them; the lachrymal glands may have the function of restoring lubrication through tears entering the nose.[6] When one sees a baby cry its head off with dry eyes until it gets hoarse, one intuitively feels that tears would be a relief—both psychologically and physiologically. The same applies to adults in situations of extreme distress.

> Home they brought the warrior dead;
> She nor swooned nor uttered cry.
> All her maidens, watching said,
> 'She must weep or she will die'.
>
> (Tennyson, *The Princess*)

Lastly, weeping may start in the child as a genuine, spontaneous overflow-reflex, but once the power of tears has been consciously or unconsciously recognized, the flow may be initiated automatically, or even voluntarily, as a weapon more subtle and more effective than mere cries of complaint or protest.* 'We seem to acquire specific visceral habits just as we pick up characteristic verbal and manual habits,' Kling has remarked,[7] and we ought to include in 'visceral habits' the exercise of the lachrymal glands. Weeping may be recruited into the service of hysteria, emotional blackmail, and even courtly behaviour (as a proof of sensibility less strenuous than swooning); it may be associated with convulsions, shrieks, and agitated display; but its true character is manifested by the person who weeps alone—helpless in her surrender to an emotion which, by its nature, can find no other outlet, whether it is caused by the thunder of a church organ, or the fall of a sparrow.

NOTES

To p. 271. So scant are the references of any significance to the subject in the technical literature, that I thought it would be useful to future students to list what I could find under a separate heading at the end of the bibliography. My indebtedness to those who helped in this is acknowledged in the Preface.

To p. 273. Romain Rolland describing the character of religious experience in a letter to Freud—who regretfully professed never to have felt anything of the sort.

To p. 274. 'The characteristic anatomical organization of the parasympathetic is correlated with absence of unitary action in this system. It is not surprising therefore that the adrenal medulla . . . has no counterpart in the parasympathetic system, and that no parasympathicomimetic hormone capable of acting extensively upon organs innervated by this system is liberated in the body.' (Macleod, ed. Bard, 1941 ed.) '. . . In contrast to the sympathomimetic hormones, the vagus substance is rapidly destroyed, and therefore produces very localized response. These effects are in line with the general behaviour of the sympathetic and parasympathetic systems of nerves.' (White and Smithwick, 1941, 2nd. ed.)

'All the viscera can be influenced *simultaneously* in one direction or the other by varying, up or down, the . . . tonic activity of the sympathetic division. And any special viscus can be *separately* influenced . . . by varying . . . the tonic activity of the special nerve of the opposed cranial or sacral [parasympathetic] division. . . . The sympathetic is like the loud and soft pedals, modulating all the notes together; the cranial and sacral [parasympathetic] innervations are like the separate keys.' (Cannon, 1929, 2nd. ed.)

In the years since this has been written the significance for psychology of the anatomical and physiological contrast between the two branches of the autonomic nervous system has become more evident, to the extent that 'rage is called the most adrenergic, and love the most cholinergic reaction' (Cobb, 1950). A further correspondence between patterns of emotive behaviour and modes of interaction between the two branches of the autonomic nervous system emerged when it was shown that the vagoinsulin system may act, in different circumstances, as an inhibitory or a catalytic agent in the glucose-utilization process and may also produce overcompensatory after effects (Gellhorn, 1943, and 1957). Hebb (1949) suggested that a distinction should be made between two categories of emotions, 'those in which the tendency is to maintain or increase the original stimulating conditions (pleasurable or integrative emotions)' and 'those in which the tendency is to abolish or decrease the stimulus (rage, fear, disgust)'. Whereas the latter have a disruptive effect on cortical behaviour, the former have not. A few years later, Olds (1959 and 1960) and others demonstrated the existence of 'positive' and 'negative' emotive systems by electric stimulation, and further showed that they were activated respectively by the parasympathetic and sympathetic centres in the hypothalamus.

These hints all seem to point in the same direction, but in fairness to the general reader I ought to point out that, while there is ample experimental proof that the hunger-rage-fear emotions are mediated by the sympathico-adrenal division, there is no direct evidence for the symmetrical correlation proposed here. Such proof can be forthcoming only when emotions outside the hunger-rage-fear class will be recognized as a worthwhile object of study by experimental psychology—which at present is not the case.

To p. 282. A psychoanalyst friend of mine, after reading the manuscript of the preceding section, objected that his patients frequently weep during the analytical hour 'in anger and frustration'. But he agreed that anger alone would not have produced the tears, and that the frustration was due, metaphorically speaking, to the analyst's refusal 'to give the patient the breast and sing a lullaby'.

XIII

PARTNESS AND WHOLENESS

Stepchildren of Psychology

The self-transcending emotions* are the stepchildren of contemporary psychology. One of the reasons is perhaps that they do not tend towards observable muscular activity but towards quietude; grief, longing, worship, raptness, aesthetic pleasure are emotions consummated not in overt but in *internalized*, visceral behaviour, with weeping as its extreme manifestation. But even the shedding of tears is not so much an activity but rather a 'passivity'.

The word 'emotion' is derived from 'motion'; and an emotion which tends to calm down motion seems to be a contradiction in terms. Yet the aesthetic or religious experiences which we call 'moving' are precisely those which induce passive contemplation, silent enjoyment. When the experimental psychologist talks of 'emotive behaviour', however, he nearly always refers to rage, fear, sex, and hunger, whereas emotions which do not beget overt activity are slurred over as 'moods' or sentiments—with the implication that they are a suspect category of pseudo-emotions unworthy of the scientist's attention. This is probably a hangover of the great ideological currents of the nineteenth century stressing the biological struggle for existence, the survival of the fittest, the acquisitive and competitive aspects of social behaviour. The ambiance of this 'Darwinistic psychology' is reflected in passages like the following, from Crile's *The Origin and Nature of the Emotions*, published in 1915:

> When the business man is conducting a struggle for existence against his rivals, and when the contest is at its height, he may clench his fists, pound the table, perhaps show his teeth, and exhibit every expression of physical combat. Fixing the jaw and showing the teeth in anger merely emphasize the remarkable tenacity of philogeny . . .

It must be admitted, though, that the social climate of the nineteenth century did not favour the contemplative life, nor the arousal of genuine self-transcending emotions. The Victorian versions of religion, patriotism, and love were so thoroughly impregnated with prudery and hypocrisy that the experimental psychologist, devoted to measuring sensory threshholds and muscle twitches could hardly be expected to take such attitudes seriously, and to put them on a par with the sex and hunger drives. Around the turn of the century, the so-called James-Lange theory of emotions emphasized the importance of visceral processes, but it was nevertheless taken for granted that the 'true' or 'major' emotions were characterized by impulses to muscular action—mainly to hit, run, or rape. When Cannon showed that hunger, pain, rage, and fear were, so to speak, variations on a single theme, it was tacitly taken for granted that *all* emotions worthy of that name were of the active, adreno-toxic, hit-run-mate-devour kind. Laughter and tears, awe and wonder, religious and aesthetic feeling, the whole 'violet' side of the rainbow of emotions was left to the poets to worry about; the so-called behavioural sciences had no room for them. Hence the paucity of the literature on weeping for instance—although it is certainly an observable behavioural phenomenon.

The emotions of the neglected half of the spectrum are as real as rage and fear; that much we know for certain from everyday experience. The theory which I have proposed assumes that they form a class, characterized by certain shared basic features. These are partly negative: the absence of adreno-sympathetic excitation alone puts them in a category apart from the emergency responses. On the positive side, emotional states as different as mourning and aesthetic enchantment share the logic of the moist eye: they are passive, cathartic, dominated by parasympathetic reactions. From the psychological point of view, the self-asserting emotions, derived from emergency reactions, involve a *narrowing* of consciousness; the participatory emotions an *expanison* of consciousness by identificatory processes of various kinds.

There exist, however, considerations of a more precise and at the same time, more general nature on which this theory of the emotions is based. These are discussed in Book Two, but I must briefly allude to them. In that wider context, the polarity between the self-asserting and participatory tendencies turns out to be merely a particular instance of a general phenomenon: namely, that every member of a living organism or social body has the dual attributes of 'wholeness' and 'partness'. It acts as an autonomous, self-governing whole on its own subordinate parts on lower levels of the organic or social hierarchy; but it is subservient to the co-ordinating centre on the next higher level. In other words it displays both self-assertive and participatory tendencies.

The Concept of Hierarchy

The word 'hierarchy' is used here in a special sense. It does not mean simply 'order of rank' (as in the 'pecking hierarchy' of the farmyard); it means a special type of organization (such as a military hierarchy) in which the overall control is centralized at the apex of a kind of genealogical tree, which branches out downward. At the first branching-out, the commanders of the land-, sea-, and air-forces would correspond to the co-ordinating centres of, say, the digestive, respiratory, and reproductive organ-systems; each of these is subdivided into units or organs on lower levels of the hierarchy with their own co-ordinating centres, C.O.s and N.C.O.s; the organs in turn are subdivided into organ-parts; and so the branching-process goes on down to the cellular level and beyond.

But each sub-organization, regardless on what level, retains a certain amount of *autonomy* or self-government. Without this delegation of powers the organization could not function effectively: the supreme commander cannot deal with individual privates; he must transmit strategical orders through 'regulation channels', which at each level are translated into tactical and sub-tactical moves. In the same way, information on what is happening in the various fields of operation (the sensory input) is selectively filtered on each level before being transmitted to the higher echelons. A living organism or social body is not an aggregation of elementary parts or elementary processes; it is an integrated hierarchy of semi-autonomous sub-wholes, consisting of sub-sub-wholes, and so on. Thus the functional units on every level of the hierarchy are double-faced as it were: they act as wholes when facing downwards, as parts when facing upwards.

On the upper limit of the organic hierarchy, we find the same double-aspect: the individual animal or man is a whole relative to the parts of his body, but a part relative to the social organization to which he belongs. All advanced forms of social organization are again hierarchic: the individual is part of the family, which is part of the clan, which is part of the tribe, etc.; but instead of 'part' we ought in each case to say 'sub-whole' to convey the semi-autonomous character and self-assertive tendency of each functional unit.

In the living organism, too, each part must assert its individuality, for otherwise the organism would lose its articulation and efficiency—but at the same time the part must remain subordinate to the demands of the whole. Let me give a few examples. The heart as an organ enjoys, of course, an advanced form of self-government: it has its own 'pacemakers' which regulate its rhythm; if one is knocked out a second automatically takes over. But the kidneys, intestines, and stomach also have their autonomous, self-regulating devices. Muscles, even single muscle cells, isolated from the body, will contract in response to appropriate stimulation. Any strip of tissue from an animal's heart will go on beating *in vitro* in its own, intrinsic rhythm. Each of these organs and organ-parts has a degree of self-sufficiency, a specific rhythm or pattern of activity, governed by a built-in, organic 'code'. Even a single cell has its 'organelles' which independently look after its growth, motion, reproduction, communication, energy-supply, etc.; each according to its own sub-code of more or less fixed 'rules of the game'. On the other hand, of course, these autonomous action-patterns of the part are activated, inhibited or modified by controls on higher levels of the hierarchy. The pacemaker-system of the heart, for instance, is controlled by the autonomous nervous system and by hormones; these in turn depend on orders from centres in the brain. Generally speaking, each organ-matrix (e.g. a cell-organelle) has its intrinsic code which determines the fixed, invariant pattern of its functioning; but it is at the same time a member of a matrix on a higher level (e.g. the cell), which in turn is a member of an organ or tissue, and so forth. Thus the two complementary pairs: matrix and code, self-asserting and participatory tendencies, are both derived from the hierarchic structure of organic life.

Complex *skills*, too, have a hierarchic structure. However much you try to disguise your handwriting, the expert will find you out by some characteristic way of forming or connecting certain groups of letters—the pattern has become an automatized and autonomous functional sub-whole which asserts itself against attempts of conscious interference. People whose right hand has been injured and who learn to write with the left soon develop a signature which is indistinguishable from the previous right-handed one—'the signature is in the brain', as a neurologist has said.[1] Again, touch-typing is a hierarchically ordered skill, where the 'letter habits' (finding the right key without looking) enter as members into 'word-habits' (automatized move-ment-sequences, each with a 'feel' of its own, which are triggered off as wholes, cf. Book Two, XII). Ask a skilled typist to misspell the word 'the' as 'hte' each time it occurs—and watch how the code of the correct sequence asserts its autonomy. Functional habits must have some kind of structural representation in the neuron-matrices of the brain; and these patterned circuits must be hierarchically organized—as organ-systems are—to account for such complex and flexible skills as, for instance, transposing a tune from one key into another.

Under normal conditions, the various parts of an organism—nerves, viscera, limbs—perform their semi-autonomous functions as sub-wholes, while at the same time submitting to the regulative control of the higher centres. But under conditions of stress the part called on to cope with the disturbance may become over-excited and get 'out of control'. The same may happen if the organism's powers of control are impaired—by senescence, for instance, or by a physiological block-age. In both cases the self-assertive tendencies of the part, isolated and released from the restraining influence of the whole, will express them-selves in deleterious ways; these range from the remorseless prolifera-tion of cancer cells to the obsessions and delusions, beyond rational control, in mental disorder (cf. Book Two, III, IV).

The single individual represents the top-level of the organismic hierarchy and at the same time the lowest unit of the social hierarchy. It is on this boundary line between physiological and social organiza-tion that the two antagonistic tendencies, which are at work on every level, even in a single cell, manifest themselves in the form of 'emotive behaviour'. Under normal conditions the self-asserting tendencies of the individual are dynamically balanced by his dependence on and participation in the life of the community to which he belongs. In the body social physiological controls are of course superseded by institu-tional controls, which restrain, stimulate, or modify the autonomous patterns of activity of its social sub-wholes on all levels, down to the individual. When tensions arise, or control is impaired, a social 'organ' (the barons, or the military, or the miners) may get over-excited and out of control; the individual, for the same reasons, may give un-restrained expression to rage, panic, or lust, and cease to obey the rules of the game imposed by the social whole of which he is part.

The participatory tendencies are as firmly anchored in the organic hierarchy as are their opponents. From the genetic point of view, the duality is reflected in the complementary processes of differentiation of structure and integration of function. We may extend the scope of the inquiry even further downward, from animal to vegetable and mineral, and discover analogous pairs of self-asserting and partici-patory forces in inanimate nature. From the particles in an atom to the planets circling the sun, we find relatively stable dynamic systems, in which the disruptive, centrifugal forces are balanced by binding forces which hold the system together as a whole. The metaphors we commonly use reflect an intuitive awareness that the pairs of opposites on various levels form a continuous series: when in rage, 'we fly off at a tangent' as if carried away by a centrifugal force; and contrariwise, we speak of social 'cohesion', personal 'affinities', and the 'attraction' exerted by an idea. These are no more than analogies; the 'attraction' between two people of opposite sex does not obey the inverse square law and is by no means proportionate to their mass; yet it remains nevertheless true that on every level of the evolutionary hierarchy stability is maintained by the equilibration of forces pulling in opposite directions: centrifugal and centripetal, the former asserting the part's independence, autonomy, individuality, the second keeping it in its place as a dependent part in the whole. Kepler kept affirming that his comparison between the moving force that emanates from the sun and the Holy Ghost was more than an analogy; the cohesion between the free-floating bodies in the solar system must have a divine cause. Newton himself toyed with similar ideas.*

I must apologize for the seemingly sweeping generalizations in the preceding section; the reader will find them substantiated in some detail in the biological chapters of Book Two. For the time being, I only meant to give some indication of the broader theoretical considerations on which the proposed classification of emotions is based—namely, that 'part-behaviour' and 'whole-behaviour' are opposite tendencies in dynamic equilibrium on every level of a living organism, and can be extrapolated by way of analogy, both upwards into the hierarchies of the body social, and downward into stable anorganic systems.

Such an approach does not imply any philosophical dualism; it is in fact no more dualistic than Newton's law of action and reaction, or the conventional method of 'thinking in opposites'. The choice of 'ultimate' and 'irreducible' principles (such as Freud's Eros and Tanatos) is always largely a matter of taste; 'partness' and 'wholeness' recommend them-selves as a serviceable pair of complementary concepts because they are derived from the ubiquitously hierarchic organization of all living matter. They also enable us to discuss the basic features of biological, social, and mental evolution in uniform terms as the emergence of more differentiated and specialized structures, balanced by more complex and delicate integrations of function.

Lastly, increased complexity means increased risks of breakdowns, which can only be repaired by processes of the regenerative, *reculer-pour-mieux-sauter* type that I have mentioned before and which will occupy us again. I shall try to show that seen in the light of the relation of part to whole, these processes assume a new significance as aids to the understanding of the creative mind.

NOTES

To p. 285. I am using 'self-transcending emotions' as a short-hand expression for 'emotional states in which the self-transcending tendencies dominate'.

To p. 290. In the only excursion into science fiction of which I am guilty, I made a visiting maiden from an alien planet explain the basic doctrine of its quasi-Keplerian religion:

'... We worship gravitation. It is the only force which does not travel through space in a rush; it is everywhere in repose. It keeps the stars in their orbits and our feet on our earth. It is Nature's fear of loneliness, the earth's longing for the moon; it is love in its pure, inorganic form.' (*Twilight Bar*, 1945.)

XIV

ON ISLANDS AND WATERWAYS

In the chapter on the 'Logic of the Moist Eye' I have discussed weeping as a manifestation of *frustrated* participatory emotions. Let me now briefly consider the *normal* manifestations of this class of emotions in childhood and adult life.

As Freud, Piaget, and others have shown, the very young child does not differentiate between ego and environment. The mother's breast seems to it a more intimate possession than the toes on its own body. It is aware of events, but not for a long time of itself as a separate entity. It lives in a state of mental symbiosis with the outer world, a continuation of the biological symbiosis in the womb, a state which Piaget calls 'protoplasmic consciousness'.[1] The universe is focussed on the self, and the self *is* the universe; the outer environment is only a kind of second womb.

From this original state of protoplasmic or symbiotic consciousness, the development towards autonomous individuation is slow, gradual, and will never be entirely completed. The initial state of consciousness may be likened to a liquid, fluid universe traversed by dynamic currents, by the rhythmic rise and fall of physiological needs, causing minor storms which come and go without leaving any solid traces. Gradually the floods recede and the first islands of objective reality emerge; their contours grow firmer and sharper and are set off against the undifferentiated flux. The islands are followed by continents, the dry territories of reality are mapped out; but side by side with them the liquid world co-exists, surrounding it, interpenetrating it by canals and inland lakes, the relics of the erstwhile oceanic communion. In the words of Freud:

Originally the ego includes everything, later it detaches from itself the external world. The ego-feeling we are aware of now is

292

thus only a shrunken vestige of a far more extensive feeling—a feeling which embraced the universe and expressed an inseparable connection of the ego with the external world. If we may suppose that this primary ego-feeling has been preserved in the minds of many people, to a greater or lesser extent, it would co-exist like a sort of counterpart with the narrower and more sharply outlined ego-feeling of maturity, and the ideational content belonging to it would be precisely the notion of limitless extension and oneness with the universe.[2]

It is this 'oceanic feeling' which mystics and artists strive to recapture on a higher level of development—at a higher turn of the spiral.

Until the end of the second or third year, while the separation of ego and non-ego is as yet incomplete, the child tends to confuse the subjective and the objective, dream and reality, the perceived and the imagined, its thoughts and the things thought about. Children and primitives not only believe in the magical transformations which occur in myths and fairy tales, but also believe themselves capable of performing them. The child at play becomes at will transformed into a horse, the doctor, a burglar, or a locomotive. Some primitives believe that they change at night into certain animals; if the animal is killed, they have to die. Magic causation precedes physical causation; to wish for an event is almost the same as producing it; children are great believers in the omnipotence of thought. As thought becomes increasingly centred in verbal and visual symbols, these become instruments of wishful evocation—of word-magic and symbol-magic.

This erstwhile method of establishing magic connections between events—regardless of distance in space, succession in time, or physical intermediaries, is a basic feature of primitive, but also of some highly developed societies, particularly in the East. Lévy-Bruhl—an anthropologist now somewhat out of fashion who greatly influenced Freud, Piaget, and Jung—had called this phenomenon *participation mystique* or the 'Law of Participation'.[3] It is reflected in innumerable rites and observances; in the individual's experience of a quasi-symbiotic communion between himself, his tribe, and his totem; between a man and his name, a man and his portrait, a man and his shadow; between the deity and its symbol; between a desired event—rain, or a successful hunt—and its symbolic enactment in dance, ritual play, or pictorial representation. Here is the ancient, unitary source out of which the dance and the song, the mystery plays of the Achaens, the calendars of the Babylonian priest-astronomers, and the cave-paintings of Altamira were to branch out later on—a magic source which, however great the distance travelled, still provides artist and explorer with his basic nourishment.

At an even earlier stage of social evolution, magic participation could be achieved by still more direct methods: the physical prowess of animals, the courage and wisdom of other men, the body and blood of the sacrificed god, could be acquired and shared by the simple means of eating them.* The sacrament of Holy Communion reflects, in a symbolic and sublimated form, the ecstasies of the Dionysian and Orphic mystery-rites: the devouring of the torn god. The participatory magic of trans-substantiation operates here not only between the communicant and his god, but also between all those who have partaken in the rite, and incorporated the same substance into themselves. A ghastly degeneration of this ritual was revealed when the circumstances of taking the Mau-Mau oath became known. A more harmless form of it is the 'blood-brother' ceremony among Arab tribes, performed by drinking a few drops of the elected brother's blood; a socially valuable survival of it are the rites of conviviality—from the symbolic sharing of bread and salt, to the ceremonial banqueting of the Chevaliers du Taste-Vin. The emotions derived from the feeding-drive seem to be of the purely self-assertive type; in fact, commensality, with its archetypal echoes, invests them with a more or less pronounced participatory character.

The progress from the historically earlier, or infantile forms of symbiotic consciousness towards voluntary self-transcendence through artistic, religious or social communion, reflects the sublimation of the participatory tendencies—emerging at the other end of the tunnel, as it were. Needless to say, the culture in which we live is not very favourable to this progress; the majority of our contemporaries never emerge from the tunnel, and get only occasional intimations of a distant pinpoint of light. The forces which effect the gradual replacement of the child's subjective by objective reality arise through continuous friction between self and environment. Hard facts emerge because objects are hard, and hurt if one bangs against them; wishes do not displace mountains, not even rocking horses. A second type of friction, between the self and other selves, drives home the fact that these latter too exist in their own right. Biological communion with the mother is dissolved by a succession of separative acts: expulsion from the womb, weaning from the breast, the cessation of fondling and petting, Western man's 'taboo on tenderness'. Things and people wage a continuous war of attrition on the magic forms of participation —until the floods recede, and the waterways dry up. Symbiotic consciousness wanes with maturation, as it must; but modern education provides hardly any stimuli for awakening cosmic consciousness to replace it. The child is taught petitionary prayer instead of meditation, religious dogma instead of contemplation of the infinite; the mysteries of nature are drummed into his head as if they were paragraphs in the penal code. In tribal societies puberty is a signal for solemn and severe initiation rites, to impress upon the individual his collective ties, before he is accepted as a part in the social whole. Vestiges of these rites still survive in institutions such as the Church and the Army; yet the majority of individuals take their place in the body social not by a process of integration, but as a result of random circumstances and pressures. The romantic bursts of enthusiasm in adolescence are like a last, euphoric flicker of the self-transcending emotions before they submit to atrophy and begin to shrivel away.

But they are never completely defeated. For one thing, the attritive forces of the social environment affect different strata of the personality in different ways. The most affected are the conscious, rational surface-layers directly exposed to contact; whereas the non-socialized, non-verbalized strata become the natural refuge of the thwarted participatory tendencies. The more remote from the surface, the less sharp the boundaries between the self and non-self; in those depths the symbiotic channels still remain navigable in the dream and other games of the underground, from which mysticism, discovery, and art draw their intuitions.

There exists, however, a whole range of more ordinary phenomena through which the self-transcending emotions manifest themselves in everyday life, and which I must briefly mention. The most banal of these is *perceptual projection*, which does not properly belong in this context—except in so far as it demonstrates that the boundaries of the self in our subjective experiences are not as clear-cut as we are wont to believe. 'Projection' in this technical sense means that the processes which take place in the retina and the brain are experienced as taking place not where they actually do take place, but yards or miles away. (This becomes at once obvious when one remembers that very low-pitched sounds are experienced—correctly—as reverberations *inside* the ear, and dazzling flashes, again correctly, as occurring in the *retina*.) Similarly, when you drive a nail into the wall you are aware, not that the handle has struck your palm, but that its head has struck the nail, as if the hammer had become part of your body.[4] These are not inventions of psychologists to make the simple appear as complicated, but examples of our tendency to confuse what happens in the self with what happens outside it—a kind of 'perceptual symbiosis' between ego and environment.

Projective empathy—again in a technical sense—is based on a similar confusion: an arrow drawn on paper is felt to manifest a dynamic tendency to move (probably a consequence of our own unconscious eye-movements); a church spire seems to 'soar' upwards, a picture has 'movement' and 'balance', and so on. Not only motions, but emotions too are projected from the self into lifeless objects; my car, climbing a hill, 'groans' and 'pants' under its 'effort'; the weeping willow weeps, the thunder growls. The tendency to animism, to project unconsciously life and feeling into inanimate bodies, is well-nigh irresistible—witness the two millennia of Aristotelian physics; we can only conclude that it is a basic feature of our psychic make-up.

Equally inveterate is the tendency to project our own emotions into other living beings—animals and people. The first leads to anthropomorphism—ascribing to our pet dogs, horses, and canaries reasoning processes modelled on our own; the second to what one might call 'egomorphism'—the illusion that others *must* feel on any subject exactly as I do. A more complicated projective transaction is *transference*—where A projects his feelings, originally aimed at B, on to a substitute, C: a father figure, sister figure, or what have you, each further transferable to D, E, etc. The Who's Who of the subconscious seems to be printed with coloured inks on blotting paper.

Introjection is meant to signify the reverse of projection, though the two phenomena are often indistinguishable from each other.* When somebody bangs his head on the doorpost, I wince; when a forward in a soccer game has a favourable opportunity to shoot, I kick my neighbour's shin. Adolescents unconsciously ape their hero's mannerisms; our super-egos were supposedly moulded by our parents at a time when the self was still in a fluid state. Throughout his life, the individual keeps introjecting chunks and patterns of other people's existence into his own; he suffers and enjoys vicariously the emotions of those with whom be becomes entangled in identificatory *rapports*. Some of these personality-transactions have lasting effects; others are more transitory, but at the same time more dramatic. Laughter and yawning have an instantly infectious effect; so have cruelty, hysteria, hallucinations, religious trances. In the *hypnotic* state 'the functions of the ego seem to be suspended, except those which communicate with the hypnotizer as though through a narrow slit in a screen' (Kretschmer); the personality of the hypnotizer has been substituted for the dormant parts of the ego; the 'slit' acts as a gap in the frontier between the self and non-self, letting in the contraband.

Freud, though disappointed at an early stage with hypno-therapy, kept stressing the affinities between hypnosis and love on the one hand, hypnosis and mass-behaviour on the other. In states of extreme enamouredness (the German technical term is *Hörigkeit*—bondage, servitude, subjection) its object replaces the super-ego or the hypnotist. The poetry—or pathology—of the condition lies in the total fascination of the bondsman by the bond, an attenuated but protracted variant of the hypnotic rapport. Awareness is focussed on the object of worship, the rest of the world is blurred or screened. The perfect symbol of the hypnotic effect is in Stendhal's *Charterhouse of Parma*: young Fabrice, in his prison cell, stares for hours on end through a narrow slit in the screen covering his window, at the figure of Clelia across the street.

The 'hypnotic effect' of political demagogues has become a cliché, but one aspect of mass-psychology must be briefly mentioned. The type of crowd or mob to which Le Bon's classic descriptions still apply, is fanatical and 'single-minded' because the subtler individual differences between its members are temporarily suspended; the whole mass is thus *intellectually* adjusted to its lowest common denominator,* but in terms of dynamic *action* it has a high efficacity, because the impulses of its members are aligned through narrow slits—or blinkers—all pointing in the same direction; hence their experience of being parts of an irresistible power. This experience of partness within a dynamic whole leads to a temporary suspension of individual responsibility— which is replaced by unconditional subordination to the 'controlling centre', the leader of the crowd. It further entails the temporary effacement of all self-assertive tendencies: the total surrender of the individual to the collectivity is manifested in altruistic, heroic, self-sacrificing acts—and at the same time in bestial cruelty towards the enemy or victim of the collective whole. This is a further example of the self-transcending emotions serving as catalysts or triggers for their opponents. But let us note that the brutality or heroism displayed by a fanaticized crowd is quasi-impersonal, and unselfish; it is exercised in the interest, or supposed interest, of the whole. The same S.S. detachments which mowed down the whole male population of Lidice were capable of dying at Oradur like the defenders of Thermopylae. The self-assertive behaviour of a mass is based on the participatory behaviour of the individual, which often entails sacrifice of his personal interest and even his life. Theories of ethics based on enlightened self-interest fail to provide an answer why a man should sacrifice his life in the defence of his family—not to mention country, liberty, beliefs. The fact that men have always been prepared to die for (good, bad, or futile) causes, proves that the self-transcending tendencies are as basic to his mental organization as the others. And since the individual cannot survive without some form of social integration, self-preservation itself always implies a component of self-transcendence.

Excepting saints and maniacs, our emotions nearly always consist of mixed feelings, where both tendencies (and both branches of the autonomous nervous system) participate in the mixture. Love, of course, is a many-splendoured thing, both with regard to its variety (sexual, platonic, parental, oedipal, narcissistic, patriotic, canine-directed, or feline-oriented as the technicians would say), and also with regard to the extraordinary cocktail of emotions which each variety represents. Much less obvious is the fact, that even such a simple and scientifically respectable drive as hunger should give rise to mixed emotions. If I may return to the subject (p. 294) for a moment: on the one hand, food is 'attacked'; it is 'wolfed'; one 'puts one's teeth into it'; biting and snapping are the very prototypes of aggression. On the other hand, the 'feeding drive' is stimulated or inhibited by the company participating in the meal; and the sacred element in the rituals of mensality (still surviving, for instance, in the funeral and wedding feasts) I have already mentioned. The teeth are tools of aggression, but the mouth is a preferential zone of affectionate bodily contact in billing and kissing. The German idiom 'Ich habe dich zum Fressen gerne' —I love you so much I could eat you—and the English 'devouring love' are symbolized by the behaviour of young mothers mock-devouring the baby's fingers and toes; it may be a distant echo of the gentle cannibal. Incidentally, we are told that among certain tribes practising ritual cannibalism, to be eaten is regarded as a great compliment; perhaps the male of the praying mantis feels the same way.

Lastly, the seemingly most altruistic social behaviour may have an admixture of conscious or unconscious self-assertion. Professional do-gooders, charity tigresses, hospital matrons, prison visitors, missionaries, and social workers are indispensable to society, and do an admirable amount of good; to pry into their motives, often hidden to themselves, would be ungrateful and churlish.

Summary

Weeping is an overflow reflex for an excess of the participatory emotions, as laughter is for the self-asserting emotions. Its nervous mechanism and bodily manifestations are the opposites of those of laughter with regard to facial expression, respiratory pattern, bodily posture. In laughter tension is exploded, emotion denied; in weeping it is gradually drained away without break in the continuity of mood; thought and emotion remain united. The self-asserting emotions worked off in laughter depend on the sympathico-adrenal system, which galvanizes the body into activity; lachrymation is controlled by the parasympathetic division whose action is inward-directed and cathartic. The self-transcending emotions which overflow in tears cannot be satisfied by any specific muscular activity; they tend towards passivity and self-abandonment, and are consummated in glandular and visceral reactions.

The various causes of weeping which have been discussed—raptness, weeping in sorrow, in joy, in sympathy, or in self-pity—all have a basic element in common: a craving to transcend the island boundaries of the individual, to enter into a symbiotic communion with a human being or some higher entity, real or imaginary, of which the self is felt to be a part. Owing to the peculiarities of our cultural climate, the participatory emotions have been virtually ignored by contemporary psychology, although they are as real and observable in their manifestations as hunger, rage, and fear. They are grounded in the hierarchic order of life where every entity has the dual attributes of partness and wholeness, and the dual potentialities of behaving as an autonomous whole or a dependent part. The classification of emotions which I have proposed is based on this general principle of polarity, to be found on every level of the organic and social hierarchies (cf. Book Two). The dual concept of adaptable matrices with fixed invariant codes is derived from the same principle.

In the development of the individual, as in the evolution of cultures, the manifestations of the participatory tendencies show a progression, comparable to that of the aggressive-defensive emotions from primitive and infantile to adult forms. The 'symbiotic consciousness' of infancy, with its fluid ego boundaries, is partly relegated to the sub-conscious strata—from which the artist and the mystic draw their inspirations; partly superseded by the phenomena of projection and introjection, empathy and identification, transference and hypnosis. Similarly, the participatory bonds of primitive magic are gradually transformed into symbolic rituals, mythological epics, and mystery plays: into the magic of illusion. The shadows in Plato's cave are symbols of man's loneliness; the paintings in the Lascaux caves are symbols of his magic powers.

The participatory emotions, like their opposites, can be accompanied by feelings of pleasure or un-pleasure which form a continuous scale, and add a third dimension to emotional experience. Lastly, identification, in itself a self-transcending experience, can serve as a vehicle (or trigger) for vicarious emotions of anger and fear.

NOTES

To p. 294. The point has been succinctly made by Walter de la Mare:

> It's a very odd thing—
> As odd as can be—
> That whatever Miss T. eats
> Turns into Miss T.

To p. 296. 'In relation to the dissolution of the ego complex, identification can receive a somewhat different interpretation according as ego-components are projected into the outside world or as elements from the outside world are incorporated into the personality. In very fluid dream processes such a distinction cannot usually be very accurately drawn; but in schizophrenia, for example, both possibilities can be most clearly experienced.' (Kretschmer, 1954, p. 93.)

To p. 297. The expression *'lowest* common denominator' is mathematically nonsensical; it should, of course, be 'highest'. But the 'highest common denominator' in a crowd of large numbers is still pretty low; thus the faulty idiom conveys the right idea, and the correct expression would only create confusion.

B. VERBAL CREATION

XV

ILLUSION

The Power of Illusion

Literature begins with the telling of a tale. The tale represents certain events by means of auditory and visual signs. The events thus represented are mental events in the narrator's mind. His motive is the urge to communicate these events to others, to make them relive his thoughts and emotions; the urge to *share*. The audience may be physically present, or an imagined one; the narrator may address himself to a single person or to his god alone, but his basic need remains the same: he must share his experiences, make others participate in them, and thus overcome the isolation of the self.

To achieve this aim, the narrator must provide patterns of stimuli as substitutes for the original stimuli which caused the experience to occur. This, obviously, is not an easy task, for he is asking his audience to react to things which are not there, such as the smell of grass on a summer morning. Since the dawn of civilization, bards and story-tellers have produced bags of tricks to provide such *Ersatz*-stimuli. The sum of these tricks is called the art of literature.

The oldest and most fundamental of all tricks is to disguise people in costumes and to put them on a stage with masks or paint on their faces; the audience is thereby given the impression that the events represented are happening *here* and *now*, regardless of how distant they really are in space and time. The effect of this procedure is to induce a very lively bisociated condition in the minds of the audience. The spectator knows, in one compartment of his mind, that the people on the stage are actors, whose names are familiar to him; and he knows that they are 'acting' for the express purpose of creating an illusion in him, the spectator. Yet in another compartment of his mind he experiences fear, hope, pity, accompanied by palpitations, arrested breathing, or tears—all induced by events which he knows to be pure make-believe. It is indeed a remarkable phenomenon that a grown-up person, knowing all the time that he faces a screen onto which shadows are projected by a machine, and knowing furthermore quite well what is going to happen at the end—for instance, that the police will arrive just in the nick of time to save the hero—should nevertheless go through agonies of suspense, and display the corresponding bodily symptoms. It is even more remarkable that this capacity for living in two universes at once, one real, one imaginary, should be accepted without wonder as a commonplace phenomenon. The following extract from a London newspaper report may help to restore our sense of wonder: [1]

Twice a week, with a haunting, trumpeted signature tune and a view of terraced roofs stretching away into infinity, *Coronation Street*, Granada Television's serial of North Country life, goes on the air. It has now had 200 issues and is coming up to its second birthday next week. It is one of Britain's most popular television programmes. Enthusiasts call it a major sociological phenomenon. In fact all marathon TV serials with fixed settings and regular characters are cunningly designed to turn the viewer into an addict. *Coronation Street* eschews glamour and sensational curtains and concentrates on trapping the rugged smug ambience on North Country working and lower middle-class life. It will follow a local event like a council election or an amateur theatrical through instalment after instalment with the tenacity of a parish magazine. Its characters provide parts that actors can sink their teeth into and digest and assimilate. They have become deeply planted, like the permanent set of seven terraced houses, the shop on the corner, the Mission Hall, and the pub.

The characters have devotees who insist on believing in their reality. When the buxom Elsie Tanner was involved with a sailor who, unknown to her, was married, she got scores of letters warning her of the danger. Jack Watson, the actor who played the sailor, was stopped outside the studio by one gallant mechanic who threatened to give him a hiding if he didn't leave Elsie alone.

The strongest personality of them all, the sturdy old bulldog bitch, Ena Sharples, has a huge following. When she was sacked from the Mission Hall of which she was caretaker, viewers from all over the country wrote offering her jobs. When she was in hospital temporarily bereft of speech, a fight broke out in Salford between a gang of her fans and an Irish detractor who said he hoped the old bag would stay dumb till Kingdom come.

Moreover, when one of the seven houses on the set became 'vacant' because its owner was said to have moved—in fact because the actor in question had been dropped from the programme—there were several applications for renting the house; and when at a dramatic moment of the serial the barmaid in the 'Rover's Return' smashed an ornamental plate, several viewers sent in replacements to comfort her.

Of course, these people know that they are watching actors. Do they nevertheless believe that the characters are real? The answer is neither yes nor no, but yes and no. The so-called law of contradiction in logic—that a thing is either A or not-A but cannot be both—is a late acquisition in the growth of individuals and cultures (Book Two, XV). The unconscious mind, the mind of the child and the primitive, are indifferent to it. So are the Eastern philosophies which teach the unity of opposites, as well as Western theologians and quantum physicists. The addicts of *Coronation Street* who insist on believing in the reality of Ena Sharples have merely carried one step further the momentary split-mindedness experienced by a sophisticated movie-audience at the climax of a Hitchcock thriller; they live in a more or less permanently bisociated world.

The Value of Illusion

But where does beauty, aesthetic value, or 'art' enter into the process? The answer requires several steps. The first is to recognize the *intrinsic value* of illusion in itself. It derives from the transfer of attention from the 'Now and Here' to the 'Then and There'—that is, to a plane remote from self-interest. Self-assertive behaviour is focussed on the Here and Now; the transfer of interest and emotion to a different time and location is in itself an act of self-transcendence in the literal sense. It is achieved through the lure of heroes and victims on the stage who attract the spectator's sympathy, with whom he partially identifies himself, and for whose sake he temporarily renounces his preoccupations with his own worries and desires. Thus the act of participating in an illusion has an inhibiting effect on the self-asserting tendencies, and facilitates the unfolding of the self-transcending tendencies. In other words illusion has a cathartic effect—as all ancient and modern civilizations recognized by incorporating various forms of magic into their purification-rites and abreaction therapies.

It is true that illusion, from Greek tragedy to horror comics, is also capable of generating fear and anger, palpitations and cold sweat, which seems to contradict its cathartic function. But the emotions thus generated are *vicarious* emotions derived from the spectator's participation in another person's existence, which is a self-transcending act (cf. pp. 278-9). Consequently, however exciting the action on the stage, the anger or fear which it generates will always carry a component of sympathy, an irradiation of unselfish generosity, which facilitates catharsis—just as a varying amount of high-voltage current is always transformed into heat. At a later stage, when the climax of the drama is passed, and the tension ebbs away, the whole amount of the current is consumed in a gentle inner glow.

The Dynamics of Illusion

In the comedy, the accumulation of suspense, and its subsequent annihilation in laughter take place at distinctly separate stages (although the two may overlap in the smiling, anticipated pleasure of the joke to come). In the tragedy, on the other hand, excitation and catharsis are continuous. Laughter explodes emotion; weeping is its gentle overflow; there is no break in the continuity of mood, and no separation of emotion from reason. The hero, with whom the spectator has identified himself, cannot be debunked by slipping on a banana-skin or by any sudden incongruity in his behaviour. The gods of the Greek and Hindu pantheon might change into any shape—a swan, a bull, a monkey, a shower of coins—and yet their paramours would lovingly surrender to them. On the bas-reliefs of Indian temples Shiva is often seen making love to Parvati while standing on his head, without appearing ridiculous. When the events in epic or drama take an unexpected turn—Odysseus's companions transformed into swine or chaste Ophelia singing obscene songs—emotion, if aggressively tainted, refuses to perform the jump and explodes in laughter; if sympathetic, it will follow the hero through all viscissitudes. The abrupt change of situation which required an equally quick reorientation of the mind to a different associative context, led in the first case to a rupture between emotion and reason, in the second to a transfer of emotion to the new context whereby its harmonious co-ordination with reason is preserved.

Thus incongruity—the confrontation of incompatible matrices—will be experienced as ridiculous, pathetic, or intellectually challenging, according to whether aggression, identification, or the well-balanced blend of scientific curiosity prevails in the spectator's mind. Don Quixote is a comic or a tragic figure, or a case-history of incipient paranoia, depending on the panel of the tryptich in which he is placed. In all three cases the matrices of reality and delusion—of windmills and phantom-knights—confront each other in the reader's mind. In the first case they collide, and malice is spilled in laughter. In the second, the two universes remain juxtaposed, reason oscillates to and fro between them, compassion remains attached to it and is easily transferred from one matrix to the other. In the third case, the two merge in a synthesis: the (emotionally 'neutral') diagnosis of the clinician.

Thus compassion, and the other varieties of the participatory emotions, attach themselves to the narrative told on the stage or in print, like faithful dogs, and follow it whatever the surprises, twists, and incongruities the narrator has in store for them. By contrast, hostility, malice, and contempt tend to persist in a straight course, impervious to the subtleties of intellect; to them a spade is a spade, a windmill a windmill, and a Picasso nude with three breasts an object to leer at. The self-transcending emotions seem to be guided by the maxim *tout comprendre c'est tout pardonner*; the self-asserting emotions are designed for assertion, not comprehension. Hence, when attention is suddenly displaced from one frame of reference to another, the self-asserting impulses, deprived of their *raison d'être*, are spilled in the process, whereas the participatory emotions are transferred to the new matrix.

The physiological considerations which lend support to this view I have already discussed (pp. 56 ff; 274, 283). Anger and fear owe their persistence and momentum to the sympathico-adrenal machinery, which causes them to become occasionally dissociated from reasoning. The self-transcending emotions, on the other hand, are accompanied by parasympathetic reactions which are in every respect the opposite of the former; since they are devoid of massiveness and momentum, there is no cause for their falling out of step with the higher mental activities, and the normal co-ordination of thought and emotion will prevail. If your mind has the nimbleness of migrating, at a moment's notice, into Romeo's in sixteenth-century Verona, then you will also be capable of shedding tears at Juliet's death.

We must remember, however, that emotions are complex mixtures; our amusement at Charlie Chaplin's adventures is full of compassion. All that is required for a mildly comic effect is that an aggressive factor should be present of sufficient strength to provide a certain inertia of feeling—or anaesthesia of the heart.

Illusion, then, is the simultaneous presence and interaction in the mind of two universes, one real, one imaginary. It transports the spectator from the trivial present to a plane remote from self-interest and makes him forget his own preoccupations and anxieties; in other words, it facilitates the unfolding of his participatory emotions, and inhibits or neutralizes his self-asserting tendencies.

This sounds like an escapist theory of art; and in spite of its derogatory connotations, the expression contains a grain of truth—though no more than a grain. The analysis of any aesthetic experience requires, as said before, a series of steps; and the escape offered by transporting the spectator from his bed-sitter in Bayswater to the Castle of Elsinore is merely the bottom step of the ladder. But, nevertheless, it should not be under-estimated. In the first place, if illusion offers escape it is escape of a particular kind, sharply distinguished from other distractions such as playing tennis or bingo. It teaches us to live on two planes at once. Children and primitive audiences who, forgetting the present, completely accept the reality of the events on the stage, are experiencing not an aesthetic thrill, but a kind of hypnotic trance; and addiction to it may lead to various degrees of estrangement from reality. The aesthetic experience depends on that delicate balance arising from the presence of *both* matrices in the mind; on perceiving the hero as Laurence Olivier and Prince Hamlet of Denmark at one and the same time; on the lightning oscillations of attention from one to the other, like sparks between charged electrodes. It is this precarious suspension of awareness between the two planes which facilitates the continuous flux of emotion from the Now and Here to the remoter worlds of Then and There, and the cathartic effects resulting from it. For when interest is deflected from the self it will attach itself to something else; when the level of self-assertive tension falls, the self-transcending impulses become almost automatically dominant. Thus the creation of illusion is in itself of cathartic value—even if the product, judged by more sophisticated standards, is of cheap quality; for it helps the subject to actualize his potential of self-transcending emotions thwarted by the dreary routines of existence. Liberated from his frustrations and anxieties, man can turn into a rather nice and dreamy creature; when he changes into a dark suit and sits in a theatre, he at once shows himself capable of taking a strong and entirely unselfish interest in the destinies of the personae on the stage. He participates in their hopes and sufferings; his frustrated cravings for communion find their primeval outlet in the magic of identification.

To revert to Aristotle, the cathartic function of the tragedy is 'through incidents arousing horror and pity to accomplish the purgation of such emotions'. In cruder terms, a good cry, like a good laugh, has a more lasting after-effect than the occasion seems to warrant. Taking the Aristotelian definition at face value, it would seem that the aesthetic experience could purge the mind only of those emotions which the stage-play has created; that it would merely take out of the nervous system what it has just put in, leaving the mind in the same state as before. But this is not so. The emotion is not created, but merely stimulated by the actors; it must be 'worked up' by the spectator. The work of art does not provide the current, like an electricity company, but merely the installations; the current has to be generated by the consumer. Although this is obvious once we remember it, we tend to fall into the mistake of taking a metaphor at face value and believing that the stage 'provides' us with a thrill against cash payment for a seat in the stalls. What we buy, however, is not emotion, but a sequence of stimuli cunningly designed to trigger off our latent participatory emotions which otherwise would remain frustrated or look for coarser outlets, and to assure their ultimate consummation. Life constantly generates tensions which run through the mind like stray eddies and erratic currents. The aesthetic experience inhibits some, canalizes others, but above all, it draws on unconscious sources of emotion which otherwise are only active in the games of the underground.

Thus the concept of catharsis assumes a twofold meaning. Firstly, it signifies that concentration on the illusory events on the stage rids the mind of the dross of its self-centred trivial preoccupations; in the second place it arouses its dormant self-transcendent potentials and provides them with an outlet, until they peacefully ebb away. Peaceful, of course, does not necessarily mean a happy ending. It may mean the 'earthing' of an individual tragedy in the universal tragedy of the human condition—as the scientist resolves a problem by showing that a particular phenomenon is an instance of a general law. It may dissolve the bitterness of personal sorrow in the vastness of the oceanic feeling; and redeem horror by pity. Tragedy, in the Greek sense, is the school of self-transcendence.

The projections of a single cine-camera with its rotating Maltese cross arouse anger, terror, and righteous indignation in up to five successive audiences on a single day, as if it were a machine designed for the wholesale manufacture of adrenalin. Yet the emotions aroused even by a cheap thriller-film are vicarious emotions derived from one of the primordial games of the underground: the transformation of one person or object into another (Chapter VIII, p. 187 f.). The fear and anger experienced by the audience is experienced on behalf of another person; the adrenalin secreted into their bloodstream is secreted to provide another person with excess energy for fight or flight; the magic of identification is at work.

It enters into illusion in two stages. The first is the partial identification, in the spectator's mind, of the actor with the character he is meant to represent; the second is the partial identification of the spectator with one or several of the characters. In both cases the identification is only partial, but nevertheless the magic is powerful enough to provide the palpitations and activate the supra-renal glands. And when I speak of magic, I am not speaking metaphorically; the 'magic of the stage' is a cliché which originates in the sympathetic magic practised by all primitive and not-so-primitive cultures, rooted in the belief in the substantial identity of the masked dancer with the demon he mimes; of the impersonator with the power he impersonates. The unconscious self, manifested in the beliefs of the child and the dreams of the adult, is, as we saw, immune to contradiction, unsure of its identity, and prone to merging it with others'. 'In the collective representations of primitive mentality, objects, beings, events can be, though in a way incomprehensible to us, both themselves and something other than themselves.'[2] This description of tribal mentality by a Victorian anthropologist could be applied almost without qualifications to the audiences of *Coronation Street*.

I have taken a short-cut from primitive to contemporary magic, but the development is in fact historically continuous: the latter is a direct descendant of the former. Dramatic art has its origin in ceremonial rites—dances, songs, and mime—which enacted important past or desired future events: rain, a successful hunt, an abundant harvest. The gods, demons, ancestors and animals participating in the event were impersonated with the aid of masks, costumes, tattooings and make-up. The shaman who danced the part of the rain-god *was* the rain-god, and yet remained the shaman at the same time. From the stag dances of the Huichol Indians or the serpent dances of the Zuni, there is only one step to the goat dance of the Achaeans, the precursor of Greek drama. 'Tragedy' means 'goat-song' (*tragos*—he goat, *oide*—song); it probably originated in the ceremonial rites in honour of Dyonysius, where the performers were disguised in goat-skins as satyrs, and in the related ceremonies in honour of Apollo and Demeter. Indian and Chinese stage craft have similarly religious origins. Etruscan drama derived from funeral rites; modern European drama evolved from the medieval mystery plays performed on the occasion of the main church festivals. But though the modern theatre hardly betrays its religious ancestry, the magic of illusion still serves essentially the same emotional needs: it enables the spectator to transcend the narrow confines of his personal identity, and to participate in other forms of existence. For—to quote for a last time the unfashionable Lévy-Bruhl, to whom Freud, Jung, and others owe so much:

> The need of participation remains something more imperious and intense, even among people like ourselves, than the thirst for knowledge and the desire for conformity with the claims of reason. It lies deeper in us and its source is more remote. During the long prehistoric ages, when the claims of reason were scarcely realized or even perceived, it was no doubt all-powerful in all human aggregates. Even today the mental activity which, by virtue of an intimate participation, possesses its object, gives it life and lives through it—finds entire satisfaction in this possession.[3]

The Dawn of Literature

The dawn of literature, too, was bathed in the twilight of mysticism and mythology. 'The recitation of the Homeric poems on the Panathanaea corresponds to the recitation elsewhere of the sacred texts in the temple; the statement of Phemios that a god inspired his soul with all the varied ways of song expresses the ordinary belief of early historical times.'[4] But the earliest *literati*—priests, prophets, rhapsodes, bards—had less direct means to impress their audiences than their older colleagues, the masked and painted illusion-mongers. They had to 'dramatize' their tales, by techniques which we can only infer from hints. The dramatization of an epic recital aims, like stage-craft from which it is derived, at creating, to some extent at least, the illusion that the events told are happening now and here. Perhaps the oldest of these techniques is the use of direct speech, to make the audience believe that it is listening not to the narrator but to the characters themselves; its use is still as frequent in the modern novel as it was in the Homeric epos. In the ancient forms of oral recital it was supplemented by imitation of voice and gesture—another tradition still alive in the nursery room. The minstrels and troubadours, the joculators or jugglers, the scôps and the *chansonniers de geste*, were direct descendants of the Roman mimes—actors who, having lost their livelihood when the Roman theatre decayed, became vagabonds and diverted their patrons with dancing, tumbling, juggling and recitals as much acted as told. The early minstrels were called *histriones*, stage-players; the bard Taillefer, who sang the *Chanson de Roland* during the battle of Hastings, is described as a *histrion* or *mimus*.

There is hardly a novelist who had not wished at times that he were a *histrion*, and could convey by direct voice, grimace, and gesture what his characters look like and feel. But writers have evolved other techniques to create the illusion that their characters are alive, and to make their audience fall in love with a heroine who exists only as printer's ink on paper. The real tears shed over Anna Karenina or Emma Bovary are the ultimate triumph of sympathetic magic.

XVI

RHYTHM AND RHYME

Pulsation

The effect of the rhythm of a poem, wrote I. A. Richards, 'is not due to our perceiving pattern in something outside us, but to our becoming patterned ourselves'.[1] Rhythmic periodicity is a fundamental characteristic of life. All automatic functions of the body are patterned by rhythmic pulsations: heart-beat, respiration, peristalsis, brain-waves are merely the most obvious ones. For there is also an inherent tendency in some parts of the nervous system, particularly on its phylogenetically older levels, to burst into spontaneous activity when released from the inhibitory control of the higher centres by brain-damage, toxic states, or by patterns of stimuli acting as triggers.

Perhaps the most striking example of such a trigger-effect is the experimental induction of fits in epileptic patients by shining a bright flickering light into their eyes, where the frequency of the flicker is made to correspond to a characteristic frequency in the patient's electro-encephalogram. This, of course, is an extreme example of a trigger-effect by direct physiological stimulation; moreover, the incoming rhythm is synchronized with an inner rhythm to produce an unholy resonance effect. The convulsions of voodoo-dancers, on the other hand, which have been compared to epileptic fits, are certainly not caused by the rhythmic beat of the tom-tom alone; other factors, of a psychological nature, must be present to produce the effect. But it is nevertheless true that our remarkable responsiveness to rhythmically patterned stimuli and our readiness 'to become patterned ourselves' arises from the depths of the nervous system, from those archaic strata of the unconscious which reverberate to the shaman's drum.

Needless to say, even the contemporary Rock-'n'-Roll or Twist are restrained and sublimated displays compared to the St. Vitus's dance which spread as an infectious form of hysteria through medieval Europe. Likewise, if rhythm in poetry is meant, as Yeats said, 'to lull the mind into a waking trance', that entrancement carries only a faint, remote echo of the incantative power of the muezzin's call, or of the recitation of the Homeric poems on the Panathanaea. On the other hand, we do experience a common kind of 'waking trance' when we keep repeating a silly phrase to the rhythm of the wheels of a railway carriage; hypnotists used to rely on metronomes, flickering candles, monotonously repeated orders or passes; and the rocking motions accompanying the prayers of Oriental religions and mystic sects serve the same purpose. Thus experience, both of the exalted and trivial kind, indicates that the mind is particularly receptive to and suggestible by messages which arrive in a rhythmic pattern, or accompanied by a rhythmic pattern.

This is true even on the elementary levels of perception. We are more susceptible to musical tones than to noises, because the former consist of periodical, the latter of a-periodical air-waves. Similar considerations apply to pure colours; or to the symmetry and balance which lend a design its 'unity in diversity'. Plato decreed that all heavenly motions must take place in perfect circles at uniform speed, because only such regular periodicity could assure the steady, eternal pulsations of the universe. Perhaps the compulsive pattern-walking ritual of certain neurotics, who must always step into the centre of pavement-stones, is motivated by the same unconscious craving for order and regularity as a protection against the anxiety-arousing threat of change.

Measure and Meaning

'The superimposition of two systems: thought and metre,' wrote Proust, 'is a primary element of ordered complexity, that is to say, of beauty.'[2] But this superimposition—in our jargon, the bisociation of rhythm and meaning—is again trivalent: it can be put to poetic, scientific, or comic use. When rhythm assumes a rigidly repetitive form, it no longer recalls the pulsation of life, but the motions of an automaton; its superimposition on human behaviour is degrading, and yields Bergson's formula of the comic: the mechanical encrusted on the living. But here again, all depends on one's emotional attitude: pre-war films of German soldiers marching the goose-step—or if it comes to that, the changing of the Guard at Buckingham Palace—will strike one spectator as comic, and appeal to the tribal, or romantic, emotions of another. Once one is in a marching column, it is extremely difficult to keep out of step; one has become patterned by the rhythmic motion in which one participates. But the comedian as an army recruit falling chronically out of step is comic, for obvious reasons.

In the natural sciences, the analysis of rhythmic periodicities—the numerical patterns underlying the phenomena of naïve experience—play a dominant part. The Pythagoreans regarded the universe as a large musical box, the organism as a well-tempered instrument, and all material phenomena as a dance of numbers. The metre of the poet, the metronome of the musician, the centimetre of the mathematician, are all derived from the same root, *metron*: measure, measurement. Yet the quantitative patterns in themselves would be meaningless to us if they were not accompanied by the sensory qualities of colour, sound, heat, taste, texture, and so on; and the rhythms of our brain-waves on the electro-encephalogram would be meaningless if we were not conscious of thinking. The scientist takes a 'bi-focal' view of life; and so does the reader whose attention is focussed simultaneously both on the measure and the message of the poem.

Without the message, the rhythm is of course meaningless, in poetry as in science. A monotonous rhythm, for instance, can be either sleepy-making or exciting, according to the message which it carries. Rhythmic stroking of the skin may be soothing or sexually exciting—it depends on the message. The rhythmic rattle of the wheels on a train journey will lull one to sleep, as a superior form of counting sheep, if one is in a relaxed mood; but I can remember at least one ghastly journey, when I found myself in a predicament of my own making, and the wheels kept repeating, 'I *told* you so, I *told* you so, I *told* you so' with such hallucinatory clarity and insistence that I found it difficult to convince myself that the other passengers in the compartment did not hear it. Rhythm penetrates so deeply into the unconscious strata that it makes us suggestible even to self-addressed messages—from the Yogic recitation of *mantras* to Coué's 'every day in every way . . .'.

However, unlike the beat of the tom-tom, or the rattle of the carriage wheels, a strophe of verse does not consist in a simple repetitive rhythm, but in complex patterns of short and long, stressed and light syllables, further complicated by super-imposed patterns of assonance or rhyme. As music has evolved a long way from the simple, repetitive figures of monochords and drums, so the various metric forms in poetry contain their substructure of rhythmic pulsation in an *implied*, and no longer in an explicit form. In free verse, the rhythmic substructure has become so implicit, as to go sometimes unnoticed.

This development from the explicit to the implicit, from the direct statement to the veiled hint, is a phenomenon which we have already met (pp 84 ff.), and shall meet again in other provinces of art, as a characteristic factor in the evolution of creative techniques in general.

Repetition and Affinity

The rhyme is a relatively late offspring of rhythm. Both words are derived from the same Greek root, *rhutmos*; up to the sixteenth century they were treated as practically synonymous. Metric patterns based exclusively on the regular succession of ups and downs of intonation—the only form of verse in Greek and Latin poetry—were later combined with patterns based on the repetition of single consonants and vowels; and thus, via alliteration and assonance, the rhyme came into being—as melody was born out of originally unmodulated, rhythmic beats.

But although conscious rhyming was only admitted into formal literature in the Middle Ages (at first as the internal rhyme in Leonine verse), it has, like rhythm, its primordial roots in the unconscious. The *repetition* of syllables is a conspicuous phenomenon at the very origins of language. In the early stages of learning to speak, children seem to have an irresistible impulse to jabber repetitive variations of sound patterns—from ma-ma and pa-pa to obble-gobble, minky-pinky and so on *ad infinitum;* gibble-gabble was the Victorian word for it. Similarly, in many primitive languages as far apart as Polynesian and Bantu, words like Kala-Kala or Moku-Moku abound; and why does the name Humpty-Dumpty hold such a charm for child and adult alike?

Next to repetition, *association by sound affinity*—punning—is one of the notorious games of the underground, manifested in dreams, in the punning mania of children, and in mental disorders. The rhyme is nothing but a glorified pun—two strings of ideas tied in an accoustic knot. In normal, rationally controlled speech, association by pure sound is prohibited, for, if given free rein, it would destroy coherence and meaning. Thus, on re-reading the previous sentence, it occurs to me that 'des-troy' lends itself to a pun (Helen was fated to destroy Troy); once one 'tunes in' to the matrix of sound-associations, a number of quite idiotic puns and rhymes will invade the mind. No effort is required to produce them; on the contrary, when concentration flags, and the rational controls are relaxed, thinking has a tendency to revert, by its own gravity as it were, to matrices governed by more primitive rules of the game. Among these, association by sound-affinities plays a prominent part; the free associations of the patient on the analyst's couch belong as often as not to this category. Let us also remember (pp. 186 f.) that other games based on sound-affinity have exercised a perennial attraction on the most varied cultures; anagrams, acrostics, and word-puzzles; incantations and verbal spells; hermeneutics and Cabala, which interpreted the Scriptures as a collection of the Almighty's hidden puns, combining letter-lore with number-lore.

Thus rhythm and assonance, pun and rhyme are not artificially created ornaments of speech; the whole evidence indicates that their origins go back to primitive—and infantile—forms of thought and utterance, in which sound and meaning are magically interwoven, and association by sound-affinities is as legitimate as association based on other similarities. Rationality demands that these matrices should be relegated underground, but they make their presence felt in sleep and sleeplike states, in mental illness and in the temporary regression—the *reculer-pour-mieux-sauter*—of poetic inspiration. But before we come to that, let me once more quote additional evidence from neurology, more precisely, from brain surgery—a field rarely bisociated with the poetic faculty.

Compulsive Punning

The phenomenon to be described is known as 'Förster's syndrome'. It was first observed by Förster, a German surgeon, in 1929, when he was operating on a patient suffering from a tumour in the third ventricle— a small cavity deep down in the phylogenetically ancient regions of the mid-brain, adjacent to structures intimately concerned with the arousal of emotions. When the surgeon began to manipulate the tumour, affecting those sensitive structures, the (conscious) patient burst into a manic flight of speech, 'quoting passages in Latin, Greek, and Hebrew. He exhibited typical sound associations, and with every word of the operator broke into a flight of ideas. Thus, on hearing the operator ask for a *Tupfer* [tampon] he burst into "*Tupfer . . . Tupfer, Hupfer, Hüpfer, hüpfen Sie mal . . .*" On hearing the word *Messer*, he burst into "*Messer, messer, Metzer, Sie sind ein Metzel, das ist ja ein Gemetzel, metzeln Sie doch nicht so messen Sie doch ·Sie messen ja nicht Herr Professor, profiteor, professus sum, profiteri.*" These manic responses were dependent on manipulation of the tumour and could be elicited only from the floor of the third ventricle.'[3]

Förster's patient opened up a curious insight into the processes in the poet's brain—in an unexpectedly literal sense of the word. The first flight of ideas, *Tupfer, Hupfer,* etc.—'tampon, jumper, go and jump into the air'—has a gruesome kind of humour coming from a man tied face down to the operating table with his skull open. The second flight, translated, runs as follows: *Messer, Metzer,* etc.—'Knife, butcher, you are a butcher in a butchery; truly this is a massacre [*Gemetzel*]; don't go on butchering [*metzeln*], take measurements [*messen*]; why don't you measure, Herr Professor, *profiteor, professus sum,*' and so on.

Thus the patient's apparently delirious punning and babbling convey a meaningful message to the surgeon—his fear of being butchered, and his entreaty that the surgeon should proceed by careful measurements, that is, in a more cautious, circumspect way. His train of thought seems to move under dual control. It is controlled by alliteration and assonance—for he has regressed to the level of sound-association and must abide by its rules. But it is also controlled by his intermittent, rational awareness of his situation on the operating table. Without this, his flight of words would become meaningless (and does so at times). Without the tyranny of the other code, he would address the surgeon in simple, sensible prose. As it is, he must serve both masters at the same time.*

Let us take a blasphemous short-cut from patient to poet. We have seen that the creative act always involves a regression to earlier, more primitive levels in the mental hierarchy, while other processes continue simultaneously on the rational surface—a condition that reminds one of a skin-diver with a breathing-tube. (Needless to say, the exercise has its dangers: skin-divers are prone to fall victims to the 'rapture of the deep' and tear their breathing-tubes off—the *reculer sans sauter* of William Blake and so many others. A less fatal professional disease is the Bends, a punishment for attempting to live on two different levels at once.)

The capacity to regress, more or less at will, to the games of the underground, without losing contact with the surface, seems to be the essence of the poetic, and of any other form of creativity. 'God guard me from those thoughts men think/In the mind alone,/He that sings a lasting song/Thinks in a marrow bone' (Yeats);

or, to quote A. E. Housman:

> . . . I could no more define poetry than a terrier can define a rat, but we both recognize the object by the symptoms which it provokes in us. One of these symptoms was described in connection with another object by Eliphaz the Temanite: 'A spirit passed before my face: the hair of my flesh stood up.' Experience has taught me, when I am shaving of a morning, to keep watch over my thoughts, because, if a line of poetry strays into my memory, my skin bristles so that the razor ceases to act. This particular symptom is accompanied by a shiver down the spine. . . . I think that the production of poetry, in its first stage, is less an active than a passive and involuntary process; and if I were obliged, not to define poetry, but to name the class of things to which it belongs, I should call it a secretion; whether a natural secretion, like turpentine in the fir, or a morbid secretion, like the pearl in the oyster. I have seldom written poetry unless I was rather out of health, and the experience, though pleasurable, was generally agitating and exhausting.[4]

The next quotation, in a more academic vein, is from Paul Valéry's *A Course in Poetics* (the italics are in the original):

> When the mind is in question, everything is in question; all is disorder, and every reaction against that disorder is of the same kind as itself. For the fact is that disorder is the condition of the mind's fertility. . . .
> . . . The constitution of poetry . . . is rather mysterious. It is strange that one should exert himself to formulate a discourse which must simultaneously obey perfectly incongruous conditions: musical, rational, significant, and suggestive; conditions which require a continuous and repeated connection between rhythm and syntax, between *sound* and *sense*. . . .

... There is a poetic language in which words are no longer the words of free practical usage. They are no longer held together by the same attractions; they are charged with two different values operating simultaneously and of equivalent importance: their sound and their instantaneous psychic effect. They remind us then of those complex numbers in geometry; the coupling of the *phonetic variable* with the *semantic variable* creates problems of extension and convergence which poets solve blindfold—but they solve them (and that is the essential thing), from time to time.[5]

The sceptical reader may object that all these metaphors about the blindfold poet thinking in his marrow-bones while secreting pearls like an oyster, reflect a too romantic view of the profession; and that I have put altogether too much emphasis on the role of the unconscious. The answer is partly to be found in the chapter on 'Thinking Aside', which shows that the unconscious is neither a romantic nor a mystic fancy, but a working concept in the absence of which nearly every event of mental life would have to be regarded as a miracle. There is nothing very romantic about the wheels of the railway carriage screaming 'I told you so'; it is simply an observed fact.

In the second place, though unconscious processes cannot be governed by conscious volition, they can at least be coaxed into activity by certain tricks acquired at the price of a little patience. Friedrich Schiller learned to get himself into a creative frame of mind by smelling rotten apples, Turgenev by keeping his feet in a bucket of hot water, Balzac by drinking poisonous quantities of black coffee; for lesser mortals even a pipe or pacing up and down in the study might do.

And lastly, there is the long process of conscious elaboration—of cutting, grinding, polishing the rough stone which inspiration has unearthed. Here the range of variations from one writer to another—and from one work to another by the same writer—is as enormous as with the elaboration and formulation of a 'nuclear discovery' in science. An excellent account of this process is to be found in an essay, far too little known, by A. E. Housman from which I have already quoted:

> Having drunk a pint of beer at luncheon—beer is a sedative to the brain, and my afternoons are the least intellectual portion of my life— I would go out for a walk of two or three hours. As I went along,

thinking of nothing in particular, only looking at things around me and following the progress of the seasons, there would flow into my mind, with sudden and unaccountable emotion, sometimes a line or two of verse, sometimes a whole stanza at once, accompanied, not preceded, by a vague notion of the poem which they were destined to form part of. Then there would usually be a lull of an hour or so, then perhaps the spring would bubble up again. I say bubble up, because, so far as I could make out, the source of the suggestions thus proffered to the brain was an abyss which I have already had occasion to mention, the pit of the stomach. When I got home I wrote them down, leaving gaps, and hoping that further inspiration might be forthcoming another day. Sometimes it was, if I took my walks in a receptive and expectant frame of mind; but sometimes the poem had to be taken in hand and completed by the brain, which was apt to be a matter of trouble and anxiety, involving trial and disappointment, and sometimes ending in failure. I happen to remember distinctly the genesis of the piece which stands last in my first volume. Two of the stanzas, I do not say which, came into my head, just as they are printed, while I was crossing the corner of Hampstead Heath between the Spaniard's Inn and the footpath to Temple Fortune. A third stanza came with a little coaxing after tea. One more was needed, but it did not come: I had to turn to and compose it myself, and that was a laborious business. I wrote it thirteen times, and it was more than a twelvemonth before I got it right.

NOTE

To. p. 316. Less dramatic than Förster's syndrome but equally convincing were experiments by Luria and Vinagradova, which demonstrated that subjects who normally associated words by their meaning regressed to association by sound when they were made drowsy by chloral hydrate (*Br. J. of Psychol.*, May, 1959).

XVII

IMAGE

The Hidden Analogy

In Chapters VII–VIII I have spoken at length of the close relatedness between the scientist seeing an analogy where nobody saw one
before, and the poet's discovery of an original metaphor or simile.
Both rely on the mediation of unconscious processes to provide the
analogy. In the scientist's Eureka process two previously unconnected
frames of reference are made to intersect, but the same description may
be applied to the poet's *trouvaille*—the discovery of a felicitous poetic
comparison. The difference between them is in the character of the
'frames of reference', which in the first case are of a more abstract, in
the second of a more sensuous nature; and the criteria of their validity
differ accordingly. But the difference, as we have seen, is a matter of
degrees; and often the two overlap. The discovery of perspective and
fore-shortening, for instance, belongs to both geometrical science and
representative art; it establishes formal analogies between two-dimensional and three-dimensional space, but at the same time has a direct
sensory impact.

Here is another example which I have already mentioned—the
account, by one of Freud's earlier biographers, of how the master
suddenly hit upon the idea of the sublimation of instinct:

> It happened while he was looking at a cartoon in a humorous
> periodical which showed the career of a young girl in two subse-
> quent stages. In the first she was herding a flock of young geese with
> a stick, in the second she was shown as a governess directing a group
> of young girls with her parasol. The girls in the second picture were
> arranged exactly in the same groups as the goslings in the first.[1]

The two cartoons provided the hidden (though not all to deeply
hidden) analogy for the Eureka process. But vice versa, the two

cartoons may be regarded as a metaphorical illustration of it. The same reversibility applies to Kekulé's snake and Faraday's cosmic lines of force. Lastly, on the third panel of the triptych, the governess or the snake can be turned into a joke—as was actually done by malicious contemporaries.

Emotive Potentials

Among the simplest metaphors are cross-references from one of the senses to another: a 'warm' colour, a 'sweet' voice, a 'sharp' light; the 'blind lips' of Swinburne, the 'blind hands' of Blake. Such combinations of different sensory matrices lend a new richness or multi-dimensionality to experience so that, again with Swinburne, 'light is heard as music, music seen as light'.

The aesthetic satisfaction derived from metaphor, imagery, and related techniques (which I shall treat as a single category) depends on the *emotive potential* of the matrices which enter into the game. By emotive potential I mean the capacity of a matrix to generate and satisfy participatory emotions. This depends of course partly on individual factors, partly on the collective attitudes of different cultures, but also on objective factors: on the intrinsic 'calory value', as it were, of some associative contexts—mental diets the ingredients of which have, for instance, a religious or mythological flavour.

On the simplest and most general level, the emotive potentials of the sense-modalities—sight, sound, odour, touch—differ widely with different people. Robert Graves[2] has confessed that his favourite poems have 'without exception' a tactile quality. He quoted as an example for it the Early English:

> Cold blows the wind on my true love
> And a few small drops of rain—

'where', he comments, 'I feel the rain on my hands and hair rather than see it.' He goes on to say that he always liked Keats and disliked Shelley because 'the characteristic of Keats is, I find, his constant appeal to the sense of touch, while Shelley's appeal is as constantly to the sense of movement'. Graves's stimulating essay (published in 1925) ended with the suggestion that psychologists should engage in 'intense research' on this question; it is a pity that it has not been followed up. (My guess would be that more people than one suspects can *smell* poetry—but that, needless to say, is a generalization based on personal experience, for I can always smell the dust-cloud raised by the galloping horses in a Western film; and the lines 'Cold blows the wind' convey to me mainly the fresh smell of the rainy wind and of True Love's wet hair.)

However, granted such personal idiosyncrasies, man lives primarily by his eyes and ears. The emotive potentials of patterned sound I have already discussed; it adds to the virtues of language the dynamism of the dance, the melody of the song, and the magic of incantation. It may even happen that the magic makes us forget the message—as when (quoting Graves) 'people read Swinburne for the mere glorious rush of his verse, without any more regard for the words than will help to a vague scenic background'; and with Blake one often feels that the emotive calories generated by the matrix have burnt up the meaning.

The Picture-strip

Much the same could be said of the emotive power of some visual imagery—including Blake's own. We have seen (Chapter VII) that 'thinking in pictures' dominates the manifestations of the unconscious in the dream, in hallucinatory states, but also in the creative work of scientists. In fact, the majority of mathematicians and physicists turned out to be 'visionaries' in the literal sense—that is, visual, not verbal thinkers.

But we have also seen that pictorial thinking is an earlier and more primitive form of mentation than conceptual thinking—in the evolution of the individual as in that of the species. The language of children is 'picturesque'—again in the literal sense of the word; and the language of primitives is 'like the unfolding of a picture strip, where each word expresses a pictorial image, regardless as to whether the picture signifies an object, an action, or a quality. Thus "to strike" and "a blow" are expressed by the same word. These languages are not merely deficient in the more abstract type of imagery, but in practically all higher grammatical construction' (Kretschmer).[3]

Let me give a concrete example from Kretschmer's textbook, followed by the comments of that excellent German psychiatrist—whose work, comparable in importance to Jung's, is far too little known to the English-speaking public. The example is a simple story told in the Bushman language. It is about a Bushman who worked as a shepherd for a white man until the latter ill-treated him; whereupon the Bushman ran away, and the white man engaged another Bushman, to whom the same thing happened. Translated into Bushman language, this story is picturized as follows:

Bushman-there-go, here-run-to-Whites, White-give-tobacco, Bushman-go-smoke, go-fill-tobacco sack, White-give-meat-Bushman, Bushman-go-eat-meat, get-up-go-home, go-merry, go-sit, graze-sheep Whites, White-go-strike-Bushman, Bushman-crymuch-pain, Bushman-go-run-away-Whites, White-run-after-Bushman, Bushman-there-other-this-graze-sheep, Bushman-all-away.

Kretschmer comments:

The thought of primitive peoples allows of but little arrangement and condensation of separate images into abstract categories; but the sensory perceptions themselves, retained directly as such in memory, unwind themselves before us unchanged, like a long picture roll. The discrete visual image dominates the scene throughout, whilst the relation between the separate pictures is barely indicated. Logical connections are as yet quite tenuous and loose. If we wish to conceive of speech at a slightly lower level still, we shall have to dispense with even those slight hints of a syntax which are present; we shall then find that the thought-processes of a people using such a language would consist entirely of an asyntactical series of pictures.

Some passages in the Old Testament seem to reflect the transition from predominantly pictorial to abstract thought:

I returned, and saw under the sun, that the race is not to the swift, nor the battle to the strong, neither yet bread to the wise, nor yet riches to men of understanding, nor yet favour to men of skill; but time and chance happeneth to them all. (Ecclesiastes.)

The tendency to stick to concrete visual images is still evident; but the characters in the picture-strip no longer represent individuals—the swift, the strong, the wise are collective nouns, abstracted universals. Incidentally, George Orwell once wrote a parody of this passage in modern academic jargon to highlight the contrast between vivid imagery and desiccated abstraction:

Objective consideration of contemporary phenomena compels the conclusion that success or failure in competitive activities exhibits no tendency to be commensurate with innate capacity, but that a considerable element of the unpredictable must invariably be taken into account.

While dreaming, even a paragon of normality regresses in time not merely to Ecclesiastes, but to the earlier mythological creations of the Babylonians and the visual concreteness of the Bushman's statements. But on awakening 'all the charm is broken, all that phantom world so fair, vanishes'—as at the call of the gentleman from Porlock. It may be just as well—the quick effacement from memory of the majority of our dreams may be a normal protective device of the mind (as distinct from pathological repression). In the hallucinatory psychoses, however, the regressions are more intense, realistic, enduring, and unforgettable in a painful sense; hence the remarkable affinities between the paintings of schizophrenics and primitive art. To quote Kretschmer again: 'Schizophrenic symbols, like primitive and dream symbols, are the pictorial antecedents of concepts and are not developed beyond that stage.' He then relates the case of one of his patients, a gifted young man who, between periods of normality and abnormality, lived through a prolonged transitional phase, enlivened by what he called his 'picture show':

In these phases he passively experiences the outcropping of a mass of images which arise from abstract concepts, or which appear to exist in concrete objects. The images often 'resemble old Norse ornaments or Roman sculptures'; sometimes they are grotesque figures, sometimes sensible film-like scenes of knights and soldiers who occupy a real old castle which lies in the valley. Most interesting are the images which arise directly out of abstract thought. For example, he is reading a philosophical work of Kant, and as he reads, the abstract thoughts are continuously converted into imagery. Whilst reading Kant on the question of the infinity of space he had the following experience: 'The pictures crowded on me—towers, circles behind circles, a cylinder which thrust itself obliquely into the whole picture. Everything is showing movement and growth; the circle acquires depth and thus becomes cylindrical; the towers become higher and higher; everything is arbitrary as in an experimental picture or a dream.'

In case-histories like this we see the extreme development of tendencies which on a moderate scale are present in the normal imaginative person; just as we saw in the punning and rhyming patient on the operating table the pathological extreme of the poet's urge to convey his meaning in rhythmic patterns. And just as rhythm is not an artificial embellishment of language but a form of expression which pre-dates language, so visual images and symbols are not fanciful embroideries of concepts, but precursors of conceptual thought. The artist does not climb a ladder to stick ornaments on a façade of ideas—he is more like a pot-holer in search of underground rivers. To quote Kretschmer for the last time: 'Such creative products of the artistic imagination tend to emerge from a psychic twilight, a state of lessened consciousness and diminished attentivity to external stimuli. Further, the condition is one of "absent-mindedness" with hypnoidal over-concentration on a single focus, providing an entirely passive experience, frequently of a visual character, divorced from the categories of space and time, and reason and will. These dreamlike phases of artistic creation evoke primitive phylogenetic tendencies towards rhythm and stylization with elemental violence; and the emergent images thus acquire in the very act of birth regular form and symmetry.'

On Law and Order

Some images seem to appeal more to the intellect than to emotion because of their logical and didactic character—but nevertheless evoke an emotive response:

> And how dieth the wise man? as the fool (Ecclesiastes)

> Golden lads and girls all must,
> As chimney-sweepers, come to dust.
> > (*Cymbeline*)

> When Adam dolve and Eve span,
> Who was then a gentleman?
> > (John Ball ?)

Each of these quotes may be described as a particular illustration of a general truth: the first and second affirm that all men must die, the third proclaims that all men are equal. If we wish to be pedantic, we can enumerate the various bisociative techniques which enter into them: sense and sound in the last two; or in the first two, the joining of habitually incompatible opposites in the focal concepts 'dying' and 'dust'. We may further note the archaic, or archetypal, resonances of Adam, Eve, the sage, the fool, and the golden lads. Finally, the technique of condensation and implication in the third quote poses a kind of naïve riddle which enhances its effect. But when all these points are made, the main feature which the three quotes share remains their didactic intent of driving home a message, of demonstrating a universal law by means of concrete imagery.

Now such reductions of particular instances to universal causes or abstract laws are supposed to represent a purely intellectual pastime which has nothing to do with art and emotion; in fact, however, they give rise to the most powerful emotional release. When John Ball exhorted the peasants at Blackheath to rise against their Lords, he advertently chose 'When Adam dolve' as his text, because it enabled him to prove that their particular grievances were based on a Law ordained by the Creator: that there should be no privilege of birth. It is significant that this same text, with its indirect affirmation implied in a riddle, should have such an explosive effect—not only in England, but also during the peasant risings in Germany, where it became the marching song of the rebels ('*Als Adam grub und Eva spann—Wo war da der Edelmann?*'). Emerson's

> There came a voice without reply—
> 'Tis man's perdition to be safe,
> When for the truth he ought to die,

might serve as a motto for all appeals to the emotions which are explained and justified by reference to divine law—the Voice Without Reply.

The Will of God, or the Laws of Nature, as the organizing and harmonizing principle of the universe is one of the most powerful archetypes of human experience. No doubt it originates to a large part in feelings of insecurity, of cosmic anxiety, the need for protection—hence the reassurance and relief which are felt whenever a threatening or merely puzzling phenomenon can be 'explained' as a manifestation of some universal law or divine order. For the opposite of order is chaos—which means unpredictability of events, absence of protection, exposure to the whims of incomprehensible forces. The emergence or order from chaos is a leitmotif of all mythologies; even the blood-thirsty goddesses of the Hindus and the choleric deities of the Pantheon provided a measure of reassurance, because they were moved by human passions which could be comprehended by the mind; so that everything that befell one was satisfactorily explained.

Thus virtually any explanation—valid or not—which commands belief has a calming and cathartic effect. It can be observed on every level: from the sudden, smiling relief of the small child when some startling appearance is shown to be related to something familiar, and recognized as part of the general order of things—to the euphoria of the scientist, who has solved his problem. Even painful experiences are tempered with relief once they are recognized as particular instances of a general law. To lose a relative by a 'stupid accident' is more painful than to lose one 'lawfully', through old age or incurable illness. The only effective consolation in the face of death is that it is part of the cosmic order; if chimneysweepers were exempted from it, we should resent it very much indeed. The idea of 'blind chance' deciding our fate is intolerable; the mind abhors gaps in the lawful order as nature abhors the vacuum.

On Truth and Beauty

However, the reduction of the uncanny and vexing to the orderly and familiar, of the rustling of leaves in the dark forest to the whisper of fairies or the vibrations of compressed air—both equally reassuring—is merely the negative aspect of the power of explanation: relief from anxiety. Its positive aspect is epitomized in the Pythagorean belief that musical harmonies govern the motion of the stars. The myth of creation appeals not only to man's abhorrence of chaos, but also to his sense of wonder at the cosmic order: light is more than the absence of darkness, and law more than the absence of disorder. I have spoken repeatedly of that sense of 'oceanic wonder'—the most sublimated expression of the self-transcending emotions—which is at the root of the scientist's quest for ultimate causes, and the artist's quest for the ultimate realities of experience. The sensation of 'marvellous clarity' which enraptured Kepler when he discovered his second law is shared by every artist when a strophe suddenly falls into what seems to be its predestined pattern, or when the felicitous image unfolds in the mind

—the only one which can 'explain' by symbols the rationally unexplainable—and express the inexpressible.

Experiences of this kind, when something previously turbid becomes suddenly transparent and permeated by light, are always accompanied by the sudden expansion and subsequent catharsis of the self-transcending emotions. I have called this the 'earthing' of emotion, on the analogy of earthing (or 'grounding') an electrically charged body, so that its tensions are drained by the immense current-absorbing capacity of 'mother earth'. The scientist attains catharsis through the reduction of phenomena to their primary causes; a disturbing particular problem is mentally 'earthed' into the universal order. The same description applies to the artist, except that his 'primary causes' and 'laws of order' are differently constituted. They derive from mythology and magic, from the compulsive powers of rhythm and form, from archetypal symbols which arouse unconscious resonances. But their 'explanatory power', though not of a rational order, is emotionally as satisfying as that of the scientist's explanations; both mediate the 'earthing' of particular experiences into a universal frame; and the catharsis which follows scientific discovery or artistic *trouvaille* has the same 'oceanic' quality. The melancholy charm of the golden lads who come to dust because that is the condition of man, is due to the 'earthing' of our personal predicaments in a universal predicament. Art, like religion, is a school of self-transcendence; it expands individual awareness into cosmic awareness, as science teaches us to reduce any particular puzzle to the great universal puzzle.

When Rembrandt had the audacity to paint the carcass of a flayed ox, he taught his public to see and accept behind the repulsive particular object the timeless patterns of light, shadow, and colour. We have seen that the discoveries of art derive from the sudden transfer of attention from one matrix to another with a higher emotive potential. The *intellectual aspect* of this Eureka process is closely akin to the scientist's—or the mystic's—'spontaneous illumination': the perception of a familiar object or event in a new, significant, light; its *emotive aspect* is the rapt stillness of oceanic wonder. The two together—intellectual illumination and emotional catharsis—are the essence of the aesthetic experience. The first constitutes the moment of truth; the second provides the experience of beauty. The two are complementary aspects of an indivisible process—that 'earthing' process where 'the infinite is made to blend itself with the finite, to stand visible, as it were, attainable there' (Carlyle).

Every scientific discovery gives rise, in the connoisseur, to the experience of beauty, because the solution of the problem creates harmony out of dissonance; and vice versa, the experience of beauty can
occur only if the intellect endorses the validity of the operation—
whatever its nature—designed to elicit the experience. A virgin by
Botticelli, and a mathematical theorem by Poincaré, do not betray
any similarity between the motivations or aspirations of their respective creators; the first seemed to aim at 'truth', the second at
'beauty'. But it was Poincaré who wrote that what guided him in his
unconscious gropings towards the 'happy combinations' which yield
new discoveries was 'the feeling of mathematical beauty, of the harmony of number, of forms, of geometric elegance. This is a true
aesthetic feeling that all mathematicians know.' The greatest among
mathematicians and scientists, from Kepler to Einstein, made similar
confessions. 'Beauty is the first test; there is no permanent place in the
world for ugly mathematics', wrote G. H. Hardy in his classic, *A
Mathematician's Apology*. Jacques Hadamard, whose pioneer work on
the psychology of invention I have quoted, drew the final conclusion:
'The sense of beauty as a "drive" for discovery in our mathematical
field, seems to be almost the only one.' And the laconic pronouncement
of Dirac, addressed to his fellow-physicists, bears repeating: 'It is more
important to have beauty in one's equations than to have them fit
experiment.'

If we now turn to the opposite camp, we find that painters and
sculptors, not to mention architects, have always been guided, and
often obsessed, by scientific and pseudo-scientific theories—the golden
section, the secrets of perspective, Dürer's and Leonardo's 'ultimate
laws' of proportion,* Cézanne's doctrine 'everything in nature is
modelled on the sphere, the cone and the cylinder'; Braque's substitution of cubes for spheres; the elaborate theorizings of the neo-impres-
sionists; Le Corbusier's modulator theory based on the so-called
Fibonacci sequence of numbers—the list could be continued endlessly.
The counterpart to *A Mathematician's Apology*, which puts beauty
before rational method, is Seurat's pronouncement (in a letter to a
friend): 'They see poetry in what I have done. No, I apply my method,
and that is all there is to it.'

Both sides seem to be leaning over backwards: the artist to rationalize
his creative processes, the scientist to irrationalize them, so to speak. But
this fact in itself is significant. The scientist feels the urge to confess his
indebtedness to unconscious intuitions which guide his theorizing; the

artist values, or over-values, the theoretical discipline which controls his intuition. The two factors are complementary; the proportions in which they combine depend—other things being equal—foremost on the *medium* in which the creative drive finds its expression; and they shade into each other like the colours of the rainbow.

The act of creation itself, as we have seen, is based on essentially the same underlying pattern in all ranges of the continuous rainbow spectrum. But the criteria for judging the finished product differ of course from one medium to another. Though the psychological processes which led to the creation of Poincaré's theorem and of Botticelli's virgin lie not as far apart as commonly assumed, the first can be rigorously verified by logical operations, the second not. There seems to be a crack in Keats's Grecian urn, and its message to sound rather hollow; but if we recall two essential points made earlier on, the crack will heal.

The first is that verification comes only *post factum*, when the creative act is completed; the act itself is always a leap into the dark, a dive into the deeps, and the diver is more likely to come up with a handful of mud than with a coral. False inspirations and freak theories are as abundant in the history of science as bad works of art; yet they command in the victim's mind the same forceful conviction, the same euphoria, catharsis, and experience of beauty as those happy finds which are *post factum* proven right. Truth, as Kepler said, is an elusive hussy —who frequently managed to fool even Galileo, Descartes, Leibniz, Pasteur, and Einstein, to mention only a few. In this respect, then, Poincaré is in no better position than Botticelli: while in the throes of the creative process, guidance by truth is as uncertain and subjective as guidance by beauty.

The second point refers to the verifiability of the product *after* the act; we have seen that even in this respect the contrast is not absolute, but a matter of degrees (Chapter X). A physical theory is far more open to verification than a work of art; but experiments, even so-called crucial experiments, are subject to interpretation; and the history of science is to a large part a history of controversies, because the interpretation of facts to 'confirm' or 'refute' a theory always contains a subjective factor, dependent on the scientific fashions and prejudices of the period. There were indeed times in the history of most sciences when the interpretations of empirical data assumed a degree of subjectivity and arbitrariness compared to which literary criticism appeared almost to be an 'exact science'.

I do not wish to exaggerate; there is certainly a considerable difference, in precision and objectivity, between the methods of judging a theorem in physics and a work of art. But I wish to stress once more that there are continuous transitions between the two. The diagram on p. 332 shows one among many such continuous series. Even pure mathematics at the top of the series had its logical foundations shaken by paradoxes like Gödel's theorem; or earlier on by Cantor's theory of infinite aggregates (as a result of which Cantor was barred from promotion in all German universities, and the mathematical journals refused to publish his papers). Thus even in mathematics 'objective truth' and 'logical verifiability' are far from absolute. As we descend to atomic physics, the contradictions and controversial interpretation of data increase rapidly; and as we move further down the slope, through such hybrid domains as psychiatry, historiography, and biography, from the world of Poincaré towards that of Botticelli, the criteria of truth gradually change in character, become more avowedly subjective, more overtly dependent on the fashions of the time, and, above all, less amenable to abstract, verbal formulation. But nevertheless the experience of truth, however subjective, must be present for the experience of beauty to arise; and vice versa, the solution of any of 'nature's riddles', however abstract, makes one exclaim 'how beautiful'.

Thus, to heal the crack in the Grecian urn and to make it acceptable in this computer age we would have to improve on its wording (as Orwell did on Ecclesiastes): Beauty is a function of truth, truth a function of beauty. They can be separated by analysis, but in the lived experience of the creative act—and of its re-creative echo in the beholder—they are inseparable as thought is inseparable from emotion. They signal, one in the language of the brain, the other of the bowels, the moment of the Eureka cry, when 'the infinite is made to blend itself with the finite'—when eternity is looking through the window of time. Whether it is a medieval stained-glass window or Newton's equation of universal gravity is a matter of upbringing and chance; both are transparent to the unprejudiced eye.

NOTES

To p. 329. 'PROPORTIONS OF THE HUMAN FIGURE.
'From the chin to the starting of the hair is a tenth part of the figure.
'From the chin to the top of the head is an eighth part.

'And from the chin to the nostrils is a third part of the face.

'And the same from the nostrils to the eyebrows, and from the eyebrows to the starting of the hair.

'If you set your legs so far apart as to take a fourteenth part from your height, and you open and raise your arms until you touch the line of the crown of the head with your middle fingers, you must know that the centre of the circle formed by the extremities of the outstretched limbs will be the navel, and the space between the legs will form an equilateral triangle.

'The span of a man's outstretched arms is equal to his height.' (From Leonardo's *Notebooks*, quoted by R. Goldwater and M. Treves, eds., 1947, p. 51.)

FIGURE 10

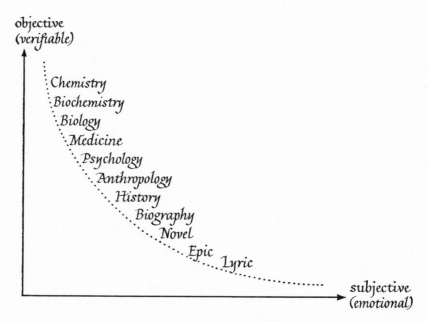

See text on pages 28, 331

XVIII

INFOLDING

Let me return once more to the three main criteria of the technical excellence of a comic work: its originality, emphasis, and economy; and let us see how far they are applicable to other forms of art.

Originality and Emphasis

From antiquity until well into the Renaissance artists thought, or professed to think, that they were copying nature; even Leonardo wrote into his notebook 'that painting is most praiseworthy which is most like the thing represented'. Of course, they were doing nothing of the sort. They were creating, as Plato had reproached them, 'man-made dreams for those who are awake'. The thing represented had to pass through two distorting lenses: the artist's mind, and his medium of expression, before it emerged as a man-made dream—the two, of course, being intimately connected and interacting with each other.

To start with the medium: the space of the painter's canvas is smaller than the landscape to be copied, and his pigment is different from the colours he sees; the writer's ink cannot render a voice nor exhale the smell of a rose. The nature of the medium always excludes direct imitation. Some aspects of experience cannot be reproduced at all; some only by gross oversimplification or distortion; and some only at the price of sacrificing others. The limitations and peculiarities of his medium force the artist at each step to make choices, consciously or unconsciously; to select for representation those features or aspects which he considers to be relevant, and to discard those which he considers irrelevant. Thus we meet again the trinity of *selection, exaggeration, and simplification* which I have discussed before (pp. 82–6; 263 f.). Even the most naturalistic picture, chronicle, or novel, whose maker naïvely hopes to copy reality, contains an unavoidable element of bias, of selective emphasis. Its direction depends on the distorting lenses in the artist's mind—the perceptual and conceptual matrices which pattern his experience, and determine which aspects of it should be regarded as relevant, which not. This part-automatic, part-conscious processing of the experience, over which the medium exercises a kind of 'feedback-control', determines to a large extent what we call an artist's individual style.

Theoretically, the range of choice before him is enormous. In practice, it is narrowed down considerably by the conventions of his period or school. They are imposed on him not only by external pressures—the public's taste and the critics' censure—but mainly from inside. The controls of skilled activities function, as we saw, below the level of awareness on which that activity takes place—whether it consists in riding a bicycle or 'taking in' a landscape. The codes which govern the matrices of perception are hidden persuaders; their influence permeates the whole personality, shapes his pattern of vision, determines which aspects of reality should be considered significant, while others are ignored, like the ticking of one's watch. For centuries painters did not seem to have noticed that shadows have colours, nor the fluidity of contours in hazy air; and if we were to add up those aspects of existence which literature has ignored at one time or another, they would cover practically the whole range of human experience. Conversely, every period over-emphasizes some particular aspects of experience and produces its special brand of 'stylization' and compulsive mannerisms—obvious to all but itself. For instance, the emphasis on contour in classical painting is still so firmly embedded in our frames of perception that we are unaware of the impossibility of seeing foreground figure and background landscape simultaneously in sharp focus. But we are aware of the absence of shadows in Chinese painting —or the absence of sex in Victorian fiction.

The measure of an artist's originality, put into the simplest terms, is the extent to which his selective emphasis deviates from the conventional norm and establishes new standards of relevance. All great innovations, which inaugurate a new era, movement, or school, consist in such sudden shifts of attention and displacements of emphasis onto some previously neglected aspect of experience, some blacked-out range of the existential spectrum. The decisive turning points in the history of every art-form are discoveries which show the characteristic features already discussed: they uncover what has always been there; they are 'revolutionary', that is, destructive and constructive; they compel us to revalue our values and impose a new set of rules on the eternal game.

Most of the general considerations in the chapter on 'The Evolution of Ideas' equally apply to the evolution of art. In both fields the truly original geniuses are rare compared with the enormous number of talented practitioners; the former acting as spearheads, opening up new territories, which the latter will then diligently cultivate. In both fields there are periods of crisis, of 'creative anarchy', leading to a break-through to new frontiers—followed by decades, or centuries of consolidation, orthodoxy, stagnation, and decadence—until a new crisis arises, a holy discontent, which starts the cycle again. Other parallels could be drawn: 'multiple discoveries'—the simultaneous emergence of a new style, for which the time is ripe, independently in several places; 'collective discoveries' originating in a closely knit group, clique, school, or team; 'rediscoveries'—the periodic revivals of past and forgotten forms of art; lastly 'cross-fertilizations' between seemingly distant provinces of science and art. To quote a single example: the rediscovery of the treatise on conic sections by Apollonius of Perga, dating from the fourth century B.C., gave the ellipse to Kepler who built on it a new astronomy—and to Guarini, who introduced new vistas into architecture.

Economy

Yesterday's discoveries are today's commonplaces; a daringly fresh image soon becomes stale by repetition, degenerates into a cliché, and loses its emotive appeal. The newborn day or the piercing cry are no longer even perceived as metaphorical: the once separate contexts of birth and dawn have merged, there is no juxtaposition—reverting to jargon, bisociative dynamism has been converted into associative routine.

The recurrent cycles of stagnation, crisis, and new departure in the arts are to a large extent caused by the gradual saturation which any particular invention or technique produces in artist and audience. A child or a savage, who is taken to the cinema for the first time, derives wonder and delight not so much from the context of the film as from the magic of illusion as such. In the sophisticated theatre-goer's mind, illusion in itself plays a relatively subordinate part—except when, watching a thriller, he regresses to infancy; the two matrices have become virtually integrated into one, so that he is capable of thinking critically of the quality of the acting and of appreciating at the same time the merits of the play. But to recapture the erstwhile magic, in all its freshness, he must turn to something new: experimental theatre, *avant-garde* films, or Japanese Kabuki, perhaps; novel experiences which compel him to strain his imagination, in order to make sense of the seemingly absurd—to participate, and re-create.

When the styles and techniques of an art have become conventionalized and stagnant, the audience is exempted from the necessity to exert its intelligence and imagination—and deprived of its reward. The 'consumer' reads the conventional novel, looks at the conventional landscape, and watches the conventional play with perfect ease and self-assurance—and a complete absence of awe and wonder. He prefers the familiar to the unfamiliar, because it presents no challenge and demands no creative effort. Art becomes a mildly pleasant pastime and loses its emotive impact, its transcendental appeal and cathartic effect. The artist, in growing frustration, senses that the conventional techniques have become 'stale', that they have lost their power over the audience, and become inadequate as means of communication and self-expression. Of course the technique itself cannot become 'stale': blank verse has the same rhythmic qualities today as it had three centuries ago; Fragonard's nymphs and shepherds are as delightful as ever, but they dance no more. We have become immunized against their emotional appeal—at least for the time being. We may again become susceptible to them at the next romantic revival, at some future turn of the spiral.

The history of art could be written in terms of the artist's struggle against the deadening cumulative effect of saturation. The way out of the cul-de-sac is either a revolutionary departure towards new horizons, or the rediscovery of past techniques, or a combination of both. (Egyptian art went through a revival of archaic styles under the twenty-sixth dynasty, in the seventh century B.C.; Rome had a Renaissance of sorts in the second century A.D. when Hadrian built his Athenaeum; and so on to the pre-Raphaelites and the relatively recent rediscovery of primitive art.)

But in between these dramatic turning points one can observe a more gradual evolution of styles which seems to proceed in two opposite directions—both intended to counteract saturation. One is a trend towards more pointed *emphasis*; the other towards more economy or *implicitness*. The first strives to recapture the artist's waning mastery over the audience by providing a spicier fare for jaded appetites: exaggerated mannerisms, frills, flamboyance, an overly explicit appeal to the emotions, 'rubbing it in'—symptoms of decadence and impotence, which need not concern us further. The opposite trend is towards economy and implicitness in the sense previously defined (p.82 et seq.); it has been eloquently described by Mallarmé in a passage which outlined the programme of the French symbolist movement:

> Je pense qu'il faut qu'il n'y ait qu'allusion. La contemplation des objets, l'image s'envolant des rêveries sucitées par eux, sont le chant: les Parnassiens, eux, prennent la chose entièrement et la montrent; par là il manquent de mystère; ils retirent aux esprits *cette joie délicieuse de croire qu'ils créent*. Nommer un objet, c'est supprimer les trois quarts de la jouissance du poème, qui est fait du bonheur de deviner peu à peu: le suggérer, voilà le rêve. C'est le parfait usage de ce mystère qui constitue le symbol: évoquer petit à petit un objet pour montrer un état d'âme, ou, inversement, choisir un objet et en dégager un état d'âme, par une série de déchiffrements. . . .
>
> (*Enquéte sur l'Évolution Littèraire*.)

(It seems to me that there should be only allusions. The contemplation of objects, the volatile image of the dreams they evoke, these make the song: the Parnassians [the classicist movement of Leconte de Lisle, Heredia, etc.] who make a complete demonstration of the object thereby lack mystery; *they deprive the [reader's] mind of that delicious joy of imagining that it creates*. To *name* the thing means forsaking three quarters of a poem's enjoyment—which is derived from unravelling it gradually, by happy guesswork: to *suggest* the thing creates the dream. Symbols are formed when this secret is used to perfection: to evoke little by little, the image of an object in order to demonstrate a mood; or, conversely, to choose an object and to extract from it a mood, by a series of decipherings.)

However, it was not the French symbolists who invented the trend from the explicit statement to the implicit hint, from the obvious to the allusive and oblique; it is as old as art itself. All mythology is studded with symbols, veiled in allegory; the parables of Christ pose riddles which the audience must solve. The intention is not to obscure the message, but to make it more luminous by compelling the recipient to work it out by himself—to re-create it. Hence the message must be handed to him in implied form—and implied means 'folded in'. To make it unfold, he must fill in the gaps, complete the hint, see through the symbolic disguise. But the audience has a tendency to become more sophisticated with time; once it has mastered all the tricks, the excitement goes out of the game; so the message must be made more implicit, more tightly folded. I believe that this development towards greater economy (meaning not brevity, but implicitness) can be traced in virtually all periods and forms of art. To indulge in a little law-making, let me call it the 'law of infolding'. It is the antidote to the law of diminishing returns in the domain of the emotions.

Greek tragedy, as far as we can tell, starts with the 'goat song', derived from the worshipful ceremonies in honour of Bacchus-Dionysius. These in turn originate even further back in the past, in rituals accompanied by human sacrifice, which the Bacchantae enacted in symbolic ways, that is, by implication; their traces can still be found in Euripides. At some stage, the epic recital of events branched off from their direct representation by actors in disguise. The early bards were probably still impersonating their heroes by voice and gesture, as the *mimes* and *histriones* did in medieval days; but economy demanded that histrionics be banned from recitation—it is practised now mainly by artistically minded nannies, and on the B.B.C. children's hour. And even legitimate histrionics, the art of acting, shows a trend towards less emphasis, more economy. Not only do Victorian melodramatics strike one as grotesque; but even films no more than twenty years old, and highly valued at the time, appear surprisingly dated—overdone, obvious, over-explicit.

Somewhere around 600 B.C. the Homeric epics were consolidated in their final version, disguised in written symbols, and folded into parchment. The actor in his mask impersonated the hero; the bard imitated his voice; the printed book evokes the illusion that somebody is talking by a pair of inverted commas—yet we can almost hear Karenina's whisper or Uriah Heap's ingratiating whine.

We have gone a long way in learning to create magic by the most frugal means. Only a hundred years ago the average Victorian novelist did not shrink from crude methods of dramatization: printed illustrations, the use of the historic present, invitations addressed to the gentle reader to follow the narrator to a certain house in a certain town on a winter evening of the year 183 . . ., and peep through the window. Here, as in pre-Raphaelite painting, we find emphasis sans economy at work—a safe criterion of bad art.

One method of economy is 'leaving out'—firstly, everything that by the writer's standards is irrelevant, in the second place everything that is obvious, i.e. which the reader can and should supply out of his own imagination. 'The more bloody good stuff you cut out the more bloody good your novel will be,' Hemingway advised a young writer. Modern prose had to accelerate its pace, not because trains run faster than mailcoaches, but because the trains of thought run faster than a century ago, on tracks beaten smooth by popular psychology, the mass-media, and torrents of print. The novelist no longer needs to crank up the reader's imagination as if it were a model-T car; he pushes the button of the self-starter and leaves the rest to the battery. A glance at the opening lines of *Mountains like White Elephants*, or *Cat in the Rain*, will show that the comparison is hardly exaggerated.

But there exist other, different, methods of infolding—obliquity, compression, and the Seven Types of Ambiguity—a modest estimate of Empson's. The later Joyce, for instance, makes one realize why the German word for writing poetry is '*dichten*'—to condense (certainly more poetical than 'composing', i.e. 'putting together'; but perhaps less poetical than the Hungarian *költeni*—to hatch). Freud actually believed that to condense or compress several meanings or allusions into a word or phrase was the essence of poetry. It is certainly an essential ingredient with Joyce; almost every word in the great monologues in *Finnegans Wake* is overcharged with allusions and implications. To revert to an earlier metaphor, economy demands that the stepping-stones of the narrative should be spaced wide enough apart to require a significant effort from the reader; Joyce makes him feel like a runner in a marathon race with hurdles every other step and aggravated by a mile-long row of hieroglyphs which he must decipher. Joyce would perhaps be the perfect writer—if the perfect reader existed.

Evidently, if the infolding technique is pushed too far, obscurity results, as witnessed by much contemporary poetry. It may be only a passing effect, due to a time-lag between the artist's and his public's maturity and range of perception; it may also be a conscious or half-conscious deception, practised by the artist on his public—including himself. To decide which of these alternatives applies to a difficult work of art is one of the trickiest problems for the critic; here, as a warning example, is Tolstoy's assessment of the French symbolists:[1]

The productions of another celebrity, Verlaine, are not less affected and unintelligible, . . . I must pause to note the amazing celebrity of these two versifiers, Baudelaire and Verlaine. . . . How the French . . . could attribute such importance to these versifiers who were far from skilful in form and most contemptible in subject-matter, is to me incomprehensible.

The Last Veil

We have seen the Law of Infolding at work in the evolution of humour —from the coarse comedian's rubbing in of the joke to the mere hint, the New Yorker type of riddle. The *comic simile* starts with comparing a man to a pig or an ass (neither of them comic any longer, but simply a colloquial adjective)—and progresses to Heine's esoteric comparison of a girl's face to a palimpsest. A similar progression could be shown towards more oblique or condensed forms of *metaphor* and poetic imagery, replacing explicit analogies which, through wear and tear, have shrivelled to empty clichés. Long before the Symbolists, Blake realized the drawbacks of trying to make 'a complete demonstration of the object' and thereby depriving it of its mystery:

> The vision of Christ that thou doest see
> Is my vision's greatest enemy. Thine has a great
>   hook nose like thine
> Mine has a snub nose like to mine.

Rhythm has undergone a similar evolution. Unlike the beat of the tom-tom or the rattling of the carriage wheels, metre does not consist of simple repetitions, but of intricate patterns of short and long stressed and light syllables, on which patterns of assonance and alliteration have further been superimposed. As music has travelled a long way from the simple repetitive figures performed on monochords and other primitive single-tone instruments, so has metre. Its original, simple pulse is only preserved in its sub-structure—implied, but no longer pounded out.

In his analysis of metric form, I. A. Richards[2] calls its effect 'patterned expectancy':

Rhythm and its specialized form, metre, depend upon repetition, and expectancy. Equally where what is expected recurs and where it fails, all rhythmical and metrical effects spring from anticipation. As a rule this anticipation is unconscious. . . . The mind, after reading a line or two of verse . . . prepares itself for any one of a number of possible sequences, at the same time negatively incapacitating itself for others. The effect produced by what actually follows depends very closely upon this unconscious preparation and consists largely of the further twist which it gives to expectancy. It is in terms of the variation in these twists that rhythm is to be described. . . . This texture of expectations, satisfactions, disappointments, surprisals, which the sequence of syllables brings about, is rhythm. . . . Evidently there can be no surprise and no disappointment unless there is expectation. . . . Hence the rapidity with which too simple rhythms, those which are too easily 'seen through', grow cloying or inspid.

If the mind is to experience the 'waking trance' which Yeats promised as poetry's reward, it must actively co-operate by filling in the missing beats and extending the sequence into the future. The witch-doctor hypnotizes his audience with the monotonous rhythm of his drum; the poet merely provides the audience with the means to hypnotize itself.

While elaborate metric forms impose a strain on our patterned expectation, the *rhyme* is its sudden and full reward; it has the same cathartic effect as the harmonious resolution of a musical phrase. It is gloriously explicit in its affirmation of unity in variety; of the magic connection between sense and sound; of the oggly-gobbly delights of sheer repetition. That is obviously the reason for its unpopularity with contemporary poets; it offends against the ascetic diet imposed by the law of infolding. I am old-fashioned enough to regret its passing, as I regret the passing of the barrel-organ.

Emphasis derives from the selection, exaggeration, and simplification of those elements which the artist chooses to regard as significant; it is a means to *impose* his vision on his audience. *Economy* is a technique designed to *entice* the audience into active co-operation, to make them re-create the artist's vision. To do so the audience must decipher the implied message; put into technical terms, he must (cf. pp. 84–6) *intrapolate* (fill in the gaps between the 'stepping stones'); *extrapolate* (complete the hint); and *transform* or reinterpret the symbols, images, and analogies; unwrap the veiled allegory. Now these operations which the audience must perform (interpolation, extrapolation, transformation) to get the artist's implied message, correspond—like mirror images, as it were—to the devices for lending a message emphasis: exaggeration, simplification, selection. The artist, intent on driving home his message, exaggerates and simplifies—the audience co-operates by filling in the gaps and extending the range of the communication. He chooses what he considers to be the significant aspect among other aspects of a given experience—the audience discovers the significance by reinterpreting the message. All this may sound a little abstract, but it leads to a simple conclusion: explicit works of art with an emphatic, pointed message contain all the elements in ready-made form which otherwise the audience would have to contribute. The surest symptom of decadent art is that it leaves nothing to the imagination; the muse has bared her flabby bosom like a too obliging harlot—there is no veiled promise, no mystery, nothing to divine.

The law of infolding affects science too, though in a different way. Aristotle had thought that nearly everything worth discovering about the ways of the universe had already been discovered; Francis Bacon and Descartes believed that to complete the edifice of science would take but a generation or two; Haeckel proclaimed that all the seven riddles of the universe had been solved. The idea of progress (in science and any other field) is only about three centuries old; and only since the collapse of mechanistic science around the turn of the last century did it begin to dawn on the more far-sighted among scientists, that the unfolding of the secrets of nature was accompanied by a parallel process of infolding—that we were learning more and more about less and less. The more precise knowledge the physicist acquired, the more ambiguous and oblique symbols he had to use to express it; he could no longer make an intelligible model of sub-atomic reality, he could only allude to it by formal equations which have as much resemblance to reality 'as a telephone number has to the subscriber'. One might almost think that physical science is determined to implement the programme of the French symbolists.

It may seem that I have laid too much stress on the law of infolding. But quite obviously it plays an essential role in the progress of art and understanding; and it is in fact a characteristic of the human condition. For man is a symbol-making animal. He constructs a symbolic model of outer reality in his brain, and expresses it by a second set of symbols in terms of words, equations, pigment, or stone. All he knows directly are bodily sensations, and all he can directly do is to perform bodily motions; the rest of his knowledge and means of expression is symbolical. To use a phrase coined by J. Cohen,[3] man has a metaphorical consciousness. Any attempt to get a direct grasp at naked reality is self-defeating; Urania, too, like the other muses, always has a last veil left to fold in.

Summary

Art originates in sympathetic magic; in the illusions of stagecraft its origin is directly reflected. In the mind of naïve audiences, the impersonator becomes identified with the character impersonated, as in ancient days the masked dancer became identified with the rain-god. On the other hand, sophisticated audiences are conscious and critical of the actors' performance, but are nevertheless caught by the illusion to the extent of producing the physical symptoms of intense emotion; their awareness suspended between two planes of experience, they exemplify the bisociative process in its purest form.

The escapist character of illusion facilitates the unfolding of the participatory emotions and inhibits the self-asserting emotions, except those of a vicarious character; it draws on untapped resources of emotion and leads them to catharsis.

Rhythm and rhyme, assonance and pun are not artificial creations, but vestigial echoes of primitive phases in the development of language, and of the even more primitive pulsations of living matter; hence our particular receptiveness for messages which arrive in a rhythmic pattern, and their hypnotic effect. Association by sound affinity is still employed in subconscious mentation; it is manifested in the punning mania of children, in sleep, fatigue and mental disorder. The poet creates by bisociating sound and sense, metre and meaning; his voice is bi-vocal—so to speak.

Metaphor and imagery come into existence by a process, familiar from scientific discovery, of seeing an analogy where nobody saw one before. The aesthetic satisfaction derived from the analogy depends on the emotive potential of the matrices which participate in it. Synesthetic cross-references from sight to touch, for instance, may enrich the experience, depending on personal preferences. Visual imagery, derived from the most important sense organ, carries a special emotive appeal; the 'picture-strip' language of concrete imagery pre-dates conceptualized thought. The highest emotive potential is found in images which evoke archetypal symbols and arouse unconscious resonances. They lead to the 'earthing' of emotion by relating particular experiences to a universal frame, the temporal to the eternal —as the scientist relates particular phenomena to general laws and ultimate causes. In both cases the flash of spontaneous illumination is followed by emotional catharsis; 'truth' and 'beauty' appear as complementary aspects of the indivisible experience. The difference between the two in objective verifiability is a matter of degrees, and arises only after the act; the act itself is in both cases a leap into the dark, where scientist and artist are equally dependent on their fallible intuitions.

Originality, selective emphasis, and economy are certainly not the only criteria of literary excellence, but they proved to be a kind of handy mariner's compass for the critic at sea; and the 'law of infolding' appears to be equally valid—and tantalizing—in science as in art.

XIX

CHARACTER AND PLOT

Identification

In his monologue in Act II, after the First Player's dramatic recital, Hamlet asks a pertinent question:

> Is it not monstrous that this player here,
> But in a fiction, in a dream of passion,
> Could force his soul so to his own conceit
> That from her working all the visage wann'd,
> Tears in his eyes, distraction in 's aspéct,
> A broken voice . . .
>   . . . and all for nothing,
> For Hecuba!
> What's Hecuba to him, or he to Hecuba,
> That he should weep for her?

The answer to Hamlet's question was given by Flaubert: *Emma Bovary, c'est moi.*

The magic tie is identification. Without it, why indeed should our tear-glands become active on Hecuba's behalf? Goethe's early novel, *The Sorrows of Young Werther*, unleashed an epidemic of suicide in Germany; every romantic young man felt that he was Werther.

The extent to which a character in a novel 'lives' depends on the intensity of the reader's participatory ties with him. To know what Hamlet feels while listening to the ghost, is the same thing as to know how it feels to be Hamlet. I must project part of myself into Hamlet, or Hamlet into myself—'projection' and 'introjection' are metaphors referring to the partial breakdown of the crust of personal identity. This remains true, regardless whether the reader admires, despises,

345

hates, or loves the fictional character. In order to love or hate something which exists only as a series of signs made with printer's ink, the
reader must endow it with a phantom life, an emanation from his
conscious or unconscious self. The major contribution will probably
come from the unconscious, which takes phantoms for granted and is
apt to confuse personal identities.

Thus the figments of Bovary, Little Lord Fauntleroy, and Alyosha
Karamazov which float around us in the air, are projections which
body forth from our intimate selves, like the medium's ectoplasm. The
author has created the prototype-phantoms, and the reader creates out
of himself a copy, which he assumes to be like the original, though this
is not necessarily the case. Whether the Elizabethans saw Shylock in a
tragic or grotesque light, my own Shylock is a tragic figure—he has a
great hook nose like mine, not a snub nose like to thine.

Some novelists give meticulous descriptions of the visual appearances
of their characters; others give little or none. Here again the general
trend is away from the over-explicit statement towards the suggestive
hint which entices the reader to build up his own image of the character.
I am always annoyed when the author informs me that Sally Anne has
auburn hair and green eyes. I don't particularly like the combination,
and would have gone along more willingly with the author's intention
that I should fall in love with Sally Anne if he had left the colour-scheme
to me. There is a misplaced concreteness which gets in the way of the
imagination. It is chiefly due to the misconception that 'imagination'
means literally seeing images in the mind's eye; and consequently that,
for a character to come alive, I must carry a complete picture of it in
my mind. Now this is an old fallacy which affects the subject we are
discussing only indirectly, but has a direct bearing on certain basic
assumptions about the nature of perception and memory, on which
the present theory rests. These are discussed in Book Two, which also
contains the detailed evidence for the rather summary remarks which
follow.

Phantoms and Images

In the first place, the evidence shows that there are people endowed
with the faculty of so-called eidetic imagery—that is, of really *seeing*
mental images with dream-like, hallucinatory vividness; but this
faculty, though relatively frequent in children, is rare in adults. The
average adult does not really *see* anything approaching a complete and

sharp image when he recalls a memory—for instance, the face of a friend—though he may deceive himself into believing that he does. How do we know that he is deceiving himself? Here is one way of proving it—among many others. The experimenter lets the subject look at a square of, say, four rows of four letters (which do not form any meaningful sequences) until the subject thinks he can see them in his mind's eye. He can, in fact, fluently 'read' them out after the square has been taken away—or so he believes. For when he is asked to read the square backwards, or diagonally, his fluency is gone. He has, in fact, learned the sequence by rote without realizing it—which is quite a different matter from forming a visual image. If he could really see the square, he could read it in all directions with the same ease and speed.

The ordinary citizen, who does not happen to be a painter, or a policeman, or of a particularly observant type, would be at a loss to give an exact visual description even of people whom he knows quite well. What we do remember of a person is a combination of (a) certain vivid details, and (b) what we call 'general impressions'. The 'vivid detail' may be a gesture, an intonation, an outstanding visual feature—the mole on Granny's chin—which, for one reason or another, has stuck in one's memory, like a fragment from a picture-strip, and which functions *pars pro toto*—as a part, or sign deputizing for the whole.

The 'general impression' on the other hand, is based on the opposite method of memory-formation: it is a schematized, sketchy, quasi 'skeletonized' outline of a whole configuration, regardless of detail. A woman may say to a man, 'I haven't seen you wearing that tie before'—though she has not the faintest recollection of any of the ties he has worn in the past. She *recognizes* a deviation from memories which she is unable to *recall*. The explanation of the paradox is that although she cannot remember the colour or pattern of any single tie which that man wore in the past, she does remember that they were generally subdued and discreet, which the new tie is not. It deviates not from any particular past experience, but from the general *code*, from an abstracted visual quality that these past experiences had in common. Such perceptual codes function as selective filters, as it were; the filter rejects as 'wrong' anything which does not fit its 'mesh'; and accepts or 'recognizes' anything that fits it, i.e. which gives the same 'general impression'. The gentleman with the new tie, for instance, can get his own back with the remark, 'You have done something to your hair, haven't you?' He has never noticed her previous hair-dos at all, but he does notice that the present one just doesn't go with her mousy appearance. Here the code is 'mousiness' which, like all visual schematizations, is difficult to describe in words, but instantly recognized by the eye. We talk of an 'innocent' or 'lascivious' expression, of 'sensitive' or 'brutal' features—characteristics which defy verbal description, but which can be sketched with a few lines—as emotions can be indicated by a few basic strokes indicating the slant of mouth and eyes. Other codes of recognition may combine form and motion, or vision and hearing: a characteristic gait, the timbre of a voice.

Thus recognizing a person does not mean matching a retinal image against a memory image of photographic likeness. My memory of John Brown is not a photographic record; it consists of several, simplified and schematized 'general impressions' whose combination, plus a few 'vivid details', enable me to recognize him when we meet, or to remember him in his absence. But that remembrance is only partly of a pictorial nature, and much less so than I believe it to be—see the experiment with the letter-square. The reason for this self-deception is that the process of combining those simplified visual and other schemata and adorning them with a few genuine 'photographic' fragments, is unconscious and instantaneous. The perceptual codes function below the level of awareness; we are playing a game without being aware of the rules. We overestimate the precision of our imagery, as we overestimate the precision of our verbal thinking (quite often we think that we have understood the meaning of a difficult text and discover later that we haven't really) because we are unaware of the gaps between the words and between the sketchy contours of the schemata. All introspective 'visual' thinkers, from Einstein downward, emphasized the vagueness, haziness, and abstract character of their conscious visual imagery. True picture-strip thinking is confined to the dream, and other manifestations of the subconscious.

The point of this apparent digression was to show that if the above is true regarding our mental images of real people whom we know, it must be all the more true regarding our images of fictional characters which lack any sensory basis. A character may indeed be 'alive' with the utmost vividness in the reader's mind, but this vividness need not be of a visual nature. The reader may fall in love with Karenina, despair when she throws herself under the train, mourn her death—and yet be unable to visualize her in his mind's eye or give a detailed description of her appearance. Her 'living image' in the reader is not a photographic image, but a multi-dimensional construct of a variety of aspects of her general appearance, her gestures and voice, her patterns of thinking and behaving. It is a combination of various 'general impressions' and 'vivid details'—that is, *constructed on much the same principles as images of real people.*

In fact, there is no sharp dividing line between our images of people whom we have met in the flesh, and those whom we know only from descriptions—whether factual or fictional (or a combination of both). The dream knows no distinction between factual and fictitious characters, and children as well as primitives are apt to confuse the two.

Thus the phantoms of Bovary and Karenina which float around us are not so very different from our apparently solid memories of Joe Smith and Peter Brown; both varieties are made of the same stuff. In one of Muriel Spark's novels, a wise old bird asks his woman friend: 'Do you think, Jean, that other people exist? . . . I mean, do you consider that people—the people around us—are real or illusory? Surely you see that here is a respectable question. Given that you believe in your own existence as self-evident, do you believe in that of others? Do you believe that I for instance, at this moment exist?'[1]

The only certainty that other people exist, not merely as physical shapes, but as sentient beings, is derived from partly conscious, but mostly unconscious, inference, i.e. empathy. We automatically infer from minute pointers in a person's face or gestures—which we mostly do not even register consciously—his character, mood, how he will behave in an emergency, and a lot of other things. Without this faculty of projecting part of one's own sentient personality into the other person's shell, which enables us to say 'I *know* how you feel', the pointers would be meaningless. Lorenz has shown that the various postures and flexions of the wolf's tail are indicative of at least ten different moods. As we have lost our tails we cannot empathize with these moods—but since our labial muscles are not very different, we feel at once the significance of bared teeth.

The semi-abstract schematizations which we call 'general impressions' of appearance, character, and personality, are intuitive pointer-readings based on empathy. It is by this means that we assign reality and sentience to other people. Once more, the process differs from bringing a fictional character alive in our minds mainly by the nature of the pointers. A bland face at a cocktail party uttering the conventional type of remark may provide less pointers for empathy and imagination than the cunningly planted hints of the novelist, specially

designed to produce positive or negative identifications. Some phantoms can be more real to the mind than many a bore made of solid
flesh. The distinction between fact and fiction is a late acquisition of
rational thought—unknown to the unconscious, and largely ignored
by the emotions.

Conflict

Drama strives on conflict, and so does the novel. The nature of the
conflict may be explicitly stated or merely implied; but an element of
it must be present, otherwise the characters would be gliding through
a frictionless universe.

The conflict may be fought in the divided heart of a single character; or between two or more persons; or between man and his destiny.
The conflict between personalities may be due to a clash of ideas or
temperaments, to incompatible codes of behaviour or scales of value.
But whatever its motif, a quarrel will assume the dignity of drama only
if the audience is lead to accept the attitude of both sides as valid, each
within its own frame of reference. If the author succeeds in this, the
conflict will be projected into the spectator's or reader's mind, and
experienced as a clash between two simultaneous and incompatible
identifications. 'We make out of our quarrels with others rhetoric,
but of our quarrels with ourselves poetry,' said Yeats.

Dramatic conflict thus always reveals some paradox which is latent
in the mind. It reflects both sides of the medal whereas in our practical
pursuits we see only one at a time. The paradox may be seemingly
superficial, as when our sympathies are divided between Hamlet and
Laertes, two equally worthy contestants, with the resulting desire to
help both, that is to harm both. But at least the double complicity in
the double slaughter is prompted not by hate but love, and we are
made to realize that it was destiny, not their own volition, which made
them destroy each other; the paradox is 'earthed' in the human
condition.

Thus the artist compels his audience to live on several planes at
once. He identifies himself with several characters in turn—Caesar,
Brutus, Antony, projecting some aspect of himself into each of them,
and speaking through their mouths; or introjecting them, if you like,
and lending them his voice. He presents Brutus and Caesar alternately
in situations where they command sympathy and impose their patterns
of reasoning, their scales of value, until each has established his own

independent matrix in the spectator's mind. Having acquired these multiple identities, the spectator is led to a powerful climax, where he is both murderer and victim; and thence to catharsis. In the *Bhagavid Gita* the Lord Krishna appears on the battlefield in the role of charioteer to his disciple Arjuna, whom he cures of his pacifist scruples by explaining that the slayer and the slain are One, because both are embodiments of the indestructible Atma; therefore 'the truly wise mourn neither for the living nor for the dead.' I doubt whether this doctrine, taken literally, had a beneficial effect on the ethics of Hinduism,* but to be both Caesar and Brutus in one's imagination has a profound cathartic effect, and is one way of approaching Nirvana.

Brutus is an honourable man; so is Caesar; but what about Iago? Through pitying Desdemona, and sharing Othello's despair, we are compelled to hate Iago; but we can hate Iago only if he has come to life for us and in us; and he has come to life in us because he too commands our understanding and, at moments, our sympathy—the resonance of our own frustrated ambitions and jealousies. Without this unavowed feeling of complicity, he would be a mere stage-prop, and we could hate him no more than a piece of cardboard. Iago, Richard III, Stavrogin, the great villains of literature, have an irresistible appeal to some common, repressed villainousness in ourselves, and give us a wonderfully purifying opportunity to discover what it feels like to be frankly a villain.

But true-black villains are limit cases; the more evenly our sympathies are distributed among the antagonists, the more successfully the work will actualize latent aspects of our personalities. Caliban and Prospero, Faust and Mephisto, Don Quixote and Sancho Panza, Christ and the Great Inquisitor—each pair is locked in an everlasting duel in which we act as seconds for both. In each of these conflicts two self-contained frames of reference, two sets of values, two universes of discourse collide. All great works of literature contain variations and combinations, overt or implied, of such archetypal conflicts inherent in the condition of man, which first occur in the symbols of mythology, and are restated in the particular idiom of each culture and period. All literature, wrote Gerhart Hauptmann, is 'the distant echo of the primitive word behind the veil of words'; and the action of a drama or novel is always the distant echo of some ancestral action behind the veil of the period's costumes and conventions. There are no new themes in literature, as there are no new human instincts; but every age provides new variations and sublimations, new settings and a different set of rules for fighting the old battles all over again. To quote G. W. Brandt: 'There is basically only a limited number of plots; they can be seen, in different guises, recurring down the ages. The reason is in life itself. Human relationships, whilst infinitely varied in detail, reveal—stripped down to fundamentals—a number of repetitive patterns. Writers straining to invent a plot entirely fresh have known this for a long time. Goethe quoted Gozzi's opinion that there were only thirty-six tragic situations—and he added that Schiller, who believed that there were more, had not even succeeded in finding as many as that.'[2]

Integrations and Confrontations

If the individual act of discovery displays essentially the same psychological pattern in science and in art, their collective progress differs in one important respect. We have seen (Chapter X) that the evolution of science is neither continuous nor cumulative in a strict sense; but it is nevertheless more so than the evolution of art.

In the discoveries of science, the bisociated matrices merge in a new synthesis, which in turn merges with others on a higher level of the hierarchy; it is a process of successive confluences towards unitary, universal laws (at least, this applies to a given province of science in a given period or cycle). The progress of art does not display this overall 'river-delta' pattern. The matrices with which the artist operates are chosen for their sensory qualities and emotive potential; his bisociative act is a *juxtaposition* of these planes or aspects of experience, not their *fusion* in an intellectual synthesis—to which, by their very nature, they do not lend themselves. This difference is reflected in the quasi-linear progression of science, compared with the quasi-timeless character of art, its continual re-statements of basic patterns of experience in changing idioms. If the explanations of science are like streams joining rivers, rivers moving towards the unifying ocean, the explanations of art may be compared to the tracing back of a ripple in the stream to its source in a distant mountain-spring.

But I must once more repeat, at the risk of being tedious, that in all domains of creative activity intellectual and aesthetic experience are both present in various mixtures; that 'science' and 'art' form a continuum; that changes of fashion are common in the zig-zag course of science, while on the other hand, development of a given art-form over a period often shows a distinct 'river-delta' pattern.* The modern atom-physicist knows more than Democritus, but then Joyce's Ulysses also knows more than Homer's Odysseus; and in some respects this progress in knowledge, too, is of a cumulative order.

Archetypes

Always bearing these qualifications in mind, we might spin out the metaphor: if the great confluence towards which science strives is the universal *logos*, the ultimate spring of aesthetic experience is the *archetypos*. The literal meaning of the word is 'implanted' (*typos* = stamp) 'from the beginning'. Jung described archetypes as 'the psychic residua of numberless experiences of the same type' encountered by our ancestors, and stamped into the memory of the race—that is, into the deep layers of the 'collective unconscious' below the level of personal memories. Hence, whenever some archetypal motif is sounded, the response is much stronger than warranted by its face value—the mind responds like a tuning fork to a pure tone.

One need not be a follower of Jung to recognize the same archetypal experiences crystallized into symbols in the mythologies of cultures widely separate in space and time. Examples of such recurrent patterns are the death-and-resurrection motif; the extension of the sexual duality into the metaphysical polarities of masculine logic and feminine intuition, mother earth and heavenly father, etc.; the strife between generations—and its counterpoint, the taboo on incest; the Promethean struggle to wrest power from the gods—and the imperative need to placate them by sacrifice; the urge to penetrate to the ultimate mystery—and the resigned admission that reality is beyond the mind's grasp, hidden by the veil of Maya, reduced to shadows in Plato's cave. These perennial patterns of victory and defeat recur in ever-changing variations throughout the ages, because they derive from the very essence of the human condition—its paradoxes and predicaments. They play an all-important part in literature, from Greek tragedy down to the present, permeating both the whole and the part: the plot, and the images employed in it. The poetic image attains its highest vibrational intensity as it were, when it strikes archetypal chords—when eternity looks through the window of time.

William Empson[3] has given a convincing analysis of the archetypal imagery in Nash's famous lines—which, however often quoted, never lose their power: 'Brightness falls from the air./Queens have died young and fair./Dust hath closed Helen's eye./I am sick, I must die./Lord have mercy upon us.'

'If death did not exist', wrote Schopenhauer, 'there would be no philosophy—nor would there be poetry.' That does not mean that either philosophy, or art, must be obsessively preoccupied with death; merely, that great works of art are always transparent to some dim outline of the ultimate experience, the archetypal image. It need not have a tragic shape, and it may be no more than the indirect reflection of a reflection, the echo of an echo. But metaphor and imagery yield aesthetic value only if the two contexts which are involved in the comparison form an ascending gradient—if one of them is felt to be nearer to the source of the stream. *Mutatis mutandum*, a scientific theory need not be directly concerned with the ultimate secret of the universe, but it must point towards it by bringing order and harmony into some obscure corner. To clinch the argument, I must quote once more Housman's essay on *The Name and Nature of Poetry*:

In these six simple words of Milton—

Nymphs and shepherds, dance no more—

what is it that can draw tears, as I know it can, to the eyes . . . ? What in the world is there to cry about? Why have the mere words the physical effect of pathos when the sense of the passage is blithe and gay? I can only say, because they are poetry, and find their way to something in man which is obscure and latent, something older than the present organization of his nature, like the patches of fen which still linger here and there in the drained lands of Cambridgeshire.

Cataloguing Plots

Let me mention a few examples of archetypal patterns in literature—without any attempt at cataloguing Goethe's thirty-six basic plots.

The Promethean striving for omnipotence and omniscience is symbolized in Jacob's struggle with the angel, the Tower of Babel, the flight of Icarus, the Faustus legend, and so on through Voltaire's *Candide*, down to the broken Promethean heroes of H. G. Wells (Dr. Moreau) or Dostoyevski (Stavrogin in *The Possessed*). In the modern development of the theme, it is of course treated in a more allusive, implicit manner; but in the mass media and pulp magazines, Supermen, Space Cadets, and Black Magicians are all happily running true to archetype.

The next catalogue-heading would be 'Individual against Society', with several subheadings, such as 'from Oedipus to Schmoedipus, or shall we love mamma?' Next would come 'polygonal patterns of libidinous relations' (triangles, quadrangles, etc.); a title I have actually borrowed from a learned publication by a field-anthropologist; it shows that if you collect archetypes methodically, they crumble to dust. Yet under this heading belongs at least half the total bulk of world literature, from the Vulcan-Venus-Mars triangle onward. Next might come the War of the Sexes—from the Amazon myths through Lysistrata to *Ann Veronica* and Simone de Beauvoir; next, love triumphant, or defeated—the Song of Songs alternating with Isolde's *Liebestod*. Lastly, the Conquest of the Flesh, from the Buddha to Aldous Huxley.

Still under the heading 'Man and Society' would come the subheadings: the *hubris* of Power; the *hubris* of Cleverness; the *hubris* of the Ivory Tower and, less obvious, the *hubris* of Sanctity. The last is either an offence to God (Job; the ten righteous men who find less favour than the one repentant sinner) or to society, because the hero's personal scales of value deviate from the conventional. He must therefore either be an inspired fool, or play the fool to escape sanction, or suffer martyrdom—'The time is out of joint; O cursed spite, / That ever I was born to set it right!' Examples range from the Perceval legend and *The Lay of the Great Fool*, through Don Quixote, Ulenspiegel and The Good Soldier Schweik to Prince Mishkin in Dostoyevski's *The Idiot*, and Camus' *L'Étranger*.

Under the heading 'The Divided Heart' would fall, as sub-categories, conflicts between Love and Duty; between Self-Preservation and Self-Sacrifice; between Ends and Means; and between Faith and Reason.

Puppets and Strings

To end this pedantic—and yet very incomplete—catalogue, I must mention one of the most powerful archetypes, which appears in countless variations in the history of literature: the Puppet on Strings, or Volition against Fate. In *Oedipus Rex* fate appears in the shape of malevolent powers who trap the King into performing his disastrous deeds apparently out of his own free will. In all plots of the *Appointment in Samara* type, apparent coincidences are the means by which destiny defeats the will of man (cf. coincidence in comedy, p. 78). In Christian theology, the ways of God become less arbitrary, but more inscrutable; man proposes, God disposes; original sin chokes his designs. In the Eastern religions he is tied to the wheel of rebirth; in Islam he carries his fate fastened round his neck. The great theological disputes between Calvinists and Lutherans, Jansenites and Jesuits turned mainly on the question of predestination, or more precisely, on the length of the rope left to man to hang himself.

With the rise of Natural Philosophy, a change in the character of destiny began to take shape. Romeo and Juliet still die as a result of fatal misunderstandings ('One writ with me in sour misfortune's book'). But in Shakespeare's later works, destiny acts no longer only from outside but also from inside the personae; they are victims not so much of blind fate, but of their blind passions: 'the fault, dear Brutus, is not in our stars, but in ourselves'. These are great, brave words; but they did not solve the dilemma, they merely polished its horns. Divine predestination was transformed into scientific determinism, which left man even less scope than before for exercising his will and making free choices. The hairshirt of the penitent had allowed him some freedom of movement, but the laws of heredity and environment wove a strait-jacket so tight that it became indistinguishable from his living skin. Even the word 'volition' was banned from psychology as empty of meaning. Chromosomes and glandular secretions took over from the gods in deciding a man's fate. He remained a marionette on strings, with the only difference that he was now suspended on the nucleic acid chains determining his heredity, and the conditioned-reflex chains forged by the environment.

The most explicit adoption of this schema for literary uses is found in the naturalist movement of the nineteenth century. Its programme was formulated in Zola's *Le Roman Experimental*, inspired by the *Introduction à l'étude de la médicine experimentale* by the great Claude Bernard (who discovered the vaso-motor system of nerves, and the glucose-producing function of the liver). Zola urged his fellow writers to take a 'physiological view' of man as a product of nature devoid of free will and subject to the laws of heredity and environment. Fortunately, in spite of the naturalist vogue in Germany, Russia, and Scandinavia, writers accepted his views in theory only—as they are wont to do. The creative mind knows how to draw on archetypal symbols without degrading them by misplaced concreteness.

You can make an X-ray photograph of a face, but you cannot make a face from an X-ray photograph. You can show that underlying the subtle and complex action of a novel there is a primitive skeleton, without committing *lèse majesté*, or foolishly assuming that the plot makes the novel. There is only a limited number of plots, recurring down the ages, derived from an even more limited number of basic patterns—the conflicts, paradoxes, and predicaments inherent in man's condition. And if we continue the stripping game, we find that all these paradoxes and predicaments arise from conflicts between incompatible frames of experience or scales of value, illuminated in consciousness by the bisociative act. In this final illumination Aristotle saw 'the highest form of learning' because it shows us that we are 'men, not gods'; and he called tragedy 'the noblest form of literature' because it purges suffering from its pettiness by showing that its causes lie in the inescapable predicaments of existence.*

NOTES

To p. 351. Hindu apologists would have us take Krishna's exhortations to belligerence as allegorical references to wars fought inside the human soul. The argument is as far-fetched as the Christian apologists' attempts to represent the Song of Songs as an allegory of Christ's love for His Church.

To p. 352. Eric Newton (*An Introduction to European Painting*) actually uses the same metaphor.

To p. 357. At least this seems the most plausible explanation of the cryptic remark in the *Poetics* that we take pleasure in tragedy because learning is pleasurable, and tragedy involves learning.

XX

THE BELLY OF THE WHALE

The Night Journey

One archetype remains to be discussed, which is of special significance for the act of creation. It is variously known as the Night Journey, or the Death-and-Rebirth motif; but one might as well call it the meeting of the Tragic and the Trivial Planes. It appears in countless guises; its basic pattern can be roughly described as follows. Under the effect of some overwhelming experience, the hero is made to realize the shallowness of his life, the futility and frivolity of the daily pursuits of man in the trivial routines of existence. This realization may come to him as a sudden shock caused by some catastrophic event, or as the cumulative effect of a slow inner development, or through the trigger action of some apparently banal experience which assumes an unexpected significance. The hero then suffers a crisis which involves the very foundations of his being; he embarks on the Night Journey, is suddenly transferred to the Tragic Plane—from which he emerges purified, enriched by new insight, regenerated on a higher level of integration.

The symbolic expressions of this pattern are as old as humanity.[1] The crisis or Night Journey may take the form of a visit to the underworld (Orpheus, Odysseus); or the hero is cast to the bottom of a well (Joseph), buried in a grave (Jesus), swallowed by a fish (Jonah); or he retires alone into the desert, as Buddha, Mahomet, Christ, and other prophets and founders of religions did at the crucial turn in their lives.

I went down to the bottoms of the mountains: the earth with her bars was about me for ever.

The journey always represents a plunge downward and backward to the sources and tragic undercurrents of existence, into the fluid magma, of which the Trivial Plane of everyday life is merely the thin crust. In most tribal societies, the plunge is symbolically enacted in the initiation-rites which precede the turning points in the life of the individual, such as puberty or marriage. He is made to undertake a minor Night Journey: segregated from the community, he must fast, endure physical hardships and various ordeals, so that he may experience the essential solitude of man, and establish contact with the Tragic Plane. A similar purpose is served by the symbolic drowning and rebirth of baptism; the institution of periods of retreat found in most religions; in fasts and other purification rituals; in the initiation ceremonies of religious or masonic orders, even of university societies. Illumination must be preceded by the ordeals of incubation.

Freudians and Jungians alike emphasize the intimate relation between the symbolism of the Night Journey, and the unconscious craving for a return to the womb. The connection is no more far-fetched than our references to 'mother earth', 'mother ocean', or 'mother church'.

Not only do we speak of 'Mother Church', but even of the 'womb of the Church', and in the ceremony of the 'benedictio fontis' of the Catholic Church the baptismal font is even called the 'immaculatus divini fontis uterus' (the immaculate uterine font of divinity). . . .[2]

The maternal aspect of the church is impersonated in the Virgin Mary. In Donne's 'Annunciation', the Angel greets her with:

That All, which alwayes is All every where,
Which cannot sinne, and yet all sinnes must beare,
Which cannot die, yet cannot chuse but die,
Loe, faithfull Virgin, yeelds himselfe to lye
In prison, in thy wombe; . . .
                    . . . yea thou art now
Thy Makers maker, and thy Fathers mother;
Thou 'hast light in darke; and shutst in little roome,
Immensity cloystered in thy deare wombe.

The craving for the womb, for the dissolution of the self in a lost, vegetative oneness—Freud's Nirvana principle—is further symbolized in the image of mother ocean in whose calm depths all life originates. Mythology is full of these symbols—the metaphors of the collective unconscious. However bewildering they may appear to the waking mind, they are familiar to the dreamer, and recur constantly in the sleep of people who have nothing else in common. The Night Journey is the antipode of Promethean striving. One endeavours to steal the bright fire from the gods; the other is a sliding back towards the pulsating darkness, one and undivided, of which we were part before our separate egos were formed.

Thus the Night Journey is a regression of the participatory tendencies, a crisis in which consciousness becomes unborn—to become reborn in a higher form of synthesis. It is once more the process of *reculer pour mieux sauter*; the creative impulse, having lost its bearing in trivial entanglements, must effect a retreat to recover its vigour.

Without our regular, minor night journeys in sleep we would soon become victims of mental desiccation. Dreaming is for the aesthetically underprivileged the equivalent of artistic experience, his only means of self-transcendence, of breaking away from the trivial plane and creating his own mythology.

The Guilt of Jonah

Among the many variations of the Night Journey in myth and folk-lore, one of the most forceful is the story of Jonah and the whale—perhaps because in no ancient civilization was the tension between the Tragic and Trivial planes more intensely felt than by the Hebrews. The first was represented by the endless succession of invasions and catastrophes, the exacting presence of Jehovah and of his apocalyptic prophets; the second by the rare periods of relatively normal life, which the over-strung spiritual leaders of the tribe condemned as abject. Jonah had committed no crime which would warrant his dreadful punishment; he is described as a quite ordinary and decent fellow with just a streak of normal vanity—for he is, justifiably, 'very angry' when, in the end, God does not raze Nineveh as Jonah had prophesied at His bidding, and thus makes Jonah appear an impostor or fool.

Now this very ordinary person receives at the beginning of the story God's sudden order to 'go to Nineveh, that great city, and cry against it'—which is a rather tall order, for Jonah is no professional priest or prophet. It is quite understandable that he prefers to go on leading his happy and trivial life. So, instead of responding to the call from the Tragic Plane, he buys a passage on a ship to Tarshish; and he has such a clean conscience about it, that while the storm rages and the sailors cry 'every man unto his god' and throw the cargo into the sea, Jonah himself is fast asleep. And therein—in his normality, complacency, in his thick-skinned triviality and refusal to face the storm, and God, and the corruption of Nineveh; in his turning his back on the tragic essence of life—precisely therein lies his sin, which leads to the crisis, to the Night Journey in the belly of the whale, in 'the belly of hell'.

The waters compassed me about, even to the soul: the depth closed me round about, the weeds were wrapped about my head . . . *yet hast thou brought up my life from corruption, O Lord my God.* When my soul fainted within me I remembered the Lord: and my prayer came in unto thee. . . . *They that observe lying vanities forsake their own mercy.*

The story sounds in fact like an allegory of a nervous breakdown and subsequent spiritual conversion. Jonah might serve as a symbol for Dimitri Karamazov, or any of the countless heroes of fiction who progress through crisis to awakening. For I must repeat that Jonah's only crime was to cling to the Trivial Plane and to cultivate his little garden, trying to ignore the uncomfortable, unjust, terrible voice from the other plane. Melville understood this when, in the great sermon in *Moby Dick*, he made his preacher sum up the lesson of Jonah and the whale in this unorthodox moral:

Woe to him who seeks to pour oil upon the waters when God has brewed them into a gale! Woe to him who seeks to please rather than to appal! Woe to him whose good name is more to him than goodness! Woe to him who, in this world, courts not dishonour!

And the author of the Jonah story himself must have been aware of its vast implications, of the impossibility of treating all men who lead an ordinary life as harshly as Jonah—for the story ends with an unusual act of clemency by the otherwise so vengeful desert-god, which comes as a curious anticlimax full of ironical tolerance for the inadequacy of man:

Then said the Lord. . . . And should I not spare Nineveh, that great city, wherein are more than six score thousand persons that cannot discern between their right hand and their left hand: and also much cattle?

Just as there is no mythology without some mention of the death and rebirth motif, so there is hardly any epoch in world literature without some variation of it. Maud Bodkin[3] has made an exhaustive study of its occurrence in works as wide apart as *The Ancient Mariner*, Morgan's *The Fountain*, Eliot's *The Waste Land*, and D. H. Lawrence's *The Plumed Serpent* and *The Man Who Died*. Even such an urbane novelist as E. M. Forster has in each of his five novels one central episode in which the hero or heroine, who previously walked with self-assurance on the smooth surface, seems to fall into a manhole with its lid off, and re-emerge as a changed character—like Mrs. Moore, after her visit to the primeval Marabar caves. With the great Russian novelists, crisis and conversion is a central theme; in German literature one can trace it from *Faust II* to *The Magic Mountain*. It pops up in such un-expected places as *The Short Happy Life of Francis Macomber*, or the last page of *To Have or Have Not*; and it was elevated to a philosophy in Kierkegaard's *Fear and Trembling* and in Sartre's existentialist credo: man is what he makes out of his anguish, he becomes 'free' through the realization of his nothingness.

Needless to say, not all great novels are—or should be—'problem novels' aiming at us a constant heavy barrage of the tragic and the archetypal; if they were, literature would be very monotonous indeed. But indirectly and implicitly every great work of art has some bearing on man's ultimate problems. Yeats had a loathing for 'those learned men who are a terror to children and an ignominious sight in lovers' eyes'; because 'Art bids us to touch and taste and hear and see the world, and shrinks from what Blake calls mathematical form, from every abstract thing.' And yet he knew better—when, for instance, he evoked the purely sensual delight of Cleopatra dancing alone under her 'topless towers':

> 'She thinks, part woman, three parts a child,
> That nobody looks: her feet
> Practise a tinker's shuffle
> Picked up on a street.
> *Like a long-legged fly upon the stream*
> *Her mind moves upon silence.*'

The refrain, recurring after each of the three stanzas of the poem, connects (as the context clearly indicates) Cleopatra's meditations during her childish dance with the monumental archetype of the spirit of God moving upon the face of the waters.

A flower, even if it is only a daisy, must have a root; and a work of art, however gay, precious, or serene, is in the last instance fed, however indirectly, invisibly, through delicate capillary tubes, from the ancient substrata of experience. If it has a humorous message, it produces a smile—a subdued laugh or *sous-rire*; if it is tragic, it produces a *sous-pleurer*, that rapt stillness and overflowing of emotion where, to quote Donne again, *with a strong, sober thirst, my soule attends.*

The Tightrope

The ordinary mortal in our urban civilization moves virtually all his life on the Trivial Plane; only on a few dramatic occasions—during the storms of puberty, when he is in love or in the presence of death—does he fall suddenly through the manhole, and is transferred to the Tragic Plane. Then all at once the pursuits of his daily routines appear as shallow, trifling vanities; but once safely back on the Trivial Plane, he dismisses the realities of the other as the products of overstrung nerves or adolescent effusions. Sudden catastrophes—famines, wars, and plagues—may shift a whole population from the Trivial to the Tragic Plane; but they soon succeed in banalizing even tragedy itself, and carry on business as usual among the shambles. During the Spanish Civil War, one of my fellow prisoners, a youth condemned to death by shooting, and suffering from appendicitis, was put on a milk diet two days before his execution.

The force of habit, the grip of convention, hold us down on the Trivial Plane; we are unaware of our bondage because the bonds are invisible, their restraints acting below the level of awareness. They are the collective standards of value, codes of behaviour, matrices with built-in axioms, which determine the rules of the game, and make most of us run, most of the time, in the grooves of habit—reducing us to the status of skilled automata which Behaviourism proclaims to be the only condition of man. What Bergson called 'the mechanical encrusted on the living' is the result of protracted confinement to the Trivial Plane.

But, glory be, man is not a flat-earth dweller all the time—only most of the time. Like the universe in which he lives, he is in a state of continuous creation. The exploratory drive is as fundamental to his nature as the principle of parsimony which tends towards the auto-matization of skilled routines; his need for self-transcendence as basic as the necessity of self-assertion; lastly, we shall see that the *reculer pour mieux sauter* of the creative act itself has its evolutionary precedents in the phenomena of organic regeneration and in the 'original adapta-tions' of which animals are capable in a crisis.

Life on the Trivial Plane is a state of unnoticed confinement—but also a condition of social and intellectual stability. The belly of the whale cannot be made into a permanent residence. Neither emotionally, nor intellectually, can we afford to live for more than brief transition periods on the Tragic Plane, surrounded by archetypes and Ultimates. Emotionally, it would mean the journey of no return of Blake—or of the Yogi entering into final *samadhi*. Intellectually, it would mean the abdication of reason. For the entities encountered on that plane, the members of its matrix—eternity, infinity, ultimate causes, archetypal paradoxes—are irreducible absolutes which do not lend themselves to logical manipulation. They disrupt all rational operations, as the mathematical symbols for nought and the infinite do if introduced into a finite equation. Malraux's '*une vie ne vaut rien—mais rien ne vaut une vie*' is a perfect expression of this. The physicist can deal with infinite space in an abstract symbol-language, but in ordinary ex-perience it is just the infinite, a thing that passeth understanding, and there the matter ends.

Absolutes are too inhuman and elusive to cope with, unless they are connected with some experience in the tangible world of the finite. In fact, eternity is a pretty meaningless notion—unless it is made to look through the window of time. 'Immensity' is a bore—unless it is 'cloystered in thy deare wombe'. The absolute becomes emotionally effective only if it is bisociated with something concrete—dovetailed, as it were, into the familiar. The rain of *manna* on the children of Israel which lasted forty years was an act of incomprehensible divine largesse which, as we learn from Exodus, did not particularly impress them; the miracle of the loaves and fishes was a true miracle.

Where the Tragic and Trivial Planes meet, the Absolute becomes humanized, drawn into the orbit of man, while the banal objects of daily experience are transfigured, surrounded by a halo as it were. The meeting may have the majesty of an incarnation where the *logos* becomes flesh; or the charm of Krishna's descent to dally with the shepherdesses. On a less awe-inspiring scale, the tragic and the trivial may meet in golden lads and chimney-sweeps; in the petrified boot which the Pompeian boot-mender holds in his petrified hand; in the slice of pig's kidney which Bloom fingers in his pocket during the funeral service. Laplace regarded it as the ultimate aim of science to demonstrate from a single grain of sand the 'mechanics of the whole universe'.

The *locus in quo* of human creativity is always on the line of intersection between two planes; and in the highest forms of creativity between the Tragic or Absolute, and the Trivial Plane. The scientist discovers the working of eternal laws in the ephemeral grain of sand, or in the contractions of a dead frog's leg hanging on a washing-line. The artist carves out the image of the god which he saw hidden in a piece of wood. The comedian discovers that he has known the god from a plum-tree.

This interlacing of the two planes is found in all great works of art, and at the origin of all great discoveries of science. The artist and scientist are condemned—or privileged—to walk on the line of intersection as on a tightrope. At his best moments, man is 'that great and true amphibium, whose nature is disposed to live, not only like other creatures in divers elements, but in divided and distinguished worlds'.

C. VISUAL CREATION

XXI

MOTIF AND MEDIUM

Looking at Nature

Kepler, contemplating a snow-crystal melting on his always sweaty palm, saw in it the harmony of the spheres reflected in miniature. Let a less romantically disposed person look for the first time at a snowflake under a microscope: he will catch his breath and wax equally lyrical: 'How strange—how beautiful—how clever is nature', et cetera. Yet the symmetrical pattern of hexagons thus marvellously revealed, loses all its magic when drawn on a drawing-board. It becomes aesthetically neutral for lack of a second context—the familiar sight of the feathery snowflake. It is the superimposition of the two matrices—the trivial object revealing the mathematical regularity of its micro-cosmic architecture—which creates the impact, and gives rise to the aesthetic experience.

Whether Odysseus saw in the sky at dawn 'rosy-fingered Athene lift her golden ray', or whether you share the sorrow of the weeping willow, there is inevitably a second frame of reference superimposed on the picture. Man always looks at nature through coloured glasses —through mythological, anthropomorphic, or conceptual matrices— even when he is not conscious of it and believes that he is engaged in 'pure vision', unsullied by any meaning. The 'innocent eye' is a fiction, based on the absurd notion that what we perceive in the present can be isolated in the mind from the influence of past experience. There is no perception of 'pure form' but meaning seeps in, and settles on the image (though the meaning need not be expressed in verbal language, about which more later).

The idea that looking at nature is self-rewarding, and that landscapes devoid of action can give rise to aesthetic experiences, is of relatively recent origin; so is landscape painting.* Dr. Johnson regarded mountains as 'rather uncouth objects'; in the literature of the eighteenth century precipices were branded as 'frowning' and 'horrid'.[1] The further we go back in time the less appreciation we find of the purely visual aspects of form and colour in inanimate nature:

> Considering the bulk and value of Greek literature, and the artistic brilliance of Athens, the feeling for nature . . . was but poorly developed among a people whose achievement in the dramatic and sculptural arts has been unsurpassed; it is seriously lacking in Homer, even when he refers to the sea or to the famous garden of Alcinous, and it can hardly be said to enter Greek drama save in the *Oedipus at Colonnus* and in some of the lyrical choruses of Euripides. Indeed, the continent of nature had to wait for a thorough and minute exploration until the romantic movement of the nineteenth century: Byron, Shelley, Wordsworth, Goethe, first brought the ocean, the rivers, and the mountain ranges into their own. . . . For primitive man earth and sea are simply the perennial source of those material goods on which life depends, and mountain peaks are uninteresting and unattractive because they are barren and bleak (Listowel).[2]

The same could be said about the underprivileged classes and nations in our own time. The peasants in the alpine village where I live in summer never cease to marvel at the silliness of tourists who talk about the 'beauty' of the mountains—which to them means so much timber, pasture, and hay. Travelling in India one is amazed by the indifference, even among the educated classes, towards landscape and scenery, birds and plants.

All this does not mean that earlier civilizations derived no emotional experiences from nature. But they were derived from different sources: the supernatural powers and magic forces which animated the visible world. The Babylonians populated the starry heavens with lions, virgins, and scorpions. The Sicilian straits were to the Greeks not a landscape but the seats of Scylla and Charybdis. To Homer, a storm at sea signified the anger of Poseidon; to Mr. Babitt it signifies the majesty of nature, a vaguely personalized Power manifested in the spectacle before his eyes. *There is always a second matrix active behind, or superimposed upon, the visual appearance.* The beholder may be convinced that he is simply perceiving images on his retina, but he is in fact perceiving with the whole of his brain; and what he sees is modified by the perceptual codes which operate in it, resonances of his racial and personal past, floating images of touch and smell, even kinesthetic sensations or incipient muscular stresses. When an appearance gives rise to an aesthetic experience, it always represents or symbolizes or expresses something behind and beyond its retinal image—exactly as the pigment on a canvas always refers to something beyond its frame.

A human face is also an object of nature, a landscape of live tissue. To evoke aesthetic feeling, it must point at something beyond itself in the beholder's mind. The analogue of the snow-crystal is here that scaffolding of perfect symmetry and proportions, whose geometrical laws the painters of Greece and the Renaissance tirelessly pursued. The golden section and other basic proportions were thought to be the ultimate constituents of organic form—as the Pythagorean scale of music was thought to regulate the heavenly motions, and as simple geometrical units, the architect's elementary 'modules', combined to make Gothic cathedrals. The philosophers of classicism, from Pliny to Leonardo and Dürer, saw beauty wherever mortal flesh testified to the immortal axioms of Euclidean geometry.

However, the ideal to which the bloated Venus of Willendorf testifies with her pendulous breasts and enormous hips, is not Euclid, but the goddess of Fertility. Our whole manner of perceiving the human frame depends on our ideas about its purpose or function—on the selective code which determines our criteria of significance and patterns our vision. I am using here the word 'function' in the dictionary sense, as referring to a 'mode of action by which [a thing] fulfils its purpose'. The definition, of course, takes it for granted that we know what the purpose of the thing in question is. Now if the thing is a railway engine, the answer is clear; but the purpose of the thing called a human body is open to various interpretations. And according to the interpretation of human purpose which we accept, our ideas will change, and our manner of seeing the human body in its functional aspect will change accordingly. In the drawings of some lunatics, adolescents, lavatory artists, and tribesmen, the dominant functional aspect is shown by a huge genital part, while the remainder of the body is only indicated by a sketchy outline. On Egyptian wall-paintings and reliefs, conventionalized and schematized figures are shown functioning as fishermen, hunters, builders, servants, or parts of a state procession. The size of the figures is usually proportionate to their rank —not to bodily but to social stature; male skin is painted dark brown, female skin pale yellow; the code which provides the criteria of relevance is not visual but *conceptual*. For three thousand years the sculptors and painters of Egypt produced no original discoveries in the technique of visual representation. They had no visual curiosity. In its indifference to colour, movement, human anatomy, Egyptian painting was more single-mindedly functional than any before or after; but 'function' was defined as *social* function, a person's rank and occupation in the social hierarchy. Apart from that, individuals are interchangeable, without personal identity, and their appearance devoid of interest.

In the golden age of Greek art, the human body was seen in a totally different aspect, that of its *physical* function: in throwing a disc, tying a sandal, or simply lifting an arm; vision is attuned to geometrical proportion, to the play and co-ordination of muscles and joints; and by the criterion of a perfect physique, with facial expressions limited to types, the curve of the buttocks becomes as important and expressive as the curve of the brow. Again, in Byzantine painting the human body functions as an indifferent, and often awkward, shell of the spirit; and if the spirit commands the saint to bend his head back and gaze rapturously into the sky, the artist has no qualms in breaking his neck and letting the body float upward with all limbs out of joint. The Renaissance once more gave the body its due; and in the centuries that followed it became the carrier of an individual head, and hence of an expression and mood. For the courtiers of Louis XV, the principal function of human bodies was to play, suitably covered and uncovered, hide-and-seek between trees and bosquets, and to fall into each other's arms. For the impressionist painter, the function of the body is to demonstrate the impermanence of appearances in the luminous blurr of colours; for the cubist, to prove God's preference for cubes; and so on.

Which aspects of reality dominate the visual matrix of a culture or group depends ultimately on its conception of the purpose and meaning of existence. Accordingly, its norms of beauty will always reflect the archetype of some kind of functional perfection: the rigid dignity of Pharaoh, through whose eyes eternity looks in stony silence at time; the play of muscles in the Greek adolescent's perfect anatomy; the spirituality in the transfigured face of the Byzantine madonna; the harmonious resolution of the body into Euclidean forms, or a patchwork of coloured blobs. Whichever aspect is dominant, its matrix acts as a kind of optical polariscope, through which the particular appearance is seen as a thing of general significance, an embodiment of some universal law or meaning.

Abstract painting is a misnomer, a contradiction in terms as 'pictorial philosophy' would be. The concept of justice is an abstraction. The concept of a square is an abstraction. A picture of Solomon meting out justice is concrete. But the picture of a blue square on a yellow ground is equally concrete.

'Non-representational art' and 'expressionist art' are serviceable labels for certain styles of painting; but if they are supposed to describe a philosophy or a programme, they are equally misleading and can create only confusion. A pattern of pigment on canvas always means, or expresses, or represents something which is not the canvas plus pigment. However, it does not represent objects or events, but the artist's mental experiences or imaginings of the nature, causes, shape, and colour of objects and events. It does not represent a model, but the artist's vision of the model; not a young lady called Lisa, but the way Leonardo saw his Lisa. It invites the spectator to share an experience which the artist had; it provides him with an illusion—not the illusion of seeing a thing, but the illusion of seeing through the artist's eyes. Without that illusion there will be no response, and the spectator will behold the canvas through the eyes of a dead fish.

Art was always 'expressionist' in the legitimate sense of the word: it expressed a subjective, biassed vision—even if the artist deluded himself into believing that he was 'copying nature'. And pigment on canvas always 'represents' something outside its frame—for instance the impact of a green arrow on the blue square when placed next to it on the yellow ground. That impact does not take place on the canvas, but in the artist's mind, and in the beholder's mind. The pigment of the blue square remained static and unchanged. But in the beholder's eye its colour, shape, and weight have undergone a dynamic change. To produce this illusionary change was the artist's intention; it is as if he were saying: Look what my green arrow can do to my blue square. The canvas expresses or represents an idea in the artist's head, and if all goes well it will cause a similar experience to occur in the beholder's head: he will read something in the picture which strictly speaking is not there. Apologies for the pedantic demonstration, but one has to revert to elementary issues to escape the muddle created by the writings of some expressionists and anti-representationalists.

Much of this confusion (as in other impassioned controversies in the past) is due to the fact that visual experiences cannot be traduced into verbal statements without suffering major impoverishment and distortion. All verbal analysis tends to make implicit, part-conscious experiences explicit and fully conscious—and to destroy them in the process. There seems to exist a kind of biological rivalry between the eye and the vocal cords, epitomized by the painter puffing at his pipe in contemptuous silence while the garrulous art-critic is holding forth. We always see a work of nature or art 'in terms of' a selective matrix governed by this or that criterion of significance; but these 'terms' are not verbal terms, and if we attempt to verbalize them the result is unavoidably a gross 'clumsification'—a medley of clichés and psychological jargon. The matrix may carry emotive echoes of some archetypal experience, but our vocabulary is extremely poor where emotions are concerned. If we say that it responds to the sight of the ocean with associations of 'eternity', 'infinity', and so forth, this sounds as if we were referring to *verbal* associations. Such words *may* present themselves to the mind, but words are the least important part of the experience, and detract from rather than add to its value. We cannot help using words in referring to processes which in the listener's mind are not crystallized into words. The alternative is to say a rose is a rose is a rose, and leave it at that.

Another difficulty is that at moments of intense aesthetic experience we see not only with our eyes but with the whole body. The eyes scan, the cortex thinks, there are muscular stresses, innervations of the organs of touch, sensations of weight and temperature, visceral reactions, feelings of rhythm and motion—all sucked into one integrated vortex. A literary narrative or a piece of music unfolds in stages, but in a still-life time is fore-shortened as it were, and by taking it in with a single sweep of the eye (or so it seems) this multitude of experiences blends into one near-simultaneous process, so that it is extremely difficult to sort out the various elements which went into its making. The trouble with explaining visual beauty, and also its fascination, is that so much is happening at the same time.

The Two Environments

What is happening is, put into our jargon, a series of bisociative processes involving the participatory emotions.

At the base of the series we again find *illusion*—the magic transformation of the carved tree into a god. The painted mask, the carved idol, are perceived at the same time as what they are and what they represent. The witch-doctor works his evil spell by sticking a needle into the rag-doll representing the victim; the cave-artist of Altamira made sure of a plentiful supply of meat by populating the rock with painted bison and wild horses.

To those with naïve tastes, illusion in itself is sufficient to evoke aesthetic experience, and 'life-likeness' is regarded as the supreme criterion of art. As mentioned before, even Leonardo wrote 'that painting is most praiseworthy which is most like the thing represented'. However, the 'most like' has an infinite number of interpretations— and that for two solid reasons: the *limitations of the medium* and the *prejudices of vision*. The range of luminosity in the painter's pigment is only a fraction of that of natural colours; the area on the canvas only a fraction of the visual field; its coarse grain can accommodate only a fraction of fine detail; it lacks the dimension of depth in space, and motion in time. (Even a photograph is far from being a true likeness; apart from its obvious limitations of colour and light = sensitivity, it increases the ratio of focal to peripheral vision about a hundredfold —which may be one of the reasons why nature is so much prettified on picture postcards.) Hence the painter is forced to cheat, to invent tricks, to exaggerate, simplify, and distort in order to correct the distorting effects of the medium. The way he cheats, the tricks he uses, are partly determined by the requirements of the medium itself—he must think 'in terms of' stone, wood, pigment, or gouache—but mainly by the idiosyncrasies of his vision: the codes which govern the matrices of his perception. Whether Manet's impression of 'The Races of Longchamp' looks more 'life-like' than Frith's academically meticulous 'Derby Day' depends entirely on the beholder's spectacles. An artist can copy in plaster, up to a point, a Roman copy of a Greek bronze head; he cannot 'copy' on canvas a running horse. He can only create an appearance which, seen in a certain light, at a certain distance, in a certain mood, will suddenly acquire a life of its own. It is not a copy, but a metaphor. The horse was not a *model*, but a *motif* for his creation—in the sense in which the landscape painter looks for a romantic or pastoral motif.

In the terminology of behaviourist psychology we would have to say that looking at the model constitutes the 'stimulus', and putting a dab of paint on the canvas the 'response'—and that is all there is to it. But the two activities take place on two different planes. The stimulus comes from one environment—the outer world: the response

acts on a different environment: a square surface. The two environments obey two different sets of laws. An isolated brush-stroke does
not represent an isolated detail. There are no point-to-point correspondences between the two planes of the motif and the medium;
they are bisociated as wholes in the artist's mind.

Visual Inferences

Once the artist has acquired sufficient technical skill to do with his
material more or less what he likes, the question *what* he likes, i.e.
what aspects of reality he considers relevant, becomes all-important.
In other words, of the two variables I mentioned—the limitations of
the medium, and the prejudiced eye beholding the motif, the first can
be regarded, within a given school, as relatively stable, and we can
concentrate our attention on the second. There can be no unprejudiced
eye for the simple reason that vision is full of ambiguities, and all perception, as we saw, is an inferential construction which proceeds on
various levels, and most of it unconsciously (cf. pp. 38–44). The *visual
constancies* (p. 43) which enable us to perceive objects as stable in shape,
size, colour, etc., in spite of their unstable, ever-changing appearances
are a first step in the interpretation of our confusing, ambiguous retinal
images. They are automatic skills, partly innate, mostly learned in
early childhood. The process is reversed in some of the so-called optical
illusions where the unconscious code governing preception draws the
wrong inferences in an unusual situation. But even these primitive
mechanisms, which normally function below the level of awareness,
can suddenly become a problem in interpretation for the painter. I
have mentioned (p. 43) that owing to the mechanism of brightness-
constancy a black glove looks as black in sunlight as in the shade—
until you look at it through a reduction screen in the experimental
laboratory or through the impressionist painter's crooked index-finger.
The various constancies are unconscious inferences we draw to make
sense of our sensations, to lend stability to the unstable flux of appearances. They transform what the eye *sees* so as to suit the requirements
of reason, of what we *know* about the external world. Between the
retina and the higher centres of the cortex the innocence of vision is
irretrievably lost—it has succumbed to the suggestion of a whole series
of hidden persuaders.

Perceptual projection, which I have already mentioned (p. 295), is one of them: the unconscious mechanism which makes us project events, located in the brain, into a distance of yards or miles (as opposed to the dazzling flashes which are 'correctly' located on the retina). *Foreshortening* and *perspective* are consciously added twists to unconscious projection—like sensations in a phantom-limb: the flat canvas is the amputation stump. (The analogy is actually quite precise: pain, too, is located in the brain, but projected to the locus of the injury; the phenomenon of the phantom-limb is a secondary projection.)

Projective empathy is another hidden persuader which I have briefly mentioned before (p. 296). Vernon Lee[3] regarded aesthetic experience as primarily derived from 'the attribution of our own moods of dynamic experience, motor ideas, to shapes. We attribute to lines not only balance, direction, velocity, but also thrust, strain, feeling, intention, and character.' Jaensch has been able to demonstrate in a fascinating series of experiments that the eidetic image (p. 346) of a straight horizontal line will expand considerably in length if a pull is exerted on the horizontally outstretched arms of the subject.[4] And vice versa, the sensation of the scanning motions performed by the eye, and of other subliminal muscle-impulses and stresses—not to mention Berenson's 'tactile values', the 'feel' of texture—all interfere with perception.

Again, the painter can consciously exploit these unconscious processes, and give them an added twist. In Seurat's 'divisionist' theory, horizontal and 'gently' ascending lines, as well as 'cool' colours convey a mood of calm and content, 'swift' and 'animated' lines and 'warm' colours make for gaiety, and so on. (The adjectives in quotes have become so current that we tend to overlook their synesthetic origin). Juan Gris, though certainly far removed from Seurat's neo-impressionism, talked in the same vein of 'expansive' and 'contractile' forms, of the physiological effects of various types of symmetry.[5] The theorizings of the 'abstracts' are not at all new. Linear rhythm, chromatic harmonies, and their combined effects have always played, consciously or unconsciously, an important part. In non-figurative painting the motifs are, instead of a landscape and a human body, say blue squares and green arrows. But ultimately these too are derived from nature— the blue and the green, the square and the arrow. Let me invoke the authority of the greatest and most eclectic painter of our time:

There is no abstract art. You must always start with something. Afterwards you can remove all traces of reality. There's no danger then anyway, because the idea of the object will have left an indelible mark. It is what started the artist off, excited his ideas, and stirred up his emotions. . . . When I paint a picture I am not concerned with the fact that two people may be represented in it. Those two people once existed for me but they exist no longer. My vision of them gave me an initial emotion, then little by little their presence became blurred; they became for me a fiction, and then they disappeared altogether, or rather they were transformed into all kinds of problems, so that they became for me no longer two people but forms and colours—forms and colours which nevertheless resume an experience of two people, and preserve the vibration of their life.[6]

I must add a word on a more primitive kind of attitude to colour. Some reactions to the 'temperature-values' of colours seems to be common to most people within the same culture circle; Rimbaud even tried to co-ordinate each vowel with a different colour. But the emotive associations of specific colours vary from person to person, and can be very strong. Wollberg[7] had a schizoid patient who reacted to red with intense anxiety, to blue with a feeling of elation; yet under deep hypnosis, Wollberg reversed these reactions. Valentine[8] quotes the case of a patient born blind who, after a successful operation, felt intense pleasure at his first sight of red, and was physically sick at the first sight of yellow. Man not only 'thinks with his hands', he quite often sees with his bowels.

The visual constancies and illusions, perceptual projection, empathy and synesthesia form an ascending series of inferential processes. One step higher in the series we come to the phenomenon of the 'face hidden in the tree', the 'image in the cloud', the Rohrschach-blot: the projection of meaning into the ambiguous motif. Once more we have here an unconscious process which has been consciously exploited from antiquity to the expressionists. Pliny recounted the anecdote of an artist who tried in vain to paint the foam at a dog's mouth until, in exasperation, he threw a spongeful of paint at his canvas—and there was the foam. The story reappears in Leonardo's *Treatise on Paintings* —where he makes 'our Botticelli' say that if you just throw a sponge at a wall it will 'leave a blot where one sees a fine landscape'. There is an oft-quoted passage in that classic treatise which bears being quoted once more:

You should look at certain walls stained with damp, or at stones of uneven colour. If you have to invent some backgrounds you will be able to see in these the likeness of divine landscapes, adorned with mountains, ruins, rocks, woods, great plains, hills and valleys in great variety; and then again you will see there battles and strange figures in violent action, expressions of faces and clothes and an infinity of things which you will be able to reduce to their complete and proper forms. In such walls the same thing happens as in the sound of bells, in whose stroke you may find every named word which you can imagine.[9]

This passage inspired the eighteenth-century English landscape painter Alexander Cozens to publish a book[10] recommending the use of random ink-blots 'from which ideas are presented to the mind', to serve as landscape motifs. It seems that Rohrschach's method of psychological testing by inviting subjects to interpret ambiguous blot-shapes was derived from Cozens—and thus from Leonardo, and thus from Pliny. Similar methods were used by Chinese artists from the eleventh century onwards. The bisociations of form and meaning are inexhaustible.

In these cases the motif (the cloud, the patterned wallpaper, or the ink-blot) and also the meaning read into it, are both of a visual nature. But the matrix which provides the meaning can also be governed by non-visual conceptual codes—for instance, a verbal suggestion such as Hamlet uses on Polonius to make the cloud change from weasel to whale; or by the various notions entertained by Egyptian, Greek, and Byzantine artists on the function and purpose of the human body. In some forms of insanity, and in the experimental psychoses induced by drugs, the patient sees serpents, genitals, archaic creatures budding out of every curve of an ornamental design. The cubist's vocabulary consists of cylinders and cubes; the pointillist's of daub's; classical composition obeyed the grammar of harmony and balance; the Egyptian painter saw in stereotyped clichés; so does the Japanese Zen artist.

Codes of Perception

This leads us to the most powerful single factor among the many factors which enter into the processing of the visual input: the power of convention as a hidden persuader (p. 42 f.). Perception is a part-innate, part-acquired skill of transforming the raw-material of vision into the 'finished product'; and every period has its conventional formulae and methods of interpretation for doing this. The ordinary mortal thinks most of the time in clichés—and sees most of the time in clichés. His visual schemata are prefabricated for him; he looks at the word through contact-lenses without being aware of it.

The extreme example is ancient Egypt—but merely because it lasted so long; contemporary Zen painting and calligraphy, as already said, obeys almost as rigid rules of the game. The Egyptian painter unvaryingly represented the human figure with head in profile, eye frontally, legs in profile, chest frontally, and so on, showing each part in its most characteristic aspect. Whether the ordinary Egyptian perceived his fellow creatures this way we cannot tell, and—remembering that we perceive a tilted coin still as a circle, and not foreshortened into an ellipse—he probably could not tell either. But we do know that the moment he translated motif into medium, his vision became stereotyped. It is highly improbable that conformity was enforced on artists against their will for a full three thousand years. There exist exceptions to the rule, relief figures dating as far back as 2400 B.C.,[11] which show foreshortening and dynamic motion; if there had been a taboo on such innovations, they would hardly have been preserved. But the exceptions became less, not more frequent as time went by; for reasons beyond our understanding, Egyptian art, as Egyptian society, remained static, and habit prevailed over originality.

Greek art, between the sixth and fourth century B.C. was, compared with Egypt, in a state of permanent revolution, which carried it within no more than six or seven generations from the archaic style to the *trompe l'œil*. Yet, although originality and innovation were valued as never before, it could not avoid developing its own clichés. 'After all,' wrote Gombrich, 'Greek art of the classical period concentrated on the image of man almost to the exclusion of other motifs, and even in the portrayal of man it remained wedded to types. This does not apply only to the idealized type of physique which we all associate with Greek art. Even in the rendering of movement and drapery the repertoire of Greek sculpture and painting has turned out to be strangely limited. There are a restricted number of formulas for the rendering of figures standing, running, fighting, or falling, which Greek artists repeated with relatively slight variations over a long period of time. Perhaps if a census of such motifs were taken, the Greek vocabulary would be found to be not much larger than the Egyptian.'[12]

That vocabulary—and its Euclidean grammar of proportion—

remained as indelibly printed on European art as the categories of Aristotle on European philosophy. The Byzantine painter and mosaic maker had given up the aspiration to copy nature, but he used the approved Greek stock-formulae to represent faces, hands, gestures, and draperies. Warburg[13] has shown that the artists of the Renaissance were prone to fall back on Greek models whenever they wanted to indicate emotion by a gesture or attitude: he called these emotive clichés *Pathosformeln*.*

'Even Dutch genre paintings that appear to mirror life in all its bustle and variety will turn out to be created from a limited number of types and gestures'—if for instance, one compares them with news-paper-photographs of crowd scenes. The quotation is again from Professor Gombrich,[14] whose *Art and Illusion* proved an invaluable source of illustrative examples.

Skilled routine in perceiving as in thinking, has its positive and negative side. Without certain conventional rules of the game, which were acquired by learning but function unawares, we could not make much sense either of nature or of art. 'The art of seeing nature', Constable wrote, 'is a thing almost as much to be acquired as the art of reading Egyptian hieroglyphs.'[15] On the other hand, conventions tend to harden into rigid formulae—the matrix freezes up, and makes us ignore those aspects of reality which do not fit into the schema. The Greek sculptor is indifferent to individual expression, the Byzantine painter to anatomy, the Chinese to shadows, and so on. But there exist far more striking examples of the single-minded neglect by the eye of anything which the mind does not consider relevant. They are engrav-ings dating from the sixteenth to the nineteenth century, which show that even artists reputed for their meticulousness can be indifferent or blind to features which are considered irrelevant or offensive to the conventional rules of the game. One of them was Merian, an extremely skilful illustrator who obviously tried hard to make a faithful 'copy'—it looks actually like an architect's drawing—of the Cathedral of Notre-Dame. And what happened? '. . . As a child of the seventeenth century, his notion of a church is that of a lofty symmetrical building with large, rounded windows, and that is how he designs Notre-Dame. He places the transept in the centre with four large, rounded windows on either side, while the actual view shows seven narrow, pointed Gothic windows to the west and six in the choir.'[16] He could not go against the code which governed his visual perception.

Nor could those medieval artists, who drew lions, elephants, and other exotic animals 'from life', but, incapable of visually digesting the startling appearance, produced monstrosities reminding one of Greek chimeras—creatures compounded of a lion's head, a goat's body and a serpent's tail. The reason is simple. The codification of experience into 'rules of the game' is as indispensable in perceptual skills as in manual or reasoning skills. The learning process starts in the cot and ends only when the artist has learned to forget what he has learned—but that is only for the chosen few. The medieval artist—like the contemporary amateur taking a correspondence course in draftsmanship—did not start by drawing from nature, but by learning, from drawing-books, the tricks and formulae of how to draw heads, hands, and feet, birds, stags, trees, and clouds. There were hundreds of such works published, from Villard de Honecourt's *Album of Patterns* in the first half of the thirteenth century to date—including such classics as Dürer's *Dresden Sketchbook* or Fialetti's *The True Method and Order to Draw All Parts and Limbs of the Human Body*—which seems to contain every conceivable shape and mis-shape of ears, eyes, and noses under the sun. To succeed in drawing an ear with an untutored eye requires genius; even Dürer, so we are told, got the anatomy of the human eye wrong.

To quote Constable again: an artist who is self-taught is taught by a very ignorant person indeed. He must acquire a vocabulary—not only to express himself, but to read meaning into appearances. The same Villard de Honecourt whose album of patterns contains the most admirably schematized swans, horses, ostriches, and bearded heads drew a lion 'from life', as he assures us—and produced a chimera. We do not know for how long he had the chance of looking at the lion or how coherent his sketch was. But it is evident that where he had to fill in features from memory, he could only do so by supplanting the forgotten details of the strange creature by parts of more familiar animals. He had certainly not intended to falsify deliberately—any more than Merian did in his drawings of Notre-Dame. But neither of them could digest the unfamiliar motif because it could not be re-solved into familiar schemata, pigeonholed, labelled, and confined to memory—or jotted down in shorthand, as it were, by means of a ready-made formula. They were in the same position as the subjects in the psychological laboratory who are made to witness an unexpected sequence of events—and, when asked to relate what happened, give notoriously divergent, unreliable accounts. Their verbal reproduction is jumbled, not because they lack the skill to express themselves, but because they were unable to take in a sequence of events which did not fit their scheme of things.

Not only the medieval artist used formulae like recipes from a cookery-book. Camper, an eighteenth-century anatomist, wrote a book on *The Connection Between the Science of Anatomy and the Arts of Drawing, Painting, Statuary, etc.*, in which he described the standard procedures of portraiture in his time: 'The portrait painters of the present day generally describe an oval upon their panel before the person to be painted sits to be drawn, make a cross in the oval, which they divide into the length of four noses and the breadth of five eyes; and they paint the face according to these divisions to which it must be accommodated, let the proportions themselves be ever so much at variance.'[17] The oval with its subdivisions represented the matrix with its fixed code; the filling-in of details was a matter of elastic strategy.

Convention and Creation

Regardless of the period at which we look, every work of art betrays the prejudiced eye, governed by selective codes which lend coherence to the artist's vision, and at the same time restrict his freedom. The ensemble of these codes provides the 'rules of the game', the routine aspect of his work; while his 'strategy' must be adapted to the double environment of motif and medium. The greatness of an artist rests in creating a new, personal idiom—an individual code which deviates from the conventional rules. Once the new idiom—a new way of bisociating motif and medium—is established, a whole host of pupils and imitators can operate it with varying degrees of strategic skill.

It does not mean belittling the creative mind to point out that every artist has his cookery recipes for the basic ingredients of the dishes he serves. But we must distinguish between true creativity—the invention of a new recipe, on the one hand, and the skilled routine of providing variations of it. The whole, vexed question of the artistic value of brilliant forgeries and copies hinges on this distinction (see Chapter XXIV).

But whether the rules of the game were imposed by convention or originally designed by the artist, they have an equal sway over him. Rubens' *puttis* sometimes look mass-produced, and even some of the portraits of his children seem to obey the same formula; similar blasphemies could be uttered about Renoir's pneumatic nudes, Henry Moore's convexities and concavities-with-a-hole, or Bernard Buffet's

obsessive angularities. One cannot help feeling that artists who spend
the rest of their lives exploring the possibilities of a single formula
which they discovered in their truly creative period, resemble the
'one-idea-men' in the history of science. The difference is that the
concrete language of the painter's brush permits endless variations on
a single theme without losing its enchantment—which the abstract
symbol-language of science does not.

The reader may have felt, in following the last few pages, an uneasy
suspicion that I was deliberately confusing the tricks and formulae
for drawing a pussycat with the artist's vision of the pussycat, and the
history of painting with a history of seeing. But in fact the two interact
so intimately in the artist's mind (and in the responsive beholder's
mind) that they cannot be separated. Take seeing first; already Pliny
knew (what Behaviourist psychology managed to forget) that 'the
mind is the real instrument of sight and observation' and the eyes merely
act 'as a kind of vehicle, receiving and transmitting the visual portion
of consciousness'.[18] But the mind is also the real instrument of manual
dexterity, in a much deeper sense than we generally realize, including
those quirks of manner and style which can be 'left to the muscles' to
be taken care of. Renoir, when his fingers became crippled with
arthritis, painted with a brush attached to his forearm, yet his style
remained unchanged. It would be psychologically just as absurd to
assume the reverse—that a pattern of expression so deeply ingrained
should have had no effect on his pattern of perception, as it would be
to assume that his perception had no influence on what his hand was
doing. The two activities are bisociated; in the terminology of the
communication engineer, the medium 'in terms of' which the artist
must think, influences by feed-back his pattern of vision.

An obvious example is provided by the way in which the study
of anatomy—even if merely demonstrated by a lay-figure—trans-
forms the artist's perception of the human body. A less obvious
example is the following—which I again owe to Gombrich. Cozens,
the eighteenth-century painter who advocated the ink-blot technique
to inspire his pupils to paint 'Rohrschach' landscapes, also drew for
their benefit a series of schemata of various types of cloud-formation—
as Guercino had given recipes for drawing various types of ears.
Constable studied and faithfully copied these crude schematizations of
'streaky clouds at the top of the sky' or 'bottom of the sky' or clouds
'darker at the top than the bottom'. By learning to distinguish different
types of cloud-formation—acquiring an articulate cloud-vocabulary as

it were—he was able to perceive clouds, and to paint clouds, as nobody had done before, His brush, like the poet's pen, 'turned them into shapes, and gave to airy nothing a local habitation and a name'. The result is that Constable addicts see real clouds in Constable's terms, as Van Gogh addicts see the fields of Provence in Van Gogh's terms— and in either case much to their benefit. Some French authors—Lalo, I believe was the first, and among contemporaries, Malraux—have proposed that our aesthetic appreciation of nature is derived from having seen landscapes in paint. That may be the case with many of us, but it only means—as suggested already at the beginning of this chapter— that man has always looked at nature through a frame. Through the painter's frame, or the frame of mythology, or the frame of science; through half-closed eyes or eye glued to the lens of the telescope. Constable called landscape painting an inquiry into the laws of nature; and Richardson, discovering that the difficulties of his pupils were caused as much by their unskilled eye as by their unskilled fingers, drew the conclusion:

> For it is a certain maxim, no man sees what things are, that knows not what they ought to be. That this maxim is true, will appear by an academy figure drawn by one ignorant in the structure, and knitting of the bones, and anatomy, compared with another who understands these thoroughly . . . both see the same life, but with different eyes.[19]

NOTES

To p. 366. I am speaking of Europe: landscape painting in China has a much older tradition.

To p. 378. Incidentally, there is a bridge waiting to be built between art criticism and the physiology of gesture. To give an example: the neurologist Kurt Goldstein (1947) has made a study of the way in which people point with their arms at an object. If the object is to the front and to the right, the person will point with the extended arm, which will form with the frontal plane of the body an angle of approximately forty-five degrees. If the object is moved further to the right, the person will start turning his trunk to the right, so that the angle between body and arm remains 45 degrees. But if the object is placed straight in front of him, he will turn his body to the left and the angle will still be the same. There are obvious anatomical reasons for this. But if you make your figure point an *accusing* finger straight ahead, fully facing his adversary, you get a 'pathos-formula'.

XXII

IMAGE AND EMOTION

The trouble with putting into words the aesthetic experience
aroused by a picture is, as we saw, that so much is happening
at the same time; that only a fraction of it becomes conscious,
and an even smaller fraction verbalized. 'The forceps of our minds', to
quote H. G. Wells again, 'are clumsy things, and crush the truth a
little in the course of taking hold of it.' Wells was talking of the
difficulties of putting *ideas* into words; when it comes to putting aesthetic experiences into words, nothing short of a caesarian will help. The
surgical tool that I proposed was 'bisociation'; and the operation consisted in disentangling the various bisociative, or bifocal, processes
which combine in the experience. I have mentioned a number of
these; I shall have to mention one or two more, and discuss briefly the
emotional reactions which they call forth.

Virtues of the Picture Postcard

The essence of the aesthetic experience consists, as I have tried to show,
in *intellectual illumination*—seeing something familiar in a new, significant light; followed by *emotional catharsis*—the rise, expansion, and ebbing away of the self-transcending emotions. But this can happen only
if the matrix which provides the 'new light' has a higher emotive
potential or 'calory value' (pp. 321-31); in other words, the two
matrices must lie on an *ascending gradient*.

Let us see in what manner the various bisociative patterns mentioned
earlier on fulfil this requirement. Take illusion once more, which
enters art in a variety of guises and disguises, on its most naïve level:
the discovery that something can be itself and something else at the

same time. A small child, fascinated by dad's amateur efforts as a draftsman, will beg '*make* me a donkey', '*make* me an elephant', thus unconsciously evoking Pygmalion's power. I shall not hark back to Altamira and the witch-doctor—merely dot my i's by pointing out that the gradient leads in that direction.

Or take the simplest illusion of space: the delighted shock of looking for the first time through fieldglasses, and seeing the distant church-spire leap to within grasp. Here again unconscious analogies, echoes of sorcery enter into play: the power to be in two places at once; the conquest of space by magic carpet; action-at-a-distance. The reverse experience is the illusion derived from a perspective landscape—or a Chinese silk painting which, with a few brushstrokes, makes the horizon recede into infinity. To call perspective and *trompe l'œil* 'magic' is a cliché, because their genuine magic has succumbed to the law of diminishing returns; but to the unsophisticated eye the hole in the wall through which it looks into a different world has the dream-like quality of Alice stepping through the looking-glass; dream-like, because the creation and annihilation of space is a favoured game of the underground.

I have made a slighting mention of the 'prettification' of nature on picture postcards, which bring the whole scenery within the range of focal vision. But there is a genuine appeal to the emotions in the fact that a landscape painting can be taken in almost at a glance, without the half-conscious, constant scanning which the real scenery requires. To have it all there simultaneously laid out before his view, gives the beholder a kind of naïve Olympian feeling, a sense of power entirely harmless, since his only aim is passive contemplation; enhanced by the circumstance—and here the next bisociation enters into the process —that he is looking at the scenery not through his own, but through Claude's or Courbet's eyes.

Another facet—or pair of facets—of the many-sided experience of looking at a picture is synesthesia (p. 321). Berenson's dictum 'the painter can accomplish his task only by giving tactile values to retinal impressions' does not only mean that the bisociation of vision with touch lends an added dimension to experience and more solidity to illusion. Berenson's emphasis on tactile values also indicates that the sense of touch had a special appeal to him—as it had to Keats (p. 321). But neither of them was exceptional in this respect; after all, the adjective 'touching'—that is, emotionally moving—is derived from touch; and 'touching' in the verbal sense is a primary impulse not only among lovers; the texture of silk or polished stone also provides minor pleasures. The brocade fineries of Van Eyck's figures have a strong tactile appeal; the impact of the gangrened flesh of Christ in Grünewald's Isenheim altar is one of horror redeemed by pity. It is perhaps only matched in power by Flaubert's rendering of the legend of St. Julian sharing his bed with the leper.

Taste and Distaste

This brings us to a subject which I have not mentioned so far, although it used to play an important part in aesthetic theories of the hedonistic type, and was a wonderful source of confusion: I mean the polarity of agreeable and disagreeable, attractive and repellent sense-impressions.

The first necessity, if we wish to avoid similar confusion, is to make a clear distinction between tastes and distastes directly affecting the *senses* (the tongue, the nose, the ear); and the pleasure-unpleasure tone of complex *emotional states* mediated by the autonomous nervous system. The distinction may seem pedantic, and a sharp line cannot always be drawn, because the different levels in the nervous system interact with each other; the palate can be 'educated' to delight in rotten Chinese eggs, and the smell of honeysuckle can become nauseating to the rejected lover. Whether the selective codes which govern our spontaneous reactions of taste and distaste are inborn or acquired in early childhood is irrelevant in this context; and the fact that these reactions can be altered in later life does not affect the argument. What matters is to distinguish between the aesthetic experience—or the experience of beauty if you like—on the one hand, and sensory gratification on the other; and to get away from such definitions as the *Concise Oxford's* of beauty: 'Combination of qualities . . . that delights the sight; combined qualities delighting the other senses', etc. Evidently, by these criteria not only Grünewald, but the vast majority of works of art would be beyond the pale of beauty and could never give rise to aesthetic experience—defined by the *Concise Oxford Dictionary* as 'the appreciation of the beautiful'.

I do not mean to flog the dead horse of hedonist aesthetics but to emphasize the difference between sensory gratification and aesthetic satisfaction—a difference of levels deriving from the hierarchic organization of the nervous system (Chapter XIII and Book Two). Take an obvious example from music. Periodic sounds—musical tones—

are more pleasing to the ear than a-periodic noises; and some screeching noises—rubbing a blackboard with a dry sponge for instance—are so offensive that they give gooseflesh to some people. Again, among musical chords, the octave, fifth, and major third are more agreeable to the European ear than others; and some dissonances, heard in isolation, can put one on edge. But the flattery or offensiveness of individual chords has only an indirect bearing on the emotional effect of a string quartet as a whole. There is no numerical relation between the number of consonances and our aesthetic appreciation. The pattern of alternation between sweet and bitter sounds is merely one among several relevant patterns interacting with each other in the multi-dimensional experience.

Sensory preferences—the discrimination between sensory stimulations which 'agree', and those which 'disagree' with our innate or acquired dispositions—do not provide the clue to the nature of aesthetic experience, but they provide one of the clues: particularly those preferences which are part of the human heritage, and shared by all. The Chinese taste for music differs from ours considerably; but all men are subject to the pull of gravity and prefer keeping their balance to losing it. A leaning tower, or a big head on a thin neck give rise to disagreeable sensations mediated by projective empathy (p. 296). But this again is only part of the story. Inverted, top-heavy, disturbing forms may combine in the picture with forms in repose, creating a total pattern with a balance of a higher order—in which the parts with positive and negative balance play the same role as consonant and dissonant chords, or beats and missed beats in a metric stanza.

One of the most haunting pictures in this particular respect is Pollaiulo's 'Martyrdom of St. Sebastian' (in the London National Gallery). The saint stands with his naked feet on the sawn-off stumps of two branches of a dead tree, his hands tied behind his back, looking as if he were bound to topple over any moment. He is held up by another, hardly visible, branch of a tree which rises behind him, and to which his hands are presumably tied; but even so he is bound to fall. What prevents him, in the beholder's eye, from falling is a trick in the composition of the picture: the figure of the saint forms the apex of a solid, well-balanced triangle. The sides of the triangle are six figures in symmetrical poses, performing symmetrical gestures. The imbalance of the part is redeemed by the balance of the whole, by the triangle which lends unity to diversity. The fact that the figures are the saint's executioners, shooting their murderous arrows into him, belongs to a different level of awareness.

Empathy projects our own dynamic experiences of gravity, balance, stress, and striving into the pigment on the canvas representing human figures or inert shapes. Thus vertical and horizontal lines acquire a special eminence; a vertical line looks longer than a tilted line of the same length, and right angles are so much singled out, that an angle of, say, ninety-five degrees is seen as an imperfect, 'bad' angle of ninety degrees. Patients with brain lesions sometimes give freer rein than normal people to the hedonistic bias of their eyes, and do not notice deviations up to ten degrees from the horizontal or vertical. They indulge in 'wishful seeing' as others in wishful thinking. And to a lesser extent that is true of all of us. Goethe knew that after-images which appear on the retina tend to reduce irregularities and asymmetries, and to transform squares into circles. The Gestalt school has shown that the raw material of the visual input is subjected to yet other kinds of processing than those I have mentioned: the 'closure principle' makes us automatically fill in the gaps in a broken outline; 'Prägnanz' (conciseness), 'good continuation', symmetry, simplicity are further built-in criteria of excellence which prejudice our perceptions. But once again, it can hardly be maintained that the delights of looking at a perfect circle with a closed circumference, and the disgust with circles marred by a bulge, enter directly into the aesthetic experience. If that were the case, the perfect picture would be a perfect circle with a vertical and a horizontal line intersecting in its centre; all hedonistic principles and Gestalt-criteria would be satisfied by it. The innate bias in our taste-buds in favour of sweet compared with acid stimuli is a fact which every theory of culinary aesthetics must take into account; but it does not make syrup the ideal of culinary perfection. Symmetry and asymmetry, closure and gap, continuity and contrast, must combine, like consonances and dissonances, into a pattern on a higher level of the perceptual hierarchy—as far removed from Freud's pleasure-principle as from the *Oxford Dictionary*'s definition of beauty.

Motion and Rest

That pattern is in fact our old friend, unity-in-diversity; or rather unity *implied* in diversity, for here the 'law of infolding' asserts itself with a vengeance. If a work of art strikes one as hopelessly dated, it is not because its particular idiom dates from a remote period, but because it is spelt out in a too obvious, explicit manner. The Laocoon group is more dated than the archaic Apollo of Tenea in spite of the vastly superior representational skill of the Hellenistic period—which the sculptor displays with such self-defeating ostentation. Pollainolo's delight in the recently discovered laws of perspective, and the resulting over-emphasis on geometrical structure has a somewhat chilling effect; the same could be said of Uccello's 'The Rout of San Romano'. Again (as Eric Newton has pointed out), the triangular scaffolding in Raphael's treatment of the Madonna and Child theme is a shade too obvious. To discover the principle of unity hidden in variety must be left to the beholder's imagination. Leonardo has given a 'formula' how to draw trees: if you draw a circle round the crown of a tree, the sections of all the twigs must add up to the thickness of the stem; the bigger the radius of the circle, the more twigs it will cut, but because the sections get thinner, the result is the same. Though the law is not exact, it holds the secret which lends unity to the tree drawn in its full foliage, and implied symmetry to its irregularly shaped branches and twigs.

Unity-in-variety can be debased to a formula: the portrait painter drawing his oval and dividing it into the length of four noses; it can also be a peephole to eternity. 'Motion or change,' wrote Emerson, 'and identity or rest, are the first and second secrets of nature: Motion and Rest. The whole code of her laws may be written on the thumb-nail or the signet of a ring. The whirling bubble on the surface of a brook, admits us to the secrets of the mechanics of the sky. Every shell on the beach is a key to it. A little water made to rotate in a cup explains the formation of the simpler shells; the addition of matter from year to year, arrives at last at the most complex form; and yet so poor is nature with all her craft, that, from the beginning to the end of the universe, she has but one stuff—but one stuff with its two ends, to serve up her dream-like variety. Compound it how she will, star, sand, fire, water, tree, man, it is still one stuff, and betrays the same properties.'

I owe this quotation from Emerson's essay on 'Nature' to G. Kepes' *The New Landscape*—one of the most remarkable books on art in recent years. It opens up a world as unattainable to the limited range of our senses—the 'narrow biological filter of perception'—as light and colour are unattainable to the blind. 'Of the total stimuli flooding the world with potential messages, the visible and audible ranges accessible to our bodies represent a tiny segment.'[1] But it has now become possible to decipher these signals and bring their message into visible focus by instruments which expand and compress events in time, penetrate space near to the border where granules of matter are revealed as patterns of concentrated energy, and enable the eye to see 'in terms of' ultra-violet and infra-red radiations. All of us have seen an occasional photograph of a spiral nebula or a snow-crystal, but these are like early daguerreotypes compared with the new landscapes seen through the electron-microscope. They show the ultra-structure of the world —electric discharges in a high voltage arc which look like the most elaborate Brussels lace, smoke molecules of magnesium oxide like a composition by Mondrian, nerve-synapses inside a muscle suspended like algae, phantom-figures of swirling heated air, ink molecules travelling through water, crystals like Persian carpets, and ghostly mountains inside the micro-structure of pure Hafnium, like an illustration to Dante's Purgatorio. What strikes one is that these landscapes, drawn as it were in invisible ink, possess great intrinsic beauty of form. The aesthetic experience derived from them seems to be directly related to what Emerson called the first and second secrets of nature: 'Motion or change, and identity or rest'—and also to the fact that the universe is made of only one stuff with a finite set of basic geometrical patterns in an infinite number of dynamic variations.

'There are two basic morphological archetypes,' wrote Kepes, 'expression of order, coherence, discipline, stability on the one hand; expression of chaos, movement, vitality, change on the other. Common to the morphology of outer and inner processes, these are basic polarities recurring in physical phenomena, in the organic world and in human experience.' They are 'the dynamic substance of our universe, written in every corner of nature'. . . . 'Wherever we look, we find configurations that are either to be understood as patterns of order, of closure, of a tendency towards a centre, cohesion and balance, or as patterns of mobility, freedom, change, or opening. We recognize them in every visible pattern; we respond to their expression in nature's configurations and in human utterances, gestures, and acts. Cosmos and chaos . . . the Apollonian spirit of measure and the Dionysian principle of chaotic life, organization and randomness, stasis and kinesis . . . all these are different aspects of the same polarity of configuration.'[2]

Thus the cliché about unity-in-variety represents one of the most powerful archetypes of human experience—cosmos arising out of chaos. We have seen it at work in the scientist's search for universal law; and when we see it reflected in a work of art, or in any corner of nature, however indirectly, we catch a faint echo of it.

Ascending Gradients

When I compared the landscape of the smoke micrograph to a Mondrian composition, I was not merely indulging the metaphoric consciousness; for another strange thing about these shapes not meant for the human eye is that *they all look like something else*. But not in the same way as the ink-blot which serves as a passive receptacle for our projections; they are so precise and well-defined that they seem to ask for an equally definite meaning. The electric discharge *does* look unmistakably like lace-work, the various unexpected shapes which a water-drop assumes during its fall through the air look unequivocally like a chain of semi-precious stones; and when no concrete interpretation presents itself, some painter's work comes to mind. To be told that the Brussels lace is actually the 'portrait of an alternating current reversing its direction a hundred and twenty times per second' provides an additional shock: the sudden substitution of a new matrix, a different contact-lens has the effect of a sudden illumination. The sparkling electric discharge still looks *like* lacework, and the Hafnium crystal still looks *like* a mountain in Hades, but the original interpretation has now become a metaphor, which supplies an additional dimension, and feeds more calories to the experience.

The mind is insatiable for meaning, drawn from, or projected into, the world of appearances, for unearthing hidden analogies which connect the unknown with the familiar, and show the familiar in an unexpected light. It weaves the raw material of experience into patterns, and connects them with other patterns; the fact that something reminds me of something else can itself become a potent source of emotion. Girls fall in love with men who remind them of father; men get infatuated with a reflection of Botticelli in a vacuous profile; every face is a palimpsest. The willow's shoulders droop, limp like a mourning widow's; the ripples on the lake reflect the Pythagorean harmonies; the whirlpool on the surface of the brook 'admits us to the mechanics of the sky'. When a painting is said to represent nothing but 'significant form'—to carry no meaning, no associative connections, no reference to anything beyond itself—we can be confident that the speaker does not know what he is talking about. Neither the artist, nor the beholder of his work, can slice his mind into sections, separate sensation from perception, perception from meaning, sign from symbol.

The difficulty of analysing the aesthetic experience is not due to its irreducible quality, but to the wealth, the unconscious and non-verbal character of the matrices which interlace in it, along ascending gradients in various dimensions. Whether the gradient is as steep and dramatic as in a Grünewald or El Greco, or gently ascending through green pastures, it always points towards a peak—not of technical perfection, but of some archetypal form of experience. We thus arrive at the same conclusion as in our discussion of literature: a work of art is always transparent to some dim outline of ultimate experience—even if it is no more than the indirect reflection of a reflection, the echo of an echo. Those among the great painters who had a taste for verbal theorizing, and the articulateness of translating their vision into words, almost invariably evoked absolutes and ultimates—the tragedy, or glory of man's condition, the wrath or mercy of divinity, the universal laws of form and colour harmony, the norms of beauty hidden in the mysteries of the golden section or anchored in Euclid's anxioms. 'Everything has two aspects,' wrote Chirico, 'the current aspect, which we see nearly always and which ordinary men see, and the ghostly and metaphysical aspect, which only rare individuals may see in moments of clairvoyance and metaphysical abstraction. A work of art must narrate something that does not appear within its outline.'

Regardless of the site we choose for our excavation, we shall always hit at the same ancient underground river which feeds the springs of all art and discovery.

Summary

The aesthetic experience aroused by a work of art is derived from a series of bisociative processes which happen virtually at once and cannot be rendered in verbal language without suffering impoverishment and distortion. At the base of the series we once more find illusion. But 'life-likeness' is a matter of interpretation, dependent on the limitations of the medium and the prejudices of vision. Perception is loaded with unconscious inferences, from the visual constancies, through spatial projection, empathy, and synesthesia, to the projection of meaning into the Rohrschach blot, and the assigning of purpose and function to the human shape. The artist exploits these unconscious processes by the added twists of perspective, rhythm and balance, contrast, 'tactile values', etc. The conventions of a period or school lend coherence to its vision, but also tend to crystallize—as in all domains of science and art—into fixed 'rules of the game': into formulae, stereotypes, visual clichés; these may be so firmly established that the artist becomes snowblind to aspects of reality which do not fit into them. The originality of genius, here as elsewhere, consists in shifts of attention to aspects previously ignored; in seeing appearances in a new light; in discovering new relations and correspondences between motif and medium.

Tastes and distastes on the sensory level play, like consonances and dissonances, only a subordinate role in the aesthetic experience, as one among many patterns of unity-in-variety. The pre-condition of the experience to occur is once more that the emotive potentials of the matrices participating in it should form an ascending gradient, and provide a hint, however tentative or teasing, of some hidden reality in the play of forms and colours.

XXIII

ART AND PROGRESS

In the discussion which followed a lecture at an American university on the subject of this book, one of the 'resident painters' remarked angrily:

'I do not "bisociate". I sit down, look at the model, and paint it.'

In a sense he was right. He had found his 'style', his visual vocabulary, some years earlier and was quite content to use it, with suitable variations, to express everything he had to say. The two planes of motif and medium had become firmly welded together at a fixed angle, and the original bisociative act had become stabilized into a skilled routine—highly flexible, but governed by a fixed code. It would be very foolish to underestimate the achievements of which skilled routine is capable. By working tirelessly to improve his technique, the pupil or imitator may—as the history of doubtful attributions and outright forgeries proves—equal and sometimes surpass the master in technical perfection. But technical virtuosity is one thing, creative originality another.

Cumulative Periods

Original discoveries are as rare in art as in science. They consist in finding new ways of bisociating motif and medium. Art historians who lived in periods of rapid transition, considered 'progress' in terms of discoveries of new techniques: Pliny called each innovator a *heuretes*—a 'finder' entitled to utter Archimedes' triumphant shout. The innovations which he and Quintilian listed as quasi-scientific discoveries were feats such as rendering difficult, contorted motions; making the first statue with an open mouth; showing the course of the veins; paying attention to light and shadow. They regarded each discovery

393

as a landmark on the road towards the mastery of reality; and during the second great awakening, the Renaissance, Vasari, Leonardo, and Dürer took a similar attitude. Vasari described the triumphant advance of painting from Giotto to the sixteenth-century masters in terms almost comparable to a history of sea-farers, where each of the great captains puts a new continent on the map. Leonardo thought in all seriousness that it was 'a wretched pupil who did not surpass his master'; and if we recall that less than two centuries, or six generations, separate Giotto and Duccio on the one hand, from Raphael and Titian on the other, we can appreciate his point of view. Greek sculpture, from Polymedes of Argos to Praxiteles (also a span of about six generations), and Italian art from the early fourteenth to the early sixteenth century, advanced indeed in a cumulative way—each genius 'stood on the shoulders of giants' and could look a little further than his predecessors.

But here a dangerous misunderstanding might arise. 'Cumulative progress' means in this context merely that each painter could make use of the discoveries of his predecessors without having to make them again. Foreshortening, perspective, anatomy, a whole series of steps in the rendering of light and colour, of textures, movements, expressions; these and many other innovations in the treatment of the medium and the perception of reality, once made, could be easily absorbed by pupils and imitators. When Leonardo spoke of the pupil's duty to 'surpass' his master, he meant only this—that the pupil was free to incorporate at his ease the discoveries of his elders into his repertory and to look for new pastures. But neither he nor Vasari meant that those who came later were better painters in an absolute sense than those on whose shoulders they stood. Moreover, Leonardo knew that the pupil was free not only to accept, but also to reject the discoveries of his elders. The deliberate distortions and asymmetries in the face of Mona Lisa, and the equally deliberate ambiguities of contour in the corners of mouth and eyes, are deviations from the canon; but they were based on a knowing rejection of certain aspects of 'scientific realism' in painting—not on naïve ignorance. In this sense the achievements of art are indeed cumulative and irreversible, as those of science are. The artist can decide to go against them, but he cannot ignore them.

'Florentine painting', wrote Eric Newton,[1] 'starts, like a sprint, with a pistol shot, In 1280 it hardly exists. By 1300 it is racing ahead.' Quite a number of modern art-historians share, with Pliny and

Vasari, a belief in the cumulative progress of art. Ruskin and Roger Fry thought the history of painting from ancient days was a progressive shedding of prejudices and the recovery of our lost 'innocence of the eye'. 'It has taken from Neolithic times till the nineteenth century to perfect this discovery,' wrote Fry, 'European art from the time of Giotto progressed more or less continuously in this direction, in which the discovery of linear perspective marks an important stage, whilst the full exploration of atmospheric colour and colour perspective had to await the work of the French impressionists.'[2] Eric Newton sees the development of European art 'as a great river system in which many tributaries are gradually drawn together';[3] and his diagram of the outstanding artists and trends from 1300 to 1940 is a map of branches and confluences representing 'the cycle of realism that had begun with Giotto and ended with Cézanne'. Lastly Gombrich, though puzzled by the representational skill of the prehistoric cave-painters, agrees that 'all representations can be somehow arranged along a scale which extends from the schematic to the impressionist'.

Stagnation and Cross-Fertilization

On the other hand, it is easy to match, in the history of every culture or country, the relatively brief periods of rapid cumulative advances with much longer periods of stagnation, onesidedness, mannerism and estrangement from reality. The parallel between the dizzy zig-zag curves in the development of the sciences and arts is obvious; and so is the kinship between the defenders of scientific and of artistic orthodoxy—the phalanxes of inertia. 'The more we become aware of the enormous pull in man to repeat what he has learned, the greater will be our admiration for these exceptional beings who could break this spell and make a significant advance on which others could build.'[4]

Because visual discoveries are so difficult to verbalize, we have hardly any introspective records of the painter's 'moment of truth' which could be compared to the accounts left by scientists; we do not know how the games of the underground enter into the picture. But if we consider the history of art as a whole—in its aspect of a collective enterprise, as Vasari saw it—we shall find that the great innovators all stand at draughty corners of world-history, where air-currents from different culture-climates meet, mix, and integrate. The Greek awakening in the sixth century B.C. probably started under the impact of the seemingly incompatible Egyptian, Oriental, and Cretan art forms on the tribes of northern origin—when they became sufficiently settled to take an interest in these matters. Later Alexander reversed the process: in the wake of his conquests, Hellenistic art invaded Egypt, the Middle East, and India; even the Buddha was made to put on a Greek smile. Gothic art originates in the particularly draughty climate of the migrations and incursions from the north, and led to the integration of pagan and Roman-Christian traditions. Another great synthesis, of the Byzantine and the Gothic, started the chain-reaction in Sienna and Florence; the rediscovery of Greek statuary gave it a further boost. Brunelleschi married the Gothic invention of vaults carried by pillars and ribs with the columns and pillasters of classic Roman architecture —and created that wonderful hybrid, the Renaissance style. And so it goes on—to Chinese Chippendale, the impact of Japanese colour-prints on Manet and Degas, and of primitive African sculpture on the moderns. Equally important were cross-influences from not directly related fields: the discovery of the laws of perspective, and the re-discovery of Apollonius' work on conic sections; the revival of anatomy (Leonardo himself dissected more than thirty corpses); the invention of oil-paint, of the woodcut, of lithography, and photography; the evolution of colour-theory in physics.

To sum up: it seems to be undeniably true, as Pliny was the first to suggest, that art evolves, like science, in a cumulative manner—but only for a while, and within limits, until all that can be done has been done along that particular line; at the great turning points, however, which initiate a new departure along a new line, we find bisociations in the grand style—cross-fertilization between different periods, cultures, and provinces of knowledge.

Statement and Implication

I have compared (p. 72 f.) the cartoonist's technique of reducing a face to its bare essentials, to the scientist's technique of representing a process by a diagram, schema, map, or model. In the third panel of our tryptich, the artist applies similar techniques. He too is engaged in making models of phenomena in his particular medium, using a par-ticular set of formulae, and concentrating on those aspects of reality, to the detriment of others, which are significant to him, or to the fashions and conventions of his time. (Let me repeat, though, that the reality which he represents need not be a tangible object in three-dimensional space any more than the elusive 'objects' represented in the physicist's equations.) Thus unavoidably, artist, scientist, and caricaturist alike must use the techniques of *selective emphasis*, exaggeration, and simplification, to underline those aspects or features which seem relevant to them.

They must also observe the rules of *economy*. As the laws of physics become more universal in character, the symbols which represent them become more elusive and implicit. In the history of art we can trace the effects of the 'law of infolding' in every period. On Egyptian tomb-paintings, each part of the body is still shown explicitly, in its most characteristic aspect; but the young girl picking flowers on a famous wall-painting in Stabiae impertinently turns her back on us. What we see of her face is only the merest hint of a profile, leaving it to us to extrapolate her lovely features. The deliberate return of Byzantine art to pre-Hellenistic rigidity and 'naïvety', expressed a rejection of worldly realism in favour of a more implicit manner of conveying its message. Much the same could be said of the deliberate simplicity and discreet, almost apologetic, use of perspective by Fra Angelico; and of all the later, unceasing attempts by artists to escape saturation, evade the obvious, and appeal to the beholder's imagination. It was Leonardo who invented *sfumato*—the smoke-screen of ambiguous shadows, the blurred contours at the corners of Mona Lisa's eyes, which kept people guessing through four centuries; and it was Titian who in his later years invented the technique of the bold and 'rough' brushstroke, those 'crudely daubed strokes and blobs'—as Vasari admiringly described them—which, looked at from close quarters, make no sense at all. A similar progression from the neat and meticulous to the loose and evocative brush can be seen in Rembrandt's rendering of textiles and embroideries: the law of infolding asserts itself both in the evolution of individual artists and in the historic development of any particular form of art. A striking example of the latter are the two views of the same Venetian motif (the Campo San Zanipolo) by Canaletto in 1740, and by Guardi in 1782—the first neat and explicit like a photograph, the second suggestive, impressionistic, and 'modern'.

One can hardly accuse Reynolds of exaggerated modernism; some of his nice little girls hugging their nice little doggies have precisely that sweet-and-sticky quality which, by its over-explicit attack on the emotions, defeats its own purpose. But as he was an accomplished master of his craft, he was capable of seeing the reverse of the medal; and in his 'Discourse' commemorating the work of Gainsborough, there is a surprising passage: 'I have often imagined that this un-finished manner contributed even to that striking resemblance for which his portraits are so remarkable. Though this opinion may be considered as fanciful, yet I think a plausible reason may be given, why such a mode of painting should have such an effect. It is presupposed that in this undetermined manner there is the general effect; enough to remind the spectator of the original; the imagination supplies the rest, and perhaps more satisfactorily to himself, if not more exactly, than the artist, with all his care, could possibly have done.'

From the middle of the nineteenth century onwards, the trend to-wards the implicit, the oblique hint, the statement disguised as a riddle kept gathering speed and momentum—so much so that it sometimes gave the impression of art not merely 'folding in' but folding up. In im-pressionist painting, Gombrich remarked, 'the direction of the brush-stroke is no longer an aid to the reading of forms. It is without any support from structure that the beholder must mobilize his memory of the visible world and project it into the mosaic of strokes and dabs on the canvas before him. The image, it might be said, has no firm anchor-age left on the canvas—it is only "conjured up' in our minds".'[5] From here it was only a step to cutting the anchor and doing away with illusion as something altogether too obvious. Picasso's women shown part *en face* and part in profile, sometimes with a third eye or limbs shuffled around, rely on the beholder's knowledge of the female form and on his willingness to participate in the master's experiments with it; like Leonardo's experiments with his chimeras, they are a challenge and an invitation to explore the possible worlds implied in the visible world. At the opposite extreme of the scale we find the meticulous realism of a series of great portrait painters—from Holbein to, say, Fantin Latour. From a purely optical point of view they seem to be completely explicit statements; and yet they contain a mystery in another dimension—the mystery of character and personality summed up in a single expression, breathing through the pigment of the canvas. A photograph can convey the truth of a moment; a portrait can inti-mate the truth of a whole life.

Thus there exist various dimensions of infolding—various direc-tions in which the beholder must exert his imagination and complete the hint. One is reflected in the development which started with the veiled *sfumato* and the loose, evocative brush—with Eastlake's 'judicious unfinish of the consummate workman'—and ends, for the time being, with the baffling challenges offered by contemporary art. Another is the avoidance of any too overt appeal to the emotions—whether in a human face or in a Neopolitan sunset. The less there is left to divine, the quicker the process of saturation sets in, which rejects any further offer of the mixture as before as sentimental, melodramatic, pornographic, or just slushy *kitsch*. Rembrandt's famous warning to the spectator to keep his distance—'don't poke your nose into my pictures, the smell of paint will poison you'—could be reversed: 'don't turn your canvas into flypaper to catch my emotions, I can't bear the feel of it.' Even patterns of unity-in-diversity, for all their archetypal echoes, become boring if they are too obvious—as rhythm becomes monotonous unless its pulsation is perceived beneath the surface only of a complex musical or metric pattern.

The Japanese have a word for it: *shibuyi*. The colour-scheme of a kimono so discreet, subdued, and apparently dull that there seems to be no scheme at all, is *shibuyi*. A statue whose grace is hidden by a rough, unpolished, seemingly unfinished surface, is *shibuyi*. So is the delicious taste of raw fish, once the acrid tang which hides it is overcome. The Chinese, however, discovered the law of infolding much earlier on. A seventeenth-century manual of painting advocates the technique of 'leaving out', illustrated by drawings of the familiar kind where the simple outline of a face, minus features, serves as a surprisingly expressive formula: 'Figures, even though painted without eyes, must seem to look; without ears, must seem to listen. There are things which ten hundred brushstrokes cannot depict but which can be captured by a few simple strokes if they are right. That is truly giving expression to the invisible.'[6]

But economy of means and avoidance of the obvious should not be misinterpreted as lack of spontaneity or a tendency towards moderation. Sesshu, perhaps the greatest of Japanese painters (a contemporary of Leonardo's), was a master of the leaving-out technique; yet he used not only his brush, but fistfuls of straw dipped in ink to impart to his landscapes their powerful and violent sense of motion. Goya's 'Disasters' combine a maximum of economy with a maximum of horror. On the other hand, Royal Academy portraits in the approved tradition display all the virtues of moderation, yet in their pedestrian explicitness 'deprive the mind', to quote Mallarmé once more, 'of that delicious joy of imagining that it creates'.

The artist's aim, we saw at the beginning of this book, is to turn his audience into his accomplices. Complicity does not exclude violence—but it must be based on a shared secret.

XXIV

CONFUSION AND STERILITY

The Aesthetics of Snobbery[1]

In 1948, a German art restorer named Dietrich Fey, engaged in reconstruction work on Lübeck's ancient St. Marien Church, stated that his workmen had discovered traces of Gothic wall-paintings dating back to the thirteenth century, under a coating of chalk on the church walls. The restoration of the paintings was entrusted to Fey's assistant, Lothar Malskat, who finished the job two years later. In 1950 Chancellor Adenauer presided over the ceremonies marking the completion of the restoration work, in the presence of art experts from all parts of Europe. Their unanimous opinion, voiced by Chancellor Adenauer, was that the twenty-one thirteenth-century Gothic saints on the church walls were 'a valuable treasure and a fabulous discovery of lost masterpieces'.

None of the experts on that or any later occasion expressed doubt as to the authenticity of the frescoes. It was Herr Malskat himself who, two years later, disclosed the fraud. He presented himself on his own initiative at Lübeck police headquarters, where he stated that the frescoes were entirely his own work undertaken by order of his boss, Herr Fey; and he asked to be tried for forgery. The leading German art experts, however, stuck to their opinion; the frescoes, they said, were without doubt genuine, and Herr Malskat was merely seeking cheap publicity. An official Board of Investigation was appointed, and came to the conclusion that the restoration of the wall-paintings was a hoax—but only after Herr Malskat had confessed that he had also manufactured hundreds of Rembrandts, Watteaus, Toulouse-Lautrecs, Picassos, Henri Rousseaus, Corots, Chagalls, Vlamincks, and other masters, and sold them as originals—some of which were actually found by the police in Herr Fey's house. Without this *corpus delicti*, it is doubtful whether the German experts would ever have admitted having been fooled.

My point is not the fallibility of the experts. Herr Malskat's exploit is merely one of a number of similarly successful hoaxes and forgeries —of which the most fabulous were probably van Megeeren's faked Vermeers. The disturbing question which they raise is whether the Lübeck saints are less beautiful, and have ceased to be 'a valuable treasure of masterpieces', simply because they had been painted by Herr Malskat and not by somebody else? And furthermore, if van Megeeren can paint Vermeers as good as Vermeer himself, why should they be taken off the walls of the Dutch and other National Galleries? If even the experts were unable to detect the difference, then surely the false Vermeers must procure as much aesthetic pleasure to the common run of Museum visitors as the authentic ones. All the curators would have to do is to change the name on the catalogue from Vermeer to van Megeeren.

There are several answers to this line of argument, but before going into them I want to continue in the part of the devil's advocate by considering an example of a forgery in a different field: Macpherson's *Ossian*. The case is so notorious that the facts need only be briefly mentioned. James Macpherson (1736–1796), a Scottish poet and adventurer, alleged that in the course of his wanderings in the High-lands he had discovered some ancient Gaelic manuscripts. Enthusiastic Scottish *littérateurs* put up a subscription to enable Macpherson to pursue his researches, and in 1761 he published *Fingal, an ancient Epic Poem in Six Books, together with several other poems composed by Ossian, the Son of Fingal.* Ossian is the legendary third-century hero and bard of Celtic literature. *Fingal* was soon followed by the publication of a still larger Ossianic epic called *Temora*, and this by a collected edition, *The Works of Ossian.* The authenticity of Macpherson's text was at once questioned in England, particularly by Dr. Johnson (whom Macpherson answered by sending him a challenge to a duel), and to his death Macpherson refused, under various unconvincing pretexts, to publish his alleged Gaelic originals. By the turn of the century the controversy was settled; it was established that while Macpherson had used fragments of ancient Celtic lore, most of the 'Ossianic texts' were of his own making.

Yet here again the question arises whether the poetic quality of the work itself is altered by the fact that it was written not by Ossian the son of Fingal, but by James Macpherson? The 'Ossianic' texts were translated into many languages, and had a considerable influence on the literature and cultural climate of Europe in the late eighteenth and early nineteenth centuries. This is how the *Encyclopedia Britannica* sums up its evaluation of Macpherson (my italics):

> The varied sources of his work and its worthlessness as a transcript of actual Celtic poems do not alter the fact that he produced a work of art which . . . *did more than any single work to bring about the romantic movement in European, and especially in German, literature* . . . Herder and Goethe . . . were among its profound admirers.

These examples could be continued indefinitely. Antique furniture, Greek tanagra figures, Gothic madonnas, old and modern masters are being forged, copied, counterfeited all the time, and the value we set on the object is not determined by aesthetic appreciation and pleasure to the eye, but by the precarious and fallible judgement of experts. And it will always be fallible for the good and simple reason that genius consists not in the perfect exercise of a technique, but in its invention; once the technique is established, diligent pupils and imitators can produce works in the master's idiom which are often indistinguishable, and sometimes technically more accomplished than his.

Some years ago, at a fancy-dress ball—in Monte Carlo, I believe—a competition was held to decide which among the dozen or so guests masquerading as Charlie Chaplin came nearest to the original. Chaplin himself happened to be among them—and got only the third prize. In 1962, the Fogg museum of Harvard arranged a private exhibition for connoisseurs, where some of the exhibits were fakes, others genuine; the guests were to decide which was which. Included were, among other items, an original portrait by Annibale Carracci, one of the most influential painters of the Italian baroque, and a contemporary copy thereof; also an original Picasso drawing of a Mother and Child, and two forgeries thereof. The result was similar to that of the Chaplin competition; among those who plumped for one of the forgeries were the chairman of Princeton's Art Department and the Secretary of the Fogg; the director of the Metropolitan Museum refused to submit to the test, while other experts 'scored themselves on sheets of paper, compared their verdicts with the officially announced facts, and quietly crumpled their papers'.[2]

Let me repeat: the principal mark of genius is not perfection, but originality, the opening of new frontiers; once this is done, the conquered territory becomes common property. The fact that even professional experts are unable to point out the difference in artistic merit between the true and the false Picasso, Caracci, or Vermeer, is conclusive proof that no such difference can be registered by the layman's eye. Are we, then, all snobs to whom a signature, an expert testimony based on X-ray photography, or the postmark of a period is more important than the intrinsic beauty of the object itself? And what about the contested works of Shakespeare and Johann Sebastian Bach? Are their dramatic and poetic and harmonic qualities dependent on the technical controversies between specialists?

The answer, I believe, can be summed up in a single sentence: our appraisal of a work of art or literature is hardly ever a unitary act, and mostly the result of two or more independent and simultaneous processes which interfere with and tend to distort each other. Let me illustrate this by a story which I have told elsewhere at greater length.[3]

A friend of mine, whom I shall call Catherine, was given as a present by an unobtrusive admirer a drawing from Picasso's classical period; she took it to be a reproduction and hung it in her staircase. On my next visit to her house, it was hanging over the mantelpiece in the drawing-room: the supposed reproduction had turned out to be an original. But as it was a line-drawing in ink, black contour on white paper, it needed an expert, or at least a good magnifying lens, to show that it was the original and not a lithograph or reproduction. Neither Catherine, nor any of her friends, could tell the difference. Yet her appreciation of it had completely changed, as the promotion from staircase to drawing-room showed. I asked her to explain the reason for her change of attitude to the thing on the wall which in itself had not changed at all; she answered, surprised at my stupidity, that of course the thing had not changed, but that she *saw* it differently since she knew that it was done by Picasso himself and 'not just a reproduction'. I then asked what considerations determined her attitude to pictures in general, and she replied with equal sincerity that they were, of course, considerations of aesthetic quality—'composition, colour, harmony, power, what have you'. She honestly believed to be guided by purely aesthetic value-judgements based on those qualities; but if that was the case, since the qualities of the picture had not changed, how could her attitude to it have changed?

I was labouring a seemingly obvious point, yet she was unable to see that she was contradicting herself. It proved quite useless repeating to her that the origin and rarity-value of the object did not alter its qualities—and, accordingly, should not have altered her appreciation of it, if it had really been based on purely aesthetic criteria as she believed it to be. In reality, of course, her attitude was determined not by those criteria, but by an accidental bit of information—which might be right or wrong, and was entirely extraneous to the question of aesthetic value. Yet she was by no means stupid; in fact there is something of her confusion in all of us. We all tend to believe that our attitude to an object of art is determined by aesthetic considerations alone, whereas it is decisively influenced by factors of a quite different order. We are unable to see a work of art isolated from the context of its origin or history; and if Catherine were to learn that her Picasso was after all a reproduction, her attitude would again change according to the changed context. Moreover, most people get quite indignant when one suggests to them that the origin of a picture has nothing to do with its aesthetic value as such. For, in our minds, the question of period, authorship, and authenticity, *though in itself extraneous to aesthetic value*, is so intimately mixed up with it, that we find it well-nigh impossible to unscramble them. The phenomenon of snobbery, in all its crude and subtle variants, can always be traced back to some confusion of this type.

Thus Catherine would *not* be a snob if she had said: 'A reproduction of this line-drawing is to all practical purposes indistinguishable from the original, and therefore just as beautiful as the original. Nevertheless, one gives me a greater thrill than the other, for reasons which have nothing to do with beauty.' But alas, she is incapable of disentangling the two different elements which determine her reactions, and to a greater or lesser extent we are all victims of the same confusion. The change in our attitude, and in the art dealer's price, when it is discovered that a cracked and blackened piece of landscape displaying three sheep and a windmill, bears the signature of Broeckendael the Elder, has nothing to do with beauty, aesthetics, or what have you. And yet, God help us, the sheep and the mill and the brook *do* suddenly look different and more attractive—even to the hard-boiled dealer. What happened was that a bit of incidental information cast a ray of golden sunlight on those miserable sheep; a ray emitted not by the pigment but by the cerebral cortex of the art-snob.

The Personal Emanation

Let me now present the case for the defence. The appraisal of a work of art is generally the result of two or more independent processes which interact with each other. One complex process constitutes the aesthetic experience as such, which has been discussed in previous chapters; it implies a system of values, and certain criteria of excellence, on which we believe our judgement to be based. But other processes interfere with it, with their different systems of values, and distort our judgements. I shall mention two types of such interfering systems.

The first is summed up in the statement of a little girl of twelve, the daughter of a friend, who was taken to the Greenwich Museum, and when asked to name the most beautiful thing she had seen there, declared without hesitation: 'Nelson's shirt.' When asked what was so beautiful about it, she explained: 'That shirt with blood on it was jolly nice. Fancy real blood on a real shirt which belonged to somebody really historic.'

Her sense of values, unlike Catherine's, was still unspoilt. The emotion that she had experienced was derived from the same kind of magic that emanates from Napoleon's inkpot, the relic of the saint carried in the annual procession, the rope by which a famous murderer was hanged, the galley-proof corrected by Tolstoy's hand. Our forbears believed that an object which had been in the possession of a person became imbued with his emanations, and in turn emanated something of his substance. 'There is, I am sure,' a columnist wrote in the *Daily Express*, 'for most of us a special pleasure in sinking your teeth into a peach produced on the estate of an Earl who is related to the Royal Family.'[4] You might even come to feel that you are a member of the family if you persist long enough in this somewhat indirect method of transubstantiation.

We can no more escape the pull of magic inside us than the pull of gravity. Its manifestations may take a more or less dignified form; but the value we set on the peach from the Earl's estate or the splinter from the saint's bone, on Dickens's quill or Galileo's telescope, is derived from the same source of sympathetic magic. It is, as the little girl said, jolly nice to behold a fragment of a marble by Praxiteles—although it has been battered out of human shape, with a leper's nose and broken ears. The contact with the master's hand has imbued it with a kind of effluvium which has lingered on, and emanates the same thrill as the real blood on Nelson's shirt—or the real ink from Picasso's pen.

The inordinate importance that we attribute to the original and authenticated, even in those borderline cases where only the expert can decide on questions of authenticity, has its unconscious roots in this particular kind of fetish-worship. Hence its compelling power—who would not cherish a lock from an Egyptian mummy's head? Yet, as every honest art dealer will admit, borderline cases are so frequent as to be almost the rule. I am no longer referring to forgeries, but to the classical practice of the master letting his pupils, apprenticed to his workshop, assist in the execution of larger undertakings; and 'assistance' could mean anything from the filling in of background and minor details, to the painting of a whole picture after the master's sketch. We are made to realize how common this practice was by the emphasis which Michelangelo's admiring contemporaries put on the fact that he painted the ceiling of the Sistine Chapel 'alone and unaided'. If we remember that even the experts were at a loss to tell the Caracci portrait from its contemporary copy—probably by a pupil —we must conclude that for the great majority of mortals, including connoisseurs, the difference between an authenticated masterpiece, a doubtful attribution, and a work 'from the school of', is in most cases not discernible. But the fact remains that an 'attribution', perfect in its genre but not authenticated, is held in lower esteem than a work of lesser perfection, guaranteed to have come from the ageing master's hand. It is not the eye that guides the museum visitor, but the magic of names. The English nation forked out a million pounds to prevent the sale to America of a Leonardo sketch to which it had never paid any attention; and the hundreds of thousands of good citizens who queued to see it could not have told it from a page in an art-student's sketchbook; they went to see Nelson's shirt.

The Antiquarian Fallacy

The second 'interfering system' is period consciousness. A Byzantine icon, or a Pompeian fresco is not enjoyed at its face value, but by a part-conscious attunement of the mind to the values and techniques of the time. Even in paintings from periods whose idiom is much closer to ours—a Holbein portrait, for instance—such externals as costume and headdress drive it mercilessly home to us that the man with the unforgettable, timeless face belonged to the court of Henry VIII. The archetypal quality is there, but period-consciousness intrudes; and the danger is that it may dominate the field.

Thus we look at an old picture through a double frame: the solid gilt frame which isolates it from its surroundings and creates for it a hole in space; and the period-frame in our minds which creates for it a hole in time, and assigns its place on the stage of history. Each time we think we are making a purely aesthetic judgement according to our lights, the stage-lights interfere. When we contemplate the Gothic wall-paintings on the church in Lübeck for the first time, believing them to be authentic, and then a second time, knowing that they were made by Herr Malskat, our experience will indeed be completely changed, although the frescoes are the same as at the time when they were hailed as masterpieces. The period-frame has been changed, and with it the stage-lights.

Apart from being unavoidable, this relativism of aesthetic judgement has its positive sides: by entering into the spirit and climate of the period, we automatically make allowances for its crudities of technique, for its conventions and blind spots; we bend over the past with a tender antiquarian stoop. But this gesture degenerates into antiquarian snobbery at the point where the period-frame becomes more important than the picture, and perverts our scale of values. The symptoms are all too familiar: indiscriminate reverence for anything classified as Italian Primitive or Austrian Baroque (including its mass-produced puffy, chubby, winged little horrors); collective shifts of period-consciousness (from anti-Victorian to pro-Victorian in recent years); the inanities of fashion (Fra Angelico is 'in', Botticelli is 'out').

The Comforts of Sterility

The mechanism responsible for these perversions is the same as discussed previously, and provides us with a handy definition: *snobbery is the result of a mix-up between two frames of reference, A and B, with different standards of value; and the consequent misapplication of standard A to value-judgements referring to B.* The art-snob's pleasures are derived not from the picture, but from the catalogue; and the social snob's choice of company is not guided by human value, but by rank or celebrity value catalogued in the pages of *Who's Who*. The confusion may even affect his biological drives—his taste and smell preferences, his sexual inclinations. A hundred years ago, when oysters were the diet of the poor, the snob's taste-buds functioned in a different manner. In the days before Hitler there was a young woman in Berlin who worked for a publisher and was well known in the literary world for a certain peculiarity: she had carried on a number of affairs with authors, regardless of age or sex—but only with those whose books had sold more than 20,000 copies. Her own explanation was that with less successful authors she was unable to obtain physical satisfaction.

It is a depressing anecdote because it has a ring of clinical authenticity; at the same time it displays the familiar pattern of the comic: the clash of two incompatible contexts. But to the poor heroine of the story it was no joke, because she could not see their incompatibility; the *Kama Sutra* and the best-seller list were hopelessly mixed up in her mind. The reader may have wondered why I have devoted a whole chapter of this book on human creativity to the seemingly trivial subject of snobbery. The answer is in the question: snobbery is, I believe, by no means a trivial phenomenon, but a confusion of values which, in various forms, permeates all strata of civilized societies, present and past (see, for instance, Petronius's *Banquet of Trimalchio*); and it is in many respects a negation of the principle of creativity.

We have seen how laughter is sparked off by the collision of matrices; discovery, by their integration; aesthetic experience by their juxtaposition. Snobbery follows neither of these patterns; it is a hotchpotch of matrices, the application of the rules of one game to another game. It uses a clock to measure weight, and a thermometer to measure distance. The creative mind perceives things in a new light, the snob in a borrowed light; his pursuits are sterile, and his satisfactions of a vicarious nature. He does not aim at power; he merely wants to rub shoulders with those who wield power, and bask in their reflected glory. He would rather be a tolerated hanger-on of an envied set than a popular member of one to which by nature he belongs. What he admires in public would bore him when alone, but he is unaware of it. When he reads Kirkegaard, he is not moved by what he reads, he is moved by himself reading Kirkegaard—but he is blissfully unaware of it. His emotions do not derive from the object, but from extraneous sources associated with it; his satisfactions are pseudo-satisfactions, his triumphs self-delusions. He has never travelled in the belly of the whale; he has opted for the comforts of sterility against the pangs of creativity.

One cannot discuss the act of creation without devoting at least a few pages to the act of desecration. Snobbery is a poor word with too specifically modern connotations for that benightedness, due to the confusion of values, which is one of the leitmotifs of the history of man; he always seems to be groping his way through a labyrinthine world, armed with a compass which always points in the wrong direction. The symbol of creativity is the magic wand which Moses used to make water come out of the rock; its reverse is the faulty yardstick which turns everything it touches into dust.

BOOK TWO
HABIT AND ORIGINALITY

INTRODUCTION

So far I have discussed creativity in science and art, that is to say, the highest forms of mental activity, with only occasional references to the humbler routines of existence. I started at the roof, as it were—what remains to be done is to build up the walls which support it.

The main purpose of this somewhat perverse procedure was to deal first with those subjects which are of primary interest to the general reader and to establish a wider theoretical framework afterwards. But there exist additional considerations to justify this reversal of order. At the Hixon Symposium in 1948 K. S. Lashley quoted with approval a French author writing in 1887. 'The study of comparative grammar,' Lashley said, 'is not the most direct approach to the physiology of the cerebral cortex, yet Fournié has written, "Speech is the only window through which the physiologist can view the cerebral life." '[1] The word 'only' is, of course, an unwarranted exaggeration, but perhaps no more unwarranted than the opposite claim, that the 'only' legitimate window is that through which we watch the workings of the salivary reflex in dogs or the behaviour of rats in mazes. To repeat an argument from the Preface to Book One: in the history of most sciences we find alternations between the downward approach from roof to basement, from the complex to the elementary, and the upward approach from the elementary to the complex; until the two finally merge. It was the study of complex electro-magnetic phenomena which provided the clue to sub-atomic structures. Torn out of the larger context in which the 'elementary part' functions, it ceases to be a true elementary part —whether we speak of electrons, tissue-cells, or 'elements of behaviour'. Genetics started with morphological classifications and comparisons of whole organisms long before anything was known about chromosomes, genes, and nucleic acids. The use of undefined, 'dirty' concepts as black boxes in theory-making has led into many cul-de-sacs in the history of science, but was nevertheless indispensable for its progress.

413

In experimental psychology the pendulum oscillated in the course of the last century between the 'upward' and the 'downward' approach: from the atomism of the English associationists to the introspectionism of the Würzburg school; from the chain-reflex theory of Watsonian behaviourism to the Holism of Gestalt, and back again to the more sophisticated behaviourism of the forties and fifties. But there are signs which indicate that the controversies between 'cognitive' versus 'stimulus-response' theories of behaviour have become sterile, and that a new synthesis is in the making.

So much by way of justification for the order of the two parts of this book. The methodological approach of the second is meant to be the reverse of the first. It starts 'from the bottom' with some elementary considerations which are non-controversial. Yet gradually, I hope, a structure will emerge which makes contact with and lends support to the controversial theories of creative activity outlined in Book One.

I

PRENATAL SKILLS

Organic life, in all its manifestations, from embryonic development to symbolic thought, is governed by 'rules of the game' which lend it coherence, stability, and an appearance of purpose (or 'goal-directedness' if you prefer that term). These rules or codes, whether phylogenetically or ontogenetically acquired, function on all levels of the hierarchy, from the chromosomes to the neuron-circuits responsible for verbal thinking. Each code represents the fixed, invariant aspect of an adaptable skill or matrix of behaviour. I shall take the stylistic licence of using the word 'skill' in a broad sense, as a synonym for 'matrix', and shall speak of the morphogenetic skills which enable the egg to grow into a hen, of the vegetative skills of maintaining homeostasis, of perceptual, locomotive, and verbal skills.

We shall find as a fundamental characteristic of codes on all levels that they function on the trigger-release principle, so that a relatively simple signal releases pre-set, complex action patterns. The signal may be mechanical, as in artificial parthenogenesis induced by a pin-prick; chemical (e.g. inducers and evocator substances); or neural (Tinbergen and Lorenz's Internal Releasive Mechanisms). But the pre-set action pattern activated by the code is generally an elastic pattern, not a rigid automatism (such as suggested, for instance, in Tinbergen's schema). Skills have varying degrees of flexibility. The restraints imposed by the code do not exhaust the degrees of freedom possessed by the matrix; there are usually various alternative choices left to provide for a flexible strategy according to the 'lie of the land'—i.e. guided by feedback from the environment. Matrices thus function under the dual control of an invariant code and a variable environment. These two factors jointly determine which members of the matrix should enter into action and in what order.

The members of the matrix are sub-matrices governed by their sub-codes. Facing 'upward' and 'inward' in the organismic hierarchy, they act as dependent parts; facing 'downward' and 'outward', they act as relatively autonomous sub-wholes. On every level of structure and function in the living organism we find the same phenomenon of Janus-faced entities which behave partly as wholes, yet wholly as parts, as it were. The 'irreducible, elementary particle' has turned out to be a will-o'-the-wisp, even in inorganic chemistry; in the organism, the firing of a single nerve-cell turns out to be not an event, but a complex, autonomous pattern of events.

Structure and Function

I shall take as my starting point two complementary aspects of the evolutionary process: differentiation of structure and integration of function. Regardless of what causal theory one adopts to account for the evolution of higher forms of life, the *means* by which progress is achieved is the development of more complex and specialized bodily structures and of more elaborate ways of co-ordinating their function. These are two *aspects* of a unitary process, not two processes. In fact both terms, 'structure' and 'function', are abstractions derived from imaginary cross-sections along the spatial or temporal axis of indivisible spatio-temporal events.

Structure is a static concept of a process frozen in the specious present. 'Anatomy abstracts from time. It studies the organism conceived "at an instant".'[1] A kidney, or a single kidney cell, which has stopped functioning no longer has the same spatial structure as before; and while it is still functioning its structure is changing at every moment. All living matter continuously alters its shape and composition; it can be said to preserve its identity only if both structure and function are taken into consideration. Vice versa, function detached from structure is the grin detached from the cat. Physiological processes, unlike mechanical automata, are 'open systems'; Ostwald compared them to the flame of a gas-burner. The flame is a relatively stable phenomenon; but how is one to distinguish between its structure and function, between combustible and combustion?

Most of the time it is both convenient and necessary for the biologist and physician to forget that when he is speaking of 'structure' and 'function' he is using 'dirty concepts'—otherwise his work would come to a standstill. However, we shall soon come across problems where the tacit implications of both terms will become relevant.

A second catch is the semantic ambiguity of the word 'function'. It can either mean the role or part which my liver *ought* to play to keep me in good health, *or* it can refer with heartless matter-of-factness to what is in fact *happening* in my liver, i.e. not to its function in the first sense but to its actual 'functioning'. In the first case, the organ is considered as *part* of the organism; in the second case it is treated, *prima facie*, as an independent whole. Whenever a distinction is indicated, I shall use the word 'function' in the first sense, and 'functioning' in the second.

The complementary aspects of structural differentiation and functional integration are reflected at every step in the process of morphogenesis.

The giant molecules of DNA (dioxyribonucleic acid) in the chromosomes of the fertilized egg are said to represent the blue-print of the future organism. Let us consider for a moment this first code which we meet at the base of the hierarchy. It is a 'code' in the twofold meaning in which I have used that term: a canon of rules for making an organism, represented in a 'coded', compressed language. The way in which the coding is done deserves some attention. Each DNA molecule is supposed to be capable of storing something of the order of 10^{10} bits of information.[2] According to the Watson-Crick model, the molecule has the shape of a ladder twisted into a double helix. The two sides of the ladder consist of uniform, linear chains of sugar groups alternating with phosphate links. The rungs of the ladder are pairs of nitrogenous bases attached on each side to the sugar groups in the double helix. There are four of these bases: adenine, guanine, cytosine, and thymine, or A, G, C, T for short. A is always paired with T, and G always with C, so that the two sides of the ladder are complementary. The sequence of bases as read down along one side of the ladder is the genetic code, written in the four-letter alphabet, 'A', 'G', 'C', 'T'. Here, then, floating in the nuclear sap, is the code which governs the skill of creating a six-foot drum major with a slight squint and dimpled cheeks, out of an egg with a diameter of a few microns.

The code's remarkably complex activities are set off by a relatively simple signal: the impact of the fertilizing agent. The principle involved must indeed be relatively simple, because in virtually all main groups of animals, including rabbits and sheep, normal development of the egg can be induced by stimulation with non-specific, physical, or chemical agents: heat or cold, salinity, ultra-violet rays, galvanic currents, or puncture with a fine needle. Though it may be hurtful to the male's pride, his seed seems to be a dispensable commodity. Its primary function is to trigger off the egg; but—with frogs at least —a platinum needle will do just as well.*

The main task of the growing cell is the manufacture of proteins which constitute the basic stuffs of the body, and of protein-enzymes, which control all its biochemical activities. The growing cell is primarily a protein-producing factory, or rather a group of specialized plants, each engaged in synthesizing one variety at a time among the thousands of different types of protein-molecules. The order and quantity in which each substance is produced, is regulated by the genetic code. The key-substances are the enzymes, which can be regarded as structural embodiments of the genetic instructions coded in the DNA chains. Each discrete set of instructions—a code-word composed of several hundred code-letters—contains the recipe, as it were, for a specific enzyme. It is usual to call these sets of instructions 'genes' (although the meaning of this traditional term has become somewhat blurred and some geneticists prefer more non-committal words). Each code-word is composed of sub-wholes: three-letter syllables like CTA, AAG, etc. Each of these sub-units in the code-sequence is capable of 'recognizing' and transporting one particular kind of sub-unit which goes into the making of proteins. These sub-units or 'building-blocks' are the amino acids; there are twenty common varieties of them. A protein usually contains all or most of the twenty varieties of amino-acid units, strung together into a chain of two hundred or more in a specific sequence. The number of permutations of twenty units in a sequence of several hundred links is of course enormous, and accounts for the impressive variety of proteins and protein-enzymes which go into the making of our all-too-solid flesh. Thus the main process in morphogenesis seems to consist in transcribing the implicit, 'functional' four-letter alphabet of the code into the explicit 'structural' twenty-letter alphabet of proteins.

The details of the process are only beginning to be known at the time of writing; and progress has become so accelerated in this particular field that by the time these pages appear in print much in them will be outdated. Broadly speaking, we know at present of two kinds of instruction-carriers between the genes and the protein-plants of the cell. The first is 'messenger RNA'. The chemical structure of RNA—

ribonucleic acid—is closely related to that of DNA. The DNA chain apparently manufactures 'messenger RNA' chains by the same process of base-paring by which it replicates itself. Each messenger is supposed to contain the 'recipe' of one specific enzyme, and to carry it to the protein-plant, the ribosome. A second type of messenger is 'transfer RNA'. Each variety of it is a much shorter chain, supposed to represent a triplet of code-letters corresponding to a particular variety of amino acids. When a transfer RNA unit meets an amino unit of the proper type in the proper condition, it will attach itself to the unit like a sort of locomotive, drag it to the ribosome plant, and shunt it into its proper place in the nascent protein chain, according to the instructions of its bigger colleague, the 'messenger RNA'.

This, in broad outlines, is the picture to date—in the year after the Crick-Watson-Wilkins team received the Nobel prize for 'breaking the genetic code'. It is to a large extent derived from work on the genetics of micro-organisms such as the colon bacillus, and there are reasons to believe that something essential is still missing from the picture.* But we need not be concerned with these niceties. What matters is that we find, literally *ab ovo*, fixed, invariant codes in control of the variable cell matrix. The order in which the various sub-codes—the genes—become active and engage in producing their specific varieties of messenger RNA is supposed to depend on the pre-set activities of 'operators' and 'repressors' in the chromosomes, and perhaps on some additional biological clocks. But it must also depend to some extent on feedback signals from the cytoplasm, including signals from neighbouring tissues which reach the cell through its sensitive membranes. Finally, recent experiments by Hyden[2a] have shown that in the nerve-cells of the mature organism experiences retained in learning lead to more or less lasting alterations in the chemical composition of the cell's RNA content: a fact of great significance for the problem of memory.

The Cell-Matrix

The growing cell illustrates the relativity, or complementary nature, of such terms as part and whole, or structure and function. 'What are called structures are slow processes of long duration, functions are quick processes of short duration. If we say that a function such as the contraction of a muscle is performed by a structure, it means that a quick and short process-wave is superimposed on a long-lasting and slowly running wave' (Bertalanffy).[3]

The same considerations apply to the relations between the genetic code and the cell-matrix. The latter is of course a very complex structure, equipped with an animal and a vegetal pole, with chemical and morphogenetic gradients, and with a variety of organelles—these, in their ensemble, are the members of the matrix. Each member is a sub-whole governed by its sub-code which can be turned on and off by orders 'from above', but once triggered into action follows its autonomous functional pattern. The *centrosomes* and *kinetosomes*, for instance, are organelles of apparently similar structure but vastly different functions. Both possess the privilege of self-replication when the cell divides; both have a cylindrical shape and are made up, it seems, of eleven fibres—two in the centre, nine outside. But these deceptively simple structures revealed by the electron-microscope are complete biochemical machines in miniature. The kinetosomes are attached to the cilia or flagella of motile cells and trigger off their activities. The centrosomes provide the poles of the spindle apparatus, which effects cell division; they establish connections with the chromosomes in the distant nucleus, tear the pairs of duplicated chromosomes apart as it were, and direct them towards their new locations in the centres of the two nascent daughter cells.

To take another example, let us cast a quick glance at the most glorious of organelles, the mitochondria. There are fifty to five thousand of them according to the type of cell and (together with the chloroplasts of green-leafed plant-cells) they are 'the power plants of all life on earth'. As a physicist has said, waxing lyrical on a biological peccadillo, they 'feed on negative entropy and drink orderliness from the environment'.[4] The chloroplasts do it by photosynthesis, the mitochondria by extracting a very special form of energy from the chemical bonds in glucose, fat, and proteins. The end product is ATP —adenosine-triphosphate—the universal carrier used by the organism to supply the energy needed for the contraction of muscles, the transmission of nerve impulses, the manufacture of proteins, and so on. The synthesizing of ATP is carried out in three main stages (glycolysis, Krebs cycle oxidation, and 'respiration'*) involving about fifty different successive reactions, each of them catalyzed by a specific enzyme system. A single mitochondrion may possess up to forty thousand of such enzyme systems; their assemblies are arranged in the membrane of the organelle in patterns which have been described as 'wiring diagrams'. They represent the sub-codes which govern the operations of the energy plant. It also has a complex feedback system: in the presence of an excess of ATP, for instance, the organelle will contract.

Even this very sketchy outline indicates the hierarchic organization of the living cell—once considered the ultimate 'atom' of life. The genetic code is blue-printed in the chromosomes; but the chromosomes do not deal directly with the sub-matrices on lower levels of the hierarchy. They do not interfere with the stepwise operations of breaking down glucose into phosphoglycerate, into lactate, into pyruvate, into citrate, and so forth; these operations, just as those of the spindle apparatus of the centrosomes, are governed by their own sub-codes. Each organelle is a highly integrated structure and enjoys a considerable amount of functional autonomy. Its operations are switched on or off by signals from the higher echelons; but these signals are addressed, as it were, to the code which governs the action-pattern of the whole organelle, and not to its subordinate parts. Generally speaking, we shall see that *a matrix on any level of the hierarchy is represented on the next-higher level by its code.* Or, to put it the other way round: the members of a matrix are sub-matrices which respond as functional units to signals activating their codes.

Nucleus and Cytoplasm

The fertilized egg contains the total pattern of the unborn individual. This privileged position of a single cell representing the whole is of short duration: after the first few cleavages, the daughter cells begin to differentiate; they lose their potential capacity of reconstructing the whole individual, and are reduced to being parts of the growing embryo.

The process involves both the nucleus and the cytoplasm, but in different ways. The characteristics of different types of cells, tissues, organs, are essentially the characteristics of their cytoplastic structure, which vary from type to type. The nuclei which (jointly with the cell's environment) determine that structure also differ according to cell-type, but in a subtler, more 'functional' than 'structural' way, It is generally assumed that each cell in the mature organism inherits a complete set of the genetic blue-print in the DNA chains of its chromosomes; but only a fraction of the set remains active—i.e. those genes which govern the cell's specialized functions; the remainder is permanently 'switched off'. As mentioned before, the activity of the enzyme-producing genes is supposed to be controlled by 'operators' and 'repressors' built into the chromosomes; and these regulators in turn are controlled by feedback from the cytoplastic environment.[5] Thus the changes in the nucleus could be described as *functional specialization*: only certain sub-codes—fractions of the complete code —remain operative; whereas the changes in the cytoplasm of successive generations amount to *structural individuation*.

The nuclear changes can actually be observed under the microscope. The salivary gland cells of midge larvae for instance possess large bundles of chromosomes, which are seen as sausage-like structures, with occasional swellings or puffs—the so-called Balbiani rings. The puffs are the sites of intense RNA production; it is therefore assumed that they indicate active genes. The pattern of these swellings changes according to the age of the larva and the type of cell.*

The action of the cytoplasm on the nucleus has also been directly demonstrated. When the nucleus from the salivary gland cell of a drosophila larva is transplanted into the cytoplasmic environment of a cell at an earlier stage of development, the chromosomes again undergo very marked changes: certain swellings disappear and others appear in their place. This clearly indicates the existence of a feedback mechanism whereby the development of the cytoplasm as a result of gene activity in its turn calls forth the activity of particular genes.[6]

The reverse type of experiment demonstrates the action of nuclei of different ages on the same cytoplasmic environment. The nucleus of an unfertilized frog-egg is removed, and replaced by a nucleus from a developing frog-embryo. If the transplant nucleus was taken from an embryo in the early blastular stage, the result will be a clone of normal tadpoles; if it was obtained from embryos in later stages of development, it will produce abnormal forms.

These experiments indicate not only that the nuclei undergo changes in the course of differentiation, but also that in the course of these changes they progressively lose their erstwhile 'totipotentiality'. The more the cell specializes in the role of a part, the less it is capable of creating a new whole.

This does not mean that the DNA chains which contain the genetic code of the whole organism are lost in the differentiated cell—it only means that as differentiation progresses, more and more genes are debarred from activity. Those which remain active are genetic sub-codes, governing the particular sub-skills which the specialized cell is called on to perform. Only the future germ-cells, segregated and protected from the beginning, retain their total creative potential to continue the genetic line—they specialize in immortality as it were. *Specialization, in morphogenesis as in other fields, exacts its price in creativity.*

The transplant experiments which I have briefly mentioned, and other evidence clearly show that while on the one hand the nuclear code governs the activities of the cell-matrix, the cytoplasm, on the other hand, is in communication with the cells' outer environment, and by feeding information on the total state of affairs back to the nucleus, co-determines which sub-code should be switched on next. The code as a whole is unalterable; but the choice of the sub-codes to be activated depends on the 'lie of the land', as in other skills. The destiny of a cell depends on the composition of the cytoplasm which it inherited from its mother cell (e.g. more animal or vegetal stuff) and on its spatial position in the growing embryo.* We have here the equivalent of a flexible strategy in morphogenesis: the development of the individual cell is determined by its invariant code and by the hazards of environment. The code represents the fixed rules of the game: if you get into the ectoderm, you must do this; if into the endoderm, you must do that. Both the fixity of the code and the flexibility of strategy become more evident as we turn to later stages of development—the matrices of morphogenetic fields, which differentiate, in hierarchic order, into organ-systems, organs, and organ-parts.

Regulative and Mosaic Development

In the five-day-old salamander embryo, whose development is fairly typical for vertebrates in general, transplantation experiments make it possible to distinguish well-defined areas which will give rise to the eye, gill, limbs, kidney, etc., although not the faintest indication of these organs is as yet visible. At this stage, the tissue of a limb-area transplanted into a different position on the embryo, or on another embryo, will form a complete limb; even a heart can be formed on an embryo's flank. Such autonomous, 'self-determining' tissue-areas are called *morphogenetic fields*. If half of the heart, limb, or eye area is cut away, the remainder of the field will form not half an organ, but a complete heart, limb or eye—just as, at the earlier, cleavage state, each half of a frog-egg, mechanically broken up, will form a complete frog. Moreover, if the tissue of, say, the kidney area is (by centrifuging) completely disintegrated into freely floating separate cells distributed at random, these cells, suspended in a proper medium, will in due time produce rudimentary kidneys—just as the dissociated cells of a living sponge, which has been broken up by straining through a filter, will start to form new cell aggregates and end up by forming a complete, normal sponge.[7]

Thus a morphogentic field behaves 'as a unit or a whole and not merely the sum of the cellular materials of which it is composed. The field with its organizing capacities remains undisturbed if the cellular material which it controls under normal circumstances is diminished or enlarged. The unit character of the field finds its clearest manifestation in these regulative properties.' (Hamburger.[8])

The various fields of the future organs and limbs form a mosaic in the embryo as a whole; at the same time they display remarkable regulative properties towards their own parts;—they are again Janus-faced entities. Each organ primordium is, when 'looking upward', a member of the total matrix; when 'looking downward', a self-governing, autonomous sub-whole. Although the future of the field in its entirety is clearly predetermined on the mosaic principle, the future of its parts is still dependent on regulative factors. The cell-populations which constitute an organ-primordium have lost their genetic totipotentiality, but they still possess a sufficient amount of multi-potentiality to keep the matrix of the field flexible. The shape of the future organ is fixed, but the part which a given cell-group or single cell will play in it is again dependent on biochemical gradients and inducers in the environment, which will trigger off the appropriate genes in the cells' genetic code.

The differentiation of organ systems, organ parts, etc., is a stepwise affair which has been compared to the way a sculptor carves a statue out of a block of wood. With each step in development the functions assigned to each group of cells become more precise, and more of its genetic potential is suppressed—until in the end most cells lose even their basic freedom to divide. By the time the fertilized ovum has developed into an adult organism, the individual cell has been reduced from totipotentiality to almost nullipotentiality. It still carries the coded blue-print of the whole organism in its chromosomes, but all, except that tiny fraction of the code which regulates its specialized activities, has been permanently switched off.

The embryo grows; the adult behaves. Growth is controlled by the genetic code; adult behaviour by the nervous (and hormonal) systems.* But in between the initial and the final stage there are some transient controlling agencies at work, which catalyze development by a mechanism as yet incompletely understood: the organizers or evocators.

During the earliest stages of development the growth of the embryo takes place in a fairly stable environment, so that feedback-controls play a relatively minor part. But with the beginning of gastrulation the situation changes: from now on each differentiating tissue acts as 'environment' on adjacent tissues; the various types of cell-population interact within the embryo.

A particularly important cell-population originates in the grey crescent of the zygote; reappears as an analogous crescent on the blastula; gives rise to the dorsal lip, migrates into the internal cavity of the gastrula, where it takes its place in the chorda-mesoderm, and becomes the so-called 'primary organizer' of the embryo, specifically concerned with initiating its nervous system—to which it will eventually hand over control. The tissue in the ectoderm which lies directly above it is destined to become the neural plate—but only if it remains in physical contact with the organizer. If that contact is prevented, the ectoderm will not form a neural plate and there will be no nervous system. If, on the other hand, organizer tissue from the dorsal lip is grafted on to the flank of another salamander embryo which is in the process of gastrulation, it will invade the host and produce a complete Siamese twin, composed partly of the invader's tissue and partly of host tissue. It was this remarkable experiment, first performed by Spemann and Hilde Mangold in 1925, which earned the privileged region of the dorsal lip in the gastrula the name of 'primary organizer'.

At a later stage, the organizer tissue seems to differentiate into head-, trunk-, and tail-organizers; and with the appearance of organ primordia, its inductive functions are further divided up and handed over to centres located in the organs themselves. A classic example of induction is the formation of the vertebrate eye. The rudimentary brain has two sacs, or vesicles, attached to it: the future eyes. The brain and its eye primordia originate as thickenings of the surface area which, after the in-folding of the neural tube, come to lie *under* the surface. So the eye vesicles must now move outward again to make contact with the surface, but at the same time remain attached to the brain by the optic stalks (which will develop into the optic nerves). In the process, the vesicles assume the shape of concave saucers, the optic cups. When these make contact with the surface, the skin areas overlaying the contact areas fold neatly into the hollow cups, thicken, detach themselves from the surface, and eventually become the transparent lenses. It can be shown that it is the optic cup which induces the skin to make a lens, for if the cup of a frog embryo is removed, no lens will form; and vice versa, if the eye vesicle is grafted under the embryo's belly, the belly skin will form a lens.

However, the docility of embryonic tissue has its limits. The tissue must be 'competent'[9] to react to the inductor; and 'competence' is determined by the degree of differentiation the tissue has reached—or, put in another way, by the amount of genetic multipotential which it still retains. An inductor 'cannot make any cell produce any specific response unless the cell is intrinsically prepared to do so'.[10] A given region of the ectoderm at a given stage of differentiation may retain enough genetic flexibility to become either a lens or skin-tissue; it will not be prepared to form a kidney. In the experimental laboratory, a transplanted eye-vesicle can be used to induce a lens on the salamander's belly. But under normal conditions the inductor's function is to catalyze or 'evocate' the actualization of the genetic potentials present in the appropriate tissue. Hence the term 'evocator-substance' for the chemical agent responsible for induction.

A curious fact about inductors is that they seem to be organ-specific but not species-specific. The optic cup of a frog transplanted under a salamander embryo's skin will cause it to produce a lens; the primary organizer of the salamander will induce brain structures not only in frogs but even in fish;[11] and the organizer of a frog, even of a fish, can induce secondary embryos in the obliging salamander. But the induced embryo will be a salamander, not a frog or a fish; and the frog-skin transplanted on to the salamander's head will form a frog-mouth, not a salamander-mouth. In this respect, too the evocator seems to act merely as a trigger-releaser on the genetic potential of the cell.

This assumption was confirmed when Holtfreter, J. Needham, and others discovered that rudimentary nervous systems could be inducted in salamander embryos by a great variety of living or dead organizers. These include most tissues of the adult salamander itself; mouse-liver and insect organs, molluscs, acidified salt solutions, sterols, and dye stuffs. Moreover, it was found that some tissues (such as embryonic skin and intestine) which cannot act as inductors when alive can do so when killed (in alcohol or by heating). All this points to the conclusion that the evocator of the nervous system is a non-specific chemical agent whose function is merely 'to release the true active substance from neighbouring cytolyzing cells';[12] and that the substance thus released is RNA, the carrier of the cell's genetic instructions. It has indeed been shown that there exist distinct RNA gradients in the inducted tissues, and that the highest RNA concentrations are found in nervous-systems induction. Since the evocator substances, unlike hormones, act only by direct contact, i.e. by diffusion from cell to cell, it seems that their function is merely *to activate those RNA subcodes which will specify the tissues' destiny*. This is in keeping with Hamburger's definition of embryonic induction as 'a process in which one developing structure, the "inductor", stimulates an adjacent structure to undergo a specific differentiation'.[13] Artificial induction through transplant experiments would then amount to drastic changes in the environment of a cell-population, which interfere with its biological time-clocks (the pre-set sequence of gene-activities); just as the transplantation of a nucleus into a different cytoplasmic environment causes a change in the pattern of its chromosome-puffs.

Induction is a transient method of regulating development, where the genetic potentials of certain cell-populations, or morphogenetic fields, are activated by chemical agencies diffused in their immediate environment. Although the chemistry of induction is still a problematic affair, it seems safe to assume, as Mittasch has pointed out, that 'organic catalyzers also show a rank order: beginning with the enzymes, which are adjusted most specifically to carry through a single reaction, to biocatalyzers such as the ... organizer substances in animals which regulate more or less wide complexes of processes, and up to directing biocatalyzers, such as many hormones, that influence to a large extent the whole organism psychophysically.'[14]

Past the early and transitory phase of induction, more advanced methods of co-ordination and control make their appearance. In the human embryo the heart begins to beat at the end of the third week, controlled by its own pace-maker, when the whole creature is less than a fifth of an inch long. Muscle contractions in response to external stimuli can be elicited after the eighth week, and spontaneous movements may begin in the tenth week. They are myogenic reactions of the muscle tissue to direct local stimulation, while the nervous system is still in the making. But the conspicuous readiness of the neural plate to start growing in response to non-specific 'evocators' designates it, as it were, as the heir apparent to the earlier forms of integration.

To sum up: at various stages of embryonic development, and at various structural levels, we find different biochemical mechanisms, but analogue principles at work. At every stage and level the game is played according to fixed rules but with flexible strategies (although their flexibility is normally hidden from the eye and revealed only by the transplantation and grafting techniques of experimental embryology). The overall rules of the game are laid down in the complete set of instructions of the genetic code; but the particular set of instructions operative at any level at any time is triggered off by messages from the inter- and extra-cellular environment, which vary in character according to structural level and developmental stage: fertilizing agents, cytoplasmic feedbacks, direct-contact evocators, hormones, and other catalysts.

On the level of the zygote, the cell-matrix consists of biochemical gradients and organelles; it is a structural mosaic equipped with axial polarity which under normal conditions predetermines the head and tail region, the blastopores, etc., of the embryo; but it also has striking regulative properties revealed by experimental manipulation. With progressive differentiation the regulative properties of the cell diminish, and its degrees of 'genetic freedom' freeze up. On the level of the morphogenetic field we again find self-regulating properties—half the field will still form a complete limb—and a mosaic-matrix of cell-populations. The autonomous, self-assertive character of morphogenetic fields is manifested in grafting and centrifuging experiments; their dependent, or part character by the trivial fact that they are kept in their proper size and place in the normally growing organism. This will sound less of a truism when we turn to the phenomena of regeneration (Chapter III). We shall find regulative character and mosaic character, autonomy and subservience, the self-assertion of the part and its dependence on the whole to be complementary aspects on every level of the hierarchy in normal development and behaviour; but also, that under abnormal conditions this ceases to be the case, and that the part may then assert itself at the expense of the whole, with sometimes beneficial, mostly destructive, effects.*

To p. 418. This is, of course, not meant to belittle the enormous advantages of sexual over asexual reproduction.

To p. 419. The three-letter 'dictionary', for instance, is partly a dictionary of synonyms: there are $4^3 = 64$ triplets, but only 20 amino acids, and many of the latter are represented by more than one code syllable.

To p. 420. 'Respiration' is an approximate term. The process is in fact oxidative phosphorylation.

To p. 422. In some, probably extreme cases, the nuclear changes are even more drastic. The nucleus of the fertilized egg of the gall-midge contains forty chromosomes, and in the course of the first few divisions these are faithfully duplicated. But in the fifth division, only eight sets of chromosomes in the soma cells duplicate in the orthodox manner; the other thirty-two fail to do so and gradually dissolve in the cytoplasm. The future germ cells, however, which have previously been segregated from the rest of the eggs, do not participate in the fateful fifth division and preserve their chromosome complement intact. Thus the nuclei of all specialized body cells have only eight chromosomes, whereas the germ cells have forty. Cf. Fischberg, M. and Blackler, A. W. (1961).

To p. 423. In a paper read at the British Association Meeting in August 1962, L. Wolpert suggested that differentiation resulted from the single cell's tendency to stick on to that part of the gastrula wall best suited for it (the idea seems to have been originated by T. Gusthafson). At the same meeting E. N. Willmer showed that changes in the salt balance of the surrounding medium made amoebae change from amoeboid to flagellate form, reversibly—the implication being that chemical gradients played an important part in the early stages of differentiation (*New Scientist*, No 303, 6.9.1962, p. 492).

To p. 425. During maturation in the higher species, the two types of control overlap; and pre-set biological time-clocks seem to exercise some influence throughout adult life.

To p. 428. In this necessarily simplified discussion of morphogenetic processes I have made no mention of cytoplasmic inheritance and other complicating factors, which do not affect the basic argument of this book.

II

THE UBIQUITOUS HIERARCHY

Development of the Nervous System

The pioneer work on the development of the nervous system in vertebrate embryos is G. E. Coghill's monumental study of *ambystoma*, a larval form of salamander.[1] Coghill published his results in a series of papers spread over a period of twenty-five years, 1914–39. Since they are surprisingly seldom quoted outside the technical literature—presumably because they ran against the behaviourist *Zeitgeist*—I must briefly summarize his conclusions.

The traditional assumption about the development of the nervous system was that elementary, local reflexes arise first, and are chained together at a later stage. Thus the segmental reflex arcs of the earthworm would develop first, as independent units aligned in a series perpendicular to its axis, and only later on would they become connected, like rings hanging from a festoon string, by the spinal cord. Coghill's work showed that the opposite is true. In the salamander, development starts with the growth of the motor-tracts of the cord axially from head to tail; then this central bundle sends out collateral branches into the segmental muscles, co-ordinating their actions in primitive, unitary patterns; the sensory neurons become functional only at a later stage, and the local reflex-arcs come last, as segregations of 'partial patterns' out of the 'total pattern' which preceded them. The whole development is centrifugal: the stem precedes the branches, spontaneous undifferentiated movements involving the whole neuro-muscular apparatus precede differentiated movement, total responses precede specialized local responses. To give an example: when the limbs develop, their first movements are entirely dependent on and synchronized with the movements of the trunk. Only later on do the limbs begin to move independently; the same applies to the motions of head, mouth, etc. The growth of the nervous system from beginning

430

to end is dominated by 'a totally integrated matrix, and not a progressive integration of primarily individuated units'. The organism is not a sum of its reflexes, but on the contrary 'the mechanism of the total pattern is an essential component of the performance of the part, i.e. the reflex'. The stimulus-response scheme cannot explain even embryonic behaviour, because movements appear long before the motor neurons of the reflex arc are connected with the sensory neurons. This centrifugal mode of development means that the individual acts on its environment before it reacts to its environment.

'In so far as the correlation of nervous structure and function in the development of the individual has been carried, structural provision has been found for the perpetuation of spontaneity, autonomy, or initiative as a factor in its behaviour. Any theory of motivation, therefore, that attributes this function wholly to the environment, is grossly inadequate.' The idea that instincts are chained reflexes must be abandoned; instincts represent 'total action patterns in response to relatively general situations'. Comparing the embryonic development of *ambystoma* with that of the human foetus, Coghill sums up:

> In conclusion I am convinced by a study of all available records of movement in human foetuses during the first six months, that behaviour develops in man as it does in ambystoma by the expansion of a total pattern that is integrated as a whole from the beginning, and by individuation of partial patterns (reflexes) within the unitary whole.*

We thus find in the development of the nervous system the same principles at work which we have discussed before. The neural plate starts as a primordium with multipotential cell-populations which differentiate in a series of steps into the brain, the spinal cord, and its sub-structures. The 'wiring diagram' of the organism has a standardized pattern—an invariant code; but transplant experiments again show the great flexibility of the 'neurogenetic skill' which realizes that pattern. If a limb-bud from a salamander embryo is transplanted to another embryo's flank, outgrowing nerve-fibres locate the bud and establish a normal nerve pattern. The bulb-shaped tips of the outgrowing nerves are apparently guided by sub-microscopic structures in the cell-matrix of the growing bud—at least according to the current 'contact guidance' theory.

I have called differentiation of structure and integration of function complementary aspects of a unitary process. But the 'functions' of the growing embryo are different from the 'functions' of the adult. It has been shown that the limb-buds and wing buds of chick embryos develop into almost normal legs and wings if nerves are prevented from entering them. This does not mean, of course, that differentiation of structure comes first, and integration of function later on, as a separate act. For the function of the leg-bud is to grow—not to walk. Growth is a function controlled by the genetic code; when growth is completed and the time has come to walk, the nervous system takes over control; and if it fails to do so, the muscle tissues will degenerate, as denervated adult muscles do.*

Locomotor Hierarchies

'Whatever the nature of organizing relations may be,' J. Needham wrote in 1932, 'they form the central problem of biology, and biology will be fruitful in the future only if this is recognized. The hierarchy of relations, from the molecular structure of carbon compounds to the equilibrium of species and ecological wholes, will perhaps be the leading idea of the future.'[2]

This prophecy has not come true. The Gestalt school's over-emphasis on 'wholeness', and the behaviourists' over-emphasis on 'simple elementary processes'—the so-called S.-R. (stimulus-response) scheme —created a controversy based on a fallacious alternative, and prevented a true appreciation of the multi-layered hierarchic order to be found in all manifestations of life.

Yet the idea is of course by no means new; hierarchies in nervous function were proposed by Herbert Spencer in the 1870s, and elaborated by Hughlings Jackson, Sherrington, and others.[3] The hierarchical character of skills was demonstrated in great detail by Bryan and Harter in their study of telegraphy and in Book's study of touch-typing (see below, pp. 544 ff.) at the turn of the century, but neither S-R psychologists nor Gestaltists paid attention to them. Woodger (1929) attempted a formalization, by means of symbolic logic, of certain types of hierarchies ('divisional hierarchies', 'spatial hierarchies', 'genetic hierarchies', etc.) which are of somewhat abstract interest. Heidenhain (1923)[4] proposed a hierarchy of 'histo-systems' which are 'encapsulated' into one another (e.g. neuro-fibriles, neurons, nerve fibres). Bertalanffy (1952) tried to make a distinction between 'hier-

archies of parts', 'hierarchies of processes', 'hierarchies of centraliza-
tion', etc. Tinbergen defined instinct as a hierarchically organized
nervous mechanism—but his mechanism is fixed and rigid (see below
p. 478). A stimulating discussion of the subject can be found in
Miller, Galanter, and Pribram's remarkable essay on 'Plans and the
Structure of Behaviour' (1960).

The word 'hierarchy' can be used to mean simply rank-order.
Hull's famous 'habit family hierarchy', for instance, means just that
(the ordering of a group of interchangeable responses according to
their strength), and is not a hierarchy at all in the sense in which the
term is used in this book. I have summarized what I meant by it in the
chapter 'Partness and Wholeness' (Book One, Chapter XIII). A hierarchy, in this sense, is not like a row of organ pipes; it is like a tree, arboriz-
ing downward. The structural or functional entities on each level are
autonomous sub-wholes of complex pattern, but are represented on
the next higher level as units. In every organic hierarchy, to paraphrase Gertrude Stein's statement about the rose, 'a part is a whole is a
part is a whole'.

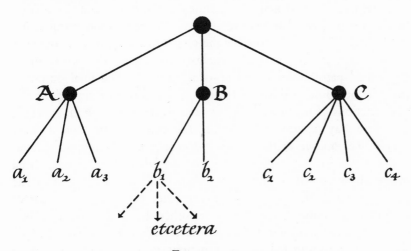

FIGURE II

Perhaps the most satisfactory theoretical treatment of the concept of
hierarchic order was given by Paul Weiss—whose experimental work
was a major contribution towards providing the concept with a firm
empirical basis. The quotation which follows is from the celebrated
Hixon Symposium; its vividness is enhanced by the fact that it is

taken from an *ex tempore* contribution by Weiss to the discussion of Lashley's paper on 'The Problem of Serial Order in Behaviour'* (my italics):

'While the physiologist and psychologist deal with the ready-made machine of the nervous system and can add to it as many properties as he thinks necessary, the embryologist must explain just how such an immensely intricate, yet orderly, thing can develop. These studies are still in their infancy, but a few things have already come out... for instance, the *relative autonomy of structured patterns of activity, and the hierarchical principle of their organization.* ... The nervous system is not one big monotonic pool whose elements can be freely recombined in any number of groupings, thereby giving an infinite variety of nervous responses. This used to be the old idea of the associationists, and it is utterly incompatible with what we have learned about the development of the nervous system and its function in animals.

'The working of the central nervous system is a hierarchic affair in which *functions at the higher levels do not deal directly with the ultimate structural units,* such as neurons or motor units, but operate by activating lower patterns that have their own relatively autonomous structural unity. The same is true for the sensory input which... operates by affecting, distorting, and somehow modifying the pre-existing, preformed patterns of central co-ordination.... The final output is then the outcome of this hierarchical passing down of distortions and modifications of intrinsically preformed patterns of excitation, which are in no way replicas of the input. *The structure of the input does not produce the structure of the output, but merely modifies intrinsic nervous activities that have a structural organization of their own.* This has been proved by observation and experiment. Coghill has shown that the motor patterns of the animal develop prior to the development of sensory innervation. I have shown, as others have, that the *removal of the sensory innervation does not abolish the co-ordination of motor activities.* Moreover, co-ordinated motor functions of limbs and other parts develop even if these parts have been experimentally prevented from ever becoming innervated by sensory fibres. Therefore, the sensory pathway can have nothing to do with the structure of the motor response. There are still some authors who try to save the old associationist idea that actually the input shapes the structure of the output. I think that they are fighting a losing fight, and I think that today's discussion ought to have given them the *coup de grâce.*

'Intrinsic automatic rhythms have been shown, for instance, by Adrian in the brain stem of the goldfish and in insect ganglia, by Prosser in other arthropods, by Bremer and by von Holst in the spinal cord, and by Bethe in jellyfish. I have shown experimentally that any group of bulbar or spinal nerve cells taken from vertebrates, if deprived of their structural bonds of restraining influences and allowed to undergo a certain degree of degradation, will display permanent automatic, rhythmic, synchronized activity of remarkable regularity. Rhythmic activity, therefore, *seems a basic property of pools of nervous elements.* . . . The rhythm is not something generated through an input rhythm, but is itself a primary rhythm which may be released and even speeded up or retarded by the input, but is not derived from the input. So we have experimental evidence that *rhythmic automatism, autonomy of pattern, and hierarchical organization are primary attributes of even the simplest nervous systems,* and I think that this unifies our view of the nervous system.'[5]

Let me enlarge on some of these points and add a few facts which have emerged since.

In the first place it has been found that intrinsic, rhythmic activity of an autonomous character is not confined to motor nerves, but that 'receptors also are spontaneously active even in the absence of stimulation from environment.'[6] This spontaneous receptor activity, while modified by environmental events, is under efferent control from the central nervous system. The central control (both of the spontaneous receptor activity and of the input) is, as we shall see, primarily of a restraining, inhibitory nature. But for the time being let us confine ourselves to motor organization.

In an earlier paper (1941 a, p. 23) Weiss distinguished the following levels of the hierarchy:

'1. The level of the individual motor unit.
'2. All the motor units belonging to one muscle.
'3. Co-ordinated functions of muscular complexes relating to a single joint.
'4. Co-ordinated movements of a limb as a whole.
'5. Co-ordinated movements of a number of locomotor organs resulting in locomotion.
'6. "The highest level common to all animals", the movements of "the animal as a whole".'

This is as far as the schema proposed by Weiss goes. Now let me extend it one step further downward in the hierarchy. Even the lowest among the six levels is a very complex affair. The individual muscle cell of a striped muscle—usually called a muscle fibre—is a long, cylindrical structure surrounded by a membrane. Its principal functions are: (a) to serve as a receptor for nerve impulses which reach it at the synapse through a chemical transmitter; (b) to re-code this message into an electro-chemical excitation spreading along its surface; (c) to relay it to the actual contractile structure, and to provide the energy for the contraction in the cell's internal energy currency—ATP; (d) to contract.* This involves at least three distinct processes (acetyl-choline transmission; sodium-potassium action potentials; activation by ATP) entering successively into action between the synaptic and the filament levels, with mechanical contraction as the end product. Thus the ultimate 'motor unit' at the base of the hierarchy is not the cell itself, but the apparatus within it which provides the contraction.

That apparatus is, broadly speaking, a kind of cylindrical cable, the fibre, composed of a bundle of fibrils, each in turn composed of bundles of filaments. The filaments are of two varieties, a thick and a thin one, the former supposed to be consisting of molecular threads of actin, the second of myosin. The combination of these two proteins—acto-myosin—is a substance which contracts when activated by the energy carrier of the cell, ATP. The mechanism of the contraction is presumed to be a telescoping into each other of the thick and fine bundles of filaments.[7]*

It is assumed, then, that muscle movement is due to the chemical action of ATP on contractile proteins; and moreover that essentially the same process is responsible for the streaming motion of amoeba, the rowing motion of cilia, and the tail-stroke motion of flagella. Amoeba, as I have mentioned before (note to p. 423, previous chapter) are capable of changing from amoeboid to flagellate form—and back. Thus at the very bottom of the hierarchy we find the same basic, universal mechanism—the archetype of organic motility as it were—throughout the whole animal kingdom from amoeba to man; and within man, we again see it at work, serving such varied functions as the swimming of his spermatozoa, the bristling of his hair, and the flexing of his muscles in a tennis-stroke. It is a mechanism or apparatus with a high degree of autonomy—and it reminds one of the equally autonomous functioning and universal occurrence of the power-plant-organelle, the mitochondria.

However close we seem to get to rock-bottom in the organic hierarchy, we find complex, integrated sub-wholes leading a relatively autonomous existence. Viruses have been compared to 'nomadic' genes (though 'freelancing' genes might be a more appropriate description).

Even a dead muscle cell (dissected and soaked in a cold glycerine solution for months, which makes it very dead indeed) will contract when exposed to the chemical trigger-action of ATP. The glycerine destroys cell-components serving its higher functions, but the essential structure of the fibrils—the structural matrix of the basic motor unit —remains intact; and it is still capable of functioning according to its built-in code. This function is of course a fixed reaction, as one would expect on the lowest level of the hierarchy; it is activated by the trigger-action of ATP on the acto-myosin. The environment of this matrix is represented by the temperature, oxygen supply, degree of fatigue in the cell, but the degrees of freedom of the fibre to adjust to these conditions boil down to an 'all-or-nothing' strategy: the alternative is to twitch or not to twitch.

On the higher levels of the hierarchy, the autonomous function-patterns of muscles and muscle-complexes are even more in evidence; at the same time the degrees of freedom in the matrix allowing for adaptable performance increase with each level. Muscles dissected from the body and put into Ringer solution will contract normally for hours. Practically any part of an animal's heart, a muscular strip, and even a single muscle cell grown on a blood clot, will continue to go on beating in its own intrinsic rhythm. The heart of the chick embryo starts beating before any nerve cells have grown into it, and the hearts of frogs and tortoises will go on beating normally if the nerve supply is cut. Some smooth muscles equally show a rhythm of their own.

But complementary to this *Eigenfunktion*, or functional autonomy, is control by a centre or system on the next higher level. The heart has its own pacemaker-system which is in itself a threefold hierarchy; under normal conditions, the sino-auricular node, the fastest part, acts as a pacemaker; but if it is prevented from doing so, the auro-ventricular node will take over, and as a last resort (in experiments carried out on frog and tortoise) yet a third centre may enter into action. The pacemaker-system is, in its turn, subject to regulatory control by sympathetic and parasympathetic nerves and by hormones, which will speed up or slow down the rate of beat by order of centres in the hypothalamus. Other organs—kidney, intestine, stomach—also have their self-regulating, intrinsic codes which assure their status as autonomous sub-wholes, while at the same time they function as parts in a multi-levelled hierarchy. Even the mid-brain centres which control temperature, metabolism, food and liquid intake, respiration, etc.—even these homeostatic controls responsible for maintaining the equilibrium of the *milieu intérieur,* turn out to be subject to the control of still higher levels. They are 'biassed homeostats' which can be 'set', as a thermostat is 'set' by the tenant to keep a higher or lower room temperature.[8] And so the top of the hierarchy which controls the controls recedes into a cloud—just as its base is embedded in the murky problem of what constitutes living matter—and ultimately dissolves into genetic mutations with thresholds on the quantum level.

The Goldfish and the Crab

Getting back to earth, that is, to the medium levels of the hierarchy— the levels 3, 4, and 5 in Weiss's schema—we find, fortunately, more precise indications about its manner of working.

Von Holst's study of the swimming motions of fish revealed a distinct three-step hierarchy: (a) the motions of the rays within a single fin, due to the alternative contractions of two antagonistic pairs of muscles; (b) the motions of the fin as a whole; and (c) the co-ordination of the motions of all the fins. In the anaesthetized goldfish, the swinging motions of each individual ray remain perfectly regular, but their co-ordination within the fin is disturbed: they flutter in disorder. The anaesthesia evidently does not affect the integrative centres on the lowest (a) level, but puts the higher nervous centres on the (b) level out of action. On the next higher, (c) level, the pectoral fin acts as a kind of pacemaker by imposing, or superimposing, its own rhythm on the caudal fins—the so-called 'magnet effect'. This whole locomotor hierarchy is relatively independent of sensory stimuli, for fishes and tadpoles go on swimming in perfect co-ordination if they have been disafferentated, i.e. if all the main sensory connections have been severed. Von Holst concludes that the stimulus-response schema does not apply to the autonomous locomotive hierarchy, and that 'the reflex is not the primary element of behaviour but a device for adapting the primary automatism to changing peripheral conditions'.[9]

Higher up on the evolutionary ladder we find increasing flexibility of motor skills. In a series of famous experiments, von Buddenbrook and Bethe have shown that the removal of one or several legs from centipedes, spiders, and other insects does not lead to disorganization, but to a spontaneous rearrangement of the whole pattern of loco-motion which is instantaneous and not preceded by trial-and-error learning. The normal progress of an insect or crab is the so-called 'cross-amble'. If 'L' and 'R' stand for left and right, and the index numbers stand for the order of legs from front to rear, the crab's locomotive code is as follows: R_1, L_2, R_3, L_4, R_5, etc., are stepping simultaneously; then L_1, R_2, L_3, R_4, L_5—are stepping simultaneously; and so on. If, now, the left front leg is removed, the pattern changes instantaneously to: R_1, L_3, R_3, L_5, etc.; followed by L_2, R_2, L_4, R_4, L_6, etc.

The crab's progress before and after loss of the left front leg:

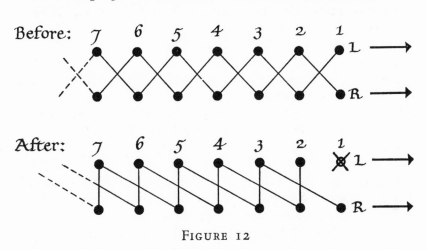

FIGURE 12

This transformation indicates that the front legs act as 'pacemakers'; this makes it impossible for the animal to adopt the simpler solution of preserving the original pattern minus L_1: for in this case R_2 would become the second pacemaker and both pacemakers would be on the right side of the animal. The crab's behaviour provides us with a rather elegant example how a motor skill can be adapted to changed conditions while preserving the basic pattern laid down in its code. I have mentioned other examples earlier on—from the spider's net to the pianist who transposes a tune from one key to another. The experiments to be described presently illustrate the challenging nature of the problem.

Weiss's transplantation experiments date back to the 1920s and proved to be, as one author said, 'of immeasurable positive significance for the appraisal of centro-peripheral co-ordination in nervous function'.[10]

Weiss grafted fully developed limbs of salamander as super-numeraries on to normal animals which thus had five limbs instead of four. The additional limb was always grafted next to a normal one, and in the process some of the nerve-fibres supplying the normal limb were severed. At first the transplant limb hung inertly from the body as a mere appendage—the fifth wheel of the cart. However, after a few weeks, it began to give signs of movement, and within a short time it functioned in complete synchronicity with the adjacent normal limb, as its equal in vigour and co-ordination.

The implications of this phenomenon were described by Weiss as follows (italics in the original):

'As could be incontrovertibly gathered from the microscopical (post-mortem) investigation and reconstruction of the course of the nerves in the original limb and in the transplanted limb, this is what took place. The severed nerve fibres had vigorously *split* up in the scar at the place of grafting. The branches had pressed forward, and some of them had eventually met the degenerated nerve paths of the transplanted limb. *As fortuitously as they were located and distributed*, they had penetrated into these and so had reached the muscles . . . in the most extraordinary and indiscriminate tangle. . . . Moreover, those few paths belonging to the normal extremity which had also been previously cut (in order to obtain severed nerve stumps capable of regeneration for the supply of the grafted limb) these too were filled with fresh nerves. In the end, therefore, the relatively small number of ganglion cells, which originally led to a small, limited section of the musculature of the normal extremity were now not only connected with this very section of muscle again, but in addition with the entire musculature of the grafted limb. . . . Thus not only have the ganglion cells involved to serve a terminal area several times as large as before; and not only have they to serve muscles altogether different from the previous ones . . . but above all the previous rule, that one ganglion cell had connections with only one muscle, now becomes the exception. Instead the rule is now a boundless confusion of conduction paths.'[11]

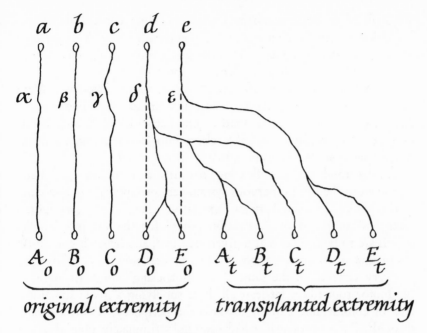

FIGURE 13

Assuming D_o and E_o to be a pair of antagonistic muscles—how can they properly function if both now depend on the same nerve supply? And what about A_t, B_t, C_t? Yet this 'boundless confusion of conduction paths' nevertheless produces perfectly co-ordinated movement. Weiss concludes that it is not the topographical layout of the pathways which matters, but the specific properties of the excitation transmitted by them; in other words, that although each muscle of the added limb will receive a chaotic medley of excitations, it will respond selectively to such excitations only which are appropriate to it:

'The means by which the central nervous system maintains concord with each muscle individually, does not consist in separate conduction paths. . . . If one and the same nerve cell has to supply excitation to several organs simultaneously, but if under these circumstances only one single route common to all these end-organs is at its disposal . . . then it is logical to assume that the periphery is so constituted that a control of its functioning in a co-ordinated manner inheres in itself. . . . We require . . . a mechanism of *positive selectivity in the end organ*, which must explain us why, when two muscles in the same state are given, one of them enters into function and the other does not,

441

although both, being connected with the same nerve cell, receive excitation equally. . . . The nature of every muscle is such that it does not react to every excitation from the centre, but *only to excitation of a quite definite form* which is characteristic for it.'[12]

To account for the specific selectivity of muscle response, Weiss uses the analogy of selective resonance in a broad sense. The acoustic analysers of the ear each respond to one particular pitch and to one only, thus analysing a complex clang into its harmonic elements. *Mutatis mutandis*, Weiss assumes that:

'. . . the total impulse flowing towards a particular peripheral region from the central nervous system can, metaphorically speaking, forthwith be designated as an "excitation clang". The "excitation clang" is composed of "excitation tones" for the varying muscles which are to be activated at a given moment, and hence is constantly fluctuating in its composition. . . . The process now is as follows: at the very same time, the same "excitation clang" flows through *all* the motor root fibres (at least all those supplying a given functional area of considerable extent) towards the periphery. It flows *equally* through *all* the fibres as if it had been indiscriminately poured into a canal system and were flooding all the channels. Thus it arrives at all the muscles which are in any way whatever connected with the centre. But when it gets to this point it is *analysed*. Every muscle, in accordance with its constitution, selects the components appropriate to it from those eventually arriving, and acts as if these components alone had arrived. And thus, although the very same impulse streams to all the muscles and across every available route, only that combination of muscles comes into action—as is now intelligible—which the central nervous system has provided for.'[13]

He then proceeds to show that the theory of selective response is not contradicted by the indiscriminate responses of muscles to electro-galvanic stimulation. The latter is an artificial, gross stimulation which compares to natural stimulation like a violent a-periodic blast to a specific clang. 'Just as, both with the clang and with the blast, the substratum carrying the movement is always the same, i.e. the air, so obviously the medium in which both the organized and the unorganized nerve impulse run their course is always the same, i.e. the conductive substance of the nerve fibre. But just as the clang sets a definite selection of resonators vibrating, whereas a noise or blast causes them to resound all at once and without an exception; so also only the organized impulse, built up of specific impulse-tones, is capable of bringing the co-ordinated selection of muscles into activity, while the artificially induced, unorganized impulse, by contrast, forces every muscle whatsoever which it reaches into function.'[14]

Let me translate the picture that emerges from the experimental evidence into the terms of the present theory. The locomotor *matrix* on level 4 of the hierarchy (p. 435) is represented by the muscular structure of the limb, plus the 'canal-system' of nervous pathways leading into it, and includes the apparatus—whatever its nature— which accounts for the selectivity of the response by enabling muscles to analyse incoming impulses. The *code* is the sequence of excitation-clangs which calls forth one complete motion—say, one step of the limb. Members of the matrix are the several joints on the next-lower level No. 3, which are triggered off in a pre-set order by their sub-codes, i.e. by the appropriate components of the excitation-clang. We may remember by way of analogy, how part-sequences of the genetic code are triggered into action in a pre-set order.

The 'motor unit' at the bottom of the hierarchy responds according to the all-or-nothing rule, but the musculature of a joint is capable of graded responses, and the motions of the whole limb follow a flexible strategy—shorter or longer step, swift or groping—dependent on the input from the environment. Weiss accounted for these variations by proposing that the excitation-clang 'is constantly fluctuating in its composition', and thus determines which single muscle should be activated at any given moment. But this conception does not seem to agree well with the basic principle that centres on high levels do not deal directly with units on low levels of the hierarchy. A way out of this difficulty is to be found in suggestions by Ruch (1951) and Miller et al. (1960), according to which pre-set patterns of skilled movements are triggered off as units by the brain; but the signal—i.e. the 'excitation clang'—would merely 'rough in' the sequence of movements 'and thus reduce the troublesome transients involved in the correction of movement by output-informed feedbacks'.[15] Since feedback circuits must be assumed to operate on every level, down to the single cell, the adjustment of the details of the 'roughed-in' movement could be handed over to lower levels. Miller et al. have made the further suggestion that this handing-down procedure may be the equivalent of converting an order coded in a 'digital' language, into a graded, 'analogue' output. The excitation-clang could thus consist in a series of 'on', 'off' signals like the dots and dashes of the Morse code; but each sub-unit could respond to its specific 'on' signal by a 'more' or 'less' intense activity, dependent on local conditions (see also below, pp. 519 ff.). These are speculations, and offered by their authors as such; but there are various alternative possibilities to account for the 'filling in' of details which were left open in the generalized excitation pattern, by feedback devices on successively lower levels.

Limits of Control

In the experiments previously discussed, a super-numerary limb was grafted next to a normal one, facing in the same direction. In another series of experiments Weiss exchanged and reversed the position of the limbs of newts. The result is again best described in his own words:

'The essential independence of the structure of motor activity is dramatically demonstrated when one exchanges and reverses the limbs of animals and then finds them crawling backwards whenever they aim to crawl forwards and vice versa. . . . This has been done in the developed animal, but the same operations have been done in embryos, and these animals have then functioned in reverse from the very beginning. What more spectacular expression can there be of the intrinsic primacy of the motor patterns of behaviour for which the external input acts only as a selective trigger?'[16]

In other transplant experiments, only the position of the two fore-limbs was interchanged and reversed:

'The grafted limbs moved just as they would have done had they been left in their original position, causing backward motion when the rest of the animal was trying to move forward, and forward motion when the rest of the animal was trying, for example, to avoid a noxious stimulus presented in front of it. A year's experience did not change this reversed movement of the grafted legs.'[17]

The experiment beautifully illustrates the autonomy of the limb-matrix. As in the fifth-limb experiment, the nerves growing out of the stump reached the muscles of the grafted limb in a random manner. Once more, the graft-limb achieved perfectly co-ordinated motion, thanks (we assume) to the analyser devices in the muscles which respond to one component in the clang signal only. But since the limb was grafted in reverse, it has to step in reverse. No doubt the poor creature senses that something is wrong if its fore-limbs move back-ward and the back limbs move forward. But owing to the principles of hierarchic order, the centre which co-ordinates the movements of the animal as a whole—level 5 in Weiss's schema—cannot interfere with the functioning of the analyser devices on level 2, to reverse their responses. It apparently cannot even prevent excitation-clangs being triggered off automatically by level 4 to the useless limbs. And when the excitation reaches the latter, they respond as they must. We have here a first, artificially produced example of 'faulty integrations' which will occupy our attention later on.

The example further illustrates a point mentioned before: *a matrix on the n-level is represented on the $n + 1$ level by its code*. There is, under normal conditions, no direct commerce between its members on the $n - 1$ level, and the co-ordinating agency on the $n + 1$ level. If the latter interferes directly with the former, routines become disorganized, and we get the 'paradox of the centipede'. Loss of direct control over automatized processes on lower levels of the body hierarchy is part of the price paid for differentiation and specialization. The price is of course worth paying so long as the species lives in an environment that is fairly stable. It is after all not part of the normal destiny of the salamander to encounter Dr. Paul Weiss.

NOTES

To p. 431. The validity of Coghill's findings for a whole range of other species—cat, bird, man—was demonstrated in a general way by authors like Coronios (1933), Herrick (1929), Kuo (1932). However, some geneticists (e.g. Windle and his associates) have maintained that functional co-ordination in higher species is the result of additive chaining of specialized local reflexes. As against this, Hooker (1950) has pointed out the undisputed fact that motor nerves are functional before the sensory nerves, and that the sensory and intercallated neurons in the reflex arc are the last to become functional, which amounts to an indirect refutation of the reflex summation view. For a summary of this controversy see Thorpe (1956) pp. 20 ff. and p. 45; also Barron (1950) and Hooker (1950).

On the other hand, Tinbergen has shown that in some patterns of complex instinct behaviour (e.g. nest building, Kortlandt, 1940), the part-performances which go into the total pattern emerge at different times, following 'a fixed time pattern just as with growing morphological structures' (Tinbergen, 1951, p. 136). Thus, for instance, fastening of twigs in the nest precedes searching for twigs. The existence of 'internal clocks' which regulate the serial activation of the various sub-codes of the integrated performance is entirely in keeping with the total pattern view. Thorpe concludes: 'Embryological studies now suggest that ontogenetically, complex muscle co-ordinations resembling fixed action patterns [see below] precede responses of the simple reflex type in mammals.' Cf. next note.

To p. 432. This confusion may have been a contributing factor in the controversy mentioned in the previous note. Since myogenic muscle contractions can be produced in embryos by electrical or mechanical stimulation before neuro-muscular integration is established, the 'isolated reflex-school' assumed such pseudo-reflexes to be true reflexes and the primary elements of adult behaviour. See, e.g. Thorpe, loc. cit.

To p. 434. The Hixon Symposium was one of the most fertile exchanges ever held between leading experts in various disciplines. Among its participants were H. Kluver, Wolfgang Köhler, K. S. Lashley, W. S. McCulloch, John V. Neumann, R. W. Gerard, Lorente de Nó, Paul Weiss, Linus Pauling, etc., to mention only a few. No wonder that Weiss, carried away by enthusiasm after hearing Lashley's brilliant paper on 'The Problem of Serial Order in Behaviour', concluded with expressing his hope that today's 'discussion will mark a turning point in the building of neurological theories'.

To p. 436. To make matters a little more complicated, we may remind ourselves in passing that muscle-contractions serve not only motility but also maintenance of tone and temperature in the organism; sometimes they serve only the last function alone (in shivering) since muscle is a main source of animal heat.

To p. 436. At the time of writing this theory still has certain difficulties to overcome; among them the fact that the energy supply of the fibre depends not only on ATP itself but also on creatin phosphate.

III

DYNAMIC EQUILIBRIUM AND REGENERATIVE POTENTIAL

Acting and Reacting

The organism', to quote Coghill once more, 'acts on the environment before it reacts to the environment.' This statement seems to apply to every level and every aspect of organic life. The lowliest creature and the highest, the moment it is hatched or born, lashes out at the environment, be it liquid or solid, with cilia, flagellae, or contractile muscle fibre; it crawls, swims, glides, pulsates; it kicks, yells, breathes, feeds, and sucks negative entropy from its surroundings for all its worth.

The patterns of these built-in motor activities we saw to be to a large extent autonomous; 'the structure of the input does not produce the structure of the output, but merely modifies it.' Moreover, the input itself is actively controlled and modified by the central nervous system from the moment it impinges on the peripheral receptor organs; and recent developments have caused, at least among an unorthodox minority of psychologists, a distinct 'shift from the notion that an organism is a relatively passive, protoplasmic mass whose responses are controlled by the arrangement of environmental stimuli to a conception of an organism that has considerable control over what will constitute stimulation.'[1]

Even below the level of the single cell, organelles such as the mitochondria and kinetosomes carry on their autonomous activities; their shadowy patterns under the electron-microscope are a reminder that the emergence of life means the emergence of spontaneous, organized exertion to maintain and reproduce originally unstable forms of equilibrium in a statistically improbable system in the teeth of an environment governed by the laws of probability. The live organism succeeds in this by creating an inner environment with which to

447

confront the outer environment—and in which the law of entropy seems to be reversed, biological clocks replace astronomical clocks, and hierarchic order reigns supreme.

An organism is said to be 'well balanced' or 'well adapted' or 'in dynamic equilibrium' if it has established a *modus vivendi* between its internal and external environment. This, of course, is a more complex form of balance than mechanical or chemical equilibrium; it implies metabolic processes required for the maintenance of form and function in an open system in perpetual flux—Bertalanffy's (1941) *Fliessgleich-gewicht*; it implies self-regulating devices which keep irritability and motility within a safe standard range; and it also implies the slow, cyclic changes of morphogenesis, maturation, and reproduction, regulated by biological clocks. If all these processes are to be lumped together under the portmanteau word 'adaptation', then we must call it adaptation of a special kind, on the organism's own terms; after all, the perfect adaptation of an organism to the temperature and chemistry of the environment is to die. In fact, the animal does not merely adapt to the environment, but constantly adapts the environment to itself. It eats environment, drinks environment, fights and mates environment, burrows and builds in the environment; and even in observing environment, it modifies, dismantles, analyses, and reassembles it after its own fashion, converting 'noise' into 'information'. 'Perception', Woodworth wrote, 'is always driven by a direct, inherent motive which might be called "the will to perceive".'

Thus the terms 'adaptation', 'environment', 'equilibrium' will be used in the following pages not in their usual passive connotations, but with active overtones, as it were. Instead of treating an animal as a 'relatively passive, protoplasmic mass whose responses are controlled by the arrangement of environmental stimuli'—a Pavlov-dog in its restraining harness—we shall regard it as a relatively self-contained organism, deploying spontaneous activities simultaneously on various levels of its constituent functional hierarchies—activities which are triggered and modified, but not created by the environment.

What is Equilibrium?

An organism can be said to function normally so long as the stresses between internal and external milieu do not exceed a certain standard range. To simplify the argument, let the term 'internal milieu' embrace all processes within the organism, and let us lump together the nature, intensity, and duration of environmental excitations in a single variable. We shall then be able to distinguish between (a) 'normal', (b) 'paranormal' or 'traumatic', and (c) destructive environmental conditions—though, needless to say, the boundaries between them cannot be sharply defined.

The term 'dynamic equilibrium' shall apply only to a normal organism functioning under 'normal' conditions. Under these conditions the organ-systems, organs, and organ-parts of the animal perform their specific, autonomous functions as sub-wholes, at the same time submitting to the regulative control imposed by the higher centres. The control is exercised by excitatory and inhibitory processes, but the latter play a vastly greater part. From the moment of conception, the genetic potentials of the individual cell are further restrained with every step in differentiation; and on every level of the growing and mature organism inhibitory blocks, negative feedbacks, growth-inhibiting hormones are at work. In the nervous system, in particular, there is censorship at every step—to prevent overloading of the information channels and overshooting of responses. Without this hierarchy of restraints, the organism would instantly blow its fuses in a kind of delirium agitans and then collapse.

Under normal conditions the part will not tend to escape the restraining influence of the whole. Under paranormal conditions the balance is upset. Thus the term 'balance' or 'equilibrium' takes on a special meaning in the context of an organic hierarchy: it is not meant to refer to relations between parts on the same level of the hierarchy, but to *the relation of a part to its controlling centre* on the next higher level. The stresses arise not between inputs 'competing for the final common path,' as the expression goes, not between 'antagonistic drives' or 'conflicting impulses' (which do not directly communicate with each other and cannot 'fight it out among themselves')—but between the excited part and the whole, whose attention it is trying to monopolize: in other words, *between the self-assertive tendencies of the part and the restraints imposed by the controlling centre.* Equilibrium is maintained in the organism by rules comparable to the procedure in a law court where the opposing parties address themselves not to each other, but to the judge.

This interpretation of equilibrium in a hierarchy was suggested in my *Insight and Outlook* (p. 139 seq.), and independently proposed by Tinbergen. In discussing the competition between various 'fixed response patterns' in innate behaviour, Tinbergen wrote: 'It should be emphasized that it is quite possible that these interconnections [between the competing centres] do not in reality run directly from one centre to the other, but go by way of the superordinated centre.'[2] Thorpe has expressed similar ideas.[3]

Super-Elasticity and Regenerative Span

An organism lives by constant transactions with the environment. As a result, stresses are set up in the parts or organs which have been aroused to carry out the transaction. The excited part may tend to 'get out of control', i.e. to assert its autonomy against the restraints imposed on it; it may tend to act to the detriment of the whole. In a 'normal' environment, these tensions between part and whole are of a transitory nature, and equilibrium is restored with the completion of the transaction. Under paranormal conditions—traumatic challenges— this is not the case, and only what one might call 'adaptations of the second order' can restore the balance. The animal's capacity to re- cover from such traumatic challenges is its regenerative potential.

A stable, monotonous environment tends to produce stereotyped and automatized reaction-patterns. A variable environment calls for flexible strategies, for behavioural matrices with sufficient degrees of freedom to cope with the changing conditions. Paranormal challenges call for a kind of super-flexibility, for adaptations of a second order which enable the animal to carry out major reorganizations on several levels of its structural or functional hierarchies. The range of this ability constitutes the animal's 'regenerative span'.

The regenerative span of a species thus provides it with an additional safety device in the service of survival, which enters into action when the limits of dynamic equilibrium are exceeded—as the shock-absorbers of a motor-car take over when the range of elasticity of the suspension springs is exceeded. But it is more than a safety device. Regeneration has been described as 'one of the more spectacular pieces of magic in the repertoire of living organisms'.[4] That may be the reason why it is so difficult to find a satisfactory definition which would embrace the whole range of phenomena to which the term is applied.

These include (a) the replication of entire individuals by asexual re- production (fission and budding); (b) the reconstitution of a whole organism from its broken-up fragments, or from a single fragment.

Sponges and hydra can be disintegrated into small clumps or even single cells by forcing them through a fine filter mesh, yet will reorganize themselves into normal, complete individuals. A single tentacle of a sweet-water polyp is capable of regenerating a complete individual; and transverse slices of a flatworm, taken from any part of its body, will regenerate the whole animal—including, brains, eyes, genitalia, and other complex organs which the segment did not contain. (c) Among the higher animals, crustaceans are capable of regenerating single organs exposed to accidental damage (antennae, stalk-eyes, etc.); among vertebrates, salamanders and newts are capable of regenerating limbs, eyes, tails, and some inner organs (lungs and gonads); the process in these cases follows closely the processes of embryonic development. (d) Equipped with high regenerative powers, some animals practise autotomy—the self-amputation of an exposed structure in the grasp of an enemy, which is subsequently replaced. Lizards let go of their tails; crabs, insects, and spiders of their legs or antennae, starfish cast off an arm. Self-amputation is facilitated by a 'breaking plane' of weakened structure somewhere near the base of the expendable appendage—rather like the perforations between stamps. (e) Among mammalia, regeneration is generally limited to the repair of damaged bone, muscle, skin, and peripheral nerves. (f) Lastly, the term 'physiological regeneration' is used for the routine replacement of tissues used up by ordinary wear and tear.

Thus regeneration appears to serve two different functions: on the one hand normal, asexual reproduction, on the other, the restoration of organs and structures lost by accidental mutilation or by wear and tear. But the two functions are in fact continuous; they shade into each other, and are often undistinguishable. If a flatworm spontaneously sheds its tail, then grows a new tail and the shed tail grows a new head, this is called asexual reproduction; if it is sliced into two in the laboratory it is called regeneration; and the same goes for budding, which is the natural way of reproduction of some marine coelenterates, but can be artificially induced by laceration of the body wall. The 'regenerative field' in the salamander's amputated leg-stump obeys the same type of code as the morphogenetic field of embryonic primordia. And vice versa: the development of twins or triplets following accidental fragmentation might as well be called a regenerative process. Hence, ontogenesis may be described as the regeneration of a complete individual from a fragment specially set aside for that purpose. But this 'setting apart' of undifferentiated embryonic cells

which 'specialize in non-specialization' occurs in regenerative processes too—for instance, in annelids, hydra, and flatworms, which store
'reserve cells' or 'regeneration cells' in various parts of their bodies
and mobilize them when the need arises. Sexual reproduction thus
appears merely as an added twist to asexual regeneration—though a
twist with momentous consequences. Instead of replicating a single
genetic code *ad infinitum*, the bisociation of two genetic codes is the
basic model of the creative act.

Although closely related species on the same level of the evolutionary hierarchy may differ widely in their regenerative power, it is
nevertheless true that, in a general way, this power decreases as we
proceed from lower to higher organisms. The essence of organic
regeneration is a release of genetic cell potentials which are normally
inhibited in adult tissue.

Physiological Isolation

These genetic potentials are the residues of the cell's erstwhile totipotentiality before differentiation set in—its original power to create
a whole new organism. Some of that power is reactivated when the
regeneration tissue—the part designed to replace the lost organ or
limb—is released from the controls which under normal conditions
keep it under restraint. For this partial or total secession of the part
from the whole, C. M. Child coined the useful concept of 'physiological isolation'.[5]

Physiological isolation may be regarded as a drastic form of dis-
equilibrium between the part and the whole. Its consequences may be
beneficial or deleterious. Child distinguishes four causes for it. (a)
Growth of the whole beyond a critical limit may make it ungovern-
able so that parts of it find themselves outside the range of central
dominance and control. This may lead in lower organisms to reproduction by fission or budding: the isolated part is either shed (as,
for instance, the planarian's tail) to form a new organism, or it may
de-differentiate and reintegrate into a complete organism by budding.
(b) Decline of the organism's powers of control (through senescence,
metabolic or hormonal disorders) may, in combination with other
causes, lead to a pathological regression of cells and tissues with un-
trammelled proliferation and without reintegration, resulting in malignant growths. (c) Partial obstruction or total blockage of (nervous and

chemical) communications, and (d) persistent local excitation beyond a critical limit, may release the part from its normal controls and activate, for better or worse, its latent potentialities.

We shall see that Child's 'isolation' concept has a wide range of applicability. In all cases, isolation of the part from the whole leads to de-differentiation or other forms of regression; in some cases this is followed by re-differentiation and reintegration. Isolation leading to regression of an irreversible kind plays a considerable part in pathology, psycho-pathology, and social pathology.* On the other hand, regression followed by a progressive rebound releases creative potentials which are normally under restraint. Its magic can be observed on every level: from asexual reproduction to the repair of structural damage and functional disorder, and further up to psychotherapy, scientific discovery, and artistic creation. In the chapter which follows I shall briefly discuss the manifestations of 'super-flexibility'—of *reculer pour mieux sauter*—on these various levels.

NOTE

To p. 453. Thus, for instance, Smithers in *A Clinical Prospect of the Cancer Problem* (1960) stresses the decisive influence which Child's *Physiological Foundations of Behaviour* had on the development of his ideas.

IV

RECULER POUR MIEUX SAUTER

Structural Regenerations

In *primitive* organisms such as the flatworm, and in the early embryonic stages of higher organisms, a physiologically isolated part tends in general 'to lose its characteristics as a part and to become or approach the condition of a new whole individual'.[1] Liberation of the part's previously restrained genetic potential 'involves a change in behaviour and structure from that of a part towards that of a whole organism'.[2] Such organisms could be said to live not only in dynamic equilibrium with their environment, but in a kind of 'regenerative equilibrium' which enables them to rise to virtually any challenge by means of these secondary adaptations.

Some *higher animals* are still capable of regenerating lost organs or limbs. Let us have a closer look how it is done. When a salamander's leg has been amputated, the tissues near the wound surface de-differentiate and the cells acquire an embryonic appearance. This is the regressive or 'catabolic' phase. Around the fourth day begins the formation of the blastema—the regeneration bud; and from here on throughout the 'anabolic' or synthetic phase the process follows closely the formation of limbs in normal embryonic development.* The blastema elongates into a cone and develops axially, the toes at its tip appearing first, and the rest of the limb gradually taking shape as it grows in length. When the organ is completed, central control is taken over by the nervous system, just as in the case of the embryo. The nervous system, however, also plays an indispensable part in initiating the first, catabolic phase. If no peripheral nerves are present in the amputation stump, regeneration does not occur.**

The 'isolated part' in this case is the amputation stump. The blastema has in the beginning the multi-potential characteristics of the organ primordia, and its re-differentiation again proceeds stepwise: if the

454

field is split in half, each half gives rise to a whole organ; if one half is removed, the remaining half will still develop into a complete limb.

Although the isolated part, transformed into a new organ primordium (or its close equivalent), enjoys a high degree of independence and controls the formation of the new limb, its ties with the higher levels of the hierarchy are not completely severed. Its function in the whole has changed; its normal controls (through the nervous system and local chemical gradients) are out of action or even reversed; but the organism as a whole nevertheless assists the regenerating part by certain emergency measures—a 'general alarm reaction' followed by a 'general adaptation syndrome', each stage indicated by metabolic changes and by the appearance of specific proteins and hormones in the circulatory system.

Thus the isolation of the part is only temporary and relative; and when the process is completed, the regenerated limb assumes its normal function in the whole. The entire regressive-progressive sequence is the means by which the animal's 'regenerative equilibrium' enables it to adjust to traumatic experiences from the environment.

Looked at from a different angle, one might say that the whole process is designed to prevent or correct malformations, i.e. faulty integrations. Without the initial nerve supply, the regressing amputation stump would be resorbed, the scar tissue would close over it, and the animal would achieve a *modus vivendi* as a cripple—a faulty integration. On the other hand, a frog which will not normally regenerate a lost limb will do so if the nerve supply to the stump is artificially augmented, providing the initial stimulus to start the process. Traumatic challenges can only be met by the liberation of the organism's latent powers—a temporary return to a more youthful or primitive condition.

Reversed Gradients

An important part in regeneration, as in morphogenesis, is played by *axial gradients*. The apical or 'head' end of the fertilized egg, the growing embryo, or the regenerating limb, are exposed to the highest degree of stimulation and show the highest rate of metabolism, protein synthesis, and RNA activity. Thus the anterior end becomes the dominant region, the 'head' in the literal and metaphorical sense, and exercises a restraining influence on the genetic potentials along the axial gradient—so that activity is highest at the front and lowest at the

tail end (higher organisms have of course a complex pattern of interacting gradients, some axial, some radial). But physical isolation by
blockage or hyper-excitation (Child's third and fourth cause) of parts
in previously subordinate positions can be shown to alter or *reverse* the
gradient. In plants, where the dominant region is the growing tip of
the shoot, pruning makes previously subordinate parts burst into
activity. If in the marine polyp, *tubularia*, a piece of the stem is cut out,
the frontal end of the fragment will normally regenerate the hydrant
which is its 'head'; but if a ligature is applied to isolate the front end
of the fragment, the gradient is reversed and the tail end, now the region
of maximum excitation, becomes dominant and grows a head.
Similarly, short pieces of planaria sometimes regenerate one head at
the front and another at the tail end, if the metabolism of both cut
surfaces is equally high.

The Dangers of Regression

Two more phenomena must be mentioned in this context: the first
illustrates the flexibility, the second the vulnerability of regenerative
processes.

If the crystalline lens of a salamander-eye is removed, part of the
iris de-differentiates, forms a vesicle, enters the cavity through the
pupil, re-differentiates, and forms a normal lens—whereas in embryonic
development the lens is formed by the epidermis overlaying the eye-
cup, without participation of the iris. Thus the morphogenetic skill of
making a lens can make use of either of two different materials; the
code is again invariant, the strategy adaptable.*

On the other hand, the factors which, in a higher organism, determine whether a given trauma will lead to regenerative or pathological
changes are of an extremely delicate nature. Thus Smithers[3] writes:

'The type of structure regenerated, or the kind of neoplasm formed,
will depend on the level of the controlling field-gradient against which
it is exerting itself, and the steepness of the gradient it can itself establish and promote as shown by its tendency towards undifferentiated
cell-reproduction. The part which is physiologically isolated then
produces an imperfect portion of a new whole, giving rise to whatever
tissues it is capable of forming under the circumstances pertaining.
This may result in malformations of all degrees, from simple overgrowth of adult tissues, through irregular mixtures of recognizable,

well-differentiated cells, to the most rapidly growing, undifferentiated tumours.'

Pathogenic regulatory responses are reactions to stimulations which are 'outside the standardized range of normal experience of the species during its developmental peak period. They do not differ from the normal regulatory responses, however, in any fundamental particular. . . . Tissue overgrowth as a response to a long-continued external irritant, is of the same order as heat regulation, wound-healing or lactation. . . . Useless or harmful regulating mechanisms and tissue responses to isolation, injury, or stimulation are not fundamentally different in kind from those favourable ones which have become incorporated into the inheritance of the species because they promoted survival through the period of reproductive activity. . . . The tissues most often called on for regeneration and repair, or most liable to recurrent stimulation into specialized activity, are those most prone to tumour formation.'[4]

'Routine Regenerations'

The last sentence that I have quoted leads into the borderland between regenerative and 'normal' processes: namely routine replacements. They range from the periodic moulting of feathers and shedding of the antlers, to the replacement of the whole human epidermis about once a month owing to wear and tear, and the replacement of red blood cells at the rate of 3×10^{11} per day; not to mention the metabolic turnover on the molecular level which consumes about thirty per cent of our total protein intake. This type of routine (or so-called 'physiological') regeneration which goes on all the time is sometimes described as a constant 'renewal' or 'rejuvenation' of the body. It is often impossible to make a clear distinction between 'wear' and 'tear'—for instance in minor abrasions of the skin. The differential factor is obviously the degree of stress, which, past a critical threshold, will bring general alarm reactions and 'adaptations of the second order' into play.

Reorganizations of Function

The transplanted salamander limb which functions normally in spite of its randomized nervous connections can be regarded as an example of both regeneration of structure and reorganization of function. The pathways leading into the limb all seem to be equipotential in their capacity as conductors of the excitation-clang. Without entering the old controversy about equipotentiality versus localization of functions in nervous tissues, it seems to be safe to say that in repetitive routines and local reflexes, equipotentiality has 'frozen up' into fixed local arrangements; whereas in case of injury to the pathways in question, the equipotentiality (or rather, multi-potentiality) of alternative 'canal-systems' is revived, and they take over the function of the injured system. To quote Lashley: 'The results indicate that when habitually used motor organs are rendered non-functional by removal or paralysis, there is an immediate, spontaneous use of other motor systems which had not previously been associated with, or used in, the performance of the activity.'[5] Nearly a century earlier Pflüger had shown that even the spinal reflexes of a frog are capable of 'crisis adaptations'. If a drop of acid is placed on the back of the left front limb of a decapitated frog, it will attempt to wipe it away with the left hind limb; but if prevented from doing so it will use the right hind limb—which it normally never does in the exercise of the wiping reflex.

Turning from the spinal level to the brain, Lashley's celebrated maze experiments have shown what astonishing regenerative adaptations the cerebral cortex is capable of. If a rat is trained to choose between two doors the one where a brighter light is shown, this habit (or at least part of it) must be localized in its optical cortex, for if this is extirpated, the habit is lost. But a rat with its optical cortex cut out can still be taught or re-taught the same skill. This means that some other cortical area has taken over the learning function after extirpation of the proper area—just as in the morphogenetic field intact tissue will deputize for lost tissue. Moreover, if a rat has learned to run a certain maze, no matter what parts of its motor cortex are injured, it will follow its path—even if it has to roll the whole way with paralysed legs; and if the injury makes it incapable of executing a right turn, it will achieve its aim by a three-quarter turn to the left. The rat may be blinded, deprived of its smell, partially paralysed in various ways— each of which would throw the chain-reflex automation, which the rat was supposed to be, completely out of gear. Yet: 'One drags himself through [the maze] with his forepaws; another falls at every step but gets through by a series of lunges; a third rolls over completely in making each turn, yet avoids rolling into a cul-de-sac and makes an errorless run. The behaviour presents exactly the same problem of direct adaptation of any motor organs to the attainment of a given end which was outstanding in my earlier observations on monkeys after destruction of the pre-central gyri. If the customary sequence of movements employed in reaching the food is rendered impossible, another set, not previously used in the habit, and constituting an entirely different motor pattern, may be directly and efficiently substituted without any random activity.'[6]

In human beings, structural regeneration—of skin, bone, muscle, and peripheral nerves—is confined to tissue-outgrowth: that is to say, the new structures are derived from cells of their own kind, not from dedifferentiating tissues. But though we have lost the amphibian's enviable powers of replacing a lost limb, we have gained a unique super-flexibility of functions in our nervous system.

On its lowest level it is manifested in certain secondary or crisis-adaptations of neuro-muscular mechanisms. The artificial limbs invented by the German surgeon Sauerbruch are flexed by muscles in the stump which formerly acted as extensors, and extended by flexors.[7] Other reversals of function are obtained by grafting operations. When the musculo-spiral nerve which activates the extensors of wrist and fingers is severed with resulting paralysis, the damage can be repaired by grafting one of the flexor-tendons from the inner side of the wrist on to the extensor-muscle. After a while the flexor will deputize for his former antagonist, although it remains attached to the 'wrong' (median) nerve—which thus carries opposite orders to the remaining flexors and to the transplanted one, along the same common path.*[8]

In these and similar grafting operations the first step is the undoing of a fixed neuro-muscular connection; thereby the nerve to be grafted becomes 'de-specialized' as it were—the functional analogue to the dedifferentiation of structures—and regains its multi-potentiality to function in more than one way. The second step, when the grafting operation is completed, is 're-specialization' of the nerve in its new role, and the reintegration of the new neuro-muscular unit into the whole. Similar considerations apply to Lashley's rats or Bethe's insects —except, of course, that in their case, the reorganization of functions is spontaneous.

Thus there is a close parallel between the regeneration of structures and the reorganization of functions after traumatic challenges; and both are continuous with the regulative principle in morphogenesis. The antithesis between 'localization of functions, fixed pathways' on the one hand, and 'mulitpotential pathways, selective responses' on the other, reflects the earlier antithesis between the mosaic character and the regulative character in embryonic development. But the seemingly opposite principles turn out to be in fact complementary aspects of development. With each successive step in the differentiation of the embryo, of the nervous system, and of adult behaviour-patterns, the regulative powers decrease, and the mosaic-character of structures and functions increases: tissues become specialized, responses localized, habits automatized—up to a point. For all matrices of structure and behaviour display varying amounts of flexibility even while the organism lives in dynamic equilibrium with its environment; but the often unsuspected amount of its regenerative potential becomes only manifest when a severe challenge induces it to retrace its steps on the genetic gradient, as it were, and make a fresh start.

Reculer sans Sauter

Hyper-excited organs or organ-systems tend to get out of control. During the repair of physical injuries, the injured part tends to monopolize the attention of the whole organism; in periods of starvation, the digestive system asserts itself to the detriment of other parts; in rage and panic, the sympathico-adrenal apparatus tyrannizes the whole; and when sex is aroused, reason (as the Austrian proverb has it) 'descends into the testes'. The over-excited part behaves as if it were in a temporary state of 'physiological isolation' (pp. 452 f.), released from its restraints; it asserts its autonomy and sometimes tends to usurp the functions of the whole.

Analogous situations occur on the cognitive level, where the 'hyper-excited part' appears in the guise of the *idée fixe*, or a 'closed system' of beliefs. Both the achievements and aberrations of human thought are to a large extent due to obsessional preoccupations with religious and scientific theories, or political ideologies, more or less closely knitted around some central idea, around a part-truth usurping the role of the whole truth.

We have seen in the previous volume how an obsessional preoccupation can force the whole mental organization into its service during the period of incubation, and give birth to a new system of thought. But these are the glorious exceptions; in the vast majority of cases, the 'over-valued idea' (to use Kretschmer's[9] term) will become segregated from the rest of the mental field, and assert itself in harmful ways. The results are all too familiar: personalities whose whole outlook is dominated by prejudice and biassed values; the compulsive rituals of neurotics; the devouring obsession of the crank; and so on to the major psychoses in which large chunks of the personality have been 'split off' and become permanently isolated from the rest. The intrusion of magic causation; inability to distinguish between fact and fantasy; delusions of grandeur, or persecution by invisible powers, are symptoms of regression to earlier levels, of the de-differentiation of thought-matrices—of *reculer sans sauter*.

Regeneration and Psychotherapy

Less extreme cases are neurotics who react to their traumatic experiences by elaborating defence systems which enable them to find some kind of *modus vivendi* with the world. One may call such behaviour-patterns 'faulty integrations'—like the newt's whose forelegs move backwards. Psychotherapy aims at undoing faulty integrations by inducing a temporary regression of the patient to an earlier level, in the hope that he will eventually reintegrate into a more stable pattern. Neurosurgery, shock-therapy, and related methods aim at releasing phylogenetically older centres of the brain from cortical restraints. In a less drastic form, Freudians, Jungians, etc., try to make the patient revert to unconscious and infantile planes of experience, and to regenerate, as it were, into a more or less new-born person.

Thus psychotherapy may be called an experiment in artificially induced regeneration. It relies on the same basic process of *reculer pour mieux sauter*, which we see operating on every level: from the flatworm which replaces a lost head, through the crab which adjusts its gait to the loss of a leg, to the rat which, unable to turn to the right, makes a three-quarter turn to the left. We found the same pattern repeated on the level of human creativity: the scientist, faced by a perplexing situation—Kepler's discrepant eight minutes' arc, Einstein's light-traveller paradox—must plunge into a 'dark night of the soul' before he can re-emerge into the light. The history of the sciences and arts is a tale of recurrent crises, of traumatic challenges, which entail a temporary disintegration of the traditional forms of reasoning and perception: a de-differentiation of thought-matrices, a dismantling of its axioms, a new innocence of the eye; followed by the liberation from restraint of creative potentials, and their reintegration in a new synthesis.

There is also a mental equivalent for the less spectacular routine regeneration of tissues, designed to compensate for wear and tear. The analogue process is the maintenance of 'mental tissues' exposed to the wear and tear of diurnal stresses, by the regenerative effect of nocturnal regressions to the primitive levels of the dream. Experimental evidence seems to indicate that the restorative powers of sleep are primarily derived from the process of dreaming. Experimental subjects who were woken up each time their EEG waves indicated the onset of dreaming, displayed symptoms of fatigue and nervous disorder; long periods of dreamless sleep could not compensate for dream-deprivation. 'Man cannot persist long in a conscious state,' wrote Goethe, 'he must throw himself back into the unconscious, for his root lives there.'

We have seen (Book One, VII, VIII) that these periodic plunges into the unconscious are accompanied by the temporary disintegration of matrices of logical thought. But they also entail a partial loss of identity, a de-differentiation of the personality—as indicated by the remarkable degree of uniformity in the contents of dreams shared by people of very different character, and by the relatedness of these contents to mythological themes and symbols. These shared patterns led Jung to postulate a 'collective'—that is, individually undifferentiated—level of the unconscious. On that level, members of the same culture seem to share some degree of psychic equipotentiality expressed in 'archetypal symbols'. These are supposed to be condensations of basic experiences of the race in the distant past; hence their great emotion-rousing potential.

To recapitulate: the fact that art and discovery draw on unconscious sources indicates that one aspect of all creative activity is a regression to ontogenetically or phylogenetically earlier levels, an escape from the restraints of the conscious mind, with the subsequent release of creative potentials—a process paralleled on lower levels by the liberation from restraint of genetic potentials or neural equipotentiality in the regeneration of structures and functions. The scientist, traumatized by discordant facts, the artist by the pressures of sensibility, and the rat by surgical intervention, share, on different levels, the same super-flexibility enabling them to perform 'adaptations of a second order', rarely found in the ordinary routines of life.

I must enlarge a little on this seemingly sweeping analogy, and try to show that it is in fact based on homologous principles, traceable on all levels of the hierarchy, and preserving their basic pattern throughout them.

Differentiation and specialization of the parts are necessary for the normal functioning of the whole; abnormal conditions call for radical measures which may include a retreat of the over-exerted part to a structurally less differentiated, functionally less specialized stage, if the whole is to survive. The 'part' may be the newt's amputation stump, or the unsolved problem in the scientist's mind which tortures and obsesses him. We have seen that such regressions are mostly patho-genic, but under favourable conditions they may redress the situation by re-activating potentials which had been operative in the past but are inhibited in the adult—such as the regulative powers of the embryo in the womb or the undifferentiated total-pattern-responses of its nervous system. The period of incubation is a similar retreat, if not into the womb, at least into long-outgrown forms of ideation, into the pre-verbal, pre-rational games of the unconscious, the wonderland-logic of the dream. The challenge which sets the process going is in all cases a traumatic experience: physical mutilation or mental lacera-tion—by data which do not fit, observations which contradict each other, emotions which disrupt approved styles in art: experiences which create mental conflict, dissonance, perplexity. The 'creative stress' of the artist or scientist corresponds to the 'general alarm re-action' of the traumatized animal; the anabolic-catabolic sequence of de-differentiation and reintegration corresponds to the destructive-constructive sequence in the creative act. The 'physiological isolation' of the over-excited part which tends to dominate, corresponds to the single-minded and obsessive preoccupation with the *idée fixe*—Kretschmer's 'over-valued idea', Kepler's pursuit of a chimera—which monopolizes the whole mind; it will either lead to its reorganization by giving birth to a new system, or to the cancerous proliferation of a degenerate tissue of ideas.

Over-excitation of an organ or part is one of the four causes of 'physiological isolation'. The other three were: growth of the whole beyond a critical limit; senescence; and (partial) blockage of com-munication (pp. 452 f.). Each situation has its parallels on the mental plane—of the individual, or the history of thought. The unmanageable size of the total body of human knowledge—or even a single province thereof—created that dissociated phenomenon, the specialist mind; senescent cultures produce degenerate art-forms; blocked communications between Ptolemaic astronomy and the main body of the physical sciences led to the untramelled proliferation of epicycles in a closed system, divorced from reality.

'It is wonderful to see how analogies can blossom when they are given a little affection', wrote the authors of a book I have repeatedly quoted.[10] Particularly, one might add, if they have solid roots in the earth. So let me carry analogy one step further. In Book One (Chapters V–VIII) I have described various aspects of the Eureka process; each of these re-structurings of thought has its obvious correlate in regenerative processes on lower levels. The 'displacement of emphasis' to a previously irrelevant part or aspect of experience corresponds to the sudden dominance of a hitherto subordinate part of an organism—such as the crab's second leg which becomes a pacemaker. The 'reversal of logic' (or of the figure-background relation) has its parallel in the reversal of physiological gradients during regeneration. When psychological textbooks describe Duncker's experiments as 'detaching' part of a visual percept from the context in which it is 'embedded', and 'attaching' it to the new context of the problem to be solved (pp. 189 f.) this description itself is based on analogies from physiological processes. During incubation, the intuitive groping of ideas towards the 'good combination', and their guidance by 'gradients in the unconscious', reminds one of the biochemical gradients in morphogenesis, or the 'contact-guidance' of out-growing nerve-processes towards their end-organ. Lastly a 'nascent', unverbalized analogy may be compared to an unarticulated organ-primordium.

But these genetic skills operate only in the embryonic stage of development; in the adult they are superseded by the integrative action of the nervous system—unless the embryonic potentials are re-activated by regenerative needs. Similarly, the adult's mental co-ordination relies on conscious, verbalized, 'logical' codes; not on the quasi 'embryonic' (infantile, pre-causal) potentials of the unconscious; again unless these are revived under the creative stress. Physical re-generations strike us as 'spectacular pieces of magic' because they derive from pre-natal skills; and creative inspirations are equally mysterious because they derive from levels which predate the conscious mind. As Polànyi wrote (in a different context): 'The highest forms of originality are far more closely akin to the lowest biotic performances than the external circumstances would indicate.'[11]

Regeneration and Evolution

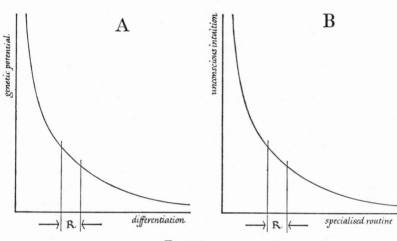

FIGURE 14

These rather fancy diagrams are solely meant to indicate in a crude way the complementary factors in the *reculer pour mieux sauter* phenomenon. In A, increase in tissue-differentiation entails a reciprocal decrease of genetic multipotentiality. In B, an analogous reciprocity prevails between unconscious intuitions and automatized routines—or, if you like, between fluid imagery and 'misplaced concreteness'. R indicates the 'regenerative span'. (The curve in A should of course have breaks and a series of discrete steps.)

It could be objected that structural regenerations merely restore the *status quo ante* whereas mental reorganization leads to an advance. But in the first place this is not always the case. Psychotherapy aims at correcting 'faulty integrations' caused by traumatic experiences—at restoring normality. In the second place the biological evolution of the species with which we are concerned has to all intents and purposes come to a standstill, whereas mental evolution continues, and its vehicle is precisely the creative individual. The Eureka process is a mental mutation, perpetuated by social inheritance. Its biological equivalent are the genetic mutations which carried the existing species up the evolutionary ladder. Now a mutation—whatever its unknown cause—is no doubt a re-moulding of previous structures, based on a de-differentiation and reintegration of the otherwise rigid genetic code. The transformations of fins into legs, legs into arms, arms into wings, gills into lungs, scales into feathers, etc., while preserving certain basic structural patterns (see, for instance, d'Arcy Thompson's *On Growth and Form*) were eminently 'witty' answers to the challenges of environment. It seems obvious that the dramatic release, at periods of adaptative radiations, of unexplored morphogenetic potentials by a re-shuffling of molecules in the genetic code, resulting in the de-differentiation and reintegration of structures like limbs into wings, is of the very essence of the evolutionary process. After all, 'ontogenesis and regenesis are components of a common mechanism',[12] which must have a phylogenetic origin.

In Book One, Chapter XX, I have mentioned the perennial myth of the prophet's and hero's temporary isolation and retreat from human society—followed by his triumphant return endowed with new powers. Buddha and Mohamed go out into the desert; Joseph is thrown into the well; Jesus is resurrected from the tomb. Jung's 'death and re-birth' motif, Toynbee's 'withdrawal and return' reflect the same archetypal motif. It seems that *reculer pour mieux sauter* is a principle of universal validity in the evolution of species, cultures, and individuals, guiding their progression by feedback from the past.

NOTES

To p. 454. It is still an open question, however, whether or how much undifferentiated 'reserve cells' (as in lower animals) contribute material to the blastema.

To p. 454. It seems that the initial role of the nervous system is to determine the main axis of the regenerate—that it acts, not as an inductor, but as a trophic agent. At the later, anabolic stages of the process no nerve supply is needed—as denervation experiments show.

To p. 456. This, actually, is the only clearly demonstrated case of metaplasia among higher animals.

To p. 459. About the ways how this is achieved, cf. McCulloch in the Hixon Symposium, p. 56.

V

PRINCIPLES OF ORGANIZATION

Before we turn to adult behaviour, a pause for stocktaking may
be in order.

In a four-dimensional continuum, embryonic development
would be represented by an ascending hierarchy of spatial levels perpendicular to the time axis. In spite of the perplexing diversity of
phenomena on different levels—cleavage, gastrulation, induction,
neuro-genesis—certain basic principles were seen to operate on every
level throughout the hierarchy. Principles (or 'laws of nature') can
only be described in symbolic language of one kind or another. The
language used in the present theory is based on four key-concepts:
motivation, code, matrix, and environment. Since these are assumed to
operate in a hierarchic framework, the dichotomy of self-asserting and
participatory tendencies of behaviour on all levels need not be separately
postulated, but derives logically, as it were, from the dual character
of every sub-whole as a sub-ordinate and supra-ordinate entity.
Let me now recapitulate some of the main points which have
emerged from the previous chapters, taken in conjunction with
Book One:

1. *Motivation* in embryonic development is a subject for the metaphysician. J. Needham's tongue-in-the-cheek phrase about 'the
striving of the blastula to grow into a chicken' indicates the directiveness of the morphogenetic process and its equifinal, regulative properties, which become particularly evident under adverse conditions.
These properties represent the genetic precursors of the motivational
drives, needs, and goal-directedness of the adult animal; during maturation, the former shade into the latter, and there is no sharp dividing line
between them.

2. 'A part is a whole is a part'. Each sub-whole is both a 'sub' and a

467

'whole'. Facing downward or outward in the hierarchy, it behaves as an autonomous whole; facing upward or inward, it behaves as a dependent part which is inhibited or triggered into action by higher controls. One might call this the 'Janus principle' in organic (and social) hierarchies.

3. The 'whole'-aspect of the sub-whole is manifested in its *autonomous* and *spontaneous* activities. The principle of autonomy is asserted on every level; from cell-organelles functioning as power plants or motor units, through the self-differentiating activities of the morphogenetic field, to the autonomous regulations of organs and organ system. In the motor hierarchy, it is reflected at every stage, from the muscle's selective response to specific excitation-patterns, through the stubborn behaviour of the reversed newt limb, to the unalterable features in a person's gait or handwriting. I have briefly mentioned (Book One, Chapters XIII, XXI), and shall discuss in more detail later, autonomous mechanism in perceptual organization—visual constancies, the automatic filtering, analysing, generalizing of the input. Lastly, thinking and communicating are based on hierarchically ordered, autonomous patterns of enunciation, grammar, logic, mathematical operations, universes of discourse.

The *dynamic* aspect of the part's autonomy is manifested in its apparently spontaneous, unprovoked rhythmic activities which are 'modified but not created by the environmental input'—a statement which equally applies to morphogenesis, to intrinsic motor patterns, to the spontaneous discharges of unstimulated sensory receptors, the electric pulses of the unstimulated brain, to drives in the absence of external stimuli or to communications addressed to imaginary audiences.

Autonomy and spontaneity taken together constitute what I have called the 'self-assertive' aspect of part-behaviour.

4. The opposite aspect is the part's dependence on supra-ordinate controls which may be said to represent the interests of the whole *vis-à-vis* the part in question. The controls are largely of an inhibitory or restraining character, to prevent overloading of information channels, over-shooting of responses, confusion and redundancy in general; while the activation of the part is effected by signals of the trigger-release type. During morphogenesis, control is exercised by the suppression of unrequired, and the release of required genetic potentials; in the mature organism by interlacing multiple hierarchies of nervous and circulatory processes, and biochemical gradients.

5. Sub-wholes on any level of the hierarchy function (a) autonomously in supra-ordination to their own parts, (b) in sub-ordination to their controlling agency, and (c) in co-ordination with their environment.

'Environment' is a relative term. On the level of the single cell, the environment of the nucleus is cytoplasm; on the level of the morphogenetic field, the environment of one cell-population is another cell-population; each organ in the adult animal is bathed in body-fluids which constitute its environment. The structure and function of any sub-whole is *determined* by (a) and (b)—its intrinsic pattern and its controls in the 'vertical' hierarchy to which it belongs; but it is also *affected* by inputs and feedbacks from its 'horizontal' environment, as it were—the lie of the land. The difference between (a) and (b) on the one hand, and (c) on the other is that the former determine the invariant pattern of the operation, (c) only its variable details. To mention a few examples: feedback from the cytoplasm to the genetic blue-print co-determines into which variety of specialized cell that particular unit will develop; but it does not alter the blue-print itself. Inductor substances in the immediate environment of a tissue will promote its differentiation into an organ—but only within the limits of the tissue's 'competence'. Environmental hazards decide the neuromuscular connections in the grafted salamander-limb, but its functional co-ordination remains unaffected by it: it is controlled by its 'vertical' hierarchy, and the lie of the land in the scar-tissue determines only the local 'tactics' of the outgrowing nerve-filaments.

Thus the function of every component in the organism is determined by two types of 'input'. The first consists of specific trigger signals from its superior controls in the hierarchy; the second are inputs and feedbacks from more or less random events in its environment. But I must stress again that the meaning of the word 'environment' depends on the hierarchic level to which it is applied. The environment of John driving his car is the traffic stream around him. The environment of John's right foot is the brake-pedal on which it rests. Let us call the former an environment on the t-level, where t stands for the top of the hierarchy controlling the various sensory, motor, and cognitive processes which constitute the skill of driving; then the brake-pedal will be an environment on the, say, t minus 4 level. Now John approaches a sign which reads 'Halt—Road Works Ahead'. This input is analysed and relayed by various stations of the perceptual and cognitive hierarchy, and is eventually re-coded into a 'sign releaser' which triggers off the pre-set patterns of slow-down-to-a-halt behaviour on lower echelons of the motor hierarchy. Thus an *environmental* input on the t-level has been transformed into a specific trigger signal in a 'vertical' hierarchy; in other words a 'category c' input on a higher level has been translated into a 'category b' input on a lower level, activating the autonomous pattern of the slowing-down skill. This consists in several sub-skills: braking, steadying the wheel, going into neutral gear at the proper moment. The foot on the brake-pedal is not responding to the 'Halt' signal from the environment; it is responding to a specific 'excitation-clang' travelling down John's spinal cord. But the foot's pre-set response is modified by feedback from the environment on its own level: the 'feel' of the pedal's elastic resistance governs the 'strategy' of braking—neither too abruptly nor too softly. Similar feedbacks influence the automatized motions of the hands on the wheel, etc.

We may perhaps speculate that the digitally coded signals: 'brake', 'steady wheel' have been converted into analogue-computing servo-mechanisms. But speculations apart, we can confidently say that an action-pattern of a general nature has been initiated on the top level, and that the details were successively filled in by feedbacks from more and more restricted local environments on the lower echelons. Similarly, the future adult is 'roughed in' in a summary way in the morphogenetic gradients of the zygote, then 'sketched in' in the organ-*Anlage* of the uncouth embryo, and so on, until the last detail is elaborated by the joint action of a cell-group's self-differentiation potential and its local environment. The performance of a skill means executing a general order by a series of progressively differentiated action-patterns, each controlled from above, and adjusted by local feedbacks.*

We thus arrive at a synthesis between the principles of hierarchic organization and feedback adjustment. To the hierarchy of autonomous sub-wholes must be added the complementary 'hierarchy of environments' and 'hierarchy of feedbacks'—of loops-within-loops, from those embracing the personality as a whole in the 'total field', down to the molecular level. An elementary but engaging model for a hierarchy of servo-mechanisms is the 'TOTE unit' proposed by Pribram.[1]

Let me dot my i's on this rather important point by a martial analogy. The commander of the N'th Army has decided, taking into account all available intelligence reports on the enemy's dispositions, to capture tomorrow at dawn the vital hill No. 607. He sends his orders to his six divisional comanders, broadly outlining their tasks. The commander of the 3rd division is assigned the task of occupying hamlet X. There are several approaches to the hamlet; to decide which is best, he sends out some reconnaissance aircraft which feed information to him. He then communicates his orders to his battalion commanders. Each of these will send out patrols to get the lie of the land allotted to them before giving orders to his company commanders; and in the end each individual soldier will have to make the best of his own small environment of protective hedges and ditches as he moves forward in obedience to the sergeant's orders.

6. It ought to be evident by now that the terms 'matrix' and 'code' are not meant to refer to separate entities, but (like 'structure' and 'function') to complementary aspects of a unitary process. The code is the invariant pattern of the process; it is not affected by environmental input. The matrix is the ensemble of part-processes, or 'members' potentially capable of being activated by the code; it thus represents the total repertory of alternative (equipotential or equifinal) variations in carrying out the process, according to feedbacks from the environment. The code is the fixed, the matrix the adaptable side of the process; the former determines the rules of the game, the latter the actual course of the game. The matrix, therefore, represents the more 'alert' or 'articulate' or 'explicit' side of the unitary process—the side turned towards the environment. The twenty-letter alphabet of protein-synthesis in the cell-matrix is more explicit than the three-letter alphabet of the genetic code; it 'spells out' what the latter implied. The articulated motions of the limb spell out the compressed message of the excitation-clang, as the pianist's fingers spell out the tune. In the perceptual and cognitive hierarchies, the codes which govern performance (e.g. grammar and syntax) function on lower levels of awareness than the performance itself.

7. The control of the whole over the parts is exercised, as in our military hierarchy, through 'regulation channels'. The genetic code does not interfere with the details of ATP synthesis: it activates the sub-code of the mitochondria. The centre co-ordinating the motion of the limbs—in newt or man—does not deal directly with individual muscles; it activates the proper sub-centres. The battalion commander does not issue orders to individual soldiers, or even squads; he signals to Company headquarters: 'D Company will advance at 1800 hours.' The Company, the limb, the mitochondria are complex sub-wholes; but they are activated from the next-higher level *as units*, through their

codes; and they in turn activate their members as units through their sub-codes.

To put it in a different way: each part-process is a pattern of *relations*; but it is manipulated from the next-higher level as a unit—a *relatum*. We shall see that as a general rule, when we ascend in any hierarchy, relations turn into relata, which enter into new relations, and so on. The code can be said to represent the invariant pattern of a relation; the matrix the ensemble of the relata. But one step up, and the code itself becomes a relatum; one step down, and the members of the matrix are seen as complex relations. We may thus add one more pair of complementary terms to characterize the Janus-faced entities in the developmental hierarchy: part < ——— > whole; structure < ——— > function, regulative < ——— > mosaic, autonomous < ——— > dependent, relation < ——— > relatum, matrix < ——— > code.

8. The stresses set up between the organism's inner and outer environment are matched by active adaptations on various scales. The term 'dynamic equilibrium' indicates adaptative processes which do not entail major changes in the pattern of the whole; 'regenerative span' refers to the organism's capacity for 'adaptations of the second order' to challenges which can be met only by a reshaping of structures or a reorganization of functions; while 'routine regenerations' occupy an intermediary position, and overlap with both.

'Equilibrium' in this context refers not to relations between parts, but between the excited part and the controls which represent the whole. Under conditions of dynamic equilibrium, the stresses between the self-assertive tendencies of the excited part and its integrative controls are of a transitory character. Paranormal challenges may lead to the phenomenon of 'physiological isolation', owing to over-stimulation of the part or blockage of communication with its normal controls. In lower organisms, the isolated part tends to develop into a new whole. If it was segregated *ab ovo*, as sex cells and regeneration cells are, this development follows a straight course; if isolation occurs at later stages, as in fissure, budding, and organ-regeneration, it involves a temporary regression of the part to an embryonic or more juvenile phase of development, and the liberation of genetic potentials which are normally under restraint. It is a safety device which enables the organism to cope with traumatic challenges, and correct faulty integrations; it furthermore confers on it a super-flexibility which plays an important part in biological and mental evolution.

On higher levels of the evolutionary scale, regenerative processes are predominantly reorganizations of *functions*. These range from the repair of neuro-muscular co-ordination to the compensation of cortical damages, and to the re-structuring of perceptual and conceptual patterns in the *reculer pour mieux sauter* of the creative process.

During the regressive, catabolic phase, the part tends to dominate the whole through the reversal of axial gradients and hierarchic controls. This may lead to irreversible changes of a pathological nature (malignant growths, *idée fixe*). To avoid snapping of the loosened ties, the isolation of the part must be temporary and not complete: after the routine-controls have gone out of action, the organism as a whole must assist the regenerative process.

'*Routine repairs*' were seen to range from the regeneration of tissues lost through wear and tear, to the restorative effects of sleep. Dreaming could be described as a de-differentiation of reasoning-matrices and even, up to a point, of personal identity.

9. These periodic fluctuations from the highest level of integration down to earlier or more primitive levels and up again to a new, modified pattern, seem to play a major part in biological and mental evolution. Their universality is reflected in the myths of death and rebirth, the 'dark night of the soul', etc. The 'magic' of organ-regenerations, and of unconscious guidance in creativity, both owe their striking character to the sudden re-activation of (morphogenetic or psychogenetic) potentials which are normally under restraint in the adult individual. The period of incubation may be compared to the catabolic phase in organ-regeneration: the former releases pre-conceptual, intuitive modes of ideation from the censorship imposed by the conscious mind; the latter triggers off embryonic growth-processes equally inhibited by the mature organism. The contact-guidance of nerves towards their end-organs and the revival of other pre-natal skills, provide enticing parallels to the unconscious gradients and ancient 'waterways' which mediate the underground rendezvous of ideas.

Summary

To the hierarchy of sub-wholes in the development and behaviour of organisms, we have now added a complementary 'hierarchy of environments', and a third hierarchy of (exteroceptive and proprioceptive) feedbacks—of loops-within-loops which connect the first and the second on every level. Certain homologue principles of organization were seen to operate on all levels, such as: (a) the dichotomy of self-assertive and participatory tendencies derived from the dual character of each part as a 'sub' and a 'whole'; and the related complementarity of regulative and mosaic development, of equipotentiality and fixed pathway, of relations and relata. (b) Control within the organic hierarchy is exercised by 'regulation channels', i.e. high centres do not normally have direct dealings with lowly ones, and vice versa. (c) Trigger-releaser devices seem to be the general rule in the activation of pre-set, autonomous patterns. (d) The releaser signals (excitation-clangs, frequency-modulation sequences?) from higher echelons were found to be of a more implicit, generalized order than the actual performance 'spelled out' by the addressee. (e) The pattern of the performance is determined by its invariant code, but sub-wholes have varying degrees of freedom for adaptable strategies (equipotential variations) dependent on feedback from their local environment. (f) Under normal conditions these flexible strategies are sufficient to restore dynamic equilibrium between the whole and its excited parts. (g) Traumatic experiences may cause irreversible, degenerative changes in the exposed part, but under favourable conditions may initiate superflexible adaptations of a second order—regenerations of structure or reorganizations of function, which are capable of redressing faulty integration, and also play an important part in biological and mental development.

The reader may consider some of these conclusions trivial, others perhaps as rash generalizations. In the following chapters their validity will be tested in the light of instinct-behaviour, learning, and problem-solving.

NOTE

To p. 470. 'Feedback' is used here in a broad sense, to include all extero-ceptive and proprioceptive inputs relevant to the ongoing activity.

CODES OF INSTINCT BEHAVIOUR

The Genetics of Behaviour

The phylogenetic origins of instinct-behaviour are among the blackest black boxes found in the sciences of life. The causative mechanism responsible for the evolution of species in their morphological aspect is perplexing enough; regarding the origin of specific behaviour-patterns, the darkness is almost complete. As one eminent ethologist laments: 'The backward position of ethology is striking. Owing to the difficulty of tracing genetically determined behaviour components, geneticists have nearly always used morphological characters as indicators of gene-function. . . . A genetics of behaviour still has to be developed.'[1]

Evolutionary genetics lies outside the scope of this book, but a brief remark in passing may be excused. If, apart from a few tentative studies,[2] the genetics of behaviour is still an uncharted territory, the reason may perhaps be an unconscious reluctance to put the already strained theoretical framework of neo-Darwinian genetics to an additional test. To quote a very trivial example: an individual songbird or jackdaw or sparrow, on spotting a predator, will give an alarm call, warning the whole flock. 'These alarm calls', Tinbergen points out, 'are a clear example of an activity which serves the group but endangers the individual.'[3] Are we really to assume that the occulo-vocal 'wiring diagram' in the sparrow's nervous system which releases the alarm call in response to a sign-Gestalt stimulus of predatory shape, arose by random mutations and was perpetuated by natural selection in spite of its negative survival value for the mutant? The same question could be asked concerning the phylogenetic origin of the ritualized tournament fights in such various animals as stags, iguana, wolves, and fish. Wolves sprawl on their backs as a token of defeat and surrender, exposing their vulnerable bellies to the victor's fangs. One is inclined to call this a rather risky attitude; and what is the *individual* survival value of *not* hitting (or biting, goring) below the belt? Or if it comes to that, of the digger-wasps' nerve-racking maternal activities?

'A female of this species, when about to lay an egg, digs a hole, kills or paralyses a caterpillar, and carries it to the hole, where she stows it away after having deposited an egg on it (phase *a*). This done, she digs another hole, in which an egg is laid on a new caterpillar. In the meantime, the first egg has hatched and the larva has begun to consume its store of food. The mother wasp now turns her attention again to the first hole (phase *b*), to which she brings some more moth larvae; then she does the same in the second hole. She returns to the first hole for the third time to bring a final batch of six or seven caterpillars (phase *c*), after which she closes the hole and leaves it for ever. In this way she works in turn at two or even three holes, each in a different phase of development. Baerends investigated the means by which the wasp brought the right amount of food to each hole. He found that the wasp visited all the holes each morning before leaving for the hunting grounds. By changing the contents of the hole and watching the subsequent behaviour of the wasp, he found that (1) by robbing a hole he could force the wasp to bring far more food than usual; and (2) by adding larvae to the hole's contents he could force her to bring less food than usual.'[4]

Let me repeat: the reason why 'a genetics of behaviour still has to be developed' seems to be that it *cannot* be developed with the existing theoretical tools without reducing the whole attempt to absurdity. It may still be possible, and even respectable today for a geneticist to state that: 'The hoary objection of the improbability of an eye or a hand or a brain being evolved "by blind chance" has lost its force.'[5] But are we also to assume that the behaviour-patterns of the digger-wasp, or of the courtship and fighting rituals of various species have all evolved 'by pure chance'? This assumption is implied in the doctrine of contemporary genetics—though rarely stated in explicit form. Similar assumptions have been made by extreme behaviourists in the field of learning theory; there is, in fact, a direct continuity between the doctrine of natural selection operating on random mutations, and reinforcement operating on random trials. Both grew out of the same philosophical climate. But while learning theory is in full retreat from that extreme position, and has a variety of alternative suggestions to offer, nothing the like is in sight in the genetics of instinct-behaviour.

Learnt behaviour is built on the foundations of innate behaviour, though it is often difficult, if not impossible, to tell where the 'foundation' ends and the 'building' starts. But the absence of fool-proof delineations between 'inheritance', 'maturation', and 'learning' need not prevent us from recognizing the existence of distinct patterns of animal behaviour which are (a) stereotyped, (b) species-specific, (c) unlearnt in the sense that they can be shown to appear, more or less completely, in animals raised in isolation. It has been objected against this view that 'innate' behaviour, e.g. the pecking of chicks, may partly be due to pre-natal influences,[6] that 'isolation' is never absolute,[7] and that learning may be practically instantaneous (as in imprinting). Such arguments are valuable in showing that pure heredity sans environment is an abstraction; but they do not alter the fact that each animal is born with a hereditary potential to feed, hoard, court, nest, fight, and care for its young in certain specific and highly characteristic ways which are as much part of its native equipment as its morphological features, and which can be modified by, but are not derived from, imitation and learning. Only the unbalanced claims of some extreme behaviourists could temporarily obscure the obvious fact that 'if the physical machinery for behaviour develops under genetic control, then the behaviour it mediates can scarcely be regarded as independent of inheritance'.[8]

Learning appears then as the adaptation of the innate potential to lived experience. To quote the convergent definitions of one ethologist and one psychologist: 'Learning is a central nervous process causing more or less lasting changes in the innate behavioural mechanisms under the influence of the outer world. . . .'[9] 'Learning is a process by which an activity originates or is changed through reacting to an encountered situation, provided that the characteristics of the change in activity cannot be explained on the basis of native response tendencies, maturation, or temporary states of the organism (fatigue, drugs, etc.).'[10]

It must be repeated, however, that outside the experimental laboratory it is virtually impossible to draw a precise distinction between the 'innate' and 'acquired' aspects or components in the adult animal's behaviour. Even the discrimination of biologically relevant sign-Gestalten in the environment seems to require a minimum of experience; and one must conclude, with Thorpe, that 'since comparison involves learning, an element of learning enters into all orientation

477

and all perception. Accordingly it is suggested that the difference between inborn and acquired behaviour is of degree rather than kind; it becomes, in fact, a difference chiefly of degree of rigidity and plasticity.'[11] In the terms of our schema, what is inherited is the specific and invariant factor in the native skill—its code. Its more or less flexible matrix develops through learning from experience. To quote Thorpe again:

'In each example of true instinctive behaviour there is a hard core of absolutely fixed and relatively complex automatism—an inborn movement form. This restricted concept is the essence of the instinct itself. Lorenz originally called it *"Erbkoordination"* or *fixed action pattern*. Such action patterns are items of behaviour in every way as constant as anatomical structures, and are potentially just as valuable for systematic, philogenetic studies. Every systematist working with such groups as birds or higher insects will be able to recall examples of the value of such fixed behaviour patterns in classification.'[12]

Tinbergen's Hierarchy

Thus on the level of instinct-behaviour 'codes' appear in the guise of fixed action-patterns, which incorporate the rules of the game of courting, nest-building, duelling, etc. Each of these activities is again a hierarchy of autonomous sub-skills. These tend to be more flexible on the higher levels which co-ordinate the drive, and more rigid on the lower levels. The autonomous sub-codes are restrained from spontaneous activity by 'inhibitory blocks', and triggered into activity by patterned impulses from higher echelons. This trigger-sensitive apparatus is called, after Lorenz, the *innate releasing mechanism*—or I.R.M. for short:

'In all the channels which flow downward from the centre [of a given drive], there is supposed to exist a physiological mechanism which effectively prevents all discharge of activity unless the animal encounters the right environmental situation and stimuli to remove or release this block. Thus there is an innate releasing mechanism (I.R.M.) ... which is in some way attuned to the biologically right stimulus in the environment ... and which is, as it were, unlocked by the appropriate releaser, thus allowing behaviour to proceed to the next lower level. These in their turn incorporate blocks and, so long as these remain, action of these lower centres cannot proceed.'[13]

Tinbergen's famous example of the hierarchic control of instinct-activity is the reproductive behaviour of the male stickleback, which I shall describe in the terminology of the present theory.

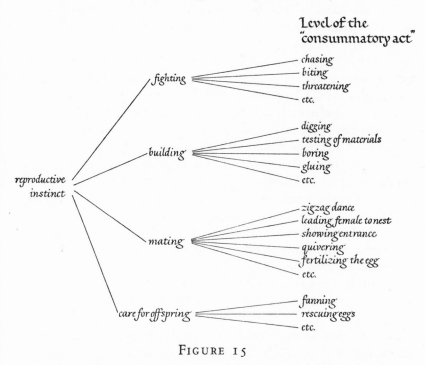

FIGURE 15

In spring the lengthening of days triggers off the small fish's 'migrating code', while hormonal activities provide the drive or motivation. The fish then migrates into shallow water and swims around until a certain environmental configuration (rise of temperature, combined with green vegetation, etc.) strikes the 'right note', i.e. releases an efferent impulse, which in turn triggers off the sub-code of the nest-building activity. This activity is again subdivided into digging, glueing, etc., each of these skills governed by its autonomous sub-code. The latter are activated by trigger releasers; the order of operations is determined by inputs from the environment and proprioceptive feedbacks. The hierarchy of mating behaviour remains blocked until nest-building is complete; but the 'fighting' hierarchy (with its five different sub-codes) may be called at any moment into action by a trigger mechanism sensitive to a specific sign-Gestalt input: 'red male entering territory'. In this case the fighting code dominates the animal's entire behaviour, and nest-building as well as other activities are inhibited while the emergency lasts: the (functional) part monopolizes the attention of the whole.

The sub-units of the behaviour-pattern tend to become more specific regarding input and more stereotyped in output on the lower levels of the hierarchy. 'Which one of the five motor responses belonging to the fighting pattern will be shown depends on sign stimuli that are still more restricted in effect.'[14] The nuptial colours of the fish are shining blue eyes and a red underbelly. Accordingly, any crude model which is red underneath will release an attack, regardless of shape and size—whereas a perfectly shaped model without nuptial colouring will not do so. Apart from colour, behaviour also acts as a releaser. 'When the stranger bites, the owner of the territory will bite in return. When the stranger threatens, the owner will threaten back; when the stranger flees, the owner will chase it; and so on. . . .'[15] But fighting is rarer than threat. The threat-behaviour of male sticklebacks is peculiar. Not only do they dart towards the opponent with raised dorsal spines and open mouth, ready to bite, but, when the opponent does not flee at once but resists, the owner of the territory does not actually bite but points its head down and, standing vertically in the water, makes some jerky movements as if it were going to bore its snout into the sand.'[16]

This of course is an exceptional example—nest-building is a rarity among fish. But the rigidity of fixed action patterns in certain classes —such as birds and insects—remains nevertheless a striking phenomenon. The ritualized rules of the game of courtship and display, of threat and danger signals, of tournament fighting and social behaviour, sometimes reminds one of the ceremonious observances at Byzantine courts, at other times of the obsessive rituals of compulsion-neurotics. And the process of 'ritualization' does indeed suggest the 'emancipation' —or isolation—of a behaviour-pattern from its original context, accompanied by intensification, stabilization, and rhythmic repetitiveness of the pattern; the reasons are as yet hardly understood.[17]

Appetitive Behaviour and Consummatory Act

In spite of the relatively stereotyped nature of fixed action-patterns— of which ritualization is an extreme example—it would be entirely wrong to regard the hierarchy of instinct behaviour as a one-way affair, in which a plastic, general drive (the 'appetitive behaviour') discharges downward along pre-formed and discrete alternative channels into the completely rigid and mechanical, fixed-action-patterns of the 'consummatory act'. This conception of the organism as an automaton whose 'adaptability' is reduced to that of a kind of automatic record-changer or jukebox, with a choice between a few dozen fixed records appropriate to the occasion, seems to have originated in a misunderstanding of the distinction made by Wallace Craig between 'appetitive behaviour' and 'consummatory act'. This point must be briefly discussed as it is of some importance for the sections which follow.

Appetite (or 'appetance') was defined by Craig (1918) as a 'state of agitation', a striving for an absent 'appeted' stimulus (conversely, a striving to escape from a noxious or disturbing stimulus); whereas the 'consummatory act' was meant to bring the activity to a close by attaining (or escaping from) the appetitive stimulus, 'after which the appetitive behaviour ceases and is succeeded by a state of relative rest'.[18] More generally, 'the term appetitive behaviour is used by present-day writers on ethology to mean the flexible or variable introductory phase of an instinctive behaviour pattern or sequence'.[19]

Thus 'appetitive behaviour' became a more refined and noncommittal name for the old, shop-soiled concepts of 'need', 'drive', 'instinct', and 'purpose'.* So far all was well; it was the 'consummatory act', which led instinct-theory into a cul-de-sac. The trouble started, rather inconspicuously, when first Woodworth[20] then, independently from each other, K. S. Lashley and Konrad Lorenz became impressed with the stereotyped character of certain 'consummatory acts' (animal rituals and automatized habits in humans), as compared with the more general 'appetitive behaviour' or drive.** Eventually the focussing of attention on such fixed patterns of behaviour led to a distortion of the whole picture: Lorenz and Tinbergen made a rigid distinction between appetitive behaviour which was supposed to be flexible, and consummatory acts which were supposed to be completely fixed and automatic. Thus Tinbergen:

'It will be clear, therefore, that this distinction between appetitive behaviour and consummatory act separates the behaviour as a whole into two components of entirely different character. The consummatory act is relatively simple; at its most complex it is a chain of reactions. . . . But appetitive behaviour is a true purposive activity, offering all the problems of plasticity, adaptiveness, and of complex integration that baffle the scientist in his study of behaviour as a whole.

... Lorenz has pointed out ... that purposiveness, the striving towards an end, is typical only of appetitive behaviour and not of consummatory actions. .... Whereas the consummatory act seems to be dependent on the centres of the lowest level of instinctive behaviour, appetitive behaviour may be activated by centres of all the levels above that of the consummatory act. ...[21] The centres of the higher levels do control purposive behaviour which is adaptive with regard to the mechanisms it employs to attain the end. The lower levels, however, give rise to increasingly simple and more stereotyped movements, until at the level of the consummatory act we have to do with an entirely rigid component, the taxis, the variability of which, however, is entirely dependent on changes in the outer world. This seems to settle the controversy; the consummatory act is rigid, the higher patterns are purposive and adaptive.'[22]

But what exactly, one might ask, constitutes a 'consummatory act'? A glance at Tinbergen's diagram on page 479, for instance, will show that *all* actual manifestations of the reproductive instinct are classified as 'consummatory acts', whereas 'building', 'fighting', etc., are merely abstract, classificatory terms in which longer sequences of consummatory acts are bracketed together. Where, then, is the 'appetitive behaviour'? In the stickleback's spring migration in search of a nesting site? But that action-pattern was, judged by its dependence on specific releasers (temperature, verdant vegetation, etc.) on the same 'consummatory' level as, for instance, 'testing of materials'. The nearest Tinbergen gets to a definition of the consummatory act is in the following passage:

'The activation of a centre of the lowest level usually, perhaps always, results in a relatively simple motor response: biting, chasing, threatening, etc., in the case of fighting. .... actual eating, actual escape, actual coition, etc., in other instincts. .... These relatively simple responses are, usually, the end of a bout of prolonged activity, and their performance seems to "satisfy" the animal, that is to say, to bring about a sudden drop of motivation. This means that such an end-response consumes the specific impulses responsible for its activation. Fighting, eating, mating, "playing the broken wing" etc., are, as a rule, "self-exhausting".'[23]

However, neither 'digging' nor 'leading female to nest' is an end-response, or self-exhausting, or leads to a 'drop in motivation'. 'Testing of materials' is not a consummation, but a part-activity in the flexible, i.e. 'appetitive', pattern of building. And the building activity is not a one-way affair in the sense of higher levels in the hierarchy discharging along fixed conduits into the lower level of consummatory acts, along irreversible gradients. On the contrary, the control of operations oscillates all the time between different levels; the operational units responsible for one kind of 'end-response' carry on until a centre on a higher level, informed by feedback, switches to some other 'consummatory act'. It is at this point that the concepts of 'hierarchies of environment' and 'hierarchies of feedback' become important. In a complex activity like nest-building, even the relatively stereotyped operations on subordinate levels are under the dual control of their fixed codes and variable environment; and furthermore, information about their activities is constantly fed back (by proprioceptive and exteroceptive channels) to higher centres, so that the whole always remains in hierarchic control 'through regulation channels' of all of its parts. Tinbergen's schema does not really represent an organismic hierarchy, but a mechanical one—rather like an automatized telephone net-work where the subscriber making a trunk call first dials the code-number of the whole town ('appetitive behaviour'), then the code of his fiancée's local exchange (semi-appetitive, semi-consummatory?), and lastly her personal number (consummatory act).

Thorpe, arguing on similar lines, has given an inventory, which fills two printed pages, of the eighteen releasers and fourteen distinct action-patterns in the Longtailed Tits' 'consummatory acts' of building a nest—ending with the exclamation: 'So much for simplicity!' He concludes:

'It seems, then, that in much of appetitive behaviour the animal's own activities . . . must be self-rewarding and self-stimulating. . . . In other words, much appetitive behaviour is also in a sense the consummatory act. . . .[24] Hinde concludes that appetitive behaviour and consummatory act differ only in degree, and that no absolute distinction can be made between them. Both are to some extent "spontaneous" in that they show evidence of external activation, and both are stereotyped to some degree and show some rigidity. Thus the classic examples of appetitive-behaviour and consummatory act can be regarded as the two ends of a series ranging from extreme variability and plasticity on the one hand to almost complete fixity on the other.'[25]

Many patterns of instinct-behaviour are of course cyclic: hunting——> capturing——> ingesting——> digesting——> hunting, etc.; and all one can say about the sub-activities in the cycle is that they are both 'appetitive' and 'consummatory', but that some are more appetitive and some more consummatory than others.

What really matters in our context is the continuous scale of gradations between rigid and flexible action-patterns. Somewhere near the middle of the scale we find the common spider, whose web-making I have already used as a paradigm for an invariant yet adaptable built-in code (Book One, p. 38). It will suspend its familiar net from three, four, or more points of attachment, according to the lie of the land; yet the centre of the polygonal web will always coincide with its centre of gravity and the radial threads will always intersect the lateral threads at equal angles. We thus have a simple fixed code, yet a highly flexible strategy. Moreover, if some of the garden spider's legs and claws are amputated, it will still construct a more or less normal net— the code remains unaffected by the elimination of some members of the matrix.

Leerlauf *and Displacement*

Towards the 'rigid' end of the scale we find reflex-like matrices, exemplified in the so-called *Leerlauf* activities. This term, too, was coined by Lorenz; the current English translation is 'vacuum activity'—but 'freewheeling' would perhaps be more appropriate. Seagulls, reared in isolation, will perform on the stone floor of the laboratory their characteristic 'tap-dance' which, under normal circumstances, would serve to bring small animals to the surface of the tidal mud. Cats will go through the motion of burying their faeces on the kitchen tiles; and hand-reared young flying-squirrels 'when given nuts, would go through all the motions of burying them in the bottom of the wire-cage, and then go away contented, even though the nuts were exposed to full view'.[26] The same author describes the behaviour of hand-reared tawny owls 'which, after being fed, would act as if pouncing upon living prey though it had never had the experience of dealing with a living mouse'.[27]

Such examples of 'stupid', automaton-like behaviour are the strongest evidence for innate codes of action. At the same time they are also additional evidence against the chain-reflex theory of instinct-behaviour: the owl, which has never seen a mouse, pounces *after* being fed, and without any visual stimulus; in the gull's case, the hard floor of the laboratory is a stimulus quite different from the soft mud—hence the 'chain-reaction' ought never to start, or to break off after the first unsuccessful attempt at 'digging' the tiles. Instincts are purposive and flexible, but their flexibility is limited to conditions more or less within the experience of the race. In a crassly unnatural environment the performance degenerates into 'freewheeling' and loses its purposive aspect.

According to Lorenz's rather controversial theory, the motivation of *Leerlauf* activity is derived from a 'damming up' of the animal's 'specific action potential' (SAP) which lowers the threshhold of the innate releasing mechanism so that the action will go off even in the absence of appropriate stimuli. Hence also the term 'overflow activity'.

Another distortion of instinct-behaviour are the so-called *displacement activities* which overlap with *Leerlauf* (and also with play). 'Displacement is the performance of a behaviour pattern out of the particular functional context of behaviour to which it is normally related. It seems to appear when the charge (SAP) attached to one instinct is denied opportunity for adequate discharge through its own consummatory act or acts and instead "sparks over" to set going the consummatory act of another instinct.'[28] A dog in its restraining harness in a Pavlov-type laboratory, while expecting the fall of food from the container, will stamp, yawn, and pant—activities which do not belong to his normal feeding behaviour; but what else, one may irreverently ask, can the poor excited creature do? Pail-fed calves will suck the ears or navels of their companions, as infants suck their thumbs. Some birds play elaborate games, throwing up and catching sticks; so do puppies; kittens will 'pretend' that a ball of wool is a mouse. *Leerlauf* and 'displacement' thus comprise a broad range of activities which occur in the absence of the proper stimulus or in the presence of normally inadequate ersatz stimuli; or when the proper response is for some reason blocked. Its human equivalents range from playful activities to repetition compulsions and the formation of neurotic ersatz symptoms.

Instinct and Originality

At the opposite end of the rigidity-flexibility scale we find adaptations of instinct-based behaviour-patterns which give the impression of original improvisation. Even the ritual-bound stickleback, that stickler for etiquette, is capable of them: 'If the normal behaviour-pattern is continually interfered with, quite large modifications in the normal instinctive orientation of the nest-building movements may be made.'[29]

Thus the denial of normal outlets can lead either to the mechanical reeling-off of the built-in pattern in freewheeling or displacement activity; or to original re-adaptations of the pattern. Which of these alternative possibilities will occur depends on the nature of the challenge, and the animal's 'ripeness' to cope with it. What solution, after all, could even a genius cat find to comply with its code of hygiene on the kitchen tiles? What creative outlet is left to the squirrel to solve his nut-hiding problem?

On the other hand, ethologists have produced many striking examples of ingenious instinct-based behaviour in the face of adversity. The female of a certain wasp, *Eumenes conica*, builds clusters of clay-cells or pots, deposits an egg in each, provisions it with caterpillars for food, then closes the cells with clay lids. If now an artificial hole is made in a cell, the wasp will first stuff the caterpillars which have fallen out back through the hole, then mend the hole with a pellet of clay—operations which are quite different from her normal building routines. Hingston[30] has described in detail the actions of another wasp—*Rhynchium nitiderium*—in repairing a man-made hole in a clay-pot. On one occasion the female tried for two hours to mend the hole with bits of material taken from the wall of the pot. Then night came and she had to give up. Next morning she flew straight to the damaged spot and set about repairing it by a different strategy. In the normal course of events the wasp works from outside. But now, in order to repair the hole, 'she examines it from both sides and then, having made a choice, elects to do the repair from within'.[31]

Equally surprising is the ingenuity of the caddis-fly larva. If a group of larvae are ejected from the tubular 'houses' which they built, and are then allowed to return, they often get mixed up and enter the wrong 'house' which is either too big or too small. The larva then sets about to cut off parts of the tube or to add to it, until it fits it exactly. Again the 'consummatory acts' in these activities are quite different from those in normal building.

Many birds, too, are capable of such 'super-flexible' behaviour in emergencies. If their brood is taken away, they will re-start their sexual cycle, court and mate out of season, and get a new family going. In some species, in the absence of the female, the male bird takes over her duties in feeding the young—which never happens under normal conditions.

Lastly, a brief mention must be made of 'supra-individual codes'—such as those which regulate activities in the honey-bee hive. Lindauer, among others, has shown that 'the programme of work carried out by the individual is not determined by the physiological state of the insect but is dictated by the needs of the colony as a whole'.[32] An individual worker-bee hardly ever builds a complete cell. She may start the cell, with wax from her own glands, then complete another cell, started by a colleague, using her own wax or that of another bee—whichever happens to be convenient. Generally, there is rigid division of labour according to age groups: each worker has to perform a different kind of 'National Service' in different periods of its life. During her first three days, she works as a cell-cleaner. For the next three days she feeds the older larvae with honey and pollen from the stores. Then she feeds the younger larvae, who get an additional diet—a liquid secreted from glands on the worker's head. At the age of ten days she is engaged in complex household chores and building activities. At twenty days she takes over guard duties at the entrance of the hive; and finally, she becomes a forager and remains one until the end of her life. But even among the foragers there is further specialization of labour: some of them become 'scouts', whose task it is to discover new sources of food, and to communicate, on their return, the nature and location of it, in their dance-language, to the hive.[33]

But this is not all. If one of the specialized age-groups is artificially eliminated from the colony, a kind of collective super-flexibility manifests itself in the hive: other age-groups deputize for the vanished group 'and thus save the superorganism. When, for instance, all pollen-and-honey foragers are taken away—usually bees of twenty days or over—young bees of scarcely six days old, who normally feed the larvae, fly out and become foragers. If all building workers are taken away—those between eighteen and twenty days old—their task is taken on by older bees who had already been builders before, but who had gone on to the stage of forager. To this end they not only change their behaviour, but also regenerate the wax-glands. The mechanisms of these regulations are not known.'[34]

Thus at one end of the scale we find rituals, fixed action-patterns, vacuum and displacement activities—rigid, automatized, and compulsive, petrified habits of unknown phylogenetic origin. At the other extreme we find supra-individual codes which govern behaviour of remarkable flexibility, and original adaptations which lie outside the animal's normal skills and habit repertory. In all forms of social organization—from courtship, mating, and fighting rituals, through territorial demarcations, up to the complex insect state, we find an interlocking of individual behaviour-patterns into a collective super-code which casts the individual bird or bee into the role of a part in the social whole. Thus we see the hierarchic part-whole relationship repeated on the level of social organization, where the integrative functions of catalyzers, inductors, and nerve impulses are superseded by interlacing systems of social releasers, including communication by signs and symbol—from display, through bird-song, to the dance-language of the honey-bee.

NOTES

To p. 481. The equivalent of the term 'appetitive behaviour' in American behaviourist theory are Hull's drive-stimulus (S_D); and his 'fractional ante-dating goal-stimuli and responses' ($S_G R_G$).

To p. 481. Out of this grew the theory that the fixed pattern of the con-summatory act—and not the 'appeted stimulus'—is the goal of the animal's striving and the source of the 'action-specific energy' of the drive; but the subject is outside the scope of this book.

VII

IMPRINTING AND IMITATION

So far we have discussed the codes of morphogenesis and innate behaviour, which emerge ready-made from the black boxes of evolution—like Ali Baba's thieves, popping out of the urns in which they were hiding.

In the chapters which follow we shall discuss the ontogenesis of behavioural codes—the acquisition of habits, knowledge, skills, by the processes of learning from experience.

The 'Following-response'

The transition from innate to learnt behaviour is sharply highlighted in the phenomena of imprinting. The follow-the-leader response of the gosling is governed by an innate code; it must stick to the mother-goose or perish. But like many phylogenetically acquired codes it seems to have been formed according to the principle of parsimony. It can be triggered off by any releaser which satisfies very broad Gestalt criteria of 'goose-likeness'—including German ethologists and even inanimate moving objects of a certain size. In a normal environment this would indeed be sufficient to ensure the gosling's survival, since the first sizeable moving creature seen would be the mother-goose. Accordingly, a young goose, reared from the egg in isolation (or in the incubator) will accept—during the brief critical period of maturation when imprinting occurs—its human keeper as its 'mother', and follow him around. Once this has happened the process becomes more or less irreversible: the 'imprinted' bird will reject the company of other geese and attach itself only to members of the human species—treating them as parents, companions, and later on as objects of sexual

489

advances. Many other birds, and possibly also some fish and insects, show the phenomena of imprinting in varying degrees.

Here, then, we have a pregnant example of the genesis of a matrix through the integration of innate and acquired behaviour-patterns. The built-in 'following response' has the characteristic autonomy of motor-patterns which we have met before: it is triggered off and modified, but not created by the environmental input. The first step in the development of the matrix is the act of imprinting itself; it must occur, as already mentioned, during the critical phase when the young bird is susceptible for it (in ducks, for instance, between eleven and eighteen hours after birth, with a pointed peak in the susceptibility curve at sixteen hours).[1] The input which triggers off the following-response is at this stage an undifferentiated and primitive sign-releaser: 'Large moving object'—much simpler in character than the more specific Gestalt stimuli which release the fighting or mating instinct in the stickleback ('red belly', 'swollen belly') or the begging response of the herring-gull chick ('red spot on beak').

The next stage is one of *perceptual learning*. After a few hours, even a few minutes, of following a human being, the gosling will follow *only* human beings—it has somehow learned to 'abstract', or 'encode' in its memory some specific Gestalt-characteristics of *homo sapiens* which distinguish it from other 'shapes that move'. On the other hand, at this stage all human beings are still 'equipotential' members of the emergent perceptual matrix. At a still later stage, the goose may become attached to one or more single individuals, that is to say, it learns to discriminate individuals within the species—as, vice versa, animal breeders learn to sharpen their perception and to distinguish one sheep or goose from another.

We thus meet, already on this level, the twin phenomena involved in all learning processes: *generalization* ('transfer', 'abstraction') and *discrimination* (segregation of pattern, selective inhibition of responses to non-specific stimuli). These basic processes will be discussed later (Chapter X); in the meantime, let us note that the innate, primitive 'rule of the game' which made the new-born animal respond to 'things-that-move', has been sharpened and elaborated into a more complex set of rules by a series of steps. Each of these steps involved a re-structuring of the perceptual matrix by successive generalizations and discriminations—which we may regard as quasi-extensions of functional integration and structural differentiation into the learning process. Morphogenesis and learning form continuous series which over-

lap during maturation; and the matrices of innate and acquired behaviour form an equally continuous hierarchy.

Bird-song and Parrot-talk

There are no sharply defined boundaries between imprinting and learning by imitation, or by trial and error. The word 'imprinting' itself is
a translation of Heinroth's *Prägung*,[2] by which he meant to indicate
the dramatic form of learning in birds which we have just discussed.
Its chief characteristics are: it is species-specific and directly dependent
on innate organization; quasi-instantaneous; and limited to a relatively
brief period in the animal's life. By applying these criteria, Thorpe has
extended the concept of imprinting to include 'a bird's instantaneous
attachment to territory, its occasional attachment not only to humans
but also to other animals and even inanimate objects; and lastly, the
song-bird's way of learning its species-characteristic song'.[3]

Apparently in some birds such as thrushes, warblers, pippits, the
whole song is genetically 'built in' and can be but slightly modified by
learning; while in others, for instance the skylark, it is mainly learned.
In chaffinches Thorpe has shown that 'while the basic pattern of the
song is innate, all the finer detail and much of the pitch and rhythm
have to be acquired by learning.'* We have here another example
of a 'roughed-in' pattern (p. 470) whose details are filled in later
by that particular type of 'feedback' process which constitutes
learning.

When we turn to *imitative* bird-song and parrot-talk, the part played
by innate organization is obviously less specific and the part played by
learning much greater; yet the difference is again one of degree. In
fact, *Prägung* means stamping (a coin), which makes the continuity
between imprinting and 'stamped-in learning' even more obvious.**
Less obvious, however, is the biological purpose or adaptive value of
the striking capacity of parrots, mocking-birds, starlings, etc., to imitate the songs of entirely alien species—including 'God Save the
King'.[4] Now parrots living in freedom in their natural environment
utter only a few fixed, simple types of cries; yet folklore apart, we have
no lesser authority than Lashley describing a captive parrot with a
'vocabulary' of between fifty and a hundred words; and there is
reliable evidence[5] that both parrots and robins can learn to utter certain
words meaningfully. Granted that vocal imitation, as McDougall

has pointed out,[6] is a special case owing to the close integration of auditory-vocal patterns, one must nevertheless admit that such imitative ability is 'a further example of pre-adaptation for apparently remote and unlikely contingencies, specialization going in advance of immediate adaptive requirement, and as such on a par with the astonishing number-sense which can be developed in many species by careful training. Such a counting ability seems to offer even less practical advantage for a wild bird than the features we have been considering; all are as yet somewhat mysterious.'[7] (The counting ability of birds was revealed in Otto Koehler's famous experiments, to be discussed later.) Ethologists such as Koehler (not to be confused with Wolfgang Köhler), Lorenz, Craig, and Thorpe all agree that the tonal purity, the 'inventiveness' and improvisation in the advanced forms of bird-song should be regarded as 'the first steps in both music and speech'.[8]

To mention one example among many: Waite, at the Museum in Sydney, owned an Australian magpie whom he taught by playing on the flute 'a fifteen-note melody in two distinct phrases'. Some years later he got a second magpie which learned the tune from the first. The two birds then developed the habit of singing it antiphonally, the first singing the first phrase, and the second only the second. 'Later the second, younger, bird died whereupon the first resumed its performance of the whole.'[9]

Examples like this show not only the great flexibility of these auditory-vocal matrices. They also show that the total pattern—the rudimentary code of the hand-reared chaffinch—develops first, and that learning the song does not consist in the chaining of individual notes according to the S.-R. scheme, but in the elaboration and variation of the pattern. We further note that originality or 'inventiveness' make their appearance at only a few removes from innate and imprinted behaviour. Lastly, the striking learning abilities of some birds, which are only revealed under the abnormal conditions of captivity— these examples of 'pre-adaptations for remote and unlikely contingencies' remind us of regenerative potentials manifested in response to traumatic challenges.

Untapped Resources

We have seen evidence of this latent super-flexibility—of 'doing wonders' in adversity—on every level: from the restoration of locomotive patterns in mutilated insects and rats, through the emergency redistribution of labour in the beehive, up to the solution of blocked problems by 'thinking aside'. In recent years, unsuspected learning abilities were revealed in such widely different classes as flatworms, dolphins, and seals—the latter, apparently, can even be taught to obey visual sign-commands printed on cards. Yet the evidence for a surplus, or reserve, of learning potentials far surpassing immediate adaptive needs has always been there in our own species: ten thousand years ago our ancestors fought with clubs and arrows, but the structure of their brains was the same as ours, and therefore potentially just as capable of learning Boolean Logics or the principles of making a nuclear bomb. Even the dumb fish have been shown to have optical capacities for form and colour discrimination far in advance of their needs under natural conditions. Thorpe comments: 'It does indeed seem to be a general feature of animal life that the precision and sensitivity of sense organs is higher than the environment would appear to justify. This fact poses a serious problem for students of evolution, since it is not easy to account for such perfection on the basis of natural selection alone.'*

It seems that this *overshooting* of the mark, this giving more than was asked for, is an inherent characteristic of the mechanism of evolution. In *homo sapiens* the 'overshooting' is demonstrated by the fact that mental evolution—learning to exploit the surplus potentials in his brain—has been going on for an astronomical period, and with no end in sight. The problem is not so much why mental evolution occurs in man, but why no similar phenomenon—learning to use their native equipment to maximum capacity—seems to have occurred in any other species, although many animals demonstrate the existence of their untapped resources in captivity. (Animals, it is true, keep no written records of their discoveries, but these could have been transmitted by imitative learning.) All this is a nice subject for speculations on a rainy day; the important point in our context is the hard core of evidence to show that various animals reveal in captivity various degrees of originality and resourcefulness which are not displayed under natural conditions. Most animals seem to have more sensitive organs than they need, and more latent capabilities than they ever learn to actualize, except when challenged under propitious circumstances. That bar-pressing experiments with rats are not the type of challenge designed to elicit original responses, need not be emphasized, and it is not surprising, therefore, that leading Behaviourists have either denied the occurrence of original responses or put them down to chance. We shall return to the subject in later chapters.

NOTES

To p. 491. The chaffinch song consists of three distinct and well-articulated phrases. Hand-reared chaffinches produce a much simplified, rudimentary variant of the song, where the first and second phrase are often inseparable, and the third partly or wholly missing. But—and this is the elegant point of the experiment— if the young bird is left to be reared by its parents, then taken away and isolated in September, that is to say, long before it starts singing, it will nevertheless burst into normal song next spring. Apparently 'these birds have by their first September learned that the song "should" be in three phrases and that the terminal phrase should contain a more or less elaborate flourish'. Thus 'on the perceptory side the process of recognizing and accepting the specific song as henceforth the "normal" for the individual (as distinct from the acquisition of the new motor habits involved in performing the song) seems to resemble the original examples of imprinting [the following response] sufficiently close to warrant considering them together' (Thorpe, 1956, p. 375).

To p. 491. In the human child, processes analogous to *Prägung* may perhaps be responsible for producing infantile fixations and fetishistic rituals. The cases of boot-fetishism, for instance, frequently reported in works on sexual pathology remind one of imprinting by inanimate objects—such as a gander's seven-year fixation on an oildrum, reported by Thorpe (p. 365). A further analogy may be found between Gestalt-sign releasers, based on the vital statistics of film-stars, and Tinbergen's simplified laboratory models of the pregnant stickleback.

To p. 493. Thorpe continues: 'However, the answer may be that the nature of sensory nervous mechanisms is such that to achieve full efficiency at the normal level of stimulation, the threshold must be much lower.' (Thorpe, 1956, p. 283). But other passages which I have quoted show that he does not regard this explanation as satisfactory.

VIII

MOTIVATION

Retrospect

Future historians will probably regard it as significant that throughout the first half of the twentieth century the dominant schools of psychology—even schools as far apart as behaviourism and psychoanalysis—recognized only one basic type of motivation, and that a negative one: the reduction of biological needs and drives, the diminution of tension, escape from anxiety. 'At the level of ego-psychology', wrote Mowrer in his survey on 'Motivation' in the *Annual Review for* 1952,[1] 'there may be said to be only one master motive: anxiety.'

The trend seems to have originated in the climate of the Darwinian revolution independently in Germany and America, with Fechner's (1873) '*Tendenz zur Stabilität*' and Thorndike's (1898) 'Law of Effect'. Freud (1920), acknowledging his indebtedness to Fechner, postulated his own Principle of Parsimony, according to which 'the course of mental events is invariably set in motion by an unpleasurable tension, and it takes a direction such that its final outcome coincides with a lowering of that tension'. Thus pleasure is derived from 'the diminution, lowering, or extinction of psychic excitation' and 'un-pleasure [*Unlust*, dysphoria, as distinct from physical pain] from an increase of it'. The organism tends towards stability—a kind of homeostasis, applied not only to autonomic regulations but also to voluntary behaviour; it is guided by 'the striving of the mental apparatus to keep the quantity of excitations present in it as low as possible or at least constant. Accordingly, everything that tends to increase the quantity of excitation, must be regarded as adverse to this tendency, that is to say, as unpleasurable.'[2]

Now this is of course true, in a broad sense, in so far as the frustration or satisfaction of primary biological needs is concerned. But it passes in silence a whole class of experiences to which we commonly refer as 'pleasurable excitement'. The preliminaries of love-making cause an increase in sexual tension and should, according to the theory, be unpleasant—which they are decidedly not. It is curious that in the works of Freud there is no answer to be found to this embarrassingly banal objection. The sex-drive in the Freudian system is essentially something *to be disposed of*—through the proper channels or by sublimation; pleasure is derived not from its pursuit, but from getting rid of it. One might argue that in Freud's universe there is no place for amorous love-play because Freud, like D. H. Lawrence, was basically a puritan with a horror of frivolity, who treated sex *'mit tierischem Ernst'*.* But arguments *ad hominem* do not explain the general trend in the first half of the century to interpret motivation as something negative. As Hilgard ruefully remarked,[3] the *'Zeitgeist* favoured our seeing incentives not as providing something sought after for what was inherent in the incentive, but something providing relief. The incentive was seen as an avenue of escape from pain, anxiety, tension.' Just as Freud's libido-theory had no room for dalliance, so learning-theory had no room for curiosity or learning-by-play.

Thorndike's 'Law of Effect' was essentially a stick-and-carrot theory; the reward (and to a lesser degree, punishment) is the factor which stamps in the correct responses in learning, and stamps out the incorrect ones. In the extreme behaviourist systems of Watson and Guthrie, the mechanization of the living organism is complete: contiguity is the basic factor in producing associative S.-R. bonds, and motivation has virtually disappeared from the picture. Nor is any theory of motivation allowed to enter into Skinner's concept of 'operant behaviour'. His system is by programme confined to the description of experimental operations, preferably in quantitative terms. The effects of different rates and sequences of positive and negative reinforcers are counted and plotted; the entity on which they act is the 'operant strength', which in turn is measured by the rate and number of responses during extinction; but the motivation of the animal is represented by a single, crude variable: the number of hours in which the rat had been deprived of food. Optimum learning results from the combination of the appropriate number of hours of deprivation with the appropriate rate of applying positive reinforcers, i.e. stimuli of the type, one might say, which are apt to deprive the organism of its deprivation. Differences between the learning abilities of various species, or of age groups within a species, are not considered to be relevant to this type of 'functional analysis' of behaviour. By the same method of selective reinforcement, by 'baiting' each step in a series of steps, pigeons can be trained to describe a figure-eight with their heads held high, and students can be trained to select the right answer among several alternatives and to punch it into the tape of the learning machine—the reinforcement in this case being that the tape moves on to the next question. Since each reinforcer is a drive-reducer, learning becomes a process of progressive de-motivation.

Hull did not share Skinner's rigidly positivistic, *hypotheses-non-fingo* attitude. He kept elaborating and modifying his theory until his death in 1951; the system has been described as the last and most impressive attempt to build an edifice on S.-R. foundations. His emphasis gradually shifted from primary to secondary drives and secondary rewards; and from need-reduction to drive-stimulus reduction (eating eliminates the *stimulus* of the hunger-drive but not the biological *need*—which will be satisfied only later by digestion). This made the system more elastic, yet in spite of these refinements, the primitive drives of hunger, sex, avoidance of pain, were considered to be the only motivational factors in learning. To quote Hebb's (1949) summing up of Hull's theory: 'Its weakest point, and clearest departure from the facts, is in the treatment of motivation as biological need. According to the theory, the rat in the maze should learn nothing about it until one of his responses is accompanied by a decrease of hunger or thirst, or escape from electric shock, or some similar reward. In actual fact, when he is allowed to run in the maze without reward or punishment, the rat learns a good deal about it. It is clear of course that the primitive drives of pain, hunger, and sex are often of overwhelming importance. We need an approach to motivation that neither minimizes these things nor fails to provide for the unrewarded learning that also occurs when the animal's belly is full and his sex drive satisfied.'[4]

If we turn to the opposite camp—Tolman and the Gestalt psychologists—the emphasis shifts from the need-reducing to the goal-seeking aspects of behaviour. In classical Gestalt theory, motivation by rewards, usually in the form of bananas, is taken for granted; it does not question the effect of reward on learning, the dispute is about whether this effect is achieved by stamping in or by insight. Similar considerations apply to Tolman's sign-learning theory, although he has progressed a considerable step further by his explicit rejection of reinforcement theories, by his emphasis on 'expectancy' and 'purposiveness', on latent learning and 'creative instability'. Lastly, Kurt Lewin's 'psychological field theory', with its complex and changing motivation, its concepts of 'ego-involvement' and 'levels of aspiration'; above all with its notion of striving after 'success' (which is subjective and relative in contrast to reinforcement by tangible rewards), played an important part in promoting that change of climate which has been increasingly noticeable since about 1950.

Decline of the Reflex

This new orientation seems to be the cumulative effect of independent developments in several fields, such as: (a) disillusionment regarding the utility of the reflex-formula both in neurology and psychology; (b) rediscovery of the fact that organisms are not passive masses of software reacting to environment, but 'open systems', feeding on 'negative entropy', engaged in spontaneous activities on all levels, and (c) that animals are capable of 'latent' learning in the absence of tangible rewards, motivated solely by their exploratory drive.

(a) The *physiological* concept of the reflex arc, which even Sherrington considered as no more than a 'useful fiction', has become an anachronism.* The Pavlovian conditioned reflex was another useful fiction which exercised at first a stimulating, then a paralysing effect— a phenomenon frequently met in the history of science. In Hebb's words: 'Pavlov has deservedly had a great influence on psychology, and his theory has not been rejected because it is too physiological but because it does not agree with experiment.' There is no need to re-capitulate the evidence which has led to this rejection.[5] 'Conditioning' is still a useful term when applied to induced changes in glandular and visceral reactions, but leads to confusion when used in a loose, analogical way for other types of learning.

The last blow to the reflex-arc concept came with the discovery that it was impossible to make a precise distinction between 'stimuli' and 'responses'. As already mentioned (p. 435) not only motor units, but also sensory receptors display constant spontaneous activity in the absence of external stimulation.[6] External events alter the pattern of this spontaneous activity, but this in itself does not yet constitute a stimulus. The receptors are under efferent control from higher levels of the central nervous system; the acceptance, suppression, or modification of the input starts on the periphery, and the centre decides what shall constitute a stimulus and what shall not. Even the stretch-sensitive receptors in muscle spindles are controlled by efferent fibres from the centre. In other words, 'stimuli' and 'responses' are not one-way processes, and cannot be isolated: 'because stimulus and response are correlative and contemporaneous, the stimulus processes must be thought of not as preceding the response but rather as guiding it to a successful elimination of the incongruity. That is to say, stimulus and response must be considered as aspects of a feedback loop. . . .'[7] These properties are a far cry from the ubiquitous S.-R. reflex arc diagrams that grace (more appropriately one wants to say "disgrace") today's texts' (Pribram).[8]

It is historically interesting that an independent but parallel softening-up process of the hard and fast S.-R. concept took place at the same time in psychology, e.g. in Skinner's and Hull's systems. Skinner was careful to state that he used the word 'reflex' not in an anatomical or neurological sense but as a purely psychological, descriptive term for the 'unit of behaviour'. But his definition of the unit was constantly shifting and changing. 'A reflex is not, of course, a theory. It is a fact. It is an analytical unit, which makes the investigation of behaviour possible.[9] The appearance of smooth curves in dynamic processes marks a unique point in the progressive restriction of a preparation, and it is to this uniquely determined entity that the term "reflex" may be assigned.'[10]

As Miller et al were to comment, to define the reflex in terms of the smoothness of curves is a 'somewhat odd approach'.[11] Yet even so it did not work: 'Skinner's "unit appropriate for experimental study" turns out, in fact, to have a measure of arbitrariness about it. . . . Some-times the functional unit is a simple response, sometimes a complex act, sometimes a rate of responding. The unit no longer has the clean dimen-sions of a correlation between a class of stimuli and a class of responses as implied in the original concept of a reflex. The atom of behaviour proves to be evasive.'[12] In the later versions of Skinner's system the stimulus no longer even precedes the response: in operant behaviour the organism emits responses in search of a stimulus as it were. The reflex as a unit of behaviour has evaporated like the physicist's hard little lumps of matter.

Skinner's experimental work had some lasting merits. He was among the first to demonstrate that 'intermittent reinforcement'—where only *some* correct responses are rewarded—can be as effective as the consistent rewarding of *all* correct responses. Humphreys[13] then showed that random rewards are actually a superior (more extinction-resistant) form of training—the rat thus trained is less discouraged when the reward is withheld, than the rat trained by the consistent-reward method. From this there was only one logical step to Tolman's theory of motivation by expectancy—a step which Skinner never took.

In Hull's case the 'softening-up' process took a different course. In his later years, Hull's attention shifted more and more from primary biological drives to secondary drives (from the 'need' to the 'taste' or 'appetite'). These secondary drives he saw manifested in anticipatory events—'fractional antedating goal-responses R_G', and 'fractional antedating goal-stimuli S_G'. 'The fractional antedating reaction (R_G) with its proprioceptive stimulus correlate (S_G), provides for the "automatic (stimulus) guidance of organismic behaviour .to goals".' The great importance Hull attached to this postulate is illustrated by his comment: 'Further study of this major automatic device presumably will lead to the detailed behavioural understanding of thought and reasoning, which constitutes the highest attainment of organic evolution. Indeed the R_G —— > S_G mechanism leads in a strictly logical manner into what was formerly regarded as the very heart of the psychic: interest, planning, foresight, foreknowledge, expectancy, purpose, and so on.'[14]

From a strictly logical point of view, the postulate makes no sense —as Hilgard has pointed out in a careful analysis—because S_G acts at the same time as a *producer* of the secondary drive S_D and as a secondary reinforcer which *reduces* S_D.[15] Hilgard put down this confusion as a sign of logical weakness in Hull;* yet he did not seem to realize that Hull was intuitively on the right track, that the contradiction is merely an apparent one, and vanishes if one stops thinking in terms of need-reducing motivation. 'That stimulus associated with reinforcement could become at once *both* a drive and a reinforcing agent' *sounds* like a contradiction, but makes eminent sense if, getting rid of the dreadful terminology, we translate it as follows: 'A rewarding experience can at the same time be both an incentive and a reward'; or even simpler: 'Some pursuits are self-rewarding'. That is the implied conclusion of Hull's eighth and last postulate which he regarded as the crowning achievement of his system. That he himself did not realize this implication only shows that the once useful S.-R. formula had by that time become a strait-jacket to thought.

It took natural philosophy nearly a thousand years to rediscover that the earth is round; it took experimental psychology nearly fifty years to rediscover, after its Dark Ages of need-reducing S.-R. theories, that rats and men are pleasure-seeking creatures, that some activities are pleasurably self-rewarding, and that exploring the environment, solving a chess problem, or learning to play the guitar are among these activities.

An interesting reflection on the spirit of the times was the long, impassioned controversy which followed the earth-shaking discovery that rats who were allowed to familiarize themselves with the maze by running around in it without reward, got quicker to the food-box when this was eventually put in than the control rats who ran the maze for the first time. How could the rat profit from its previous experience in the maze without being rewarded by food or punished by electric shock? As Berlyne put it: 'There are plenty of experiments to show that latent maze-learning can occur in the rat, which is embarrassing for those whose theories are not built to assimilate it. . . . Where does the reinforcement for these responses come from? Several writers have considered the possibility that it comes from the reduction of curiosity.'[16] Other writers suggested that it came from the drive-reducing diminution of boredom. One might as well say that composing a song is a silence-reducing activity.

There have been throughout these Dark Ages 'voices crying in the wilderness', but they were dismissed as old-fashioned. Thus McDougall (1923) kept reaffirming that the earth was round and that striving towards a goal was often more satisfactory than reaching it. Allport held that activities originally derived from biological needs may become autonomous and self-rewarding: 'The characteristic feature of such striving is its resistance to equilibrium: tension is maintained rather than reduced.'[17] Goldstein emphasized the tendency of organisms towards 'self-actualization'.[18] But the revival of a dynamic psychology which reinstated the academic respectability of such terms as curiosity, exploratory drive, purpose, only came about when experimental evidence showed that even in the rat the urge to explore may prevail over hunger and fear.

The experiments of Harlow, Montgomery, Butler, Hudson, etc., on rats and monkeys showed—what naturalists had always known—that animals are inquisitive, that they have an urge to manipulate, explore, to 'look what's inside', which is independent from such bio-logical drives as hunger, sex, and fear—or, rather, that the exploratory drive itself stems from a primary biological need. They showed that exploratory behaviour may combine with, or enter the service of, hunger or fear, but that it may also compete with and sometimes assert itself against them; and that novelty, surprisingness, or puzzle-ment are as real incentives to learning as pellets of food dropped into the Skinner box.[19]

As far back as 1930 Nissen had found that rats would cross an elec-trified grill to reach a maze which contained nothing but some unusual objects; he concluded that an exploratory urge did exist—'a biogenic drive to explore, perceive, to know'.[20] Experiments by Hudson, Berlyne, and Walley, in which rats were punished for approaching some novel visual pattern, led them to conclude that 'objects that have become associated with danger are often explored before they are shunned'.[21] Carr and Williams[22] showed that the exploratory drive varies with heredity and environment: hooded rats explore more than black rats, and black rats more than Albino rats. Montgomery and Barnett[23] showed that wild rats are more frightened, tame rats more attracted by novelty; Thompson and Heron[24] that young animals are more curious than old ones, and—as one would expect—that female rats are more inquisitive than males.[25] Confronted with novel situations, hungry rats interrupt their feeding to explore their surround-ings;[26] but rats whose cerebral cortex has been removed in part, while still capable of learning to run a maze to get at food, show a diminished tendency to exploration. They 'do not evince the preference for a variable path over a standardized path that is characteristic of a normal rat, except when the variable path is the shorter. Brain-damaged rats likewise show less variability of route in a Dashiell maze.'[27] Yet, as Lashley's rats have shown, even depriving the creature of substantial portions of its brain does not make it conform to the S.-R. ideal.

On higher levels of the animal kingdom the evidence becomes less monotonous and depressing. What a relief to get out of the Skinner box and to read Lorenz's description of curiosity battling with fear in one of his birds:[28]

'A young raven, confronted with a new object, which may be a camera, an old bottle, a stuffed polecat, or anything else first reacts with escape responses. He will fly up to an elevated perch and, from this point of vantage, stare at the object literally for hours. After this, he will begin to approach the object very gradually, maintaining all the while a maximum of caution and the expressive attitude of intense fear. He will cover the last distance from the object hopping sideways with half-raised wings, in the utmost readiness to flee. At last, he will deliver a single fearful blow with his powerful beak at the object and forthwith fly back to his safe perch. . . .' In the end 'he will grab [the object] with one foot, peck at it, try to tear off pieces, insert his bill into any existing cleft and then pry apart his mandibles with considerable force. Finally, if the object is not too big the raven will carry it away, push it into a convenient hole and cover it with some inconspicuous material.'

As for primates, we can comfortably fall back on Darwin's *Descent of Man*:

'All animals feel *Wonder*, and many exhibit *Curiosity*. They sometimes suffer from this latter quality, as when the hunter plays antics and thus attracts them; I have witnessed this with deer, and so it is with the wary chamois, and with some kinds of wild-ducks. Brehm gives a curious account of the instinctive dread, which his monkeys exhibited, for snakes; but their curiosity was so great that they could not desist from occasionally satiating their horror in a most human fashion, by lifting up the lid of the box in which the snakes were kept.' Darwin was 'so much surprised at this account' that he proceeded to the monkey-house at the Zoological Gardens armed with a stuffed snake, a dead fish, a mouse, and a live turtle:

'The excitement thus caused was one of the most curious spectacles which I ever beheld.' The greatest success was the turtle. The monkeys 'showed unbounded astonishment, as well as some fear. . . . This was displayed by their remaining motionless, staring intently with widely opened eyes, their eyebrows being often moved up and down. Their faces seemed somewhat lengthened. They occasionally raised themselves on their hindlegs to get a better view. They often retreated a few feet, and then turning their heads over one shoulder, again stared intently. . . . In the course of a few minutes some of the monkeys ventured to approach and touch the turtle. . . . I then placed a live snake in a paper bag, with the mouth loosely closed, in one of the larger compartments. One of the monkeys immediately approached, cautiously opened the bag a little, peeped in, and instantly dashed away. Then I witnessed what Brehm has described, for monkey after monkey, with head raised high and turned on one side, could not resist taking a momentary peep into the upright bag, at the dreadful object lying quietly at the bottom.'[29]

This was written half a century before Köhler's *Mentality of Apes* was translated into English—with a delay of eight years after the appearance of the German original.[30] It had the effect of something like a bombshell on American psychology, in which Pavlov and Watson were all the rage. Yet even Köhler, though he attacked Thorndike, remained essentially conservative as far as motivation is concerned; it took another quarter-century for a new crop of experimentalists to discover, in the 1950s, that the exploration of novelty, the manipulation of objects, the dismantling and reassembling of complex manual puzzles, and even scribbling and drawing were self-rewarding and self-arousing activities.

'Those who have had opportunities to observe monkeys and apes at close hand for prolonged periods invariably dwell on their addiction to looking, mauling, prodding, licking, and generally squeezing every drop of possible entertainment from whatever crosses their path.'[31] Particularly revealing is the fact that Rhesus monkeys who have learned to dismantle a complex manual puzzle of interlocking pieces performed better when there was *no* food reward put inside the puzzle than when they knew that there was one. In the second case they got impatient and tried short-cuts; in the first case they practised disinterestedly, '*l'art pour l'art*'.[32]

The Exploratory Drive

The cumulative evidence of these and similar experiments led Harlow to the conclusion:

'There are logical reasons why a drive-reduction theory of learning, a theory which emphasizes the role of internal, physiological-state motivation is entirely untenable as a motivational theory of learning.

'The condition of strong drive is inimical to all but very limited aspects of learning—the learning the ways to reduce tension. . . . The hungry child is a most uncurious child, but after he has eaten and become thoroughly sated, his curiosity and all the learned responses associated with his curiosity take place.'[33]

Montgomery came to similar conclusions, which he put into the laconic formula: 'Exploratory behaviour is motivated by the exploratory drive.'

These clarion calls of a new generation of experimentalists in fact echoed the earlier 'voices in the wilderness'—such as Woodworth's: 'To see, to hear—to see clearly, to hear distinctly—moment by moment, such concrete, immediate motives dominate the life of relation with the environment.'[34] In the meantime, however, these 'old-fashioned' views had received added, powerful support from neurophysiology. Lindsley (1951), Hebb (1955) and others have shifted their attention from tension-reducing, stabilizing processes in the nervous system to the supposedly arousing, attention-sharpening functions of certain structures in the midbrain—the so-called 'reticular activating system', RAS. Although these theories are still controversial, parallel studies on sensory deprivation have dramatically revealed the deleterious effects of protracted stimulus-starvation, and the organism's need for more or less constant stimulation, or at least a steady inflow of information—a hunger for experience and thirst for excitation probably as basic as hunger and thirst themselves. Instead of responding passively to the environment, 'human beings and higher animals spend most of their time in a state of relatively high arousal and . . . expose themselves to arousing stimulus situations with great eagerness'.[35] Two thousand years ago Juvenal had said much the same: 'Duas tantum res anxius optat, / Panem et circenses.'

Berlyne[36] has made a systematic survey of the manifestations of the exploratory drive on various levels—from orientation reflexes to artistic and scientific curiosity. At the bottom of the ladder we have Pavlov's 'investigatory' or 'what is it?' reflex. 'It is this reflex', Pavlov wrote in a famous passage, 'which brings about the immediate response in men and animals to the slightest changes in the world around them, so that they immediately orientate their appropriate receptor-organ in accordance with the perceptible quality in the agent bringing about the change, making full investigation of it.'[37] From true reflexes such as dilatation of the pupil and automatic scanning, we ascend to oculo-motor responses, movements of the head or the whole body towards the stimulating phenomenon: animals prick their ears, tense their muscles, sniff the air 'musingly'. Next comes 'locomotor exploration' which 'appears to be universal among higher vertebrates and present to some degree in other branches of the animal kingdom'; yet, as Berlyne ruefully remarks: 'It has been studied systematically in rather few species. By far the greater part of the relevant literature is concerned with the rat.' According to Darchen,[38] even the cockroach is capable of disinterested latent learning, prompted by sheer curiosity;

while kittens, puppies, and young chimps seem to spend a major portion of their time in 'locomotive exploration'. Lastly, we come to 'investigatory' or 'inquisitive' behaviour, ranging from Darwin's monkey who cannot refrain from peeping into the snake-infested Pandora's box, to the 'insatiable curiosity' of the artist and explorer.

Thus neuro-physiological considerations, laboratory work with animals, and the observations of ethologists of the Lorenz-Tinbergen school, all seem to converge in the same direction. Even the embryological studies of Coghill (pp. 430 ff.) and Weiss (p. 434 seq.), with their emphasis on spontaneous, intrinsic activities on all levels of the organic hierarchy, lend indirect support to the primacy of the exploratory drive. The lesson of fifty years of rats-in-mazes has been summed up, e.g. by Thacker in the statement that 'motivation for learning is central and neural . . . organized and proliferated cognitive structure itself is the goal towards which learning moves'.[39] In other words, *the motivation for learning is to learn.*

Thorpe, for all his habitual caution, has gone even further. He starts with a rhetorical question: 'And so it becomes important to consider how far there is evidence of learning motivated by a general drive quite independent of the motivation of particular instincts';[40] and he concludes that 'there is now substantial and precise evidence for a general drive in a number of animals, and this can be looked upon as an indication of a primary motivation which to some extent, however slight, is superior to the governing centres of any of the instincts or of their combinations, and finds its most characteristic expression in exploratory behaviour in all its various forms'.[41]

In his monograph on *The Nature of Explanation* (1943), which has inspired a great many neurologists and computer-theorists, the Cambridge psychologist K. J. Craik put forward the idea that the function of the organism's nervous system is to set up a symbolic model of the external world: 'The brain . . . imitates or models external processes. The function of such symbolization is plain. If the organism carries a "small-scale model" of external reality and of its own possible actions within its head, it is able to try out various alternatives, conclude which is the best of them, react to future situations before they arise, utilize the knowledge of past events in dealing with the present and future, and every way to react in a much fuller, safer, and more competent manner to the emergencies which face it.'[42]

To extract information from the chaotic environment is as vital to the organism as it is essential for it to extract specific forms of energy from sunlight and food. If we assume this to be an inherent tendency of all living organisms, then we must also assume the existence of an inherent primary drive to explore the environment for relevant information.

Thus the organism functions not merely by responding to the environment, but by asking it questions. The main incentive to its exploratory activities are novelty, surprise, conflict, uncertainty.* The exploratory drive may combine with, or be instrumental to, other drives—sex, nutrition, anxiety. But in its purest form—in play, latent learning, unrewarded problem-solving—'stimuli' and 'responses' are undistinguishable parts of the same feedback loop along which excitation is running in a circle like a kitten chasing its tail. 'The scientist', wrote Allport, 'by the very nature of his commitment, creates more and more questions, never fewer. Indeed the measure of our intellectual maturity, one philosopher suggests, is our capacity to feel less and less satisfied with our answers to better problems.'[43]

We have thus established a broader base for the scientist's motivation as discussed earlier on (Book One, XI). The exploratory drive may combine with the self-transcending mysticism of a Kepler or with the self-asserting vanity of a Galileo. Each original artist has an element of the explorer in him: the poet does not 'manipulate words' as Watson thought, he explores the emotive and descriptive potentialities of language; the painter is engaged, throughout his life, in learning to see.

NOTES

To p. 496. Ernest Jones says in his biography: 'Freud partook in much of the prudishness of his time, when allusions to lower limbs were improper'. He then gives several examples—such as Freud 'sternly forbidding' his fiancée to stay 'with an old friend, recently married, who, as she delicately put it, "had married before her wedding" ' (Jones, 1953, Vol. I, p. 142).

To p. 498. 'The simple reflex is probably a purely abstract conception, because all parts of the nervous system are connected together and no part of it is probably ever capable of reaction without affecting and being affected by various other parts . . . the simple reflex is a convenient, if not a probable, fiction' (Sherrington, 1906, p. 8).

To p. 500. 'His thinking was particular, not general. When he thought of secondary drive, he thought of . . . fear or anxiety. When he thought of secondary reinforcement, he thought of such things as . . . tokens substituting for food' (Hilgard, 1958, p. 177).

To p. 507. Uncertainty is more arousing than certainty—as witnessed by the universal passion for gambling which coincided with the consolidation of the

British Welfare State. Its rudiments can be found even in the rat and pigeon—as Skinner himself pointed out—when rewards are given rarely and irregularly; this treatment induces the creature to go on trying for an astonishingly long time without a single reward—just as Britons will fill in week after week their football coupons.

IX

PLAYING AND PRETENDING

L ogically every book on learning theory ought to have between the sections on 'innate behaviour' and 'acquired behaviour' a chapter on 'learning through play'—or, at least, on 'ludic behaviour' (from *ludere*, to play)—a term coined by Berlyne, presumably to make the subject sound more respectable. The role of play in the learning and practice of skills is too obvious to naturalists and pedagogues to need stressing; yet play was another stepchild of the Psychology of the Dark Ages. Its connotations of curiosity, exploration, frivolousness and *joie de vivre* did not appeal to the spirit of the times; its unpredictability did not fit the S.-R. schema; above all, its self-reinforcing motivation, dissociated from the primary physiological needs, stood in flagrant contradiction to any drive-reducing theory. Thus the concept of 'ludic behaviour' was objectionable on the same grounds as the concept of the exploratory drive; the former appears in fact to be the purest manifestation of the latter.

Difficulties of Definition

A further reason for this neglect may have been the difficulty of defining 'play'* without making the definition circular. By way of elimination, let us try to distinguish between true play and vacuum activities during maturation. A young bird toys with straws and feathers 'aimlessly' before the other action-patterns of the nest-building instinct have matured; displays of fragmentary mating behaviour before sexual maturity fall into the same category. Some of these activities look playful in the sense of serving no apparent purpose (although in fact they may be useful as 'practice runs' in developing a skill); yet they can hardly be regarded as true play because they display all the rigidity of fixed action-patterns. They are performances of isolated bits of the animal's built-in repertory, and thus contrary to appearances, in the direct service of 'primary biological needs' in the classic sense. This implies that 'true play' is dissociated from those needs; that 'it does not have a biological function that we easily recognize'.[1] But precisely at this point the danger of circular definitions comes in: to say that play does not serve a primary need reopens the whole question of what needs, drives, motivations, should be called 'primary'. Thus, for instance, in Drever's *Dictionary of Psychology* play is defined as an 'activity, which may be physical or mental, existing apparently for its own sake, or having for the individual as its main aim the pleasure which the activity itself yields; *usually involving also a detachment from serious aims and ends* . . .'. If we then ask 'What are serious aims and ends?' the answer is obviously: those which are not playful. The way out of the vicious circle is to 'take play seriously', as an activity with a definite 'primary biological function'—viz. to give free rein to the exploratory drive. But such a view can only be held once it is recognized that the exploratory drive itself originates in a 'primary need' equal in importance to the others.

It seems to be wrong, however, to go to the opposite extreme and stretch the meaning of the word 'play' so as to cover *all* manifestations of the exploratory drive—as Berlyne seems to do when he says that 'in human beings, ludic behaviour includes everything that is classified as recreation, entertainment, or "idle curiosity", as well as art, philosophy, and pure (as distinct from applied) science. . . .'[2] This, of course, is a matter of definitions, but I think it more expedient to use the word play in a more precise and restricted sense, which is closer to its colloquial usage. A small child, kicking a ball about, plays; a professional football 'player' works hard for a living. When the monkey takes the puzzle apart and puts it together again, he 'plays'; when there is food inside the puzzle he 'strives'. Two chess masters may *play* a friendly café game; in a tournament they *compete*. The examples show how fluid the borderlines are, yet the principle is clear: *the degree of 'playfulness' in an action decreases in proportion as the exploratory drive is adulterated by other drives;* or, to put it differently: as the self-arousing and self-rewarding nature of the activity, characteristic of the exploratory drive, yields to striving for specific rewards This foreshadows a similarly continuous, graded relationship betwee the dynamics of latent and reinforced learning, to be discussed later

It follows from the above that play can only arise at an evolutionary level or in such special situations, where the organism has been partially liberated from the tyranny of 'primary needs' in the traditional sense, and can afford to 'take time off' to play. This happens among animals where the young mature slowly and enjoy prolonged parental protection and care; under the sheltered conditions of domestication and captivity; and in human history, of course, with the increase of security against the hazards of the natural and social environment. To quote Thorpe again: 'The prolonged childhood of the human species [has] been of prime importance in the process of freeing appetitive behaviour from the primary needs. This and man's growing mastery of his environment have been the essential first steps not only for play but for all those activities which transcend mere maintenance and which underlie the mental and spiritual development of man; activities which, though originating in "play", have produced real advantages in knowledge and comprehension, of the scheme of things. . . .'[3]

A related process of emancipation, namely the detachment of reasoning from emotion, gave rise, as we saw, to humour. Man's emergent ability to perceive a thing or event simultaneously in two incompatible mental contexts enabled him to take the step from the 'ludic' to the 'ludicrous'. The historic link between the two is probably reflected in the word 'ludicrum'—stage play. The actor's or bard's pretence of being himself and somebody else at the same time was at the origin of tragedy and epic; a similar act of magic—carving or painting a thing which is meant to be something else—was the origin of representational art. These, of course, are activities on an incomparably higher level than the play of kittens and birds; yet as Lorenz has pointed out, both imitation and pretence occur already on the animal level. When puppies fight in play, they do not hurt each other or their masters; they conform to certain 'rules of the game'. Whether these have their phylogenetical origin in the ritualized fights of their wild ancestors or whether they are acquired by social learning, the fact remains that such fights are 'not in earnest' and necessitate 'bringing in the "higher" or more psychological concept of "pretence"'.[4]

Equally suggestive is the so-called 'sub-song' of birds. As distinct from the true or full song which is fixed and species-specific, the sub-song is 'a somewhat amorphous, rambling utterance'.[5] Birds indulge in it when their 'primary needs' are not pressing—before the mating season or in captivity—as a kind of vocal play which might either represent practice for the true song, or else a form of 'pretending': some birds which never imitate alien species in their true song do so in their sub-song. Thorpe compares this vocal imitation to the process by which human infants learn to speak—from 'amorphous' babblings to the imitation of sounds produced by their elders (echolalia). Thus imitation, pretence, as well as art, seem to have their precursors in the playful activities of the higher mammalia and birds.

To sum up: 'exploratory behaviour is motivated by the exploratory drive'. In play, its purest form, it is generalized, non-specific, and indiscriminate—a puppy let into an unfamiliar room rushes to and fro, sniffs at every corner, picks up any object, beside itself with excitement under the incentive of novelty. On the other hand, when the exploratory drive is canalized towards more specific targets, it results in latent learning and, still higher up, in problem-solving. While play is self-rewarding, in problem-solving the search itself may also be self-rewarding to varying degrees, but the principal reward is finding the solution. In this broader sense, of course, the law of effect remains valid; but the reward, the pleasure derived from success, is specific to the exploratory drive—its 'consummatory act' as it were—and not a premium extraneous to its nature. If the problem was an easy one, the solution may be both a reward and an incentive to have a go at another problem at once; if the drive was obstructed, involving stress, the solution is tension-reducing. And, of course, the solution may carry supplementary rewards—the carrot of satisfied ambition, for instance.

In laboratory experiments the animal's exploratory possibilities are restricted, and artificial motivations replace the drive as it operates in freedom. At the same time, animals in the laboratory are induced to pay attention to, and discriminate between, stimuli which under normal circumstances would be biologically irrelevant to them; or else to perform motor actions (e.g. Skinner's ping-pong playing pigeons) which are outside their natural repertory. Tricks of this kind can be taught only by stamping in; and attempts to build a universal theory of learning on such methods carry the danger of confusing a travelling circus with Plato's *Academy*.

NOTE

To p. 509. The *Concise Oxford Dictionary* gives no less than thirty-four meanings of the word.

X

PERCEPTION AND MEMORY

I must now switch from animal to man, and later back again. The manner in which animals learn holds important lessons for man; but in order to interpret the data the experimenter must make certain minimum assumptions regarding the animals' experiences; and, whether he is aware of it or not, these assumptions are based on his own human experience. We talk about the animal's pain-reaction or fear-reaction because we have experienced pain and fear; we interpret certain signs as meaning that the animal is alert or apprehensive by inferences which are often unconscious and contain an unavoidably anthropomorphic element. Even Lloyd Morgan's canon acknowledged this; it merely said that one should not be more anthropomorphic than one could help.*

Now, learning involves perception and memory; and since we know incomparably more about both in man than in cats or rats, we must discuss some aspects of man's perceptual and sensory-motor skills before we turn to learning in animals. Instead of the over-worked province of visual perception, I shall start, for a change, on hearing.

Screening the Input

It has been said that visitors to Stalin had to go through seventeen successive screenings: at the outer gate of the Kremlin compound, at several inner gates, and so forth, until the last corridor and the last door leading to the inner sanctum. 'Inputs' which aspire to become 'stimuli' apparently suffer a similar fate. Where hearing is concerned, the brain's stimulus-screening activity starts in the ear. Efferent, inhibitory fibres from higher centres to the cochlea of the cat were discovered by Galambos in 1956. In a series of remarkable experiments[1]

513

the cat's auditory nerve was tapped and wired to an amplifier, so that impulses passing from ear to brain were directly recorded. The impulses were caused by the clicking of a metronome. But the moment a mouse in a glass jar was shown to the cat the firings in the auditory nerve were diminished or ceased altogether: the cat was turning a 'deaf ear' on the metronome. The point of the experiment was to show that the process of stimulus-selection is centrally controlled, but sets in at the periphery—the outer gate of the Kremlin compound.

Attitude and expectation—the pattern of the behavioural matrix to which the organism is attuned at the time—determine what shall constitute a stimulus and what shall not. On a happy family evening, when people are talking while the radio is playing, junior is crying, and the dog is begging to be let out, each of these simultaneous inputs may be perceived as 'signal' and the rest as 'noise'. In audition, at least, the 'figure-background relation' seems to be more complicated than the Gestalt school suggests; it is not something innate in perceptual organization, but dependent on past experience and present state of mind. Women were known to sleep soundly through an air-raid but to awake at the slightest cry of their babies; people deeply asleep show sharp EEG reactions when their own name, or the name of a girlfriend, is read out in a list of other 'background' names.[2]

The point has also an indirect bearing on the controversy whether discrimination is based on the 'absolute' or relational properties of stimuli.[3] The answer seems to be, briefly, that absolute stimuli do not exist—short of sticking a knife into somebody. Yet even on the primitive level of pain, the matrix influences perception—as witnessed by the General in the American Civil War who, in the heat of battle, did not notice that his middle finger was shot away; not to mention anaesthesia by hypnosis in dentistry and child-birth—or the even more remarkable phenomena of hysterical conversion blindness.

Thus the higher centres exercise a selective influence on sensation and perception; those aspects of the input which are irrelevant will be treated as noise, and forgotten 'without leaving a trace'. But the criteria of relevance depend on the 'rules of the game' which the organism is playing at the time.

Stripping the Input

Selective control of the input is the first stage in the process of extracting information from the chaotic noises and other sensations which bombard the organism's receptors; without it, the mind would be in a kind of Brownian motion. This first stage is followed by the processing of the input in a series of relaying operations, each of them designed to strip the input of what appears to be irrelevant—according to the criteria of relevance which operate along that input-channel. One might call this a process of *de-particularization*. It is a clumsy word, but it conveys what is really implied in the terms 'generalization' or 'abstraction', with their multiple connotations.

The most familiar examples of 'de-particularization' are, of course, the visual constancies. The triangle, or the letter 'W', is stripped of the irrelevancies of retinal position, size, etc. Thanks to colour constancy the accidents of light and shadow are discarded; thanks to size constancy, my moving hand does not seem to shrink or grow—changes in perspective size are 'dis-regarded' by the regard. Yet the criteria of relevance and irrelevance depend, even in these cases of apparently spontaneous perception, to a considerable degree on interpretative frames—on perceptual matrices acquired by past experience. When an object of the appearance of a tennis ball is inflated against a homogeneous background, it will be seen as if it were retaining its size and approaching the observer.[4] This is different from size constancy because in this case the observer has to accommodate his eyes and make them converge at a closer range so that the ball gets out of focus and should be seen as a blurred double image. Yet the knowledge that tennis balls behave reasonably and do not grow into footballs somehow manages to compensate for this, and to discard the anomalies in the situation as irrelevant noise. To quote Bartlett once more: 'Even the most elementary perceptions have the character of inferential constructions.' The Baconian ideal of observation without theorizing is undermined by the mechanism of observation itself. Perception is polluted by implied hypotheses. To look, to listen, to taste, means to ask questions; and mostly they are leading questions.

To obtain a more detached view of the living organism's methods of coding and storing its experiences, let me make a naïve comparison with a typical engineering procedure. Examining a modern gramophone record with a magnifying glass, you see a spiral curve with lateral oscillations of varying amplitude and spacing—a curve where the abscissa represents time, and the ordinate the amplitude of the needle's oscillations. And yet this two-dimensional curve, with a single independent variable, can reproduce any sequence of sounds, from the Sermon on the Mount to the Ninth Symphony performed by orchestra and choir, including the buzzing of a fly and a cough in the audience. In fact the entire range of human knowledge and experience could be expressed by the function of this one independent variable, so that one is tempted to ask why the nervous system does not produce engrams in this simple type of code, instead of the incomparably more complicated methods it uses. The answer is, that a 'linear' memory trace of this type would be completely useless for the purposes of analysing, recognizing, and matching new inputs, and for working out the appropriate responses. It would merely represent the 'blooming, buzzing confusion of pure sensation sans organization' which, in the words of William James, is the new-born infant's world. Before it can be more or less permanently stored, the input must be processed, dismantled, and reassembled in various ways, which the following examples may serve to illustrate.

Dismantling and Reassembling

Let the input be fifty instruments and fifty voices performing a choral part of Beethoven's Ninth. On the gramophone record, and in the air-waves which make the ear-drum vibrate, the pitch, timbre, and loudness of the individual voices and instruments have all been superimposed on each other—scrambled together into a single variable pulse. The individuality of soprano, flute, viola, is lost in the process; it requires a human nervous system to reconstitute it.

The pulse is transmitted and amplified by the bones of the middle ear and enters through the oval window into the cochlea. Here the basilar membrane, based in viscous fluid, starts the process of un-scrambling the acoustic omelette. This is done, partly at least, by a kind of Fourier-analysis of the oscillatory curve, which breaks it down into its spectrum of basic frequencies.* The parallel fibres of the basilar membrane form a kind of spiral harp; each fibre responds to a specific frequency. This analysing mechanism operates over a range of twenty to twenty thousand cycles per second, and auditory discrimination varies from about 0.05 at low frequencies to 0.025 at 2,000 c/s (Piccolo flute). Each frequency has its separate 'place' on the spiral membrane. Each 'place' is presumed to be connected by a separate group of fibres, running through several relay stations, to a presumably fixed location in the primary reception area in the auditory cortex—area 22.

But this mechanism of transmission by fixed pathways and non-specific impulses is only half of the story; the other half is transmission of the lower frequencies by 'volleys' in a bundle of fibres firing in turn at the specific frequency of the input.[5] The details of both theories are still controversial, but the available evidence indicates that they complement each other. We have, then, here one more instance of the complementary character of two types of nervous function: conduction by specific pathways, and conduction by specific signals over equipotential pathways.

We now have our fifty singers and fifty instruments decomposed into a constantly changing mosaic pattern of excitations in area 22 where each point (or region or circuit)[6] represents the frequency of one pure tone, and in some form also its intensity—*regardless of the instrument or voice in which it originated*. This state of affairs bears no resemblance to any conceivable neural model based on S.-R. theory —or on the Gestalt physiology of Köhler and Koffka.* In fact the whole physiological theory of Gestalt, and many of its psychological postulates, break down when we come to audition. This is not surprising since Köhler concentrated entirely on *visual* perception; and in the seven hundred-odd pages of Koffka's *Principles of Gestalt Psychology* exactly one page (p. 200) is devoted to 'other (than visual) senses'. Even on this one page, the only reference to audition is the statement that 'sound' and 'stillness' have a reversible figure-background relation.

At the auditory projection area we must assume the dismantling process to end and the reassembling to start. When we listen to the symphony we do *not* hear an ensemble of the pure tones into which it has been broken up in the cochlea, but an ensemble of individual instruments and voices: that is, of organized sub-wholes. The individual timbre of an instrument is determined by its overtones—the series of partials which accompany the fundamental, and the energy-distribution of them. By superimposition of the sine curves of the partials, we obtain the periodic curve characteristic for each instrument. When we identify the sound of a violin or flute by picking out and bracketing together its partials—which were 'drowned' among thousands of other partials in the air-pressure wave—we have achieved 'timbre constancy', comparable to visual figure constancy. This, of course, is based on past experience and involves an act of recognition by the 'trained ear' of instruments previously heard in isolation.

Since all but the most elementary perceptions interact with past experience, it seems a rather unsound procedure to discuss perception divorced from the problem of memory. The question, then, is how the 'trace' was originally acquired which enables me to recognize an instrument or voice on subsequent occasions. Let us assume that I am hearing an exotic instrument for the first time, and that I am interested at the moment only in its timbre, not in the melody played on it (which, in the case of a Japanese *koto* or *samisen*, would be above my head anyway). As I am listening, the mathematical relations between the partials remain constant and enduring, whereas their pitch and loudness are changing all the time. This stable and enduring relation-pattern (the fixed ratios between the part-frequencies) will be treated by my nervous system, which is processing the input, as relevant, whereas the changes in the relata (the absolute frequencies) are discarded as irrelevant. When this filtering-out process is completed, the input will have been finally stripped of all irrelevant detail, according to the demands of parsimony, and reduced to its invariant pattern—to 'information' purified of 'noise'. If an input has undergone these transformations and was permitted to progress this far without being blocked somewhere on its way (as, for instance, the voices of irrelevant strangers at a cocktail party are) then it will tend to leave a lasting 'trace'—which will enable the nervous system to recognize in future the same voice or instrument.

We have witnessed, as it were, the formation of the code of a new perceptual skill. The organism feeds on negative entropy; in communication theory, 'entropy' becomes 'noise'. The sensorium abstracts information from the chaotic environment as the mitochondria extract, by a series of dismantling and reassembling processes, a specific form of energy from food. The abstracting and recording of information involves, as we have just seen, the sacrifice of details which are filtered out as irrelevant in a given context. But what is considered as irrelevant in one context, may be relevant in another; and vice versa. We can recognize an instrument regardless of the tune played on it; but we can also recognize a tune regardless of the instrument on which it is played. The tune is abstracted and recorded in a memory-trace de-particularized of timbre; timbre is recorded de-particularized of tune. Thus the filtering-out of redundancies as the input is relayed from periphery to centre does not proceed along a single channel, but along several channels, each with its series of filters of different colour, as it were. The different colours represent the criteria of relevance in different perceptual hierarchies. Each hierarchy analyses the input according to its own criteria of relevance; but the loss of detail incurred in the process of memory-formation along a single channel is partly counteracted by the fact that information rejected as irrelevant by its coloured filters may be admitted as relevant by another channel belonging to a different hierarchy. We shall see that this principle of multi-dimensional analysis is of basic importance in the phenomena of recognition and recall.

A Digression on Engrams

The neurophysiological problems of memory are beyond the scope of this book, but the following remarks may help to forestall possible misunderstandings. Perceptual codes of the type which enables us to recognize an instrument are devices which analyse complex acoustic inputs by some unknown process of 'matching' or 'resonance'. The quotes indicate that these words are used as metaphors only; the process must of course be incomparably more complicated than acoustic or electric resonance. What matters is that a memory-trace cannot be visualized as a mechanical record like a gramophone groove, 'stamped' into the brain and activated by specific pathways. Such an arrangement would be as useless for purposes of auditory analysis as it would be useless for the visual recognition of shapes to have an archive of photographic engrams. Instead of this, we must hypothesize some kind of 'attunement' of a cluster or clusters of neurons, with a hierarchic ogranization and containing sub-wholes which are equipotential in their response to one specific pattern of excitation and to that pattern only. Pringle[7] assumed that memory-traces function like 'coupled resonators'; Hyden's[8] theory of RNA changes which determine selective responsiveness to frequency-modulation sequences of excitation seems more plausible. Whatever the mechanism is, it must combine the principle of fixed but partly equipotential spatial connections, with selective responses to specific excitation patterns, to account for the hierarchic organization of perceptual, conceptual, and motor skills. Weiss' excitation clang was an approach in that direction. Hebb's phase sequences in neuron assemblies was another. The Pitt-McCullough model of a scanning analyser to account for figure constancies should show that basically similar principles can be applied in vision as in audition to the problem of analysing and matching the input.

The matrix of a complex skill—such as the maze-running skill of Lashley's rats—may be no more 'localized' than the programme of a political party is localized by the addresses of all members who adhere to it. If some members or groups of members are eliminated, other groups may take over. Simpler and more primitive matrices, however, are perhaps rather like the professional guilds of craftsmen concentrated in one area of a medieval town; if that area is destroyed, the skill is lost.

Tracing a Melody

We have seen that recognition of a voice or instrument is based on an invariant relation (the fixed ratios between partials or formants) which has been extracted from the variable relata. Once the instrument is perceived as a recognizable whole, the relation becomes a relatum—e.g. 'a violin'—regardless whether a verbal symbol is attached to it or not. This relatum then enters into relations with the sound of other instruments, which are analysed on higher levels according to the criteria of more complex rules of the game—harmony, melodic, and contrapuntal form—in which several perceptual hierarchies participate.

A *tune* is defined by rhythm and pitch. Rhythm derives from the hierarchic organization of beat-cum-accent into measure, measure into phrase. To qualify as a tune, the pitch-variation sequence must conform to certain codes of modality, key, harmony. These codes must also be represented in the listener's perceptual organization, otherwise there would be no musical experience, only the sensation of a medley of sounds—as when a European listens for the first time to Chinese opera. The melody itself has the structural coherence of a closed figure as distinct from an open, linear chain. It is either 'taken in' as a whole in the specious present, or learned by the integration of sub-wholes, that is of entire phrases—but never by chaining note to note in the manner of learning nonsense-syllables (though even these tend to form patterns). A chain of notes could not be transposed from one key or instrument to another; nor recognized after transposition.

A tune is a temporal pattern of notes in a given scale. The notes are the relata; by humming it in a different key, or playing it on a different instrument, the relata are changed but the relation remains invariant in all transformations. On a higher level, the tune as a whole again becomes a relatum which enters into relations with other tonal patterns; or with itself in symmetrical reversal; or contrapuntally with other themes.

Most people are capable of learning and recognizing simple melodies, and equally capable of recognizing the sound of various instruments —but few mortals share the privilege of 'absolute pitch', of being able to identify single notes. In other words, retention of a pattern of stimuli is the rule, retention of an isolated stimulus the exception. If the pattern is relatively simple, it is 'take in at a glance', as a whole: as a rule, listening to the first two transients is sufficient to identify an instrument.[9] But the more complex the pattern, the more difficult it becomes to 'take the whole in at a glance', and it can be retained only by dint of a certain amount of rote learning.

Conditioning and Insight in Perception

Once more, however, the items memorized are not discrete bits, but organized sub-wholes; and they are not summated in an open chain but interrelated in a closed figure. Thus the first movement of a sonata will fall into three sub-wholes: statement of themes, development, recapitulation; and the first of these is usually subdivided into the exposition of two themes in the order A-B-A; while in the rondo we usually have A B A C A.

Similar considerations apply, for instance, to the learning of a poem. Rhythm, rhyme, grammar, and meaning provide patterns or 'grids' superimposed on each other—matrices governed by already established codes; and the memorizing that remains to be done is not so much a 'stamping in' but a 'filling of gaps'. This is shown by the typical way of 'getting stuck' in reciting a poem; e.g.:

'. . . Cannon to left of them / Cannon in front of them / (— —) and thundered'. A word has fallen out like a piece from a jigsaw puzzle—but it merely leaves a gap; it does not break the 'chain'. The old-fashioned method of teaching history by reigns and battles is an obvious example of stamping in. Even so, the data often show some rudimentary organization into rhythmic or visual patterns, acquired spontaneously or by some memorizing trick such as rhyming jingles. Calculating prodigies memorize long series of numbers, not by chaining but by ordering them into familiar sub-groups. Nonsense syllables are easier retained by twisting them into a semblance of words, and

weaving these into a story.[10] The position of thirty men on a chessboard is easier retained than of five chessmen lying in a heap on the
floor.

How do we recognize complex patterns? Take a professional musician who has turned on his radio in the middle of a programme: 'It's
a string quartet. . . . Something by Beethoven. . . . It's a quartet of
the middle period. . . . It's the second Rasoumovsky. . . . It is probably
played by the Amadeus Quartet. . . .' The input has been matched in
rapid succession against the very complex coded constancies in several
interlocking hierarchies—timbre, melody, rhythm, accent, phrasing,
volume, density, etc.—until the last drop of 'information' has been
extracted from it. Each independent hierarchy of 'coloured filters'
activated by the input adds an additional dimension to understanding.

Perception cannot be divorced from past experience. What I have
said so far already foreshadows a continuous scale of gradations between
opposite methods of perceptual learning. At one end, in classical conditioning, we shall find stamping-in, under artificial conditions, of
excitation-patterns which outside the laboratory would be treated as
biologically irrelevant and would accordingly leave no trace. Outside
the laboratory, edible things do not emit signals by metronome-clicks,
or by displaying the figure of an ellipse on a cardboard. The dog's
perceptual organization is not 'attuned' to this kind of input-signal;
it lies outside all recognized rules of the game; and there will be no
inherent tendency in the naïve dog to abstract information from the
rate of metronome-clicks. However (see below, Chapter XII), even
the artificial stamping-in of a trace in this type of experiment is not
purely mechanical, and not comparable to the action of the recording
needle on the gramophone disc.

In the intermediary ranges of the scale we find blends of varying
proportions between 'bit learning' and 'whole' or pattern-learning;
and lastly, at the opposite end, the input is analysed in all its relevant
aspects by the various 'competent' perceptual hierarchies, until it is
saturated, as it were, with meaning. This, I shall suggest, is what we
mean by 'insight-learning'. Insight thus becomes a matter of degrees
—and not, as the Gestalt school seemed to hold, an all-or-nothing
process.

The key-word in the previous paragraph was 'competent'. The
amount of 'stamping in' needed, and the type of learning which will
occur, depends on the animal's (native and acquired) perceptual organization—in other words, on its 'ripeness' for that particular kind of

task. If this sounds like a truism, one still wonders how conditioning
—'classical' or 'operant'—could ever have been regarded as the paradigm of all learning.

Abstract and Picture-strip

Memory of a sort is found on every organic level, from protozoa
upwards. The human nervous system we assume to be equipped with
a hierarchy of memory-systems operating on various levels: from
short-lived, unstable modifications in the receptor organs, to stable
and enduring central 'engrams' and the codes of complex skills. Since
perception and memory-formation proceed in a continuous series, and
since perception filters the input, we are led to the apparently paradoxical conclusion that the most enduring memory-traces must be
those which have been most thoroughly de-particularized—that is to
say, impoverished. This seems indeed to be the case at least in so far as
one important category of hierarchies is concerned: the abstractive
category.

When one is watching a play at the theatre the successive sounds
emitted by the actors must be retained by short-term memory until
they can be bracketed together into words or larger syntactic sub-
wholes. The psychological present embraces various-sized chunks of
the immediate past (by means of a 'mnemic afterglow', of reverberating circuits, or what-have-you). By the time the actor utters his
next line, the perceptual relata—the speech-units—of the previous line
have already been forgotten, and only the wording is still retained.
A few lines further the exact wording of the first phrase is also wiped
off the memory slate, and only its content is still stored on some
higher level of the hierarchy. The next day one still has a fairly detailed
recollection of the actual sequence of scenes in the play; a few months
later only an outline of the plot as a whole remains in the 'store'.
Parsimony in memory-formation demands that only a mere skeleton
of the complex original experience should be retained on the highest
level of a given hierarchy; and vice versa, that the trace which an
input leaves shall be the more enduring, the higher the level to
which it has attained by successive stages of de-particularization and
re-coding.

The example I described was of an abstractive hierarchy governed
exclusively by logical analysis. A computer built on these lines, after
being fed a number of West End plays, would probably filter down

all that it found worth retaining, to a formula such as: isoscele marriage triangle with pet-dog at centre of gravity, or: whodunit with five independent variables (suspects).

Let us assume that at each stage of this serial abstractive process, the input activates some particular scanning- or filtering-device which is 'attuned' to that particular input. The receiving end of that device corresponds to its 'matrix' aspect: it is potentially responsive to a great many inputs which have one specific feature or pattern in common, and are thus equipotential in that respect. When an input is 'recognized' by the matrix as conforming to that pattern, it will emit a code-signal to the higher echelons. But while the matrix is 'attuned' to a great number of variations in the input pattern, the code merely signals the invariant aspect of it, e.g. 'a triangle', 'an octave', 'a fly', 'a denial'. The size and position of the triangle, the particulars of the fly, the wording of the denial are lost in the coding, and cannot be retrieved by reversing the process within that particular hierarchy (though it may have been preserved by another).

Thus the analysing-devices behave like analogue-to-digital computers, and in other respects, too, the order of events is the exact reverse—as one would expect—of the processes we have observed in motor-hierarchies. When an animal engages in some skilled action, the co-ordinating centre activates a matrix of equi-final motor patterns; which particular sub-skill will be called into activity depends on circumstances. Thus the 'roughed-in' action-programme becomes more and more particularized in the course of its descent to the periphery—while contrariwise, the peripheral input is more and more de-particularized or 'skeletonized' in its ascent towards the centre. The first is a process of progressively spelling out implicit orders; the second an equally stepwise process of abstracting the meaning implied in the mosaic of sensations. Both processes are irreversible: the exact words of the actors in the play cannot be retrieved.

It can also happen, however, that one has quite forgotten what that play, seen years ago, was about—except for one particular detail, an inflection of voice, an imploring gesture of the heroine which, torn from its context, remains engraved on one's memory. There exists, indeed, a method of retention which seems to be the direct opposite of memory-formation in abstractive hierarchies. It is characterized by the preservation of vivid details, which, from a purely logical point of view, are often quite irrelevant; and yet these quasi-cinematographic details or 'close-ups', which seem to contradict the demands of parsimony, are both enduring, strikingly sharp, and add texture and flavour to memory.

Bartlett, in a classic experiment, made his subjects read an Indian legend and then reproduce it on repeated occasions at intervals of increasing length—ranging from fifteen minutes after the first reading to several months or years. The story was about thirty lines long; it concerned a young Indian who got involved in the 'War of the Ghosts', and was wounded in the process. The last paragraph read:

> He told it all, and then became quiet. When the sun rose he fell down. Something black came out of his mouth. His face became contorted. The people jumped up and cried. He was dead.[10a]

Twenty subjects were tested. Their written recollection of the story shrank with the passage of time to a few lines which, in most cases, distorted its content almost 'beyond recognition'. But, with one exception, all the spaced-out versions of all subjects, even after several years, contained the lines: 'Something black came out (or "issued" or "rushed" or "jumped out") of his mouth.' The one exception wrote (after four months): 'My remembrance was in visual terms . . . of breath somehow materializing into a ghost.'

Fiction and autobiography abound with examples of such 'vivid-fragment-memories': the mole on Granny's chin, the fly crawling over the lump of sugar at the moment of the dramatic climax. Let us call this the 'picture strip' type of memory—although, of course, the 'vivid fragment' may be auditory or olfactory, or even a whole 'cinematographic sequence'—like the detailed, auditory-visual sequences which Penfield evoked in his patients through electric stimulation of their exposed temporal lobes (see below).

Obviously the formation of such 'picture-strip traces' must also be preceded by some filtering process; but in this case the criteria of relevance and parsimony are different, and often directly opposed to those of the abstractive hierarchies. The vivid detail is usually described as 'striking', 'attractive', 'evocative', 'nostalgic', 'frightening'; it always has some *emotional* significance. It is mostly on a pre-verbal level; but even verbal fragments—of a poem, of a chill warning or whispered endearment—are retained because of their affective quality. The filter-matrices that operate in these hierarchies must be emotionally 'attuned' —let us say to some hypothalamic controls. We may further assume that such picture-strip memories are formed on lower (pre-conceptual) levels than memories of the abstractive kind; they may be symbolic, but their symbolism too is often pre-verbal, and perhaps related to the symbolism of the dream; they may even obey their own special brand of parsimony. We have seen that occasional regression to lower levels of the hierarchy is a *conditio sine qua non* of creativeness; the combination of the abstractive and picture-strip type of memory may serve the same purpose—*vide* Coleridge and Kekulé.

We are thus led to assume the existence of various hierarchies in perception and cognition, whose criteria of relevance are determined by the attitudes, drives, emotions, which they serve; they interlace with each other on every level, and thereby provide the multi-dimensionality—or multi-colouration—of experience; at the same time they also compensate for the impoverishment of experience in the process of memory formation. The outstanding memory which some geniuses are said to have possessed may possibly be due to their many-dimensional ways of analysing and storing experiences.

Learning to See

Let us turn to vision.

Innate perceptual organization provides no more than the primitive foundation on which learning can build. The long controversy between Behaviourists and the nativistically inclined Gestalt school whether perceptual organization is innate *or* learned has finally been superseded by the more realistic question *how much* is innate and how much acquired by early learning. The consensus seems to be that colour and brightness constancy, and the recognition of line, angle, and texture are innate in rats as well as men.[11] So is 'primitive unity' (Hebb) —the segregation of simple figures as coherent entities from the background (for instance, a black splash on a white card). But when it comes to more complex figures where the contrast is less marked, even the figure-ground relation is strongly influenced by learning and expectancy. I have quoted examples from the neglected field of auditory perception where the relativity of figural unity is obvious. The radiologist whom experience has taught to *see* a peptic ulcer or a lesion of the lung, treats the much sharper contours of the ribs as 'background'. When you hunt for a collar-stud in a drawerful of miscellaneous objects, that small, insipid form, poor in Gestalt *Prägnanz*, will 'stick out a mile'; the remaining contents of the drawer are 'background'.

Thus even figural coherence is influenced by past experience and present attitude. When it comes to the *identification* and recognition of visual Gestalten, it has been shown that even the simplest of them— triangles, squares—require an element of learning. The behaviour of chimpanzees reared without pattern vision, of human beings with congenital cataract who had to 'learn to see' after they were operated on, and the cumulative evidence from other experiments indicate, in Hebb's words, 'that the normal human infant goes through the same process, and that we are able to see a square as such in a single glance only as the result of complex learning'.[12] The learning process seems to depend mainly on visual exploration: a two-year-old child will recognize a triangle that has been rotated by 120 degrees only after rotating its own head;[13] but even in the adult, perception is bound up with exploratory motions of the eyes, from conscious movements to the involuntary, minute motions ('drift', 'flick', 'tremor') which move the image across the fovea when the eye seems 'fixed' on a stationary object. Identification of a triangle or square seems to depend on serial scanning of its contours.[14] With practice, the scanning motions may become summary or subliminal; but when scanning is artificially eliminated by a mechanical device, the image disintegrates into frag-ments. '*Wir tasten mit unserem Blick das Sehfeld ab*', Exner wrote in 1891[15] (We finger over the visual field with our gaze).

Thus with the exception of brightness and colour constancy, and a few other primitive 'innate skills', visual perception is inextricably bound up with learning, i.e. with memory. What we perceive in audition is not the linear pulse of pressure-variations arriving at the eardrum, but an 'inferential construct' of individual voices, instru-ments, musical or verbal phrases; and what we perceive in vision is not the camera-image on the retina but the 'inferential construct' of people and objects which preserve their constant shape and size, regard-less of angle and distance. The eye may be a camera, but immediately behind its lens there is a series of compensating, correcting, and re-touching devices—the perceptual matrices of skilled vision.

Knowing and Seeing

The best-known among these are the matrices responsible for the visual constancies and illusions which are found in every elemen-tary textbook. Less attention has been paid to the modification of automatically functioning perceptual matrices by verbal learning and verbal suggestions, by attitude and expectation.[16] Mitscherlich, an outstanding observer, had denied that there existed any structural difference between the two types of tartaric acid of opposite optical activity. Pasteur, using the same apparatus, saw at once the asymmetric facets on the tartar crystals because his hypothesis on molecular structure demanded that they should be there.[17]

Perceptual matrices function not only autonomously, but display considerable 'self-assertion'. This is shown in a simple but drastic manner by the difficulty of breaking the arrow illusion:

Another example of 'self-assertion' is the tiresome insistence with which a tune will go round and round in your head; or the infuriating messages—'I told you so'—'I told you so' rapped out at the rate of once per second by the wheels of your railway-carriage. A more advanced but equally typical illustration for 'knowing is seeing' is this quote from Babbage: 'I will prepare the apparatus, and put you in such a position that [Fraunhofer's dark lines] shall be visible, and yet you shall look for them and not find them: after which, while you remain in the same position, I will instruct you *how to see them*, and you shall see them, and not merely wonder you did not see them before, but you shall find it impossible to look at the spectrum without seeing them.'[18]

A pretty illustration of perception impregnated by previous knowledge is in the drawing opposite.

The bear climbing on the other side of the tree is purely inferential. Yet you *see* the semi-circles plus four strokes as his paws.

Levels of Memory

Perception and memory cannot be un-scrambled. Let us consider briefly a few types of 'mnemic' processes which intervene on various levels of the hierarchy.

On the lowest, peripheral level we find automatisms designed to reduce redundancy and to 'compress' the input. It would be uneconomical if each receptor in the retina would signal to report stimulation

FIGURE 16

from a uniformly illuminated area; hence lateral inhibition between neighbouring receptor units, combined with light-adaptation, will filter down the input to signals which report only the relevant spatial *differences* in illumination—i.e. the contours of the illuminated area.[19] Likewise, the eye adapts to uniform motion—as seen in the illusion of reverse movement when the real movement stops (the 'waterfall-illusion'). These automatisms could be called memory processes confined to the psychological present (in the broad sense of 'memory = modification of responsiveness by experience').

More lasting are *after-images*—once regarded as the prototypes of 'photographic' memory. In fact, however, the after-image 'improves' on the original by achieving greater regularity and simplicity. Goethe was the first to observe that the after-image of a square will gradually become transformed into a circle—a figure of greater symmetry. Rothschild's[20] experiments showed that only regular figures with 'good' contour produce stable after-images; that figures with gaps in their contours appear 'closed' in the after-image; that small irregularities disappear, and elements which 'do not belong' to a figure, such as

529

a squiggle or tail attached to a square, become detached from it and come and go as independent units. Thus the reproduction is far from mechanical, and is controlled both by intrinsic codes and from higher centres.[21]

There are some significant parallels between after-images and images which have been artificially stabilized on the retina. The latter are obtained by a tiny projector, mounted on a contact-lens worn by the subject. The illuminated target-figure is fixed at the other end of the projector; it moves with the involuntary scanning motions of the eyeball, and its projection remains thus fixed on the same spot of the retina—subtending a visual angle of two degrees in a patch of light of five degrees, with darkness all round. Under these conditions the perceived image will vanish and reappear much as after-images do—either as a whole, or it will disintegrate into parts. If the latter is the case, the fragments will be meaningful in one way or the other: a human face will break up into its specific features or groups of features—profile or top of the head; and a composite monogram will break up into the individual letters and numbers which were hidden in it. Conversely, the elements in a meaningless pattern of curlicews will at first fade and reappear in various combinations; but after a while they will organize themselves into stable sub-wholes. Central processes fraught with past experience exert an obvious influence on these phenomena; and so does the subject's attitude.

The next step leads to *eidetic images*. These occupy an intermediate place in the memory hierarchy between after-images and the 'picture-strip' type of recall. In their direct sensory impact they are comparable to hypnagogic images and close to hallucinations. The experimenter directs the subject to inspect a picture for about thirty seconds without staring (to eliminate after-images), then to look at a grey screen. The average person sees nothing; the eidetic 'projects' the image onto the screen and behaves as if the picture were actually there. He can focus on a detail, point out its exact position on the screen, count the buttons on a coat, the number of spokes on a wheel, and 'read' the letters in a foreign-language text forward or backward.[22] It seems, therefore, that eidetic images 'are seen in the literal sense of the word'.[23] Eidetic recall may be limited to a short interval after inspecting an object or picture, or extend to 'minutes, days, years'.[24] Analogous phenomena seem to exist in other sense-modalities: Beethoven, Mozart, Wagner, and Elgar were supposed to be able to 'hear at will the full texture of an orchestra'.[25]

Eidetic memory, though rare in adults, seems to be quite common in children before puberty; 'in certain regions,' according to Kluever, 'eighty to a hundred per cent of the children are reported eidetic'.[26] This is a striking confirmation of the commonplace that the child lives in a world of images of great vividness, whereas the average adult's images are grey shadows. The eidetic type of memory seems to be irretrievably lost, in all but exceptional cases, with the transition from the perceptual and affective to the conceptual and symbolic mentality. Pictorial memory, as we saw, belongs to a phylogenetically and onto-genetically earlier level of the mnemic hierarchy.

Yet if we expect the eidetic image to be a true photographic record, we shall again be disappointed. All reports agree that the development of the image on the screen depends on the child's interest in the picture as a whole, and in its details. Exciting details come out sharply, while adjacent parts may remain blank, blurred, or even appear in com-plementary colours. Pictures which have no meaning for the child do not appear on the screen.[27] The objects in the image can be moved about, and their colour and size can be changed at will, or in response to verbal suggestions. Synaesthetic phenomena also enter: if the subject's arms are pulled while he is inspecting a horizontal line, the eidetic image of the line will be lengthened; images of the Mueller-Lyer illusion may be lengthened 'by as much as two yards'.[28]

Image and Meaning

A further step upward in the hierarchy leads to what I have called the 'picture-strip' kind of memory with emotive significance; and lastly we arrive at the phenomena referred to as 'memory images' in ordinary parlance.

An image is defined in *Drever's Dictionary* as 'a revived sense ex-perience, in the absence of the sensory stimulation'. But since most of the sensory stimulation has been irretrievably lost in the filtering-processes of memory formation, only some exceptionally sharp, vivid details are perhaps capable of being 'revived' or 'reproduced'; the remainder of the experience must be 'reconstructed'. It has been known for a long time that introspective reports on 'visual memory images' are largely based on self-deception. Visual recall—as Semon once wrote—'renders only the strongest lights and shadows';[29] but strictly speaking, even shadows are absent from visual images—as they are from Chinese paintings; and so are, as a rule, all but the crudest shades of colour. The normal adult's memory-images are much vaguer, sketchier in outline than he is wont to believe; in most cases when he believes that he possesses a visual image of a thing, he is really referring to aggregates of simplified perceptual schemata, held together by conceptual links.

This has been amply demonstrated (cf. Book One, pp. 346 seq). In the Binet-Mueller test[30] the subject is directed to memorize a letter square (comprising sixteen or twenty-five letters in random distribution) until he thinks that he has formed a visual image of it, and can 'see' it in his mind's eye. But when he is asked to read the letters in his image in backward order or diagonally, he will take up to ten times longer than when reciting them in their proper serial order from left to right.

Another classic test is the drawing of elephants by patients suffering from a form of aphasia which impairs symbolic thought but leaves perceptual faculties intact—a test first used by Pierre Marie, and later by Henry Head:[31]

Case No. 8 ('semantic' asphasia): Asked to draw an elephant, he moved his pencil about aimlessly, saying 'I can't get the idea'. Then he suddenly drew the outline of the head, back and belly, adding the four legs and an eye; the tusks were indicated but he omitted the trunk. I asked 'What is the characteristic of an elephant?' To this he replied, 'Its trunk; I see I have omitted to put in his trunk'.

Case No. 11 . . . made an incomplete drawing of an elephant to order. Asked if he had left out anything, he replied 'His ear', and made a mark on the side of the head. When I inquired 'Has an elephant got anything else?', he answered 'Trunk, eye, tail, toes', marking in each object in turn as he named it; but he forgot the tusks.

Case No. 21 (a woman of high intelligence with some semantic disorder): When I requested her to draw an elephant she produced a picture distinctly resembling this animal, except that she gave it a bushy tail and forgot the tusks. After she had finished she exclaimed 'I haven't put the tusks in. I can't remember where they come. They come from just below the eye, I think; but I don't know. I believe they are teeth and should come out of the top of the jaw really.'

The quotations show that the visual image of the elephant was not in fact a 'perceptual whole' but a mélange of perceptual *and* conceptual entities; the glue which held the visual parts together was *meaning*. Thus in a number of drawings the tusks at first appeared on top of the elephant's head as if they had been horns; and only when their function was remembered were they put in their correct place.

We have now reached the boundary between the perceptual and symbolic hierarchies—the highest level of perceptual integration, where symbolic coding must take over if further progress in learning is to be achieved. The schematized visual forms of trunk, legs, tusks, seem to be the upper limit of the patient's capability of forming true perceptual Gestalt-traces. When it comes to reproducing the 'image' of the complete elephant, the *visual pattern* of the tusk is manipulated as a *symbolic unit*, labelled a 'tusk'. It is, once more, a double-faced entity: one side is a complex and flexible perceptual whole, the other is a semantic unit which signals the word 'tusk' and is activated by the same signal.

Klangbild and Wortschatz

A similar frontier is found in audition, where perception of sound patterns turns into interpretation of language. Here one face of the entities which pass the frontier is a *Klangbild*, the other belongs to the *Wortschatz*—a distinction between 'sound-picture' and 'word-treasure' (i.e. vocabulary)—which Wernicke made in 1874.[32]

There is considerable doubt whether the discrete elements or 'segments' of speech are phonemes, syllables, or even larger units. Let us assume for argument's sake that the segments are characteristic vowel-consonant combinations—digrams or trigrams* and call these the *perceptual units* (the 'sound-pictures' of speech). In whatever way you define your unit, when it comes to the transition from perceiving the sound-picture to interpreting its *speech-value*, a considerable degree of ambiguity creeps in. Thus the speech-value of a vowel (the o-ness of an o) is independent of the frequency of its fundamental, and depends on the characteristic frequency-ranges of its two formants (its dominant partials). But these formant-ranges overlap; and accordingly 'a sound with a particular spectrum will be recognized as / ī / on one occasion and / ē / on another'.[33] Most consonants, on the other hand, vary their pitch according to the vowel with which they are associated, and are characterized not only by pitch but also by the change, and rate of change of pitch.[34] Thus the identification of language units depends to a considerable extent on their meaning-context; experimental subjects confuse m and n in nonsense syllables more frequently than when listening to meaningful speech; and the ambiguity of the input can only be resolved with reference to the preceding and following inputs in the psychological present. In discussing the practical feasibility of robots for translating speech into typescript, Fry and Denes concluded: 'It is unlikely that the mechanical speech-recognizer will be successful without the use of some form of linguistic information.'[35] It is the same as with ambiguous visual stimuli, whether they are riddles of the face-hidden-in-the-tree kind, or Frauenhofer-lines in the spectroscope. '*Es hört doch jeder nur was er versteht*', Goethe noted in his *Maximen*.

If scanning is an aid to vision, articulation is an aid to hearing. When we try to remember a tune, we hum it. The decisive factor in the emergence of human speech was not the development of the ear, but of the vocal organs and of the speech area in the motor cortex. The multiple feedbacks of auditory-vocal co-ordination exceed even those of oculo-motor co-operation. The child learns words by articulating them; adults learning a foreign language follow a similar procedure. Reading is more often accompanied by sub-vocal articulation than by images in the ear (except if you know intimately the author of what you are reading). The analysis of speech-sounds by matching them against innervation-patterns of the vocal tracts is a much simpler procedure than the acoustic analysis of the ambiguous sound spectra. However complex and variable the wave form of a vowel which reaches the ear, its identity as a language unit depends on its two formants, which in turn depend only on the resonance effects produced by the alterations of shape of two vocal cavities, mouth and pharynx. Paget[36] proposed that 'in recognizing speech sounds the human ear is . . . listening . . . to indications, due to resonance, of the position and gestures of the organs of articulation'. More recently a team of American experimentalists in the Haskins Laboratories have come to the same conclusion that 'speech is perceived by reference to articulation—that is, that the articulatory movements and their sensory [proprioceptive] effects mediate between the acoustic stimulus and the event we call perception'.[37] Lastly, Lawrence (1959) has described a method of speech-analysis which specifies such details as the frequencies of resonance of the vocal tract and the vibration frequencies of the vocal chords—a method of analysis 'which preserves all perceptually valuable features, but is vastly simpler than the acoustic wave form. From an information theory point of view it is a tremendous reduction in the bit rate—it is a reduction of the order of thirty to one. It may well be that speech is held in the short-term memory in a form like this.'[38]

Once again we find confirmed that perception is 'something the organism does, not something which happens to the organism';[39] that responses enter at every level of the hierarchy into the processing of stimuli; and that motor activities intervene to analyse the input long before it has achieved its full status as a 'stimulus'—before it has, for instance, become a meaningful word capable of stimulating the central process which is to mediate the 'response'. As Drever, Jr., has so nicely put it: 'Associationist learning theory, where it has tried to hold to a strict S——>R pattern, appears to be lapsing into an esoteric scholasticism. Where it has abandoned S——>R in favour of S——>X——>R, there are complaints that it is struggling to say things which must be said, but doing so in a language which is no longer appropriate.'[40]

Perceptual and Conceptual Abstraction

One last example of a frontier where perceptual organization can do no more for you, and symbolic thought has to take over.

When a number of objects is projected by lantern slide on a screen just long enough to be fully seen but not long enough to be counted, few people can correctly tell how many objects they have seen if the number exceeds seven; and many reach their limit of 'number perception' at five.[41] Surprisingly enough, the remarkable experiments of Otto Koehler revealed that pigeons, jackdaws, paroquets, and budgerigars can do as well, and that specially gifted jackdaws have a 'number sense' with the upper limit eight—just as the most gifted humans.

The experimental procedure consists, briefly, in training birds to open that box among several other boxes whose lid shows the same number of spots as the number of objects shown to the bird on a cue card. The sizes and spatial arrangements of the spots on the lid and of the objects on the card are not related in any way; and the rigorous experimental conditions and controls seem to have established beyond doubt that birds have a 'prelinguistic number sense'; that they 'are able to abstract the "concept" of numerical identity from groups of up to seven objects of totally different and unfamiliar appearance'.[42] Among mammals, squirrels have been shown to have the same ability.[43] The evidence suggests 'that men and animals may have a pre-linguistic "counting" ability of about the same degree, but that man's superiority in dealing with numbers lies in his ability to use, as symbols for numbers, words and figures which have not the same, or indeed any, numerical attributes.'[44] The symbolic coding of 'number Ges-talten' seems indeed a decisive step towards the formation of cardinal numbers; I shall return to the subject later (Chapter XV).

Sound-pictures, printed letters of the alphabet, number-configura-tions, are all complex perceptual wholes, and at the same time ele-mentary parts of symbolic thought: one might call them (to change the metaphor) 'amphibian' entities. They signal the transition, in mental evolution, from the 'aquatic' world of perception which keeps the organism submerged in a fluid environment of sounds, shapes, and smells, to the dry land of conceptualized thinking. The highest forms of purely perceptual abstraction on the pre-verbal level are like bubbles of air which aquatic creatures extract from the water; conceptualized thought is dry and inexhaustible, like the atmosphere.

This is not meant of course to belittle the formidable powers of perceptual abstraction found in some animals. The innate (or im-printed) releasive mechanisms, for instance, may be regarded as phylogenetically acquired skills which enable the animal to combine the colour, shape, and movement of the stimulus-pattern into a single 'constancy'. The rat learns to make a 'mental map' of the maze in its head (Chapter XII); and it has always been a mystery to me how my dog recognizes another dog on the opposite sidewalk *at sight* without using his sense of smell—for the typical reactions of staring, straining at the leash, whining, occurs at the very instant of catching sight. The other dog may be a miniature Peke, a dolled-up Poodle, or a Great Dane; how does my dog identify that apparition as a kinsman—how did he abstract the universal 'Dog'? Perhaps at a distance he merely reacts to four legs and one or two other Gestalt characteristics common to all canines, which account for their 'dogginess'—though we would be at a loss to define them.

We have discussed various forms of 'filtering' codes, both innate and acquired, which de-particularize or strip the input for purposes of recognition and storage according to the criteria of relevance in a given hierarchy. The incoming pattern is thus subjected to 'generalization' and discrimination at the same time; the two are complementary aspects of the same process. (The word 'generalization' is often used in two different senses: (a) extracting invariant features from a variety of experiences, (b) the 'spreading' of responses. I am using it in the first sense.)

Native equipment and early learning provide the basic foundations on which the different hierarchies are built, designed to filter out more and more sharply defined features. The coarse-meshed 'perceptual sieves' of the tyro acquire fine-meshed sub-analysers: perceptual learning progresses 'from the seeing of gross differences to the seeing of fine differences' (pp. 490 f.). All connoisseurship—from the chicken-sexer's to the handwriting expert's, from the wine-taster's to the art historian's, depends on the hierarchic build-up of analysing, matching, scanning codes which extract subtle similarities and make precise discriminations.

This leads to the hoary problem of the nature of 'similarity'. The simplest answer would be to eliminate it altogether from the vocabulary of psychology and to substitute 'equipotentiality' for it. Two percepts are equipotential if both can pass a given filter in a given hierarchy —if they satisfy its criteria according to the rules of the game that is played at the time; in other words, if 'for *one* intent and purpose' (but not 'for all intents and purposes') they are the same thing. Sultan discovered the 'similarity' between a branch on the castor-oil bush and a stick because they were equipotential for his purpose. A paperclip is 'similar' to a hair-pin when I have to mend a blown fuse. The answer to the old classroom question whether a red circle is more similar to a green circle than to a red triangle, depends on whether I am teaching geometry or colour-theory. In the first case, the two circles are for my purpose 'the same thing'; in the second, the two colours are 'the same thing.'*

The width of the span within which two stimuli are perceived as 'the same thing' depends on the precision of the analyser—the gauge of the sieve through which they must pass. To talk of the 'spreading' of response ('generalization' in sense (b)) is confusing; the equipotentiality of circle and ellipse to the naïve Pavlov dog is not due to any *spreading* of reactions from circle to ellipse, but to the *absence of discrimination* between two figures which for the 'intents and purposes' of the untrained animal are the same—as for my intents and purposes one sheep is the same as another. Similar considerations apply to 'transfer' (Chapter XV).

'Association by similarity' of perceptions would accordingly mean that an input-pattern A at some stage of its ascent in the nervous system initiates the recall of some past experience B which is equipotential to A with respect to the scanning process at that particular stage, but not in other respects. We might say that A and B have one 'partial' in common which causes B to 'resonate'.

Association by sound and visual form plays, as we have seen, an important part in the dream and in subconscious processes which enter into creativity. But in the ordinary routines of life, association of sensory percepts uncontaminated by conceptual thinking seems to be rare, and whether it occurs at all is anybody's introspective guess. In the Rohrschach test visual association depends on projective dynamics imbued with meaning. Verbal suggestions influence the visual matrix and distort even the eidetic image; the ambiguities of the sound-picture can only be dispelled by reference to vocabulary; children and aphasic patients often confuse p and q, or write s and e as mirror images, because the cognitive glue which holds the true perceptual units together (verticals, loops, etc.) has not yet hardened or has already decayed—like the aggregate of visual and cognitive elements which constitutes the image of the elephant. Thus hearing is inextricably bound up with interpreting, seeing with knowing, perceiving with naming. By these methods the organism is enabled to build a model of the external world into its own nervous system, without having to store lantern-slides and gramophone records of complex perceptual forms—animal, vegetable and mineral—which would not work anyway. All that the model needs in the way of perceptual 'traces' is a modest inventory of elementary root-forms—much like the cubist painter's austere repertory which Cézanne recommended: 'Everything in nature is modelled on the sphere, the cone and the cylinder. One must teach oneself to base one's painting on these simple figures—then one can accomplish anything one likes.'[45]

What we call our visual or auditory memory probably consists of a limited number of such 'root traces' or 'perceptual elements' (in Hebb's sense). These alone may have 'real form' as perceptual wholes, and at the same time enter as parts into the complex, aggregate 'pseudo-images', held together by meaningful association. If it seems to us that such complex aggregates can be 'taken in' and 'recognized at a glance' without scanning and exploration, this is perhaps because we commonly underestimate the span of the psychological present. In his review of the literature on the psychological present, Woodrow found that its maximum span is estimated to lie between 2·3 and 12 seconds.[46] No wonder there is considerable disagreement about the size of the 'discrete units of speech' in perception—whether the unit is the phoneme, syllable, word, or a whole sentence! A few seconds are ample time for those partly or wholly unconscious operations which make our perceptions into inferential constructions. If the psychological present $/P/$ be regarded as an elementary quantum of conscious experience, then the processes which go on *within* $/P/$ can *ex hypothesi not* be on a conscious level; they must remain an unanalysable and uncompressible blur.

Recognition and Recall

While new matrices are formed by learning, others may decay through disuse like old waterways overgrown by weeds. Apart from generation and decay, the traces left by past events in the nervous system also undergo dynamic changes—simplification, condensation, distortion on the one hand; elaboration and enrichment through the addition of extraneous material on the other. The 'schemata' of memory, as Bartlett called them, are 'living, constantly developing, affected by every bit of incoming sensational experience of a given kind'.[47] In other words, the past is constantly being re-made by the present.* To quote Bartlett again:

'Remembering is not re-excitation of innumerable, fixed, lifeless and fragmentary traces. It is an imaginative reconstruction, or construction, built out of the relation of our attitude towards a whole active mass of organized past reactions or experience, and to a little outstanding detail which commonly appears in image or in language form. It is thus hardly ever really exact, even in the most rudimentary cases of rote-recapitulation, and it is not at all important that it should be so.'[48]

True recall by imagery would be possible only if the de-particularized memory could be re-particularized, the irreversible process reversed. One may be able to 'hear'—while shaving, for instance—the faint, pale ghost of a voice from the past singing a simple song. To make this possible, at least three different systems of 'coloured filters', concerned with melody, timbre, and wording, must each have preserved one aspect of the original experience. One may also recall, more or less distinctly, characteristic combinations of form and motion: the stride of a person, the roll of a boat, the waddle of a tortoise. But the average person's abilities of perceptual imaging are limited to this kind of production. Hence the paradox of what one might call 'negative recognition': I visit a friend whom I have not seen for some time, look round and say: 'Something is changed in this room'—without being able to say *what* has been changed. I can only assume that my memory of the room was determined by several complementary matrices—sketchy, part verbal, part visual schemata, such as 'Regency furniture', 'L-shaped plan', 'subdued colour scheme', etc.—plus one or two 'vivid details': a picture, a flower-vase. A good many changes could be made in the room which I would not notice so long as they satisfy these criteria as 'equipotential variations'; only changes which offend against one of the codes will make me register that '*something* is wrong'. My inability to name that 'something' indicates that the code was functioning below the level of conscious awareness (Cf. Book One, XIX).*

The adjectives used to describe a face—'soft', 'bony', 'pinched', 'humorous', etc.—refer to part visual, part verbal schemata, some of which may be as simplified as the surprisingly few linear elements which suffice to indicate emotional expression by the posture and slant of mouth and eyes. The caricaturist can evoke a face by a few strokes which schematize a total impression (Hitler's moustache and lock), or he can pick out a detail which acts as a 'sign-releaser' (Churchill's cigar). It is often easier to remember a face known only from illustrations—Napoleon or Mona Lisa—than faces of living persons; perhaps because half of the compressing and coding of the visual information has already been done by the artist. Equally revealing is the police method of reconstructing the likeness of a criminal by the Identi-Kit method. This is based on 'a slide-file of five hundred and fifty facial characteristics containing, among other things, a hundred and two sets of eyes ranging from pop to squinting, thirty-three sets of lips from thin to sensuous, fifty-two chins, from weak to jutting, and even twenty-five sets of wrinkles. Witnesses pick the individual features that most closely resemble their idea of the criminal's look. From their selections a composite picture of all the features is then assembled.'[49]

If in the process of memory-formation the input is stripped down to bare essentials, recall requires dressing it up again. This seems to be done by some summary drapings, patched out with surviving fragments of picture-strip, plus some fitting garments borrowed from elsewhere—we all know how often 'vivid details' are incorporated into the recall of experiences to which they do not belong. Imaging involves imagining, which is a flexible skill. It is triggered-off by an impulse of central origin—a kind of 'excitation-clang' which unlocks 'memory releasers' and sets off the feedback-circuits of 'inferential reconstruction'; as with other plastic skills, two performances are never quite the same.

Summary

I have treated perception, recognition, and memory-formation as a continuous series. The sensory input is screened, dismantled, reassembled, analysed, interpreted, and stored along a variety of channels belonging to different hierarchies with different criteria of relevance. A tune can be stored stripped of timbre, and vice versa. The departicularization of experience in the process of memory-formation is compensated to some extent by the multiplicity of abstractive hierarchies which participate in the process, and by the retention of 'picture-strips'—vivid fragments of emotive or symbolic significance.

Central controls and motor activities participate at various stages in the processing of the input; from stimulus-selection in the end-organ and visual scanning, through resonances from the vocal tract, to the interpretation of *Klangbild* by *Wortschatz*, and of the seen by the known. Nowhere are 'stimuli' and 'responses' neatly separable; they form hierarchies of loops within loops. The mechanisms responsible for the processing are partly inborn, mostly acquired; their codes have a high degree of autonomy and show their 'self-asserting' tendencies in the tenacity of optical illusions and of 'seeing in terms of'.

The generalization and retention of perceptual forms has an upper limit where symbolic coding must take over to make further progress in learning possible. The ability of man to form 'number percepts' is not significantly superior to that of some birds; memory images are aggregates of relatively simple schematized forms, i.e. of true perceptual elements, held together by cognitive linkages, as the 'sound-pictures' of speech are given coherence by their meaning. They are double-faced entities: complex perceptual Gestalt-wholes which enter as units into the symbolic hierarchy. We must assume that there are analysing devices of this kind active in the nervous system, 'resonators' which are 'attuned' to a certain configuration in the perceptual input, and respond to it by signals in symbolic coding addressed to the higher echelons. All inputs which are equipotential with respect to that configuration—e.g. 'triangularity'—are regarded by the analyser as 'the same thing', and reported by the same signal. The process is thus the reverse of the 'spelling out' activites of the motor hierarchy—which is in some respects comparable to the unlocking of memory-releasers in recall.

'Generalization' and 'discrimination' are complementary aspects of the same process, and will be discussed, together with the ambiguities of 'spreading' and 'transfer', in later chapters.

NOTES

To p. 513. Cf. Polànyi, 1958, p. 364: 'Behaviourists teach that in observing an animal we must refrain above all from trying to imagine what we would do if placed in the animal's position. I suggest, on the contrary, that nothing at all could be known about an animal that would be of the slightest interest to physiology, and still less to psychology, except by following the opposite maxim. . . .'

To p. 516. This response is mediated either by resonance (Helmholz's theory) or, more likely, by the locus of maximum hydraulic pressure in the 'travelling wave'.

To p. 517. The latter assumes that in visual perception a spatial 'picture' is projected on to the primary optical cortex, which reproduces the retinal image. But the excitation-pattern in the auditory cortex has no 'contours' separating figure and background, and it would be difficult to imagine 'field currents' created by them.

To p. 533. There are strong arguments against the segmentation of language according to the letters of the written alphabet (cf. e.g. Paget 1930; Ladefoged in *Mechanization of Thought Processes*, 1959).

To p. 537. There exist of course both innate and acquired preferences for choosing one system of 'coloured filters' rather than another as a criterion of equipotentiality. Two notes an octave apart sound more 'similar' to man and rat than two notes close together. Evidently the nervous system finds it for its own 'intents and purposes' more convenient to regard two frequencies of the ratio $2p : p$ as more similar than two frequencies of the ratio $p : (p—r)$.

To p. 539. The protracted controversy about the existence of progressive, systematic changes in *perceptual* traces ('levelling' and 'sharpening') was unfortunately restricted to one type of change only—the reduction of 'dynamic stress' in the physical trace, predicted by Gestalt physiology—see Wulf, quoted by Koffka (1935); Hebb and Foord (1954). No psychologist would dare to deny that 'memory plays us false'; but its confidence-tricks are evidently not of the grossly mechanical type, divorced from the subject's living experience, which Köhler's theory of cortical field-processes demanded.

To p. 540. 'Negative recognition' could be called the *unconscious* variety of Woodworth's (1938) 'schema with correction'.

XI

MOTOR SKILLS

In the process of becoming an expert typist, the student must go through the whole range of learning processes variously classified as instrumental conditioning, sign-learning, trial and error, rote and place learning, insight. He is, of course, quite unaware of these categories—which, in fact, overlap at almost every stage. The essence of the process is the step-wise integration of relatively simple codes of behaviour into complex and flexible codes with a hierarchic structure. This conclusion was actually reached (although expressed in different words) in the 1890s by Bryan and Harter[1]—then buried and forgotten for nearly half a century. Woodworth was one of the few experimental psychologists who kept harking back to the subject. The following is taken from his summary of Bryan and Harter's *Studies on the Telegraphic Language. The Acquisition of a Hierarchy of Habits.*[2]

'The beginner first learns the alphabet of dots and dashes. Each letter is a little pattern of finger movements in sending, a little pattern of clicks in receiving. It is something of an achievement to master these motor and auditory *letter habits*. At this stage the learner spells the words in sending or receiving. With further practice he becomes familiar with word-patterns and does not spell out the common words. The transition from the letter habit to the *word-habit* stage extends over a long period of practice, and before this stage is fully reached a still more synthetic form of reaction begins to appear. "The fair operator is not held so closely to words. He can take in several words at a mouthful, a phrase or even a short sentence." In sending he anticipates, as in other motor performances; but in receiving, he learns to "copy behind", letting two or three words come from the sounder before he starts to copy. Keeping a few words behind the sounder allows time for getting the sense of the message.'

Let us call these three stages of habit-formation the 'letter', 'word', and 'context' levels. The letter habit is acquired by 'serial learning'. But no chain-response theory can account even for this first step in acquiring the skill—for the simple reason that the homogeneous dots and the homogeneous dashes of the Morse sequence offer no distinguishable characteristics for the forming of specific S.-R. connections. The letter 'u' is transmitted by dot-dot-dash; the letter 'w' by dot-dash-dash. In terms of S.-R. theory, the finger-movement made in sending the first dot is the initial part-response which triggers the chain, its kinaesthetic sensation acting as a stimulus which calls out the next response. But the correct response to the *same* stimulus will be *either* dot or dash; nothing in the nature of the stimulus itself indicates what the next response should be; the response is determined at this and each following step *not* by the preceding stimulus but by the total pattern. The habit cannot be represented by a linear series: · — — > — — — > · — · it can only be represented as a two-tired hierarchic structure:

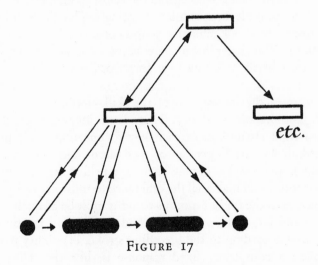

FIGURE 17

The related skill of touch-typing was studied by Book,[3] who wired his machines to time every move made by the experimental subjects. In this case the letter habit is acquired by 'place-learning'—the keyboard is hidden from the student by a screen, and he is required to form a 'map' of its layout in his head. This map, one supposes, is structured by a simple co-ordinate-system: the fixed resting position of the ten fingers on the third row of the keyboard; the result is a kind of simple 'maze' with variable target positions. But when, after a certain amount of hit and miss, the letter habit had been mastered:

> further practice gave results unexpected by the learner. He found himself anticipating the sequence of finger movements in a short, familiar word. Habits were developing for groups of letters such as prefixes, suffixes, and short words. . . . 'A word simply means a group of movements which I attend to as a whole. I seem to get beforehand a sort of feel of the whole group'. . . . The single letters were no longer thought of and each word became an automatic sequence. . . . Familiar phrases were similarly organized, the thought of the phrase calling out the whole series of connected movements.[4]

Yet even phrases ending with a full stop did not prove to be the highest units. The records showed 'no pauses between phrases' but an even flow; and here, too, 'the eyes [on the text to be copied] were well ahead of the hands'—to enable the typist to take in the meaning.

As a third example let us consider learning to play the piano (though I could find no textbook references to this not altogether unusual human occupation). The 'letter habit' here becomes a 'note habit'—hitting the intended black or white key; for 'word' read 'bar' or 'musical phrase'; and so on to more complex integrated patterns. In this case, however, even the lowest unit of the skill—hitting the right key—displays considerable flexibility. There is no longer, as on the type-writer, a rigid attribution of each key to one finger; on the piano keyboard almost any finger can be used, according to circumstances, to hit any key; several keys may be hit and held at the same time; and a hard or soft touch makes all the difference to musical quality. (Needless to say, even the typist's motion-patterns must be adaptable to small portables and large office machines, and the starting position of the finger varies according to the preceding stroke. Flexibility is a matter of degrees; a completely fixed response is, like the reflex arc, an abstraction.)

The skill of hitting the correct piano-key is not acquired by establishing point-to-point correspondences, but primarily by practising the various scales; these superimpose, as it were, structured motions on to the keyboard, sub-structured into triads, septims, etc. At an advanced stage, when improvization has become possible, the left hand will learn to accompany the right, which acts as a 'pace-maker'—a glorified form of the magnet effect in the gold-fish (p. 438); but the left can also act in relative independence, according to the commands of the score. At this level we have approximately the following state of affairs: the visual input consists in two groups of parallel rows (staves) of coded signals, of which the upper series must be referred to the right, the lower to the left hand. In the course of this procedure both rows of signals must be de-coded and re-coded. The symbols on the two rows are usually in different parallel codes ('violin clef' for the right, 'bass clef' for the left). Moreover, there are 'key signatures'— sharp and flat signs—at the beginning of a section, which modify the 'face value' of the notes; there are symbols which indicate the timing and duration of notes; and overall instructions regarding loudness, tempo and mood. All these part-dependent, part-independent de- and re-coding operations for both hands must proceed simultaneously, in the psychological present, and more or less automatically.

On an ever higher level, the concert pianist develops a repertory of *œuvres* that he can 'trigger off' as units and play by heart—though some of these units may be an hour long. Once again we must assume that this is done by a combination of several interlocking hierarchies, each articulated into sub-wholes and the sub-wholes thereof.

Then there is improvisation. It need not be creative; the bar-pianist who, half asleep, syncopates Chopin and trails off into some variation of his own, is not a composer; but he has gained additional flexibility—more degrees of freedom—in the practice of his skill. And finally there is the creative act: the composer who weaves his threads into new patterns, and the interpreter who sheds new light on existing patterns.

The learning process is, somewhat paradoxically, easiest to visualize as a reversal of the hierarchic sequence of operations which will characterize performance when learning is completed. When the typist copies a document, the sequence of operations is initiated on the semantic level, then branches down into successive lower levels with increasingly specific 'fixed action-patterns'—'word-habits' and 'letter-habits'; terminating in the 'consummatory act' of the finger muscles. The impulses arborize downwards and outwards, whereas learning proceeds in the reverse direction: the tips of the twigs of the future tree are the first to come into existence; the twigs then grow together centripetally into branches, the branches merge into the trunk. It strikes one as a very artificial procedure; but the type of mechanical learning we have discussed, where the discrete base-units must be stamped in bit by bit, is indeed an artificial procedure. The difference between this method of learning through trial and error and learning 'by insight' becomes glaringly obvious if you compare what happens during an elementary violin lesson and an equally elementary singing lesson. The choir boy can rely on his innate, multiple auditory-vocal feedbacks—operating through the air, through his bones, and through proprioceptive sensations from his vocal tract—to control his voice. But there exist no innate feedbacks between the violin student's cochlea and finger-muscles, to control their motions. No amount of theoretical insight into the working of the instrument can replace this handicap; it can only be overcome by supplementing insight with trial and error. In other words, human beings are biologically less 'ripe' for learning the violin than for learning to sing. If evolution were to produce a super-cricket or *cicada sapiens*, the opposite may be true.

To put it in a different way: the built-in feedbacks of the auditory-vocal apparatus provide a *direct insight* into the rightness or wrongness (singing out of tune) of the response; they permit an immediate 'perception of relations'—which is Thorpe's definition of insight. But once more, this insight is far from absolute: when it comes to professional singing, a heart-breaking amount of drill is required. The pupil is often taught the proper techniques of breathing with his hand on the teacher's stomach—because his insight into, and control of, his own physiological functions is limited. Verbal instructions are of little help, and are sometimes a hindrance, in the acquisition of muscle skills; to become clever with one's hands, or one's feet in dancing, requires a kind of muscle training which defies classification as either insightful or trial-and-error learning.

I have repeatedly mentioned the mysteries of riding a bicycle: nobody quite knows how it is done, and any competent physicist would be inclinded to deny *a priori* that it can be done. However, as a two-legged primate, man has an innate 'ripeness' for the acquisition of all kinds of postural and balancing skills such as skating, rock-climbing, or walking the tight-rope; accordingly, the hierarchy of learning processes in the case of the cyclist starts on a higher level of already integrated sub-skills, than in the examples previously discussed. Broadly speaking, the pupil must turn the handle-bar in the direction he is falling, which will make him tend to fall in the opposite direction, and so forth, until he gradually 'gets the feel' of the amount of correction required. This is certainly trial-and-error learning in the sense that errors are punished by a fall; but the trials are by no means random, and the errors are all in the right direction—they merely over-

or under-shoot the mark. The code which is formed by successive adjustments of the neural 'servo-mechanism' is presumably of the analogue-computer type—and the same applies probably to dancing, skating, or tennis-playing.

But once the skill has been mastered and formed into a habit, its integrated pattern is represented as a unit on the next-higher level in the hierarchy, and can be triggered off by a single (verbal or non-verbal) command. To take a more complicated example: the soccer-player must acquire a variety of basic routines of taking command of the ball—'stopping' it with foot, thigh, chest, or head; volleying it in flight without stopping; kicking it with the instep, the inner or outer side-wall of the boot; dribbling, passing, and shooting at the goal, etc. When these elementary, yet very complex, techniques have been mastered, each of them will become a self-contained sub-skill in his repertory, and he will be able to decide, in a split second, which of them to employ according to the layout of the field. The decision whether to shoot or pass is based on discrete yes-no alternatives of the digital type; but the execution of the actual move—shooting, passing, etc.—seems to require an analogue-computer type of code. A further step down the 'analogue' process of flexing the leg-muscles for a pass of appropriate length is again converted into the digital on-off processes in individual motor units; while on the top level a fluid strategy is converted into discrete tactical decisions.

It would seem that behavioural matrices on every level of a given hierarchy are triggered off by digital-type all-or-nothing impulses; if the matrix is flexible it will function as a digital-to-analogue converter; and will in its turn trigger off sub-codes at certain critical limits as analogue-to-digital converters. But theorizing about the nervous system in terms of computer models is a risky affair, and may yet lure psychology into a cul-de-sac—as the telephone-exchange model did half a century ago.*

Summary: Rigidity and Freedom

Let me recapitulate some points which emerge when the observations in the present chapter are taken in conjunction with the broader issues discussed in Book One.

On the elementary levels of learning a skill a varying amount of stamping-in is required, depending on the organism's 'ripeness' for the task; or, to put it the other way round, depending on the 'natural-ness' of the task relative to the organism's existing skills. Learning to type requires more stamping-in than learning to ride a bicycle; the former is comparable to the blindfold memorizing of a maze, the latter to the gradual adjustment of various interlocking servo-mechanisms. In both cases the learning process consists in the integra-tion of elementary skills—the members of the nascent matrix—into a single pattern which can be activated as a unit. But even in acquiring a mechanical skill like typing, bit-by-bit learning plays in fact a lesser part than seems to be the case. The typist's mental map of the key-board is not simply a rote-learned aggregation of twenty-six letters (plus numbers and signs) distributed at random; it is a 'coded' map, structured by a system of co-ordinates—the resting position of the fingers—and by the frequency-rating of letters, syllables, etc. These patterns, superimposed on the keyboard map, could be compared to the mnemonic aids used in the learning of nonsense syllables. Whole-learning invades bit-learning at every opportunity; if the meaningless is to be retained, the mind must smuggle meaning into it.

Once a skill has been mastered so that it can be activated as a unit it functions more or less autonomously and automatically. This applies to both perceptual and motor skills, from the perceptual constancies and motor reflexes upwards. Learning to find the right key on the keyboard requires concentration, focal awareness; but when the letter-habit has been acquired it becomes 'instinctive', unconscious; attention is freed to concentrate on meaning, and can 'let the fingers take care of themselves'; their control is relegated to lower levels of awareness and, in all likelihood, to lower levels in the nervous system. Thus the work of Gastaut and Beck clearly suggests that 'once we have learned something we no longer rely so much on our cortex and reticular formation. Those things we do "without thinking" . . . may depend more on the older primitive parts of the nervous system such as the limbic structures, thus releasing higher centres such as the cortex for other tasks. . . . Common sense indicates such a possibility; electro-physiology suggests it. . . .'[5*]

The same skilled action—driving a motor-car or playing a nocturne by heart—can be performed automatically, or in semi-conscious absent-mindedness, or with full concentration. But the motorist who concentrates on driving fast along a crowded road has his attention focussed on matters of general strategy—e.g. whether it is safe to over-take or not, whereas the actual manipulation of the wheel and pedals are still carried out automatically; and the pianist trying to give his best, still finds the keys automatically. We again find confirmed that the code which controls skilled behaviour always operates through sub-codes which function on lower levels of awareness. Shifting the focus of attention to these sub-codes produces the familiar 'paradox of the centipede'. Its equivalent in perception is the loss of meaning which results when a word is repeated monotonously and attention becomes focussed on the Klangbild (cf. 'ce-du, ce-du, ce-du', Book One, p. 75 f.; even more painful is the semantic paralysis which sometimes befalls a writer while correcting the proofs of a forthcoming book.

The lower we descend in the hierarchy the more stereotyped, reflex-like activities we find; and vice versa, flexibility increases with each step upward. The more complex the skill, the more alternative variations it offers for adaptable strategies: a matrix on the $n+1$ level has more degrees of freedom than a matrix on the n level. But whether they will be utilized and produce varied performance, depends on the environment. Monotonous environments induce repetitive, stereotyped habits; the degrees of freedom in the matrix freeze up. 'Overlearning' is the fixation, through repetition in unvarying conditions, of one among many possible variations in the exercise of a skill at the expense of all others. Thus habits become automatized (a) because they operate on the lower strata of the hierarchy with few degrees of freedom, like hitting a typewriter key or depressing the accelerator pedal; (b) when a complex skill is reduced through environmental monotony to a single-track habit. 'Monotony' is of course a subjective term referring to lack of change in those features of the environment which are relevant to the subject's interests. For all we know the streets of Koenigsberg through which Emmanuel Kant took his fixed walk at a fixed hour for forty years might have been wildly exciting to another person.

The integration of motor-patterns into larger and more complex skills in the process of learning is paralleled by a similar progression on the perceptual side. The telegraphist who has advanced from 'letter-habits' through 'word-habits' to 'phrase-habits' in his sending technique, has at the same time learned to take in several words and even phrases 'at a mouthful'. The pianist takes in a whole musical phrase from the score at a glance; both input and output are no longer measured in bits but in chunks.* The more complex the skill, the bigger the chunks in space or time which must be taken into account.

The skilled soccer player keeps his eye on the ball, but is at the same time aware of the positions and peculiarities of the other players on the field. The motorist, driving to his office, chooses the least congested road among several alternatives by consulting the mental map in his head. The typist, who deliberately lags a phrase or two behind dictation, expands the duration of the psychological present to take in a bigger chunk of meaning. While listening to speech or music we do the same; while talking we trigger off long sequences of muscular patterns as a whole. As we become more proficient in any skilled activity, we learn 'to put feedback loops around larger and larger segments of our behaviour'.[6]

Though motor learning proceeds, generally speaking, from lower to higher levels, and performance in the reverse direction, this does not mean that in performing we run through the whole gamut of the learning process in reverse gear. As one learns to play a sonata by heart, one needs less and less often to consult the score, and in the end the visual feedback which was indispensable during learning can be dispensed with entirely; the habit now functions autonomously. The skilled pianist can play blindfold, a man can knot his tie without looking into the mirror, the physician can tell the patient's pulse without looking at his watch, the adult reads without spelling out the letters. When the skill has been mastered, the props which served the learning process are kicked away—as Maxwell kicked away the scaffolding of his mechanical model when he arrived at his equations (see Appendix I). In this respect, too, the learning process is irreversible.

The *autonomy* of the codes which pattern behaviour is a phenomenon which we have met on all levels—from the self-regulatory activities of the morphogenetic field, through the fixed action-patterns of instinct behaviour, to the perceptual frames responsible for constancies, illusions, and our ways of seeing the world through coloured filters, as it were. But on the level of complex skills, the 'self-assertive' tendencies of acquired motor-patterns are particularly striking. To repeat an obvious example, one cannot disguise one's handwriting sufficiently to fool the expert; even the skilled burglar has his individual style in safe-breaking which gives him away. Autonomy and self-government are basic principles in the hierarchy of skills. Thus 'the performance of very quick movements', Lashley observed, 'indicates their independence of current control. "Whip-snapping" movements of the hand can be regulated in extent, yet the entire movement, from initiation to completion requires less than the reaction time for a tactile or kinaesthetic stimulation of the arm, which is about one-eighth of a second, even when no discrimination is involved. . . . The finger-strokes of a musician may reach sixteen per second in passages which call for a definite and changing order of successive finger-movements. The succession of movements is too quick even for visual reaction time. . . . Sensory control of movement seems to be ruled out in such acts.'[7]

Similar conclusions were reached, as already mentioned, by Ruch, concerning voluntary movement in general. In view of the rapidity of skilled movements which are too fast to leave room for visual or proprioceptive feedback control, Ruch, like Lashley, assumed the operation of pre-set time-tension patterns of muscle contraction in the nervous system: 'The cerebral-cerebellar circuit may represent not so much an error-correcting device as a part of a mechanism by which an instantaneous order can be extended in time . . . and thus reduce the troublesome transients involved in the correction of movement by output-informed feedbacks.'[8]

The tendency to reduce those 'troublesome' feedbacks to a minimum is the essence of habit-formation and automatization. It follows the principle of parsimony; if we had to concentrate on each movement we made, there would be no room for thought. On the other hand, this inherent tendency to form neural organizations which, one might say, jealously defend their autonomy against interference from a changing outside world, makes us all, in varying degrees, the slaves of habit. We may reduce the degree of enslavement, but the basic predicament is inherent in the hierarchic structure or nervous organization, where 'the structure of the input does not produce the structure of the output, but merely modifies intrinsic nervous activities that have a structural organization of their own'. The quotation (repeated from p. 434) referred to instinct behaviour and the lower motor functions, but it is equally applicable, as we have seen, to complex, acquired skills. These may have a high degree of flexibility, but they nevertheless operate through automatized sub-skills on the lower ranges of the hierarchy, which manifest themselves in the individual 'touch' of the pianist, the 'style' of the tennis-player, the fixed mannerisms, quirks, idiosyncrasies, and unconscious rituals which are our personal hallmarks.

How much of his potential freedom a person puts to active use depends partly on environmental factors—the novelty, intensity, vexatiousness, etc., of the stimuli to which he is exposed. But the nature and amount of stimulation derived from a given input depends, of course, on personality structure. One type of individual will respond to monotonous situations with stereotyped reactions; another type will find monotony vexatious, that is to say, *stimulating*. 'Active boredom', as this kind of reaction may be called, can provide alternatives to habituation; the subject may experience the very absence of change as a novelty—as prison is a novelty to the first offender; and since the environment refuses to offer variety, he will vary his own performance to provide it. Hence the apparently spontaneous changes in fashions and crazes, not only in human society but also in colonies of captive chimpanzees.

If, on the other hand, the challenge from the environment exceeds a critical limit, behaviour will either become distintegrated, or the challenge will be met by an original, 'super-flexible' response—a re-structuring of the pattern of the skill. We have met examples of this on all levels, from the 'prenatal skills' of morphogenesis, through Bethe's mutilated insects to Lashley's rats and Köhler's chimpanzees. The complex, acquired motor-skills, which we discussed in this chapter, are capable of equally impressive emergency-reorganizations. The first aircraftsman who, when his brakes refused to function on landing, saved his plane by opening his parachute through the rear-window, achieved a true bisociation of two unconnected skills. The violinist who finishes his piece in spite of a broken E string; the typist managing on a half-broken machine; the secret tunnel-builders in prisoner-of-war camps; the legless war pilot winning a Victoria Cross; Renoir, crippled with arthritis, continuing to paint with a brush fixed to his forearm—they all gave proof of an unexpected, creative surplus-potential in the nervous system. Such accomplishments are more impressive than the quasi-miraculous feats performed in panic or rage—the latter are of a quantitative order and do not involve the reorganization of pattern.

The homologous nature of the basic principles which operate on different levels of the hierarchy becomes evident when we remember the conclusions which emerged from the discussion of instinct behaviour: 'At one end of the scale we find rituals, fixed action-patterns, vacuum and displacement activities—rigid, automatized, and compulsive, petrified habits. At the other extreme we find . . . codes which govern behaviour of remarkable flexibility, and original adaptations which lie outside the animal's normal skills and habit repertory.'[10]

To p. 549. See, for instance, the rather desperate footnote on p. 197 of Miller et al (1960): 'One reason for much of the trouble on reaching an agreement about the way the brain works was that two of the authors stubbornly persisted in trying to talk about it in terms appropriate to the dry hardware of modern digital computers, whereas the third was equally persistent in using language appropriate to the wet software that lives inside the skull. After a decade of cybernetics you might think the translation from one of these languages into the other would be fairly simple, but that was not the case. The relation between computers and brains was a battle the authors fought with one another until the exasperation became unbearable.'

To p. 550. Experiments by S. M. Evans (*New Scientist,* 2 May, 1963) have shown that the supraoesophageal ganglia of the ring-worm (its 'brain') are essential for learning but not for memory storage since learned habits will be retained after removal of the 'brain'. Once the habit is acquired, it is apparently transferred 'to a storage centre which is presumably somewhere else in the nervous system'.

To. p. 551. Cf. also: 'in rapid sight reading it is impossible to read the individual notes of an arpeggio. The notes must be seen in groups, and it is actually easier to read chords seen simultaneously and to translate them into temporal sequence than to read successive notes in the arpeggio as usually written' (Lashley in the Hixon Symposium, p. 123).

XII

THE PITFALLS OF LEARNING THEORY

A Glance in Retrospect

In the course of the past fifty years, learning theory has been one of the central battlefields of psychology. 'One may say broadly', Bertrand Russell wrote in 1927, 'that all the animals that have been carefully observed have behaved so as to confirm the philosophy in which the observer believed before his observations began. Nay, more, they have all displayed the national characteristics of the observer. Animals studied by Americans rush about frantically, with an incredible display of hustle and pep, and at last achieve the desired result by chance. Animals observed by Germans sit still and think, and at last evolve the situation out of their inner consciousness. To the plain man, such as the present writer, this situation is discouraging. I observe, however, that the type of problem which a man naturally sets to an animal depends upon his own philosophy, and that this probably accounts for the differences in the results.'[1]

Russell's remarks remain true, even though some eminent psychologists deny that they have a philosophy at all and hold all theory-making to be 'wasteful and misleading'.[2] Not only the choice of problem, but also the choice of animals is characteristic of the experimenter's bias. Köhler, desirous to prove insight and intelligence, concentrated mainly on chimpanzees. Skinner's best-known books are called *The Behaviour of Organisms* (1938) and *Science and Human Behaviour* (1953); but—as Hilgard said—'neither title betrays that the precise data were derived largely from experiments on rats and pigeons. It is somewhat anomalous that a systematist who refuses to predict what a rat or pigeon will do—because such prediction does not belong in a scientific study of behaviour—is willing to make confident assertions about the most complex forms of human behaviour, economic, political, religious'.[3]

Hull's attempt to create an all-embracing theory of behaviour was almost entirely based on the bar-pressing activities of rats. This was considered by Hull and his school as a sufficiently solid basis to derive from them 'the basic laws of behaviour . . . including the social behaviour of man'.[4]

Lastly, the German school of ethologists—Lorenz, Tinbergen, etc. —concentrated mainly on highly ritualized forms of animal life in birds and insects. Thus each school developed its special universe of discourse, moving in a closed system, concentrating on their favourite animals in their favourite experimental situations—dogs dripping saliva through fistulae, cats raging in puzzle-boxes, rats running through mazes, geese being 'imprinted' by Dr. Lorenz ambling on all-fours.

But the data from these highly specialized, experimental trends did not add up to a coherent picture, and each school had a tendency to ignore what the others were doing. Thus, for instance, in Skinner's *Science and Human Behaviour*, which was intended as a textbook, the index contains neither the word 'insight', nor the names of Köhler, Koffka, Lewin, Tolman, Hull, Lashley, or Lorenz; only Thorndike and Pavlov are mentioned by name as theorists of learning with some merit. And vice versa, I have searched in vain for the name of Pavlov in the indices of Köhler's and Koffka's books.[5] Thus much of the controversies in learning theory resembled less a battle than a game of blind man's buff.

How, just at a time when the mechanistic conceptions of the nineteenth century had been abandoned in all branches of science, from physics to embryology; how just at that time, in the 1920s, the concept of man as a rigid mechanism of chained reflexes could become fashionable in cultures as different as the United States and the Soviet Union is a fascinating problem for the historian of science. The Pavlovian school in Russia, and the Watsonian brand of Behaviourism in America, were the twentieth-century postscript to the nineteenth century's mechanistic materialism, its belated and most consistent attempt to describe living organisms in terms of machine theory.

The Denial of Creavitity

Nearly half a century has passed since the publication of Watson's *Psychology from the Standpoint of a Behaviourist* (1919), and few students today remember its contents or even its basic postulates. In Watson's second book (1924) there is a chapter entitled: '*Talking and Thinking— Which, When Rightly Understood, Go Far In Breaking Down the Fiction That There Is Any Such Thing As "Mental" Life.*' In this chapter, the behaviouristic view on the creative activities of man is set down in a simple and striking way (all italics are Watson's):

> *How the new comes into being:* One natural question often raised is: How do we ever get new verbal creations such as a poem or a brilliant essay? *The answer is that we get them by manipulating words, shifting them about until a new pattern is hit upon.* . . . It will help us to go to manual behaviour. How do you suppose Patou builds a new gown? Has he any 'picture in his mind' of what the gown is to look like when it is finished? He has not. . . . He calls his model in, picks up a new piece of silk, throws it around her; he pulls it in here, he pulls it out there, makes it tight or loose at the waist, high or low, he makes the skirt short or long. He manipulates the material until it takes on the semblance of a dress. . . . The painter plies his trade in the same way, nor can the poet boast of any other method.[6]

The key word is 'manipulation', defined by Watson as an 'instinctive tendency sometimes exalted by calling it constructiveness. That there is an original tendency to reach out for objects, to scrape them along the floor, to pick them up, put them into the mouth, to throw them upon the floor, to move back and forth any parts which can be moved, is one of the best grounded and best observed of the instincts.'[7] That is all we learn about manipulation. It is a random activity, which, through elimination of useless movements by the trial-and-error method, gradually develops into ordered habits. The rat, put into an unknown maze, goes on manipulating its motor-organs at random until it hits upon the food in the same way as (the comparison is Watson's own[8]) Patou manipulates the piece of silk until he hits upon a new model; likewise, the poet or essayist 'shifts about' words 'until a new pattern is hit upon'. It is expressly denied that Patou, the poet, or painter has any 'picture in his mind' of the kind of thing he is planning; he simply goes on manipulating his units until the model, poem, or drama is 'hit upon'. At that moment the stimulus 'to arouse admiration and condemnation' ceases to be active, and manipulation stops—'the equivalent of the rat's finding food'.[9]

Obviously, viewed from this angle, psychology presents no problems. Yet the matter is of more than historical interest, because, although the cruder absurdities of Watsonian behaviourism are forgotten, it had laid the foundations on which the later, more refined behaviouristic systems were built; the dominant trend in American and Russian psychology in the generation that followed had a distinctly Pavlov-Watsonian flavour. 'Each of these systems', Hilgard wrote (referring to the immensely influential schools of Guthrie, Hull, and Skinner*) 'represents in its own way a fulfilment of the behaviouristic programme originally proposed by Watson.'[10] The methods became more sophisticated, but the philosophy behind them remained the same. Originality and creativeness have no place in it.

For Guthrie, the original solution of a problem 'must be in the category of luck, and hence lie outside of science'.[11] In Skinner's works, as I have just said, the word 'insight' does not occur; and the technique of problem-solving is, in Skinner's view as in Watson's, 'merely that of manipulating variables which may lead to the emission of the response. No new factor of originality is involved.'[12] Hull expressly postulated that the differences in the learning processes of man and rat are of a merely quantitative, not of a qualitative order:

'The natural-science theory of behaviour being developed by the present author and his associates assumes that all behaviour of the individuals of a given species and that of all species of mammals, including man, occurs according to the same set of primary laws.'[13] The verbal and mathematical symbolism of man, verbal communication and written records, were considered to differ only in degree, not in kind, from the learning achievements of the lower animals, epitomized in the bar-pressing activities of the rat. 'Hull did not intend merely to systematize the account of rat lever-pressing, from which most of the data for his later set of postulates derived. He intended to arrive at the basic laws of behaviour, at least the laws of the behaviour of mammalian organisms, including the social behaviour of man.'[14]**

The state of affairs in that period has been succinctly summed up by Osgood:

Lloyd Morgan's canon—that the behaviour of animals should not be explained in terms of human attributes if it can be explained on a lower level—was designed to counteract the common tendency to put oneself in an animal's place and explain its actions in terms of what we would do in that situation. . . . It is interesting that through the behaviouristic phase in which American psychology has been moving, Lloyd Morgan's canon has been subtly inverted. Many present-day psychologists are loath to attribute to *humans* any characteristics that cannot be demonstrated in lower animals.[15]

In other words, for the anthropomorphic view of the rat, American psychology substituted a rattomorphic view of man.

The Advent of Gestalt

A turning point seemed to have been reached with the publication of Köhler's *Mentality of Apes* in 1925. The Gestalt school had been steadily growing in Germany since Wertheimer's first papers in 1912. As already mentioned, the German edition of Köhler's ape book appeared in 1917, but the first American translation only eight years later. Imagine Einstein's General Relativity theory, also published in 1917, reaching America with an eight years' delay! Yet physicists are supposed to have a limited, psychologists a broad and open-minded, outlook.

The historical merit of the Gestalt school was, beside its concrete discoveries about perceptual organization, to crystallize the convergent trends towards a new, dynamic conception of the organism as a living whole—and not merely as the sum of its parts. Such trends had been developing since the beginning of the century, independently from one another, in biology, embryology, neuro-physiology, and in psychology itself. But only when the new terms 'Gestalt', 'configuration', and 'functional whole' became fashionable slogans comparable to Relativity and the Oedipus Complex—did this silent revolution penetrate into the broader public's mind and convey some vague idea of a new orientation towards the problems of organic life and the human intellect.

However, the great expectations which Gestalt aroused were only partly fulfilled; and its limitations soon became apparent. Gestalt-explanations seemed to flourish only in the area of their origin, visual perception; when it was attempted to transplant them into the fields of cognition, memory, neuro-physiology, even the other sense-modalities, they seemed to wilt away. Some of these limitations I have already mentioned in previous chapters; the ambiguities of the central concept of 'insight' will be discussed in the next one. The result was a kind of abortive Renaissance, followed by a behaviourist Counter-Reformation. The neo-Behaviourists, having incorporated some of the Gestalt findings into their theories, had indeed a remarkable come-back; the Gestaltists remained more or less firmly entrenched in their positions which displayed 'good closure' all round. The experimental evidence was mostly inconclusive; some of it proved damaging to one school, but without directly confirming the contentions of the other. Each camp was divided in itself; and (apart from the 'lone voices' of the elder generation) a 'third force' began to make itself increasingly felt, comprising such outstanding freelances as Tolman and Hebb, who stood with one foot in each camp, as it were. Hebb has compared the situation to 'the running battle between the Left and Right'[16] where each party, while shouting its own slogans, tacitly keeps adopting ideas originally advanced by its opponents. All this, of course, refers to the American scene; but in England, at least, developments followed similar lines.

In spite of this *rapprochement*, and the new outlook of a younger generation (cf. the chapter on Motivation), some basic differences still divide learning theory into two broadly outlined camps—differences not on points of fact, but on their interpretations—on explicitly stated or tacitly implied axioms, general outlook and selective emphasis. These can be briefly schematized as follows:

S.-R. Theories	contra	Cognitive Theories
Conditioning		Insight
Chained responses, stamped in bit by bit		Patterned, flexible responses adapted to the total situation
Gradual learning by trial and error		Sudden learning and problem-solving through insight.
Acquisition of habits and skills through reinforcement		Acquisition of knowledge ('cognitive structures') through latent learning
Emphasis on peripheral, sensory motor activity		Emphasis on central cognitive processes
Emphasis on discrete stimuli, on parts and perceptual elements		Emphasis on relation-patterns, wholes, perceptual Gestalten

S.-R. Theories	contra	Cognitive Theories
Motivation = reinforcement by need- or drive-reduction, or anticipation thereof		Motivation by exploratory drive, or its combination with other primary drives
Continuous linear gradient leading from rat to man		Hierarchic levels of organization

This schema follows (except for the last two points) by and large Hilgard's classification of 'issues on which learning theories divide'.[17] Only a few prominent psychologists would subscribe to *all* the principles listed in either of the two columns; but a majority of them would probably subscribe to the majority of the principles in a single column.

The core of the controversy could be summed up in shorthand as 'drill' versus 'insight'. The answer, already suggested, seems to be that the various methods of learning form a continuum extending from classical conditioning at one end to spontaneous, intelligent problem-solving at the other, while in the intermediary ranges we find various combinations between drilled-in and insightful learning, depending on the animal's ripeness for the task to be learned. This approach, which aims at synthesis, not compromise, is of course by no means original; it is shared—though for somewhat different reasons— by 'functionalists' like Woodworth, behaviourists like Hebb, and ethologists like Thorpe. Thus Hilgard wrote on the 'functionalist outlook': 'Learning is not blind on the one hand and insightful on the other; there are degrees of understanding involved from a minimum at one extreme to a maximum at the other, with most cases falling between these extremes.'[18] However, the definitions of 'insight' and 'understanding' vary, which leaves us with the same problem, only in a different formulation. Let us try to get closer to it by considering some typical examples of animal learning.

Conditioning and Empirical Induction

A newly hatched chick will peck at grains, worms, caterpillars in its neighbourhood. If a so-called cinnabar caterpillar is now placed before the chick, of which species it has no previous experience, it will peck at it as at any other small object, but reject it at once with signs of distaste. With the majority of chicks one single experience is enough to make it in the future avoid caterpillars *by sight*. (The cinnabar caterpillar has a distinct black and gold colouring, a visual pattern easy to retain.) Thus the chick has acquired a new skill, the avoidance of caterpillars, after a single experience (or one repetition in the case of less gifted chicks); and moreover, that skill, or 'cognitive structure', or knowledge, or whatever you call it, is a correct replica, in the chick's nervous system, of the relation between the visual appearance and disgusting nature of caterpillars. Must we ascribe insight to the chick; or shall we adopt the opposite viewpoint, according to which the single try was sufficient to eliminate the error of pecking at caterpillars and to establish the avoidance reaction; and are we faced with a real alternative or merely a verbal quibble? Let us, for the time being, leave the question open.

A dog is an animal of much greater intelligence than a chick, and yet in Pavlov's laboratory dogs require long series of repeated experiences for learning to relate certain perceptual signals to the imminence of food. Weeks of stamping-in are often necessary to make the dog differentiate between the food-signal values of a circle and an oval, whereas a single experience is sufficient to make the chick differentiate between the signal values in the appearances of a worm and a caterpillar.

The reason for this contrast has already been discussed (Chapter X). Caterpillars belong to the natural environment of the chick; the perception of the striped creature is a biologically relevant input while the chick is engaged in pecking; its horrid taste makes it even more relevant; the visual input will accordingly be allowed to pass through the filters of the memory hierarchy, where it will be encoded and serve as an analyser-device for future inputs. On the other hand, gongs, bells, metronomes, tuning forks, cardboard figures, red lights, and electric shocks have no biological relevance to the species dog, nor to the individual dog outside the laboratory. In its natural environment the dog would pay no attention to them, but pursue some exciting scent; the cardboard ellipse would never have a chance to form a stable trace in the dog's perceptual organization.

How should one explain, then, that the experimenter nevertheless succeeds in stamping in the response? In the first place, a Pavlov dog in its restraining harness is not a dog, but a preparation, which can only be found *in laboratorio*. It is immobilized on the experimental platform, in a soundproof laboratory, alone, cut off from all natural stimuli and habitual activities; it is, so to speak, isolated under a glass bell. This state creates a particular stress in the animal, called the dog's 'laboratory attitude', which is sharply distinguished from its behaviour outside the lab. Deprived of all other stimuli and activities, the ticking of the metronome or the figure on the cardboard are the only events on which the dog's attention can focus; there is no competition between different inputs; and thus the originally irrelevant stimuli are gradually transformed into relevant stimuli and encoded in stable traces. Relevant to what? To the only biologically important events which are allowed to occur under the glass bell: the periodic appearance of meat-powder by remote control. The dog's laboratory attitude is dominated by this periodically repeated event; and as his perceptual hierarchy becomes slowly readapted to pay attention, in the absence of other stimuli, to the irrelevant sound of the bell, the nascent trace of the bell-sound will become incorporated into the feeding hierarchy. If the sound of the bell always overlaps with the appearance of the meat-powder, then the sound will eventually trigger off the feeding code, as the first two bars of the *Marseillaise* will trigger off the following bars; the dog will begin to salivate. But salivation is merely the first, anticipatory act of its feeding behaviour, and if no meat-powder is actually presented, it will stop there; the dog will not chew and snap at nothing. In the absence of food, the feeding habit gets no 'environmental feedback', and the activity comes to a halt at the expectant, salivatory stage. It is quite untrue, therefore, to say that the 'conditioned stimulus', e.g. the bell, has been 'substituted' for the 'unconditioned stimulus', the meat-powder. What happened was that the dog has learned, by the cumulative effect of its past experience, to *expect* the appearance of the meat-powder after the bell, because that is the 'rule of the game'. He salivates, *not* because he confuses the bell with food, but because he expects the food, signalled by the bell. We can say, with Polànyi,[19] that the dog has arrived at a correct empirical induction; or with Craik, that the dog's nervous system is now functioning 'as a calculating machine capable of modelling or paralleling external events' which is 'the basic feature of thought and of explanation';[20] or in our own terms, that the invariant factor in a repeated sequence or experiences has been encoded in the dog's brain.

All this is a far cry from the conception of reflex arcs in which USs, CSs, URs, and CRs are mechanically coupled together or substituted for each other like railway carriages in a shunting yard. In fact, the dog's behaviour in the strange, artificial universe where red lights portend food and metronomes electric shocks, is eminently 'logical'; and the reason why it takes so long to stamp in the lesson is that the dog must readapt its entire attitude and hierarchy of values—of what is important in life and what is not—to that universe, where natural law is replaced by Pavlov's law; a kind of Nietzschean *Umwertung aller Werte*. Perhaps the highest achievement of the dog is learning to discriminate between more or less flattened ellipses—for unlike its sharp pitch-discrimination, based on native equipment, geometrical forms must represent the height of irrelevance in canine eyes. Yet once relevance has been revalued, and the perceptual analyser-devices have been established, the development of sharper sub-analysers or discriminatory filters must follow the stages outlined in Chapter X.*

In a seemingly casual aside, Hebb has remarked that 'the characteristic adult learning (outside of psychological laboratories) is learning that takes place in a few trials, or in one only'.[21] The implication is that the stamping-in of responses under artificial conditions in dogs, cats, or rats is quite uncharacteristic of the normal learning process. To try to base a human psychology on these procedures was a rather perverse approach.

Do Insects have Insight?

The work of Baerends, de Kruyt, Tinbergen, and Thorpe was rarely mentioned in the controversies to which I have referred, as if wasps, bees, fishes, and birds belonged to the fauna of another planet. As Thorpe remarked wistfully: 'Perhaps the arguments as to whether certain performances of rats in mazes represent insight or trial-and-error learning would have been somewhat less prolonged if the abilities of some of the "lower animals", such as insects, had been known. . . . While it surprises no one that something like latent learning should be displayed by mammals and by birds with their proverbial powers of orientation, it may come as something of a shock to comparative psychologists who work primarily with mammals to find learning of this kind displayed at a high level among invertebrates. It is true that, with the confirmation of the work of von Frisch on the orientation of the hive-bee, we are now prepared to believe almost anything of bees, but there are certainly many insects other than bees, and many invertebrates other than insects, in which latent learning and similar performances can be discerned. The neglect of the study of invertebrate behaviour has given the impression that insight-learning is a characteristically human faculty hardly to be expected in a sub-primate mammal and, of course, out of the question in an arthropod. We now see what an astonishing misconception this is.'[22]

While behaviourists denied the rat the capability to acquire a mental map of a maze, the ethologists have shown that this is precisely what insects do. Their work merits consideration in some detail—which is done best by textual quotation. Tinbergen and de Kruyt have trained wasps to find their way to the nest by a configuration of certain land-marks (such as fir-cones and twigs). When these training marks were moved, and the wasp might have been expected to show complete disorientation, it 'will suddenly utilize new landmarks completely un-related to the previous orientation marks on which it had apparently been trained—a result which has interesting and suggestive simi-larity to Krechevsky's work on hypotheses in maze-learning. Many such examples lead us imperceptibly to what we may consider as insight-learning. Ammophila hunts caterpillars which are too heavy to be brought back on the wing, and which may thus have to be dragged for a hundred yards or more across and through every imagin-able natural obstacle. Here the original learning of the territory has probably been in the main affected by observation from the air, and yet the return has to be made on foot. Although the insect may from time to time leave her prey and take short survey flights, this is by no means invariable . . . and quite often the wasp seems able to maintain orientation while on the ground as a result of earlier aerial recon-naissance.'[23] When large obstacles (metal screens 50 by 120 centi-metres) were placed in its path, 'the insect diverged just enough to carry it round the obstacle on a perfectly smooth, even course of maximum economy of effort. On one particular occasion the experiment was immediately repeated twice with the same results, but the third time the insect walked straight at the screen, climbed with perfect ease to the top and, without ever letting go of its caterpillar, flew down to the ground on the other side and continued its journey. On subsequent occasions this insect would adopt now one type of behaviour, now another, but in no instance did she ever show trial and error. The solution to the problem was always smooth, unhesitating, and eco-nomical.

'This and other individuals which behaved in the same way were then caught and transported in a dark box to a new site, a process

taking less than a minute. On release the insect might have been expected to be at least momentarily disorientated. On the contrary, it
appeared quite unperturbed and without any orientation flight set
out at once on its new course. It was again given the detour test three
times on its new course, but it reacted as efficiently as before and within a few minutes had arrived exactly on its nest. Although the insect
too, on occasion, shows some evidence of disorientation, nevertheless
the overwhelming impression given (as also recorded by Baerends
(1941) and other workers) was one of almost uncanny knowledge of
the details of the terrain.'[24] Thorpe concludes: 'In some instances it
is possible that the homing faculty depends on no more elaborate
sensory mechanism than that involved in simple taxes or light-com-
pass reactions. Nevertheless, it is certain that in a large number of
examples this is inadequate and that we have a true place memory.'[25]

In the case of at least the honey-bee, the memory is communicable.
The orientation dance of the bee is certainly as striking an example as
one could wish for, of place-learning encoded and re-coded into a
symbolic motor-pattern. Yet again the question arises: if, following
Thorpe, we call the behaviour of these insects 'insightful', have we not
stretched the word into a kind of rubber concept? And once more the
only description which implies neither too much nor too little seems
to be that the organism has contrived to build a coded model of the
invariant and significant aspects of the territorial environment into its
nervous system.

The Controversial Rat

Munn's *Handbook of Psychological Research on the Rat*, published in 1950,
contains a bibliographical list of over two thousand five hundred titles;
its rate of growth since then is anybody's guess. A considerable portion
of this research was devoted to maze studies. Not even Newton, as
Bertrand Russell remarked,[26] could learn a maze by any method other
than trial and error; yet what the rat learns is not a chain of responses,
but the pattern of the maze as a whole—as shown by the experiments
with mutilated rats, and in others where the rat takes prompt advantage of short-cuts when a wall is removed, and avoids newly
created cul-de-sacs. The evidence is equally conclusive that the rat
is capable of latent learning and of forming 'hypotheses' by 'provisional tries'. Yet the Great Rat Controversy was kept going—partly
because S.-R. theorists kept coming up with ingenious alternative

interpretations of the evidence, and partly because of the weighted character of much of the experimental procedure itself. A good illustration for this was the 'continuity versus non-continuity' dispute, where Spence and others represented the behaviourist view against Krech, Lashley, etc. The results could be interpreted either or neither way; but—as Osgood wrote, in summing up the controversy: 'It is significant with respect to methodology in psychological experimentation that, almost without exception, the studies supporting the Lashley view have used the jumping stand, while those supporting the continuity view have used a Yerkes-type discrimination box.'[27]

Not only the experimental conditions, but the experimenters' subjective attitudes seemed to exert their influence on the data obtained. In this respect Rosenthal's 'experiment on experimenters' must have come as a shock to students who had taken at least the 'hard and fast' quantitative data (if not the interpretations) of nearly half a century of rat experiments for granted. Rosenthal gave one group of his research workers rats which, he explained, were 'geniuses' specially bred from a stock with exceptionally good maze-learning records. To a second group of researchers he gave what he explained were 'stupid rats'. In fact, all rats were of the same common-or-garden breed; yet the score-sheets of the 'genius rats' showed unmistakably that they learned to run the maze much faster than the 'stupid rats'.[28] The only explanation Rosenthal could offer was that the bias in the research-workers' minds had somehow been transmitted to the rats— just how this was done he confessed not to know. These and other experiments by Rosenthal caused one science editor to comment: 'The results throw a pall over the entire range of psychological tests as reported by the psychologists over the last fifty years.'[29]

Thus I shall have little more to say about the bar-pressing and maze-running experiments with rats. In spite of the impressive mathematical apparatus, and the painstaking measurements of 'rates of response', 'habit-strength', 'fractional anticipatory goal-responses', and the rest, rarely in the history of science has a more ambitious theory been built on shakier foundations.

The Cat in the Box

The cat in the puzzle box, in Thorndike's classic experiments, is also put into a situation so designed that it can be solved only by trial and error. The box is equipped with contrivances such as rings, loops, turning bolts, pedal boards, etc., and with a door which opens, according to the experiment, when the animal operates one of these contrivances, or several of them in a given order. Thus the cat may have to turn bolt B which, however, becomes loose only after bolt A has already been turned; or it may have to pull a string, or a loop, in order to free itself. When the cat is put into the box, it 'tries to squeeze through any opening; it claws or bites at the bars or wire; it thrusts its paws out through any opening, and claws at everything it reaches; it continues its efforts when it strikes anything loose and shaky; it may claw at things within the box. It does not pay very much attention to the food outside, but seems simply to strive instinctively to escape from confinement. The vigour with which it struggles is extraordinary. For eight or ten minutes it will claw and bite and squeeze incessantly.'[30]

The cat's behaviour is typical of that phase in a 'blocked' situation, where organized behaviour disintegrates and yields to more or less random trials. The solution—pushing a bolt or pulling a loop or even licking itself—will be first hit upon by chance, and after a number of repetitions, it will be retained; the learning curve will be more or less continuous or it may show a sudden, sharp drop. The objections against this kind of experimental design are essentially the same as against classical conditioning: they create an artificial universe. 'The solution of Thorndike's problems demanded behaviours that were quite beyond the animal's normal repertoire. Cats do not get out of boxes by pressing buttons or by washing themselves; rather they try to squeeze through narrow openings or scratch at the barriers, and Thorndike's animals were observed attempting just such solutions as part of their early trial and error. In other words, the correct response in a situation like Thorndike's could *only* be hit upon by sheer, blind chance.'[31]

The conclusion which Thorndike and his followers drew from these experiments—'that animals are incapable of higher mental processes such as reasoning and insight—that they are limited to the "stamping-in" and "stamping-out" mode of trial and error'—is one of the most astonishing examples of question-begging in the history of modern science. One might just as well adapt Thorndike's method of reasoning to human education, teach children nonsense syllables which can only be learned by rote, and then conclude that children are only capable of learning by rote. And yet, to quote Hilgard: 'for nearly half a century one learning theory dominated all others in America, despite numerous attacks upon it and the rise of its many rivals. It is the theory of Edward L. Thorndike.'[32] Tolman, writing forty years after the publication of Thorndike's *Animal Intelligence*, went even further:

> The psychology of animal learning—not to mention that of child-learning—has been and still is primarily a matter of agreeing or disagreeing with Thorndike, or trying in minor ways to improve upon him. Gestalt psychologists, conditioned-reflex psychologists, sign-Gestalt psychologists—all of us here in America seem to have taken Thorndike, overtly or covertly, as our starting point.[32a]

Cat experiments of a type diametrically opposed to Thorndike's were carried out by Adams. It is amusing to compare the description of the behaviour of Thorndike's cats which I have just quoted, with the behaviour of Adams' cats:

'A piece of liver is suspended from the top of a wire-cage, so that the liver rests on the floor inside the cage, loosely held by the thread. A hungry cat in the room with the cage, but outside it, sees the liver and walks over to the cage. It hesitates for a time and its head moves up and down as though it is studying the string. Then it jumps on top of the cage, catches the string in its mouth, raises the liver by joint use of mouth and paw, and leaps down with the stick at the end of the string in its mouth.'[33]

The behaviour of Adams' cat, first 'thinking out' the solution of the problem, then acting it out in an unhesitating, smooth, purposeful manner, is of the same kind as Köhler's chimpanzees'. The contrast between this type of intelligent problem-solving, and Thorndike's stamping-in process *seems* to be complete. Yet the cat's learning in the box is by no means the blind, random process which Thorndike and his followers read into it. In the first place we must realize that the cat's handicap lies not only, as in classical conditioning, in the *irrelevance* of the clues which in its natural environment the cat would ignore; but also in the fact that the clue—say, a loop hanging from the ceiling—is hidden or 'drowned' among other equally irrelevant clues—latches, bolts, etc. The unnaturalness of the tasks set in these experiments is illustrated by the 'lick-yourself-to-escape' type of rule. Yet even in this surrealistic universe, the cat's behaviour testifies to a remarkably high I.Q. After the initial bewilderment, as adjustment to the laboratory situation progresses, the range of the cat's tries will be narrowed down, and loops, bolts, etc., will be paid an increasing amount of attention, as members of the nascent matrix. The cat develops, like Pavlov's dogs, an attitude of expectancy, of 'Means-End Readiness' (Tolman); it begins to form 'hypotheses'.[34] Thus, when the cat has learned to get out of the box by clawing at a loop, and the loop is then displaced from the front to the rear wall of the box, it will learn to free itself much quicker than before it had abstracted the loop-Gestalt from other clues. If, however, the loop is replaced by a small wooden platform hung in the same place which the loop occupied before, the animal will free itself after a short while by striking at the platform; in this case, the *location* is the clue. Thus the 'loop hypothesis' can exist side by side with the 'place hypothesis'—just as Krechevsky's rats, who had to guess whether the food was hidden by a door of a given colour, *or* of a given location, formed first a colour hypothesis, then a place hypothesis.[35]

At this stage, the cat's behaviour can be described as a series of 'provisional tries'.[36] These tries, far from being governed by chance, show great plasticity: if the cat has learned to escape by pulling a string with its foot, it may on the next occasion free itself by pulling the string with its teeth, which requires an entirely different sequence of motions. Even where the 'correct' response was the perverse action of licking its own fur, the act is reduced in the final trials 'to a mere symbolic vestige.'[37]

Whichever way we look at it, the cat's behaviour is most fittingly— if somewhat metaphorically—described as learning the rules of Thorndike's game by a process of elimination and empirical induction. The learning curve is a function of several variables: it will show gradual or sudden progress, continuity and discontinuity, according to the experimental conditions, individual learning capacity, fatigue, and chance.

NOTES

To p. 559. Hilgard calls Hull's system 'the most influential of the theories between 1930 and 1950, judging from the experimental and theoretical studies engendered by it, whether in its defence, its amendment or its refutation' (Hilgard, 1958, p. 192).

To p. 559. The objection to this is not that Hull postulated a continuous series linking rat to man, but that his 'primary laws' are epitomized by the bar-pressing act of the rat, which he regarded as the atomic unit of behaviour. The fallacy of this reasoning seems to be derived from Hull's implied notion of mental progress from rat to man as a linear gradient. Theories of this kind fail to take into account the hierarchic principle in mental evolution—reflected in the hierarchy of levels in the nervous system. If instead of linear gradients, we think in terms of levels of increasing complexity, then a difference in degrees does become a difference in kind. Since the basic mechanisms of sexual reproduction are common to all mammalian species, Hull's postulate seems to imply that detailed study of sexual behaviour in the rat would eventually yield the 'primary laws' underlying the Kinsey reports on the sexual behaviour of the American male and female. Homologue principles (such as the part-whole relation, or control by feedback) do operate on all levels, but they are general principles, not specific 'units' or 'atoms' of behaviour.

To p. 565. Coding is an irreversible act, and once the code is established, it will be relatively permanent—until it decays. If, however, the dog is fooled repeatedly and in quick succession ('massed practice'), i.e. food is withheld after the buzzer has sounded, a negative code will superimpose itself on the previous one. The first few times the response will stop at salivation short of chewing; but soon it will stop short of salivation. After a few hours' rest, however, salivation is restored by 'spontaneous recovery'—a paradox which has bedevilled learning theory for a long time. Perhaps the explanation may be sought on the following lines. The whole attitude of the dog, as it has become adapted to the laboratory situation, is based on the expectation that *all* stimuli are events relevant to food; and that the negative code (buzzer——> no food), if it has been quickly superimposed on the positive one (buzzer—— >food), is of a more temporary and brittle nature than its opponent. If, however, the unrewarded signals are spaced out over a greater length of time, i.e. if the extinction-drill approximates in thoroughness the original drill, extinction becomes final (Cf. e.g. Hebb, 1958, pp. 134-5, 147).

XIII

THE PITFALLS OF GESTALT

More about Chimpanzees

I f the S.-R. theorist's method of designing experiments seems to be aimed at printing a wiring circuit into the animal's nervous system, Köhler's method was to provide it with a do-it-yourself kit. The main task of the experimenter, as Köhler saw it, was to arrange for his chimpanzees conditions which favour original discovery by placing the necessary paraphernalia in their cage—solid and hollow sticks, crates, etc.; and to make the task just difficult enough to exceed, by a fraction as it were, the limit of the animal's repertory of skills.

I have mentioned a few typical examples of the chimpanzees' achievements in Book One (Chapter V). In the *use of tools* the decisive factor was the discovery that a previously acquired playful technique M_1 could be applied as a mediating performance to solve a problem in the blocked matrix M_2. Nueva applied her stick—which previously she had used only for pushing things about in play—to rake in a banana placed beyond her reach outside the cage. In similar ways, the chimpanzees used sticks as jumping poles to get at fruit hung high from the ceiling; as implements to make holes in the wire-netting of the cage, to dig up roots in the earth or to prise open the lid of a water-tank; they used sticks as traps to capture crowds of succulent ants, and as weapons for stabbing at fowls and killing lizards. Each of these new achievements was based on the combination of two or more already existing skills, and some of them on serial sequences of 'Eureka processes': when a chimp had discovered the use of a stick as a rake, a short stick was then used to rake in a longer stick to rake in the bananas.

In the *making of tools* we saw similar bisociative processes at work. Sultan's star achievement was the fitting of two hollow bamboo-rods together into one long rod, by pushing the end of the thinner rod into the opening of the other. Let me describe this experiment in some detail:

Sultan is given the two sticks, and the banana is placed at a distance from the bar greater than the length of each single stick. For quite a while he tries to reach the banana with one stick or the other (M_1 obstructed, random trials). He then pulls a wooden box, which has been used in a different type of experiment, to the bar (fumbling for some M_2 to provide the 'mediating performance'). He pushes the useless box away again, pushes one stick outside the bar on the ground as far as it will go and prods it with the second stick towards the banana (M_3: Sultan learned long ago to push a longer stick about with a shorter one). He succeeds in pushing the first stick into contact with the banana, but obviously cannot pull the banana in. Nevertheless, he repeats the procedure: when he has pushed one stick out of his reach and it is given back to him, he starts once more. 'But although, in trying to steer it cautiously, he puts the stick in his hand exactly to the cut (i.e. the opening) of the stick on the ground, and although one might think that doing so would suggest the possibility of pushing one stick into the other, there is no indication whatever of such a practically valuable solution [no "insight"]. Finally, the observer [i.e. Köhler] gives the animal some help by putting one finger into the opening under the animal's nose (without pointing to the other stick at all). This has no effect [still no insight]; Sultan, as before, pushed one stick with the other towards the objective. . . .'

He finally abandons the attempt altogether. These tries have lasted over an hour. The chimp was then left in the keeper's care, who reported later on:

Sultan first of all squats indifferently on the box, which has been left standing a little back from the railings; then he gets up, picks up the two sticks, sits down again on the box and plays carelessly with them. While doing this, it happens that he finds himself holding one rod in either hand in such a way that they lie in a straight line; he pushes the thinner one a little way into the opening of the thicker, jumps up and is already on the run towards the railings, to which he has up to now half turned his back, and begins to draw a banana towards him with the double stick. I call the master: meanwhile, one of the animal's rods has fallen out of the other, as he has pushed one of them only a little way into the other; whereupon he connects them again.[1]

Henceforth Sultan never had any difficulty in connecting two rods; and later on even three.

At first sight, Sultan's achievement appears not as an integration of existing skills, but as the invention of a totally new one. However, commenting on the keeper's report, Köhler says: (my italics) 'The keeper emphasized the fact that Sultan had *first of all connected the sticks in play and without considering the objective* [the banana]. The animals are constantly poking about with straws and small sticks in holes and cracks in their play, so that it would be more astonishing if Sultan had never done this [i.e. poking the thinner rod into the hole of the other], while playing about with the two sticks.'[2]

Thus the discovery again followed the familiar pattern of a playful habit being connected with a blocked matrix, with chance acting as a trigger. Later on, a third matrix was added: Sultan had learned long ago to sharpen sticks by biting off splinters, so that they could be used to poke in keyholes; now this skill was used to make two sticks fit together. Obviously, Sultan would never have invented this sophisticated method of tool-making if each of the three component skills (raking, poking, sharpening) had not been pre-existing items of his habit-repertory. The more familiar and well exercised each of the matrices, the more likely it is that the animal will solve the problem and, other things being equal, the less it will depend on the helping hand of chance. (In the case of the two bamboo rods which 'happened' to fit each other—a chance which the animal will rarely encounter in the woods—we have an example of 'guided learning': the experimenter serves as a match-maker in lieu of the favourable chance event; the rest is up to the pupil.)

Uniform Factors in Learning

Sultan's original achievements cannot be explained either by stamping-in, or by spontaneous inspiration out of the blue; they are integrations of existing, flexible skills, of previously unconnected codes of behaviour into more complex codes of a higher order. In conditioning and rote-learning, the new code has to be formed more or less from scratch, more or less bit by bit. This 'drilling in' is a gradual, cumulative process; whereas the bisociation of two matrices appears as a sudden fusion. But in between these opposite extremes we find a graded series of learning methods, with certain basic features common to all. Let me enumerate a few of these common features.

The chimpanzee, straining to reach a banana behind the bars, *remembers* the stick lying out of sight; he runs to get it and uses it as a rake. This has been mentioned in the early Gestalt literature as one of the criteria of insight learning. But memory enters into *all* learning processes. Thus retention in delayed reaction tests has been shown to last in cats from three to thirteen hours, in chimpanzees up to forty-eight hours.[3] Another feature which we find in *all* types of conditioning and learning, from Pavlov upward, is expectancy and *anticipatory behaviour*. Once the stage of initial bewilderment or frustrated rage is passed, and the animal has embarked on 'learning to learn', random trials are superseded by less random 'fumbling tries'; and these in turn by hypotheses. At the 'fumbling' stage, Sultan's behaviour in the stick-connecting experiment shows no more insight than the cat's: his fetching of the wooden box and attempts to push one stick with the second, were quite inappropriate. On the other hand, however, we have met with plenty of examples of comparable fumblings among human geniuses—of wild guesses and inappropriate tries preceding the act of discovery. If we remember that Kepler spent seven years of trial and error, pursuing false inspirations and wrong hypotheses before the discovery of his First and Second Laws, we are led to realize the subtleties and wide applications of the try-method —and how completely wrong it is to equate it with blind random behaviour. The range of learning by trial and error extends from relatively haphazard tries through the whole graded series, to the relative certainty of inductive inference. On the lower reaches the trials are explicit and often temperamental, like the frantic attempts of Thorndike's cats to get out of the box; on the higher reaches, they assume more and more the character of implicit hypothesis—Adams' cat moving its head up and down as it 'works out' the means of getting at the liver suspended from the string. Lastly, at the top of the series, the inventor toys with an idea in his head before taking the more explicit step of trying out several alternative sketches on paper; after which he may proceed to making a rough model—an even more explicit, but nevertheless merely symbolic try. The writer, groping for the right adjective, will sample several with his literary taste-buds; even the Lord Almighty, according to Genesis, proceeded by trial and error, as witnessed by the painful episode of the Flood.

So far, then, we have a continuous series of learning methods, where the amount of required stamping-in decreases in proportion to the animal's ripeness for the experimental task. But, according to the contentions of the Gestalt school, there is a decisive break in the continuity of the series which puts insightful learning into a category apart from other methods of learning; and this break is said to be reflected in the animal's characteristic behaviour at the moment the true insightful solution occurs. In this view, Sultan's trial-and-error behaviour was merely a *preliminary* to the true solution, which emerges with dramatic suddenness and all in a piece; whereas in trial-and-error learning it emerges gradually.

The chief descriptive characteristics of 'insight' which have been proposed by various authors are as follows: (a) dramatic suddeness; (b) 'the appearance of a complete solution with reference to the whole layout of the field';[4] (c) the smooth, unhesitating manner in which the solution is 'suddenly, directly and definitely'[5] carried out; (d) the solution of the problem precedes the actual execution of it;[6] (e) the solution is retained after a single performance; (f) novelty of the solution.[7] It is furthermore generally assumed that 'insight' is closely related to, if not synonymous with, intelligence and understanding and, by implication, that trial-and-error learning is not so or to a lesser degree so. This last point, however, I shall discuss later; first let us turn to the purely *descriptive* aspects of 'insight learning'.

When Köhler's experiments are discussed, the authors usually select the star performances of Sultan, and it is often overlooked that these were rather in the nature of rare limit cases. In the experiment I am going to describe, a young chimpanzee, Koko, was faced with the problem how to get a banana hung high from the wall. The only solution was to push a wooden box underneath the banana and to climb on the box. Though Koko is described by Köhler as 'just as gifted as Sultan', it took him no less than nineteen days to learn this—whereas he had learned to rake in a banana with a stick in a few minutes. The use of sticks is part of the chimpanzee's repertory of habits—but there are no wooden boxes lying about in the forest. However, before the experiment was started, Koko was given a small wooden box as a toy; 'he pushed it about and sat on it for a moment'. He was then removed to another cage and in his absence the banana was suspended from the wall, three or four yards away from the wooden box (the italics are Köhler's: by 'objective' he means banana):

> Koko . . . first jumped straight upwards several times towards the objective, then took his rope in his hand, and tried to lasso the prize with a loop of it, could not reach so far, and then turned away from the wall, after a variety of such attempts, but without noticing the box. He appeared to have given up his efforts, but always returned to them from time to time. After some time, on turning away from the wall, his eye fell on the box: he approached it, *looked straight towards the objective*, and gave the box a slight push, which did not, however, move it; his movements had grown much slower; he left the box, took a few paces away from it, but at once returned, and pushed it again and *again with his eyes on the objective*, but quite gently, and not as though he really intended to alter its position. He turned away again, turned back at once, and gave the box a third tentative shove, after which he again moved slowly about. The box had now been moved 10 centimetres in the direction of the fruit. The objective was rendered more tempting by the addition of a piece of orange (the *non plus ultra* of delight!), and in a few seconds Koko was once more at the box, seized it, dragged it in one movement up to a point almost directly beneath the objective (that is, he moved it a distance of at least three metres), mounted it and tore down the fruit. A bare quarter of an hour had elapsed since the beginning of the test.[8]

All's well that ends well. But it does not. A few minutes later the experiment was repeated—after the banana had been moved about three yards from its former position, while the box was left standing where Koko had dragged it. When Koko was led back onto the stage:

> he sprang at the new banana in the same manner as before, but with somewhat less eagerness; at first he ignored the box. After a time he suddenly approached it, seized and dragged it the greater part of the distance towards the new banana, but at a distance of a quarter of a metre he stopped, gazed at the banana, and stood as if quite puzzled and confused. And now began a tale of woe for both Koko and the box. When he again set himself in motion it was with every sign of rage, as he knocked the box this way and that, but came no nearer to the objective. After waiting a little the experiment was broken off.[9]

This tale of woe continued for nineteen days during which the experiment was repeated at varying intervals; and even afterwards, when the new skill was firmly established at last, its performance still alternated for a while with random trials.

Does Koko's behaviour satisfy the descriptive criteria of insight learning?

(a) *Suddenness*. Yes, it does—because at the climactic moment of the first experiment, the solution did appear suddenly and all of a piece. No, it does not—because prior to it Koko had made several half-hearted attempts at the correct solution and yet abandoned them. (b) 'Complete solution with reference to the whole layout to the field'. The answer is, No. (c) 'Smooth, unhesitating, direct and definitive'— on one occasion, Yes, on the others, No. (d) 'Solution precedes execution of solution'—yes and no. (e) 'Solution retained after a single performance'—definitely No. (f) Novelty—yes.

Köhler's own comments on this experiment are revealing. Although in *The Mentality of Apes* he stresses that the gulf between Trial-and-Error and Insight is unbridgeable ('the contrast is absolute'[10]), his comment on Koko's initial hesitations and fumblings with the box is: 'there is only one expression that really fits his behaviour at that juncture: it's beginning to dawn on him!'[11] Let us note that for about ten days after that first success, Koko kept manipulating the box, sometimes aimlessly, sometimes angrily, and during this whole period 'no trace of a solution appeared, except an equivalent of the words: "there's something about that box".'[12] In another passage Köhler says (italics Köhler's): 'It may happen that the animal will attempt a solution which, while it may not result in success, yet has some meaning in regard to the situation. "Trying around" then consists in attempts at solution in the *half-understood* situation.'[13]

Preconditions of Insight

No more need be said to prove that if we apply the descriptive criteria which I have ennumerated, we find a graded series from 'trying around', through the 'dawning' of the solution, to the limit case of the sudden solution. But limit cases at the end of a graded series do not require a separate set of postulates to explain them. The break in actual behaviour, the discrete and unitary character of the solution in these cases can be explained in terms which are also applicable to other forms of learning. Thus with regard to criterion (a) we can say that the suddenness of the solution is due to the trigger action of chance in a situation which was ripe for solution—that is to say, where the animal's repertory comprises all the requisite single skills, and where all that is needed is a link to combine them into a complex skill—e.g. Sultan accidentally pushing one rod into the opening of the other. In other cases—Sultan turning round to pick up the remembered stick —where chance plays no part, memory provides the link; but memory enters into all forms of learning. Regarding (c) and (d) (smooth, unitary execution of the act, indicating that it has been thought out before being acted out), we may say that the animal has formed a hypothesis, or carried out an implicit try, followed by explicit performances of the act. Rats, cats, and dogs also show this brief suspension of activity, this 'attitude of concentrated attention'[14] before they act out a hypothesis—which may or may not be the correct one. (e) Retention after a single performance can be interpreted as 'induction based on a single case'—as the chick, from a single experience, draws the correct empirical inference that all cinnabar caterpillars are to be avoided. Lastly, (f), *novelty* is of course also achieved when the cat learns the open-sesame trick in the puzzle-box. To argue that the cat's novel response was acquired by Trial and Error, the chimp's by Insight, is to argue in a circle, since novelty itself is supposed to serve as a differential criterion.

Thus Sultan's Eureka processes, *once we have got rid of thinking in S.-R. schemata*, are interpretable in terms of the same theory which covers all lower forms of learning. They make a spectacular impression, because (since the separate skills which had to be integrated into the new skill were well-exercised items in his repertory of habits), the problem to be solved was just one step beyond the limits of that repertory, and all was set for a single spark to trigger off the fusion.

At the opposite end of the learning scale, the dog in Pavlov's laboratory is not equipped with pre-existent rules of the game which could be combined with each other; it must *construct a new code of rules*, starting more or less from scratch. Therein lies the main difference. The dog must start with an agonized reappraisal of which environmental events are relevant and which are not; then extract and codify the recurrent invariant features from the stimuli promoted to significance; then discriminate between finer features within those features. The rat must piece together, bit by bit, his cognitive map of the maze;

the cat must gradually extract, by empirical induction, the rules of Thorndike's game from a surrealistic universe.

The 'missing link' in between the cat and Sultan is provided by Koko. He does not have to start from scratch; he has already played with the box; he has sat on it and pushed it about. Was his first successful solution of the problem a random try? Certainly not. It had all the 'dramatic suddenness, smoothness, directness and definiteness' that one can wish for. It was more than a 'provisional try', rather like a hypothesis which carried implicit conviction; yet on the other hand, it had been preceded by hesitant action along the correct lines which was abandoned; and it was succeeded by forgetting all but a fragment of the successful solution—the fragment 'there is something about that box'.

The reason for this paradoxical behaviour is evident. Koko had to combine two skills; the reaching-jumping-climbing skill M_1, and displacing the box to serve as a platform, M_2. But M_2 is not part of the chimp's habit-repertory; in all Köhler's experiments with manipulating boxes and putting them on top of each other, his chimps proved surprisingly stupid.* Thus the skill of manipulating boxes is not a well-exercised, 'ready-made' item in Koko's repertory; and Koko is not really ripe for the task set for him, because M_2 is still too tentative and unstable to become firmly attached to M_1; linking did occur in a lucky moment, but the link broke again. This description presupposes that the box-manipulating skill was developing *independently* from banana-collecting, as a purely playful occupation—as it did in fact when Koko was made to play with the box before the experiment started. And it further presupposes that if Koko had been given sufficient time to become proficient in that playful skill, then he would have become ripe for a true bisociative act. Instead of this, however, he was led to form a 'premature linkage' between boxes and bananas (cf. Book One, IX).

This interpretation differs from Köhler's 'appearance of a complete solution with reference to the whole layout of the field'; or rather, it specifies the condition under which such a 'complete solution' has a chance to occur. But our interpretation is borne out by later experiments by others, in which chimpanzees were given the same raking task as set by Köhler. One chimpanzee out of six had previously used sticks in play; this animal was *the only one* which had the 'insight' to rake in the food placed outside the cage; the other five failed, although the stick was lying in plain view. For the next three days all six chimps were given sticks to play with. They used the sticks, as usual, to push and poke, but never as a rake. Then the experiment was repeated—and all six sticks turned into rakes instantly.[15] Experiments with dogs reared in isolation and then set 'insight situation' tasks, gave similar results.[16]

It may seem pedantic to lay so much stress on the independent primary development of skills which are later combined in the 'moment of truth'. But the point does become relevant on higher levels. The experimental sciences of electricity and magnetism developed independently, and the discovery of electro-magnetic induction was a truly bisociative act; in comparison to it the subsequent improvements of electromagnets were a pedestrian procedure. The previous independence of the cognitive structures which are made to fuse in the creative act is, as we saw before, one of the criteria of originality; I shall return to the subject in the final chapter.

The Ambiguities of Gestalt

The Gestalt theory was developed in Germany, before Wertheimer, Köhler, and Koffka settled in America; and the original German term for insight was 'Einsicht'. In a footnote on page 291 of the English translation of The Mentality of Apes we read (my italics): 'The German word "Einsicht" is rendered by both "intelligence" and "insight" throughout this book. The lack of an adjective derived from the noun "insight", apart from other considerations, makes this procedure necessary.'

In this casual footnote we find the clue to the sad confusion which has bedevilled the controversy from its beginning: Gestalt theorists used the word 'insight' indiscriminately to mean either (A) intelligence, understanding, judgement, knowledge in general, or (B) specifically the acquisition of new understanding and knowledge under the sudden and dramatic circumstances specified in the previous section. By equating (A) with (B), the Gestaltists were led to regard (B) as the only type of 'intelligent' learning, everything else as 'blind' learning; and their explanations of why and how learning of type (B) occurs become unavoidably tautological. Thus Köhler writes:

We can, in our own experience, distinguish sharply between the kind of behaviour which from the very beginning arises out of a consideration of the structure of a situation, and one that does not.

Only in the former case do we speak of insight, and only that behaviour of animals definitely appears to us intelligent which takes account from the beginning of the lay of the land, and proceeds to deal with it in a single, continuous, and definite course. Hence follows this criterion of insight: *the appearance of a complete solution with reference to the whole layout of the field.*[17] (Köhler's italics).

But a few pages further we read: ' "trying around" consists in attempts at solution in the *half-understood* situation; and the real solution may easily arise by some chance outcome of it, i.e. it will not arise from chance impulses, but from actions, which, because they are *"au fond"* sensible, are great aids to chance'.[18] Köhler further speaks of the 'dawning' of the solution and of 'good errors'—that is, tries in the right direction vaguely sensed. Thus Köhler admits that insight in the sense (B) is a matter of approximation, and may be achieved in several steps, consisting of more or less 'sensible' hypotheses and tries; yet in other passages he asserted the exact opposite, namely that the criterion of insight was 'the appearance of a complete solution . . . in a single continuous and definite course'.

To get out of this confusion, let me distinguish between two problems; firstly, what constitutes *understanding* or Insight A; and in the second place, how *new* understanding or Insight B is acquired. Regarding the second problem, we have seen that the dramatic Eureka process is not the rule, but rather an exceptional limit case; and that understanding or Insight A enters to varying degrees into *all* forms of learning.

Let us examine for a moment the Gestalt school's answer to the first problem: the nature of understanding or Insight A. On page 219 of *The Mentality of Apes* we read that it is based 'on the grasp of a material, inner relation of two things to each other . . .'; 'relation' being further defined as an 'interconnection based on the properties of these things themselves, not a "frequent following each other" or "occurring together" '. The meaning of these formulations becomes clearer in Köhler's later book (1949). There this 'material' 'inner' relation between two things is expressed as 'our feeling of something naturally depending on something else'.[19] 'Between the attitude and its sensory basis we experience what in German is called *ihr sachlicher Zusammenhang* . . .'; and *sachlicher Zusammenhang* is translated, with some hesitation, as 'intrinsic connection'. This again is used synonymously with 'experienced determination' such as that prevailing 'between a disease and its germ'.[20] Again: 'Here not only the result is experienced, but also very much of its "why" and "how" is felt in just the actual context. Wherever this is the case we apply the term *insight.*' But 'very much' is a relative term, and its use as an all-or-none criterion—'wherever this is the case'—again confuses the issue. Turning to Koffka, we find that he explains the difficulties confronting the cat in the problem-box by the fact that the actions which it must perform to gain release are to the cat 'objectively meaningless', that they have 'no sort of internal connection with release', that they have no 'material relation' or 'intrinsic relation' with the opening of doors, and so on.

It should be clear by now that all these somewhat obscure terms are shamefaced references to *physical causality*, and that the position of the Gestalt school boils down to the tautology that the animal's behaviour is the more intelligent the more insight it has into causal relations. Nobody will quarrel with this statement; but it entirely begs the central question of learning theory: namely, by what processes and methods that insight into causal relations is *acquired*. The loop in the puzzle-box, at the beginning of its training, means nothing to the cat; at the end of its training it means escape. How is this meaning acquired? Through trial-and-error learning, hypotheses, etc. The problem can now be re-formulated as follows: can learning by trial and error *result* in 'genuine' solutions, can it provide a correct, or true, or meaningful representation of the causal connection between loop and door? We can even go one step further and ask the same question with regard to classical conditioning. If the dog could express itself in Köhler's terminology, it would no doubt answer that the sound of the gong 'signals' or 'means' food, that an 'objectively meaningful connection', an 'intrinsic connection' or *sachlicher Zusammenhang*, exists between the two. And this statement would entirely correspond to fact, because in the laboratory universe this sequence *is* natural law. Of course some connecting links are missing in the dog's inner model of that law: the intentions of God Pavlov who has decreed it are unknown to the dog. But such gaps occur on *all* levels of cognitive processes. When the average citizen turns on his radio he has about as much insight into the 'intrinsic connections' between the knob and the sound, the 'whys' and 'hows', the 'interconnections based on the properties of the things themselves', the 'total layout of the field' as Pavlov's dogs have.

Understanding is a matter of approximation. If we hold, with

Craik, that the basic achievement of the nervous system is derived from its power to parallel or model external events,[21] then the cat which has learned to open the door by tugging at the loop can be said to have made a correct, if crude, model of a causal sequence. The crudeness of the model is mainly due to the fact that the rope connecting the loop and the door is hidden from the cat's sight—whereas under normal conditions the cat can 'see what it is doing'. But this difference is one of degree not of kind; and it is not justifiable to argue —as Gestalt theorists have occasionally done—that because the cat cannot see the connection, it has no 'insight'. Because sight is our main sense organ, we have come to use the words 'I see' as synonymous with 'I understand'. The Gestalt school with its strong emphasis on visual perception has carried this tendency to extremes, and thus came to believe that to have all relevant facts of a situation or problem laid out before one's eyes is both necessary and sufficient for its understanding.[22] In fact, of course, it is neither. Rats learn to know a maze, and to form a mental map of it—which amounts to as complete an understanding of the situation as one could wish for—without having been offered a bird's eye view of it. Nor is seeing a *sufficient* condition for knowing in chimpanzees or humans, even if the 'whole field' containing all the necessary clues is laid out in full view. Thus Sultan establishes a visual connection with the banana outside the cage by pushing one stick towards it with a second stick, but that procedure does not testify to much insight. In other experiments, where a string is attached to the banana and one or more strings are laid out in the vicinity, Sultan will pull at random at any of the strings, although he can clearly see which string is connected to the banana, which is not.* The young child behaves in similar ways; Piaget has called this phenomenon 'optical realism'. It 'consists in considering things as being what they appear to be in immediate perception and not what they will become once they have been inserted in a system of rational relations transcending the visual field. Thus the child imagines that a stick can draw an object because it is beside it or touches it, as though optical contact were equivalent to a causal link.'[23]

Adults are also quite often unable to understand how a simple mechanism works although it is laid bare before their eyes. The visual concurrence of all elements which belong to the problem facilitates understanding (in various degrees according to species, see previous note), but does not guarantee or imply it; it does not provide a 'direct and complete' insight into the causal connections of the situation, nor, except in certain cases, does it occasion a 'complete answer according to the total layout of the field'. Even in relatively simple situations there are always gaps in understanding the 'intrinsic material relations' between things. Why can I pull but not push an object with a string? What are the whys and hows of rigidity, flexibility, cohesion, etc.? Why is a hemp-cord stronger than a paper-cord, and less elastic than a rubber-cord? Our insight into the 'inner material relation of phenomena' is full of missing links, so to speak; the model of the outside world which we form in the matrix of our minds represents, by the very nature of that matrix, not a point-to-point correspondence but a point-to-blur correspondence, a more or less rough approximation. Not only this blurred microstructure, but even the macrostructure of the universe, and the laws which govern it, put us into much the same perplexed condition as the cat which has to infer, by empirical induction, the laws which Thorndike made in his wisdom. And the cat's behaviour in the box is, in fact, a first approximation to the methodology of exact science as formulated by Craik: 'induction supported by experiments to test hypotheses'.[24]

It is necessary to remind ourselves of these truisms, because the controversies in learning theory have almost made us lose them from sight. The extreme wing of the Behaviourists has tried to banish the concepts of understanding, memory, purpose, consciousness, hypothesis, from the groves of Academe, to interpret trial and error as a random process, and human induction as an equally mechanical affair. Classical Gestalt theory sinned in the opposite direction; its attitude is epitomized, e.g. in the passages from Köhler already quoted: according to which true understanding can be derived only from 'an interconnection based on the properties of the things themselves, *not* a "frequent following each other" or "occurring together".' To pay attention to the 'frequent following each other' or 'occurring together' of two events, which is so contemptuously dismissed here, is the very essence of inductive inference. To quote Russell again: 'Let there be two kinds of events, (a) and (b) (e.g. lightning and thunder), and let many instances be known in which an event of the kind (a) has been quickly followed by one of the kind (b), and no instances of the contrary. Then either a sufficient number of instances of this sequence, or instances of suitable kinds, will make it increasingly probable that (a) is always followed by (b), and in times the probability can be made to approach certainty without limit. . . .'[25] Instances of a very suitable, clear-cut kind—that is to say, situations for which the animal is 'ripe', may then lead to inductive certainty derived from a single occurrence—the chick inferring that all caterpillars of appearance (a) are accompanied by a disgusting taste (b).

The mistake of the classical Gestalt school was *to identify trial-and-error learning with chain-reflex theory*—a historically understandable mistake since the two were lumped together in the S.-R. schemata of Thorndike, Pavlov, Watson, Guthrie, etc. Yet the history of science abounds with examples of brilliant discoveries which were preceded by long periods of more or less fumbling tries in half-understood situations. To try is to adventure; and to quote Russell once more: 'If an induction is worth making, it may be wrong.'[26]

The same kind of bias led to the Gestalt school's uncompromising rejection of any associationist theory of learning. Again this radical attitude is historically understandable as a reaction against mechanistic interpretations of associations as rigid neural connections, fixed pathways, conditioned reflex arcs and the rest. But the Gestalt school did not succeed in offering any valid alternative of its own for associative memory. Köhler's trace theory, elaborated by Koffka, does not give even a remote clue as to how a visual percept—say a caricature of Nelson, which is 'pictured' by an electrolytic field-current in the optical cortex—will activate, 'by similarity' the auditory trace of the word 'Trafalgar'. The influence of past experience on the present is minimized by Köhler wherever possible, and learning is virtually reduced to spontaneous 'Insight B', where new knowledge emerges all in a piece like Minerva in full armour from Jupiter's head.

According to Köhler, association has to be 'given up as a special and independent theoretical concept. It is not more than a name for the fact that organized processes leave a trace picturing their organization and that in consequence of it reproductions are possible. . . . Our conclusion is, that association depends upon organization because association is just an after-effect of an organized process.'[27] 'Organization' in this context means perceptual organization—that is to say, the animal's innate faculty to order its perceptions into Gestalt-configurations which arise spontaneously as the 'experienced direct determination' of 'objectively meaningful intrinsic connections' based on the 'whys and hows of the interaction of the properties of the things themselves'—and so on. Gestalt has become the ultimate panacea. As one critic remarked: 'The Gestalten thus become primary realities, existential ultimates, in terms of which all events should be comprehended.'[28]

As so frequently in the history of science, a school of outstanding achievements has succumbed to the magic power of a unifying formula. That formula, in its turn, is based on a metaphysical assumption: the existence of an *a priori* correspondence, or co-ordination, between the physico-chemical processes in the nervous system and the events in the outside world. Owing to Köhler's theory of 'psycho-physical isomorphism', the sight of a square gives rise to a field current in the cortex, and 'this cortical process must have the structural characteristics of the square.'[29] The 'intrinsic', 'material', or causal relations in the outer world are automatically mirrored by isomorph electro-chemical Gestalt processes in the brain, and *'insight' turns out to mean the spontaneous operation of the isomorph faculty.* Thus the organism does not have to *build* a symbolic model of reality in the nervous system by the processes of learning—such as scanning, coding, abstraction, gradual approximation through inductive hypotheses; the isomorph model in the head is pre-figured, potentially given in its native perceptual organization, and need only be *activated* by 'spontaneous insight'. To quote Polànyi: 'From this principle (isomorphism) it would follow that the whole of mathematics—whether known or yet to be discovered—is latent in the neural traces arising in a man's brain when he looks at the axioms of *Principia Mathematica*, and that the physico-chemical equilibration of these traces should be capable of producing a cerebral counterpart (a coded script) comprising the entire body of mathematics.'[30]

Thus the metaphysical assumptions of Gestalt psychology lead us (as Koffka somewhat reluctantly admits)[31] back to the kind of 'faculty psychology' abandoned about a century ago; and ultimately to Plato; whereas Behaviourism leads us ultimately back to the atomism of Democritus combined with the scepticism of Ecclesiastes. Köhler's chimps look at the world through the 'eyes of the soul'; Hull's rats are wired marionettes jerked about by a non-existent puppet player.

Putting Two and Two Together

Contiguity is the *Deus ex machina* of Behaviourists such as Watson and Guthrie, and the *bête noire* of Gestaltists, who reject association by contiguity as 'blind' and 'meaningless'.

'There is not a single example', writes Köhler, 'of an effect produced by the interaction of two things or processes quite independently of their properties. Nevertheless this is the character of the classical law of association as we find it stated in most textbooks.'[32] I cannot remember having seen anywhere the law stated in quite that form, and Köhler's description is obviously a caricature; how can two things interact 'independently of their properties'? Does not the term 'interaction' imply that properties of the interacting processes are involved? Contiguity—the overlapping of two events in spacetime—of a regular, recurrent kind is the base on which inductive inference can build. This applies, impartially, to the dog learning that the gong is a signal for food, and to Kepler observing that the tides follow the moon. Kepler concluded that there must be a causal connection between the moon and the tides, although his ideas of gravity were of the most erratic kind; and his was a correct approximation, followed by the closer approximations of Newton and Einstein—though we are perhaps as far as ever from 'grasping the intrinsic, material relations' between bodies acting at a distance. More often than not, the starting point of the scientist's inquiry is *post hoc, ergo*—let's hope—*propter hoc*. Even in the rare limit case of the Eureka process, contiguity—the simultaneous activity in the mind of the two matrices which are to be integrated—provides the link; and the provider may even be 'blind chance'—a fungus sailing through the window into Fleming's laboratory.

Learning, then, in the most general sense of the word, consists in putting two and two or A and B together. It may be done gradually, by plodding through hypotheses and eliminations; or all of a sudden, following upon a single implicit try. A and B may stand for recurrent features abstracted from a series of perceived events; or A may be a signal-pattern requiring the correct choice of reaction B among other possible choices; A and B may be codes of behaviour or universes of discourse, each complete in itself and adequate for routine tasks; but to solve a certain new task they must be put together. If the subject is ripe for the solution, the putting together can occur in a single flash. But let me repeat that such lightning inductions based on a single case are possible only if both M_1 and M_2 are well-established, flexible matrices which the subject knows 'inside out'. Only those chimpanzees discovered spontaneously the use of a stick as a rake who had previously played with sticks; those who had not, though of equal intelligence, failed to see the light.

There is a rather striking parallel between the present interpretation of discovery as a bisociative process, and the conclusions which Hebb reached regarding the sudden appearance of new insights:*

The sudden activation of an effective link between two concepts or percepts, at first unrelated, is a simple case of 'insight' . . .[33]

Insight, as a sudden perception of new relationships, can result from the simultaneous activity of two conceptual cycles in adult learning.[34]

The insightful act is an excellent example of something that is not learned, but still depends on learning. It is not learned, since it can be adequately performed on its first occurrence; it is not perfected through practice in the first place, but appears all at once in recognizable form (further practice, however, may still improve it). On the other hand, the situation must not be completely strange; the animal must have had prior experience with the component parts of the situation, or with other situations that have some similarity to it. . . . All our evidence thus points to the conclusion that a new insight consists of a *recombination of pre-existent mediating processes*, not the sudden appearance of a wholly new process. [Hebb's italics]

Such recombinations must be frequent in man's everyday living, and in a theoretical framework we must consider them to be original and creative. . . .[35]

Hilgard (1958) came to similar conclusions: 'Because all learning is to some extent cognitively controlled, the distinction between blind learning and learning with understanding becomes one of degree.'[36]

NOTES

To p. 581. Köhler made a distinction between one-box experiments and the building of two- or three-storey structures. In the latter additional difficulties arise from what he called the chimp's 'lack of a feeling for statics'. This handicap no doubt adds to the animal's perplexity; but Koko's and Sultan's behaviour in experiments of this kind (cf. pp. 47, 118, 122 ff) indicates that not only the problem of balance, but the whole box-building business goes against the chimpanzee's grain.

To p. 585. The importance of visual clues varies of course with different species. Adams' cat immediately saw that the piece of liver can be hauled up by the string to which it was attached. Köhler tried a similar experiment with his dog: a basket, containing food, was suspended from a rope outside the barred window of the room so that the dog could easily have hoisted it up with her teeth or paws. But she 'did not even attempt this simple method of self-help, and paid no attention to the string which was lying just under her nose—whilst at the same time she showed the liveliest interest in the distant basket. Dogs, and probably, for instance, horses as well . . . might easily starve to death in these circumstances which offer hardly any difficulty to human beings—or to chimpanzees'

(Köhler, 1957, p. 31). Far be it from me to suggest that cats are more intelligent than dogs; what the experiment shows is that cats are phylogenetically more ripe for this type of perceptual and manipulative skill than dogs.

To p. 589. Hebb's *Organization of Behaviour* was published in the same year as *Insight and Outlook*; his *A Textbook of Psychology* in 1958.

XIV

LEARNING TO SPEAK

Intending and Saying

Preparing to say something, whether it is a single sentence or a public lecture, is to set a hierarchy in motion.

'. . . And has the reader never asked himself', William James wrote in 1890, 'what kind of a mental fact is his *intention of saying a thing* before he has said it? It is an entirely definite intention, distinct from all other intentions, an absolutely distinct state of consciousness, therefore; and yet how much of it consists of definite sensorial images, either of words or of things? Hardly anything! Linger, and the words and things come into the mind; the anticipatory intention, the divination is there no more . . . [The intention] has therefore a nature of its own of the most positive sort, and yet what can we say about it without using words that belong to the later mental facts that replace it? The intention *to say so and so* is the only name it can receive. One may admit that a good third of our psychic life consists in these rapid premonitory perspective views of schemes of thought not yet articulate.'[1]

In other words, before the verbal hierarchy is set into motion, there is an ideational process of a highly conscious character, an intention or active expectation, which itself is not yet verbalized. Consider what is involved in preparing an ex-tempore lecture. The first step is to jot down the principal arguments or themes in key-words—in 'symbols of the second remove' so to speak. Each theme is then treated as a sub-whole, a flexible matrix of ideas with an invariant code: the logic of the argument to be conveyed. But the ways of putting it across are many: factually, whimsically, by concrete examples. My strategical choice is governed by the lie of the land: the character of the audience; and by feedback from implicit tries: their anticipated reactions. If I have decided on concrete examples, I must search for them in my memory, and then again make strategical choices. The next question is where to start, to decide on the sequential order, and the approximate time allotted to each of the various subjects so as to make a balanced whole. In this quasi-architectural planning, the arguments are still treated as sub-wholes or building blocks, whose 'contents are known but are present without adequate verbal designation'.[2] All this is still a long way from the choice of actual words; in fact the hazy intentional situation described by James repeats itself on several levels.

But as we approach the actual formation of sentences, automatisms begin to intrude, indicating that we are nearing the bottom of the hierarchy—the consummatory acts of language which terminate the appetitive behaviour of thought. The sub-codes of grammar and syntax, which now enter into action, are almost wholly automatized; and when we finally arrive at the formation of syntactic units—individual words patterned into phrases—there is a good chance that these will be 'fixed action-patterns'—verbal formulae, clichés, mannerisms, stereotyped turns of phrase, which remind one of the fighting rituals of the stickleback (e.g. 'the evidence tends to show', 'as we have seen before', 'we must bear in mind, however', etc.). Technical papers and bureaucratic utterances are conspicuous by their narrowness of vocabulary and rigidity of phrasing. Fortunately, there exist non-abstractive hierarchies whose criteria of relevance are aesthetic or emotional, which co-determine the tactics of verbal choices and counteract the tendency towards automatization.

Having gone through all these implicit motions, we end up by spelling out the actual sounds or ink marks, vocal patterns or type-written letters. Yet even on this automatized level, hierarchic organization prevails; the phonetic sequences or manual patterns are triggered off as wholes and perceived as wholes; nowhere, in the course of our descent through the hierarchy, do we strike rock-bottom, made of hard 'atoms of behaviour'.

Thus 'verbal behaviour' is initiated by unverbalized intentions at the top of the language hierarchy, and terminates in deverbalized sensory-motor activities; at each level it is governed by rules which elude verbal definition, and modified by extraneous factors acting on the plastic matrices of language. Each time we slice behaviour 'vertically'—instead of horizontally on a single level—we arrive at a series which at the top recedes into an elusive blur and at its base vanishes in the twilight of awareness.

The above description may have seemed unnecessarily verbose, since the hierarchic structure of language is so obvious that it need not be stressed. After all, nearly half a century has passed since Watson proclaimed that speech consists in the manipulation of words, and thinking in the sub-vocal manipulation of words. However, if the reader thinks that the cruder forms of Paleo-Behaviourism are a matter of the past, he should turn to the first Note* at the end of this chapter (which will also provide some light relief). It is an excerpt from a textbook for College students, published in 1961, which starts with the sentence: 'For many of you, this is your first encounter with psychology as a science.' One wonders what this first encounter will do to the mind of the trusting student who is here quite literally led to believe that human discourse consists in the chaining of S.-R. units which are best studied by bar-pressing experiments 'under the more ideal conditions in the laboratory'.

The Dawn of Symbol Consciousness

The previous section referred to speech as a performance. *Learning* to speak proceeds more or less in the opposite direction—from the bottom to the top of the hierarchy. But only 'more or less', because bit-learning plays here a much lesser part than in the acquisition of mechanical skills like typing. Let us take a closer look at a few characteristic aspects of the process.

The first vocal ventures of the child confirm the now-familiar principle (cf. Chapter II) that spontaneous motor activity precedes sensory control. The child, too, 'acts on the environment before it reacts to it'—as parents must learn in sleepless nights; cooing and babbling are spontaneous expressions of *joie de vivre*, in which a surplus of energy is discharged, as in the waving of arms and wriggling of toes.

At the early stages these spontaneous babbling sounds are the same whether they are produced by an American white or a Negro baby (i.e. the frequency spectra of the phonemes are practically identical).[3] At five to six months, however, when syllabic, speech-like sounds become increasingly frequent, the spectrum shifts noticeably towards the sound patterns produced by the adults in the child's environment; and at twenty-four months the resemblance is close. Thus the originally undistinguishable phonetic matrices of infants from different language-groups become differentiated by the imitative repetition of adult sound-patterns. Imitation is at first probably automatic, the auditory-vocal feedback apparatus being excited by the input as in the young singing bird; then shades into a more or less conscious response—from 'echolalia' to 'metalalia'.

The first correlations between a sound pattern and an object or person are probably 'stamped in' by the parents at an age when the child's nervous system is not yet mature for them. In Book One (pp. 220–3) I have mentioned two examples at opposite extremes: Watson conditioning an infant less than six months old—i.e. much too early—to say *da* each time it was given the bottle; and Helen Keller's sudden and dramatic discovery, at the age of seven—i.e. when she was over-ripe for it—that 'everything had a name and each name gave birth to a new thought'. In the average, normal child the dawn of symbol consciousness seems to be a gradual, cumulative process. From approximately the eighteenth month onward there is a sharp increase in the child's vocabulary (Book One, p. 221) and somewhere around that time it makes that 'most important discovery of its life', that verbal labels can be attached not only to particular things and events, but that everything under the sun has a name. The universe of words, and the universe of things, have become integrated and will remain inseparable. Henceforth, every word *must* mean something and everything *must* have a name.

With the emergence of language, we have attained a new level of the cognitive hierarchy, which represents a sharp break in the continuity of learning processes in animals and man. Homologue laws still operate: 'All things have names' may be regarded as yet another case of empirical induction which we have seen operating on all levels; and verbal symbolism may be regarded as an extension of sign situations. Dolphins can be taught to respond to verbal or visual commands; dogs and chimps can make their wishes be known to their masters; cats will learn that bolts and loops mean escape; bees can communicate their experiences by dancing. But such communication by signs extends only to a few particular situations; it is generalized to some extent in the laboratory situation, when it seems to dawn on the cat that 'all these contraptions are means of escape', as it dawns on the child that 'all these words are means of getting one's way'. But at this point the cat has reached the limit of its abstractive capabilities, whereas the child has only got to its first inkling of what words can do for you.*

Their first, obvious advantages to the child are that they can be utilized both as *labels*, and as *levers* which make things happen, that they serve both the progressive socialization and internalization of behaviour—communication and inner discourse. This is well-covered ground which needs no further labouring. But another phenomenon of early language behaviour is rarely emphasized: the appearance of the naming question or 'naming mania'. The child points at anything it sees, asks 'This—?' or 'What that?', and is visibly satisfied to learn the answer, without any utilitarian reward. Alternatively, it points at things, calls out their name or, if it has forgotten it, invents a new one. Here is a true paradigm of latent learning, of the exploratory drive, or of *l'art pour l'art* behaviour—whatever one wants to call it. To quote Piaget: 'It is . . . no exaggeration to say that sensory-motor intelligence is limited to desiring success or practical adaptation, whereas the function of verbal or conceptual thought is to know and state truth.'[4]

But there is another aspect to the 'name-expectation': henceforth the child's concept of a thing or event will be experienced by it as *incomplete* if there is no verbal label attached to it. The concept will behave like a molecule with a free valency, as it were. We can perhaps recapture an echo of this when we hunt for the forgotten name of a person. Also, when we learn a new language, we suddenly have a whole class of free valencies: we feel actually frustrated when we discover that the French have no word for 'snobbery' or 'understatement', and are tempted to exclaim like a child: 'But surely they *must* have a name for it?'

The behaviour of the rat exploring a maze or of the monkey fearfully peeping into the box with the snake, could be described as interrogatory, and the same description could be applied to the puzzled expressions and actions of a small child before it has learned to speak. But its first *explicit*, verbal questions refer to the *names* of things, prompted by the need to 'saturate' the free valencies in its pre-verbal object-concepts. Is it too speculative to assume that this origin of the questioning habit must influence the whole later development of thought? The fact that each naming question can be readily answered by adults, may implant the implicit belief into the child that *all* questions are both meaningful and answerable; that the nature of explanation is based on the same kind of simple and direct connections as that between 'thing' and 'name'. This implicit belief seems to have been one of the factors responsible for the aberrations of human thought.

I have talked of (pre-verbal) 'concepts' to which the verbal label becomes *attached*. *The Concise Oxford Dictionary* defines a concept as an 'idea of a class of objects; general notion'; Webster as 'a mental image of a thing formed by generalization from particulars'; Hilgard: 'When a symbol stands for a class of objects or events with common properties, we say that it refers to a *concept*';[5] Piaget[6] regards the development of 'object concepts' as one of the principal achievements of the 'sensory-motor intelligence' which precedes the rise of verbal intelligence in the child's first two years. He distinguishes six stages in the attainment of stable object-concepts, which he defines as 'a system of perceptual images endowed with a constant spatial form throughout its sequential displacements and constituting an item which can be isolated in the causal series unfolding in time.'[7] It is interesting to compare Piaget's rather abstract formulations with the lucid 'incisiveness' of Wilder Penfield—a neuro-surgeon. He too starts by securing his flanks with quotes from Webster and Oxford; then he goes on:

'The concept may be a butterfly. It may be a person he has known. It may be an animal, a city, a type of action, or a quality. Each concept calls for a name. These names are wanted for what may be a noun or a verb, an adjective or an adverb. Concepts of this type have been formed gradually over the years from childhood on. Each time a thing is seen or heard or experienced, the individual has a *perception* of it. A part of that perception comes from his own concommittant interpretation. Each successive perception forms and probably alters the permanent concept. And words are acquired gradually, also, and deposited somehow in the treasure-house of word memory—the cortico-thalamic speech mechanisms. Words are often acquired simultaneously with the concepts. . . . A little boy may first see a butterfly fluttering from flower to flower in a meadow. Later he sees them on the wing or in pictures, many times. On each occasion he adds to his conception of butterfly.

'It becomes a generalization from many particulars. He builds up a concept of a butterfly which he can remember and summon at will, although when he comes to manhood, perhaps, he can recollect none of the particular butterflies of past experience.

'The same is true of the sequence of sound that makes up a melody. He remembers it after he has forgotten each of the many times he heard or perhaps sang or played it. The same is true of colours. He acquires, quite quickly, the concept of lavender, although all the objects of which he saw the colour have faded beyond the frontier of voluntary recall. The same is true of the generalization he forms of an acquaintance. Later on he can summon his concept of the individual without recalling their many meetings.'[8]

Thus the pre-verbal concepts of the child are formed by a series of operations continuous with those described in previous chapters: the de-particularization, filtering, and coding of percepts according to those of their common features which are relevant to a given conceptual hierarchy; the formation of colour- shape- and object-constancies; the development of sensory-motor skills such as the grasping of objects, bringing them close to the eye, visual and tactile exploration, etc.; lastly, according to Piaget's schema, the 'objectification' of space and time, the gradual separation of the self from the non-self, and the beginnings of the transition from magical to more objectified kinds of implied causality. Most of these processes can be found, to a greater or lesser degree, in animal learning; but with the addition of a verbal label, the concept acquires a new dimension as it were, and the continuity of the series of learning processes in animal and man is broken. No extrapolation is possible from the behaviour of the rat to that of man.

This can be demonstrated even in maze-learning experiments with humans, where the advantages of verbalization are not at once obvious. In a famous experiment by Warden[9] forty subjects were seated in front of a table with a grooved maze on it. The maze was of the same type as in rat experiments, with various cul-de-sacs; the subject had to thread his way through it with a stylus in his hand, by purely tactile guidance, for the maze was hidden from his view by a screen. The number of trials required until the maze was completely learned varied, according to subject, between 16 and 195 (!). At the end of the experiment each subject had to report whether he had memorized the maze by the 'feel' of it, that is by motor-kinesthetic imagery; or by making a 'visual map'; or by a verbal formula—e.g. 'first left, third right, first right', etc.

The results were as follows: out of 60 subjects, 17 adopted the 'motor' method. These needed an average of 124 trials (ranging from 72 to 195 according to subject) to learn the maze. Eighteen adopted the 'visual' method; average trials: 68, ranging from 41 to 104. Twenty-five adopted the 'verbal' formula; average trials: 32, range: 16 to 62.

Thus, in round figures, the visualizers learned twice as fast, the verbalizers four times as fast as the motor learners.

This reminds one of Otto Koehler's experiments (mentioned on p. 535 f.), which showed that clever jackdaws have a 'pre-linguistic number sense' almost equal to man's and are 'able to abstract the concept of numerical identity from groups of up to seven objects'; which 'suggests that many animals may have a prelinguistic "counting" ability of about the same degree, but that man's superiority in dealing with numbers lies in his ability to use, as symbols for numbers, words and figures'.[10] The dependence of counting and calculating abilities on verbal processes is further illustrated by Penfield's studies on aphasia, about which later.

Even voluntary movements (as opposed to automatized skills) seem to be to some extent dependent on guidance by internal verbalization. Some of Head's patients with speech disorders due to brain lesions were unable to imitate correctly Head's gestures—such as touching an eye or an ear with the left or right hand—while they were sitting face to face with Head; but had no difficulty in doing so if standing in front of a mirror with Head standing behind them. In the mirror test, of course, the task is reduced to pure imitation, whereas sitting opposite the experimenter 'left' and 'right' are reversed and the patient cannot see himself:

'When the patient sitting opposite to me attempts to imitate movements of my right or left hand brought into contact with one or other eye or ear, internal verbalization occurs at a phase of the normal act. No word may be uttered, but the words "right" and "left", "eye "and "ear", are essential to correct imitation of this kind. For the same reason these patients may find considerable difficulty in carrying out the hand, eye, and ear tests when the command is pictorial (given by a drawing on a printed card) although they can execute them correctly when asked to do so by word of mouth (or even by printed command). Their difficulty is in evoking the words they require, and the verbal command supplies the necessary want.'[11]

Thus Head's patients, with their impaired command of words, were virtually reduced from the level of the verbalizers to that of the motor-learners in Warden's maze experiment. We must conclude that verbal symbolism enters even into the learning of complex motor skills—just as it provides the mortar for holding together complex visual pseudo-images (p. 531 ff.).

Owing to the immense benefits derived from verbalization, the verbal symbol, which at the dawn of symbol-consciousness was at first no more than a label attached to a pre-existing conceptual schema, soon becomes its focal member, its centre of gravity, as it were. As words are the most convenient and economical means not only of communication but also of internal discourse, they soon assume a central role in the child's mental life, whereas images and other forms of unverbalized thought are gradually pushed towards the periphery, the fringes of awareness, or sink slowly down below its surface.

This tendency of verbal thinking to dominate and monopolize consciousness has its blessings and its curses, though the latter are less obvious than the former. Some of the dangers of thought becoming enslaved to words have been discussed in Book One, VII. Woodworth's remark, 'often we have to get away from speech in order to think clearly'[12] was seen to apply to a wide range of creative activities— from mathematics and physics to philosophy, and there is no need to labour the point further. What needs stressing once more is that words are symbols for perceptual and cognitive events, but they are not the events. They are vehicles of thought, but the vehicle should not be confused with the passengers.

Let me recapitulate. (1) The child has formed a variety of pre-verbal concepts of persons, objects, and recurrent events to which later verbal symbols become attached as labels; without the previously existing person-concept, the symbol 'Mama' would have nothing to refer to; it would remain meaningless—an empty vehicle without passenger. (2) At a later stage, the word and the concept may be acquired simultaneously: 'Mummy, what does SEDUCTRESS mean?' 'A very bad woman who uses too much make-up.' (3) The *concept* 'seductress' will undergo drastic changes during adolescence and later years; the *word* SEDUCTRESS remains unchanged. It is a vehicle with a fixed, immutable structure; whereas the passengers are constantly changing, getting in and out of the bus. We may even distinguish between passengers of first and second class: trim denotations, furtive connotations, and stow-aways hidden under the seats. Dr. Watson's suggestion that the passengers themselves are subliminal omnibuses was not a helpful one. (4) The word SEDUCTRESS refers to different concepts in different people. (5) The word which is attached to a concept may become detached from it, leaving the concept more or less un-impaired. This last point needs elaboration.

One may of course forget the name of a person without forgetting the person, i.e. without losing one's concept of him or her. But does the same apply when the word refers to an abstract concept?

A certain class of Head's aphasic patients confused the names of numbers, but nevertheless carried out the correct numerical operations. The patient would call a card 'nine of hearts' when he meant 'seven of hearts', and yet play a correct game. On doing a multiplication he would say aloud 'seven nines are fifty-six' and yet write down '63' correctly. This shows that his number-concepts remained intact, although he attached the wrong verbal labels to them; he probably catalogued them by their visual labels (the written figures), but this did not impair the efficiency of his symbolic operations. The trouble of the jackdaw is not that it cannot attach *verbal* symbols to its number-concepts, but that it cannot symbolize them in any other way either. One has only to think of deaf-mutes to remind one that a symbolic language is not necessarily an auditory-vocal language.*

The clinical phenomena of aphasia are frequently open to more than one interpretation; but on the particular point under discussion this is not the case. After surveying the literature on the subject, Humphrey[13] concluded: 'the general argument from aphasia for the independence of thought and language seems, on reading the evidence, overwhelmingly strong'. ('Independence' manifested in pathological cases does not, of course, prevent interaction under normal conditions.)

More recently, Penfield and Roberts, reviewing the literature and their own case histories, came to the same conclusion: 'It is obvious that in many cases the aphasic patient is able to perceive accurately. He knows what an object is used for; he recognizes it. He must, there-fore, be able to draw upon his store of recorded experience. He is still able to record his new experience of things heard and seen, and to compare the new experience with the whole of his past similar ex-periences. Thus his capacity to perceive through other channels than the sound and form of words is preserved.'[14]

Particularly impressive is the evidence from temporary aphasia in-duced by electrical stimulation of the cortical speech areas of the con-scious and consenting patient. Penfield's usual method was to show the patient an object printed on a card and ask him to name it, while the low-voltage electrode was applied to various points of the cortex: 'The patient may remain silent, or he may use words to explain that he cannot name the object, or he may misname it. He may show perseveration.'[15]

A typical case is the following (italics in the original):

When the electrode was applied to the supramarginal gyrus at point 27, he said: 'I know what it is', and was silent. When the electrode was withdrawn, he said at once, 'tree', which was correct.

When the electrode was applied to the posterior temporal region at 28, he was completely silent. A little time after the electrode was withdrawn, he exclaimed suddenly: 'Now I can talk—butterfly [which was correct]. I couldn't get that word "butterfly" and then I tried to get the word "moth". . . .' The speech mechanism was separately paralysed, and yet the man could understand what he saw and could substitute the concept, moth, for the concept butterfly, in a reasoned attempt to regain control of the speech mechanism, by presenting to it a new idea, moth. He could also snap his fingers (as he did) in exasperation at his failure.

The words of C. H. [the patient] bring us face to face with other brain mechanisms. The concept of a moth, as distinguished from a butterfly, must also depend on a brain mechanism—a mechanism capable of functioning when the speech mechanism is selectively paralysed—a mechanism that stores something derived from the past. . . .[16]

Dropping the terminology of physiology for the moment, I may say that the patient presented the concept of a 'butterfly' to his speech mechanism, expecting that the word for it would be forthcoming. When the mechanism failed him, he cast about and selected an analogous concept from his storehouse of concepts and presented that to the speech mechanism. But again he was disappointed, and he snapped his fingers in exasperation. He could still express himself emotionally with his fingers in that way, although he would probably not have been able to write the lost words.*

Penfield concludes that there exists a 'conceptual mechanism' in the brain, and a 'speech mechanism' which is structurally separate, and functionally separable from the former.

We have seen that a considerable portion of mental activities is of a non-verbal character—in the nature of experiences which 'cannot be put into words', which remain incommunicable and inarticulate, and nevertheless play an important, sometimes even a dominant, part in a person's life. We now see that even in articulate verbal thinking, a distinction must be drawn between the ideational process and its conversion into verbal currency. I have quoted some of the clinical evidence; there is also a vast body of experimental evidence reviewed, e.g. by Humphrey (1951).[17] Among the most convincing results are those which emerged from factor analysis (Burt, 1949).*

Everyday experience points in the same direction. In states of fatigue one may read every word of a printed paragraph without understanding 'a single word of it'. And vice versa: every experienced lecturer knows that one's thoughts may race ahead, or go astray, while one goes on talking—as if talking were an automatized and autonomous skill like the typist's who 'copies behind'. More precisely, the lecturer converts into verbal currency cognitive sub-wholes on lower levels of the hierarchy, which have already been portioned out or 'pre-chewed' by the ideational process proceeding on the higher level.

We may safely conclude, then, with Humphrey: '*Clinical, experimental, and factorial results agree that language cannot be equated with thinking.* Language is ordinarily of great assistance in thinking. It may also be a hindrance.'

NOTES

To p. 594. Excerpt from the textbook *Psychology*, ed. A. D. Calvin (Boston, 1961), Section Four: 'Learning, Retention and Motivation' by F. J. McGuigan:

The experimental data that we have presented . . . have been limited to rather simple responses such as salivation and bar-pressing. In our everyday life we seldom spend much time in thinking about such isolated responses, usually thinking of more gross activities, such as learning a poem, carrying on a conversation, solving a mechanical puzzle, learning our way around a new city, to name only a few. While the psychologist could study these more complicated activities, as is done to some extent, the general approach of psychology is to bring simpler responses into the laboratory for study. Once the psychologist discovers the principles of learning for simpler phenomena under the more ideal conditions of the laboratory [sic], it is likely that he can apply these principles to the more complex activities as they occur in everyday life. The more complex phenomena are, after all, nothing but a series of simpler responses. Speaking to a friend is a good example of this. Suppose we have a conversation such as the following:

He: 'What time is it?'
She: 'Twelve o'clock.'
He: 'Thank you.'
She: 'Don't mention it.'
He: 'How about lunch?'
She: 'Fine.'

Now this conversation can be analysed into separate S.-R. units. 'He' makes the *first response*, which is emitted probably to the stimulus of the sight of 'She'.

When 'He' emits the operant, 'What time is it?', the muscular activity, of course, produces a sound, which also serves as a stimulus for 'She'. On the receipt of this stimulus, she emits an operant herself: 'Twelve o'clock', which in turn produces a stimulus to 'He'. And so on. . . .

In such a complex activity, then, we can see that what we really have is a series of S.-R. connections. The phenomenon of connecting a series of such S.-R. units is known as *chaining*, a process that should be apparent in any complex activity. We might note that there are a number of sources of reinforcement throughout the chaining process, in this example the most obvious being the reinforcement of 'She' by receiving an invitation for lunch and of 'He' by having the invitation accepted. In addition, as Keller and Schoenfeld point out, there are such sources of reinforcement as the hearer 'encouraging' the speaker to continue, the use that the conversationalists make of the information received (he finds out what time it is), etc.

This example of the analysis of a complex activity is but one of numerous possibilities that we could discuss. You should continue to think of others yourself and try to diagram the chaining process for them . . . (p. 375).

To p. 595. It is interesting to note that Hebb, an enlightened behaviourist yet a behaviourist, considers as the chief advantages of language that words can be used in varying combinations: 'In man . . . we also have a kind of behaviour, which, as far as we know, does not occur in any other species. This is language. It includes sign language as well as spoken and written words; and the chief problem does not concern the ability to make the sounds of human speech, since lower animals are not capable of sign language either. What puts language on a higher level than the purposive communication of dog or chimpanzee is the *varied combination* of the same signs (words, pictures, gestures) for different purposes. . . . The criteria of language are then: (1) that it is usually purposive communication (though a number of non- purposive uses is common also, as in talking to oneself), and (2) that two or more items of the behaviour are combined in one way for one purpose and recombined for other purposes' (Hebb, 1958, p. 209; his italics). Is that all? Or may we at least add, with Hilgard, that 'without language it would be well-nigh impossible to think of such abstract notions as justice or reciprocal tariffs' (Hilgard, 1957, p. 315).

To p. 601. In Head's gesture-imitation experiments, on the other hand, some kind of implicit verbal symbolization seems to be indispensable, because reliance on visual or kinesthetic clues leads only to the familiar mirror-confusion—as any normal person will discover by repeating the experiment.

To p. 602. One might further speculate that the patient's inability to name the object shown on the printed card, while he is perfectly capable of using words to explain that he cannot name it, may be due to the fact that single object-names like tree, moth, etc., have a more arbitrary character *qua* phonetic labels learnt by rote, and have more 'brittle' traces, than verbs and propositions which form syntactic sub-wholes. A 'tree', after all, is originally a nonsense syllable. One of Penfield's patients, shown a card picturing a foot, said, 'Oh, I know what it is. That is what you put in your shoes'. After withdrawal of the electrode, he said correctly 'foot'. Now why should 'foot' be more difficult to name than 'shoe'? Perhaps because the word 'shoe' occurred in a meaningful context—Burt's Factor II of Verbal Ability—whereas 'foot' occurred in a naming context (Factor I) which was blocked (see next note). In other words, the *naming*-code was out of action, while the semantic code continued to function.

To p. 603. Burt divided Verbal Ability into a *word factor* dealing with words in isolation and a *language factor* dealing with words in their context. The former he sub-divided into a *receptive* factor of recognizing and understanding words and into an *executive* factor for finding and selecting the right word. The language factor is similarly sub-divided into a receptive factor for understanding statements and an executive factor for literary expression and verbal fluency. Burt's divisions followed in broad outline Head's classifications of aphasia and substantiated the validity of the letter, (*The British Journal of Educational Psychology*, Vol. XIX, June and November, 1949).

XV

LEARNING TO THINK

Let me return to the early development of verbal matrices.

From about the eighteenth month onward, the child acquires new words at a faster rate; about the same time it begins to correlate single words into word-sequences, and later on into sentences. The earliest word-sequences are again produced by spontaneous, undirected vocal activity, in which meaningful words alternate with strings of nonsense syllables and with words imitated but not yet understood. Some children have the uncanny gift of imitating the phonetic patterns of adult speech so well that from the next room their babbling sounds like a meaningful monologue. If we are to believe Bertrand Russell, his daughter at the age of eighteen months, 'when supposed to be sleeping, was overheard saying to herself: "Last year I used to dive off the diving-board, I *did*." Of course, "last year" was merely a phrase repeated without understanding. . . .'[1] This philosophical comment seems to imply, oddly enough, that the remainder of the sentence was pronounced with understanding.

Frequently the first meaningful string of words refers to a sequence of events. Fenton's unusually precocious son, also at the age of eighteen months, 'uttered soon after seeing his father climb into an automobile with another man and drive away, the words, "Daddy, school, man, auto".'[2] This sounds exactly like the 'picture-strip language' of the primitive (as Kretschmer called it[3])—the unrolling of a visual sequence, where each single word symbolizes a complete event. 'The speech units of the child belong to no single class of words because they are (i.e. stand for) not single words but sentences.'[4] Even the first verbal labels have a not merely denotative, but an operative character; they do not refer to objects *in vacuo*, but to 'action-objects',[5] that is to say, to the functional relevance of the object to the child. 'Chamberlain, Tracy, Dewey, Binet and others have shown that the child's symbols are action-words, i.e., their content is action. There is also practically universal agreement on the fact that the first symbols of the child are in reality word-sentences designating action and object or subject, or all three at once.'[6]

This, of course, is again a far cry from any S.-R. theory of language learning. The command RIGHT TURN is a simple and definite verbal stimulus, which, one would think, should be easy to associate with a definite motor response; but many children and some normal adults have considerable difficulty in distinguishing between right and left. This fact is used by Hebb as an elegant proof that the *concept* (of right-left-sidedness) precedes the *word* for it: 'The child can very readily learn at the age of three that "right" and "left" each refers to a side of the body—but ah me, which one? . . . What is set up first is a conceptual organization. By the age of six the word "right" clearly and immediately means sidedness to the child. A considerable conceptual elaboration has already occurred, and the stimulus effectively arouses that structure; but it arouses no prompt, specific response. . . . With such facts, it becomes nonsense to explain man's conceptual development as exclusively consisting of verbal associations.'[7]

The point becomes clearer when we realize that between the ages of two and four many children are equally confused about 'up-down', 'back-front', etc.; but they only confuse opposites with *each other*, never 'left' with 'up' or 'front' with 'down'.[8] This shows that the child forms at an early stage sensory-motor matrices of 'up-downness', 'left-rightness', etc.; and that the verbal labels acquired later on may become attached to the matrix as a whole, before directions within the matrix are verbally discriminated. This does not mean, of course, that abstraction preceded discrimination, since both are aspects of the same process; it only means that there is often delay and confusion in the verbal labelling of pre-verbal concepts.

This brings us to the central problems of the evolution of symbolic thought: abstraction and concept-formation.

Abstraction, Discrimination, and Transfer

In common usage 'abstract' thought is regarded as a specifically human faculty, and more particularly as a prerogative of the scientific mind. The *Concise Oxford* defines abstraction as 'the process of stripping an idea of its concrete accompaniments'. There are, however, obvious analogies between the abstraction of ideas—the formation of concepts—and perceptual generalization—the extraction of invariant features, stripped of their accidental accompaniments, from varied situations. It is therefore frequently asserted or implied that abstract thought is merely the extension, along a continuous scale, of selective processes which operate already in the rat and even lower down. I shall first briefly recapitulate those aspects of the abstractive process which are indeed continuous with animal learning—until we arrive at the point where the line again breaks. I shall again use the term 'generalization' in the sense indicated above—and not in the sense of 'spreading of responses' (see p. 537 ff.).

The continuum of abstractive processes can be extended down into the inorganic domain. The green-grocer's balance abstracts from a pound of peaches and a pound of potatoes the one feature which it has been programmed to recognize as relevant, their weight. A barometer, programmed to compensate for variations of temperature, can be regarded as a model for perceptual size-constancy—the apparatus programmed to compensate for distance. The same barometer used as an altimeter may serve to illustrate the reversible figure-ground relation. Each of these programmes is represented by a code which determines which type of stimulus should be regarded as relevant and abstracted from experience, and which not.

Built-in perceptual analysers for the recognition of species-specific sign-releasers may be described as the result of the phylogenetic abstraction of biologically relevant stimulus-patterns. We may regard this abstractive power, with Lashley, as 'one of the primitive basic functions of organized nervous tissue'.[9]

Turning to acquired behaviour, we must distinguish between learning under natural and artificial conditions. In both cases the animal must learn to abstract relevant patterns from its environment as a *conditio sine qua non* of properly reacting to them. With animals in their natural habitat this happens either during maturation, or, in adult animals, after a few repetitions of a certain kind of experience. Since the animal attends only to stimuli which are biologically relevant to it —to which its perceptual organization is 'attuned'—the learning process consists essentially in the sharpening and modification of its built-in perceptual analysers. In the laboratory situation, however, the animal must in the first place readjust to an artificial universe, in which stimuli which it would normally treat as irrelevant, become all-important. When this revaluation is well under way, the cat in the box will begin to abstract from its bewildering environment the significant patterns of loops and bolts in general, regardless of variations in their position and shape. But this will be a slow, repetitive process because abstraction is a function of relevance, and relevance in this case must be inferred by induction; the cat is caught in a vicious circle. Even so, its powers of abstraction are considerable—see the perfunctory lick reduced to a symbolic performance (p. 570). The rat in the maze is in a more favourable position: it likes exploring highways and byways; and the cognitive map which it abstracts from a number of concrete tries provides it with a matrix of remarkable plasticity—see Lashley's extirpation experiments, pp. 458 f.

The child's pre-verbal concepts are derived from abstractive processes which form a continuous series with animal learning—from the early development of its perceptual constancies and its 'sensory-motor intelligence' to the crystallization of 'object concepts'. The child learns to recognize its mother before it learns the word 'ma'. Unlike the gosling whose nervous system is ready, a few hours after its birth, to receive the imprint of the mother-goose all in one piece, the helpless infant must slowly, and perhaps painfully, abstract the concept of its mother as a stable, unvarying entity from a series of her very varied appearances, all different in shape, and disconnected in time. The breast first, more tactile than visual, monopolizing the whole perceptual field; a fully-clad figure with concealed breasts, standing or bending over; a series of faces appearing at intervals, never looking quite the same—such must have been the fragmentary, concrete experiences out of which the unitary mother concept was extracted in the first three weeks of our existence—if only we could remember.

However, owing to the nursing mother's exceptional importance to, and sustained bodily contact with, the child the formation of the mother-concept must also be regarded as an exceptional process in which several successive stages are telescoped into one. Other object and action concepts emerge more slowly and hesitantly, even if the object is a person. The adult's awareness of other people's personal identity is based on empathy—which is a projective phenomenon, in some respects comparable to the stroboscopic effect. But in the babe the experience of its own identity is still hazy, and so is its awareness of the personal identity of others. When a feature F, which is important to the child, is common to several individuals whose other attributes are less important to it, then the child will abstract, conceptualize, and name that shared feature in preference to the collection of features which constitutes each individual's personal identity. This can happen even if one of the persons concerned is the father—at the stage before the father becomes functionally important to the baby. A baby is often taught the word 'da-da' before it has learned to recognize its father—except for some vague features such as largeness or bulkiness, which are equally found in other appearances. As a result, it applies the label 'da-da' 'widely and often embarrassingly to large individuals of all shapes, sizes, ages, and colours'.[10] Abstraction and discrimination are guided by relevance; and the relevant experience in this case is some feature of dada-ness shared by lots of visitors who —their colour, age, etc., being as yet irrelevant—are not discriminated as individuals. It is the same with the gosling, which in the first stage of imprinting follows all human shapes, and only later on confines its attention to the keeper. During the first stage individual differences in appearance are seen, but not 'taken in' and retained, because they are not yet relevant to the gosling; during the second stage the distinguishing marks become relevant because the gosling has learned that keepers produce food, while other humans do not. Thus the sharpenings and modifications of discriminatory codes are the result of changes in the scales of relevance. In the first stage of development, all 'dada-ish' visitors to the baby—and all human beings to the gosling—are regarded as 'for all intents and purposes the same thing'; in the second stage they no longer are, because the intents and purposes have changed.

I have laboured this point at the risk of repetitiveness because once accepted, it allows us to dispense with terms like transfer, spreading, 'generalization' (in sense b, cf. p. 537), and 'association by similarity'— and to close the lid of the semantic Pandora box. Take, for instance, Watson's famous experiment intended to establish a 'conditioned fear reflex' in an infant eleven months of age, by striking an iron bar with a hammer each time the child touched its pet animal, a white rat. After this was repeated several times within the span of a week, little Albert responded with fear, crying, etc., whenever the rat was shown to him. But he also showed fright-reactions in varying degrees to rabbits, fur coats, cotton wool, and human hair—none of which had frightened him before. Watson concluded, and a number of textbooks with him, that the conditioned reflex had 'spread' or been 'transferred' to all furry things—words which have the connotation of motion in space, conveying the image that the child had somehow lifted its fear-reaction from the rat and put it down on the piece of cotton wool. In fact the idea of the 'spreading' of the conditioned response was originally derived from Pavlov's notion of the irradiation of excitatory processes spreading across the cortical tissues. This physiological theory of Pavlov's has long been abandoned,[11] but its unconscious echoes still haunt the laboratories. On a metaphorical level there is of course no objection to saying that the child's dread had spread from rats to cotton wool, but on the technical level the concept of 'spreading' has no explanatory value, and has been the source of endless confusion. (The same applies to 'transfer', and to 'generalization' used as a synonym for spreading.) Instead of pretending that the child has shifted its response, along a so-called generalization gradient, from rat to cotton wool, we should say that it has *abstracted* the tactile quality of furriness, and *recognized* it in the cotton wool. And its reaction to it was perfectly logical, because Watson had taught it that furriness always signalled the dreaded bang. It would of course be nonsensical to pretend that this child of eleven months was incapable of seeing the difference between rabbit, cotton wool, and human hair. But at that time the tactile quality alone was relevant, and with regard to that, rabbit, rat, and fur coat were all 'the same thing' (cf. pp. 537 ff.).

We can observe the operation of the same principles on the *verbal* level at a more advanced age. Stern's daughter, Hilda,[12] at the age of nineteen months, had been in the habit of pulling at her parents' noses; when she discovered that the tips of their shoes (before having learned the name 'shoe') offered the same satisfactory opportunities, she promptly named them 'noses'. Again, instead of speaking of 'transfer', etc., we shall say that the child recognized an abstracted quality that could be found in various objects. Koffka mentions a boy of twenty-six months 'to whom "la-la" first meant song or music; later when he heard a military band, it meant soldier, and finally all kinds of noises, including sounds like claps and thuds. . . . Another little boy uttered the word "atta" at the end of his eleventh month whenever anything disappeared—when a person left the room or when a light was turned out.'[13]

The first object- and relation-concepts to be abstracted and named are those which have the greatest functional relevance to the child. At that stage no verbal distinctions are made between objects and attributes, between qualities and things in which these qualities are vested, between nouns, adjectives, and verbs. Lala refers to music; it functions as a collective name for bells, soldiers, instruments; and if we feel that Lala is a silly name for a soldier, but regard 'redcoat' or 'poilu' as reasonable, then only because wearing a red coat or being unshaven appear to us more relevant martial qualities than making music. When the child learns to use words, the functionally most important aspect of an as yet unnamed object or event will provide its name; the less important aspects of secondary qualities are then relegated to the role of 'going together with it'—its 'attributes' or 'parts' or 'functions'. But the criteria of relevance change with age; when Stern's little girl learned to walk, shoes acquired a more important function than that which they shared with noses; and with it a new name.

Of course the visual experience of Watson's baby is different when it touches a rat and when it touches a fur coat; but it is the touch that matters, the visual aspect is irrelevant, and accordingly, in its overt reactions, the baby does not discriminate between the two. Similarly, the baby mentioned by Koffka saw the difference between the shapes of its Teddy bear and of its stuffed rabbit; but this difference is irrelevant at the early age when all that matters is manipulating a soft toy; hence the name 'dolly' was sufficient to symbolize the whole class, and no motivational need arose for explicit verbal discrimination. Adults behave much the same way. The Eskimoes have several words for various kinds of snow where we have only one; but Malinovski's savages had only one word, *manna wala*, for all insects and birds— except those that could be eaten. Building workers, who shift from job to job, cannot be bothered to learn one another's names; all electricians are 'Sparks' and all carpenters 'Chippies'. Elderly ladies addicted to romantic novels from the lending library feel that the names of authors are irrelevant; all that matters is that it should be a 'nice book'.

Thus all along the line we abstract and discriminate only qualities which are relevant to us; and new discriminations arise as a result of changes in our criteria of relevance—where 'us' refers to animal and man. In the normal development of the individual these changes are due to maturation and guided learning. In the experimental laboratory, as in reformatory schools and other brainwashing establishments, rewards and punishments effect the transformation of the subject's, or victim's, scale of values. In classical conditioning all tuning forks are 'the same thing' to the dog until the difference in pitch is made significant by the giving or withholding of food. In guided learning, all pages in his algebra book look the same to the schoolboy until he learns to distinguish linear from quadratic equations at a glance.

Distinctions which are irrelevant to the subject will either go entirely *unnoticed*; or they may be *perceived but not retained*; or they may be retained but not *verbally* discriminated. Thus if we fail to observe differences, it is either because we lack the equipment for doing so ('lack of discrimination' in the colloquial sense), or because the differences are 'indifferent' to us, or not important enough to give them verbal labels (e.g. knowing stars by sight but not by name).

I have dwelt at some length on the subject of abstraction and discrimination because although most of what I have said would seem self-evident to the layman, this would not be the case with students of experimental psychology—or of philosophy, if it comes to that. Already in the twelfth century A.D. John of Salisbury remarked that the world had grown old discussing the problem, and that it had spent more time on it than the Caesars took to conquer the world. But Pavlov, Watson, and those directly or indirectly influenced by them have certainly made confusion worse confounded.*

From the genetic point of view, abstraction and discrimination appear (cf. pp. 608 f.) as the latest extensions of the basic principles which we saw at work on all levels of the hierarchy, starting with the integration of functions and differentiation of structures in morphogenesis. Abstraction, by creating pattern and order out of the chaotic stream of experience, corresponds to the former; discrimination in perception and the consequent differentiation of response correspond, as language indicates, to the latter. If we wish to indulge in analogies, we might say that the categories of Aristotle acted as embryonic inductors on the self-differentiating morphogenetic fields of conceptual thought.

The Magic of Names

We have so far distinguished several stages in the child's progress: (a) the abstraction of pre-verbal object concepts (and action concepts); (b) attaching a verbal symbol, which soon acquires central importance, to the concept; (c) the discovery, signalled by the appearance of the naming question, that *all* things have names, that the words previously learned are only particular instances of a general relation between words and things. The next step consists in the concretization of this relation itself in the concept 'name'. The child has realized that not only have all things verbal handles and labels attached to them, but that these labels and handles are called *names*.

A characteristic feature of this development is that at each step a *relation* has been abstracted and turned into a *relatum*. At the first step the relation between the varied particular appearances of the mother was turned into a single relatum 'mama', which now enters as a unit into other relations; at the last step the relation between words and things was abstracted and turned into the conceptual entity 'name'. '*Name*' is the verbal symbol attached to the relation of verbal symbolism; by being made explicit and conscious the relation is now experienced as a concrete relatum.

In fact, an over-concrete relatum. To quote Piaget: 'Names are, to begin with, situated in objects. They form part of things in the same way as do colour and form. Things have always had their names. It has always been sufficient to look at things to know their names. . . . To deform the name is to deform the thing.'[14] When a child of four and a half was asked how one knows that the sun's name is 'sun', it answered: 'Just because one sees it'. And when a child of nine was asked whether one could have given another name to the sun, he answered: 'No—because the sun is just the sun'. Another child of six and a half, when pressed, admitted that God could have given the sun another name, but in this case 'God would have done something wrong'.[16]

When Herschel discovered Uranus, the German naturalist Sachs remarked sceptically: 'What guarantee have we that the planet found by him really *is* Uranus?' Equally inspired was this philosophic reflection of an Englishman: 'English is the most logical language; a knife, for instance, is called by the French *couteau*, by the Germans *Messer*, and so on, whereas the English call it "a knife" which is after all what a knife really is.'

In the mentality of primitives, the person and his name are magically related. In Eastern religions, evocation of the names of deities—the recital of mantras—fulfils a magic function; in Tibetan Buddhism the work is left to the prayer mill. This attitude lingers on in medieval philosophy (Realists versus Nominalists); in all forms of magic, and, more covertly in modern science—in the unconscious belief that words like gravity, entelechy, or electro-magnetic 'field', etc., somehow have an explanatory value *an sich* (cf. Book One, VII). Such is the power of verbal symbols to focus attention that it confers on hazy concepts in *statu nascendi* the appearance of hard, tangible concreteness, and 'gives to airy nothing / a local habitation and a name'. The name is then experienced as a self-evident explanation, a saturation of free valencies as it were.

During its first years the child does not discriminate between nominal, attributive, and causal predications—as earlier it did not differentiate words according to grammatical categories.

When children between five and six are asked: 'Why does the sun not fall down?', they will answer: 'Because it is hot', 'Because the sun stops there', 'Because it is yellow'.[15] And the moon does not fall down 'Because it is very high up', 'Because the sun is not there', etc. The significant aspects of an experience are connected as 'going together' in an undifferentiated 'feeling of relation'.[16] Goethe's 'Connect, always connect' seems to be the motto of the child as, out of the fluid raw material of its experiences, it selects and shapes patterns and relations —relations which will be re-classed and re-grouped later on according to shifts in motivation and interest leading to the emergence of new criteria of relevance—until the final, more rigid but not always more perfect adult relation-categories emerge. The urge to connect, to aggregate matrices of experience into more comprehensive ones; the fumbling for hypotheses about the way things are held together, the tentative formulation of rules of the game—in all these fertile activities we see the participatory tendencies at work: intimations of the fundamental unity of all things. Later on they will crystallize in magic causality, with its correlates: animism and 'mystic participation' (to use an expression coined by Lévy-Bruhl for the mentality of primitives, and applied by Piaget to the mentality of the child). Needless to say, the self-asserting tendencies too play their obvious part both in the child's overt behaviour and its fantasy world.

It seems that the first relational patterns which are discriminated are relatively static forms of *attribution* (of names and other properties), and of dynamic *changes-in-time*. The latter give rise to a vague 'feeling of causal relations'[20] derived from the cumulative experience that 'things make other things do things'. At this stage, word-classes begin to emerge which roughly correspond to substantive-nouns, adjective-attributes, and action-words or verbs. But these classes, and the types of relations implied in them, remain for a long time fluid. The child's progress towards grammatically more correct forms of speech is mainly due to imitation and conventional training—which mask the fact that behind the increasingly adult forms of expression, magic ways of thought survive. They survive, of course, even in the adult, and never vanish completely. Thus the stabilization of the codes of grammar and syntax in no way corresponds to the dynamic evolution of thought, and inferences drawn from the former to the latter have for a long time misled child psychologists.[21]

With the momentous realization that 'one thing leads to another', intimations of causality emerge from the fluid pool of perceived 'togetherness' and 'relatedness'. The *homo novus* has now set out on a long and tortuous road, which has in fact no end, except where, of his own choice, he will come to rest—theological causality, mechanical causality, statistical probability—gods playing billiards or throwing dice. But children are philosophical optimists, and the same process of empirical induction which earlier on led to the discovery that all things have names, now leads to the discovery that all things have 'becauses'. The sequel is a familiar one: the naming question is replaced by the 'why' question which is many a parent's despair; just as a thing was incomplete without a name, so now an event has a free valency which must be filled by a 'because'. The actual content of the proffered explanation, the when, and how, and how much, is as yet of secondary importance; 'the sun does not fall down because it is yellow' is accepted as quite as satisfactory an answer as 'the dolly is called dolly because that's her name'. Just as, at the earlier stage, when a name was not immediately offered, it was invented to fill the vacancy, so now, when no 'because' is proffered at once, an explanation is provided *ad hoc* by the child itself. And just as the invention of names is guided by onomatopoeia or private associations, so the causal explanations of children are derived from their private matrices of thought.

The questioning mania is reinforced by the desire to attract attention and to be in the centre of events; it is a typical mixture of participatory and self-assertive motivations. Lorimer made a record of all the why's asked by a child of four years, eleven months, in the course of four days,[17] which is both charming and instructive. (One asterisk signifies that no answer was given; two asterisks: no answer given, question not repeated):

1. Why do you have this box for your feet?
2. Why did they bring the bed down from the attic?
3. *Take your dollies in now, Joyce!* Why?
4. *Fix the rug! You caught your feet under the edge of it!* Why? Why did I?
5. Why did you take two cookies?

6. Why does the watering-pot have two handles?

7. Why did he put the solder in so many places?

8. *The song-sparrow isn't pretty to look at*—Why isn't he pretty?

9. *The bobolink has a brown coat in winter.* Why?* Why?

10. *It was careless of you to lose your shovel.* Why?* Why?

11. *This is your orange juice.* Why?**

12. *You are to sit here, in Daddy's place.* Why?*—Please, Mother, tell me why.

13. Do we have bangs at the back of our heads? *No!* Why?* Why, Mother?

14. *And then he made a mast for his little boat.* Why? Please tell me why he made a mast.

15. Why do you wash the hair off (the razor)?

16. (Putting on bathrobe without putting her arms in the sleeves) Is this good? *No.* Why?*—(impatiently) Why? Speak out! (but then without waiting for an answer) Because it wouldn't stay on. *There, you thought it out for yourself, didn't you?*

17. Why did you stub your toe? *Because I wasn't watching out.* Why?

18. *I will tell you a story about this willow plate*—Why?**

19. *Please hurry, Joyce!* Why?*—Because you want me to wash?* Why didn't you wash first? Because you knew I wanted to go with Daddy?

20. See the little tea things! Why did we buy them? *Why do you think?* Because we might use the others all up.

21. Why did you use both a fork and a spoon in making that cake?

22. Why did you sit in that chair, Mother?

23. *Please don't climb in that chair!* Why?**

24. Why are you putting up that screen?**

25. Why are you opening that window?**

26. Why does the little chicken grow in the shell?

27. *You can't win by jumping up and down!* Why?

28. Jeremiah, Jeremiah. He got into a pit, didn't he? Why did they put him into a pit?

29. *Please be careful not to break the bean-plants.* Why?

30. I saw your blue apron through a crack in the door. I thought it was a spider. *A spider isn't blue, dear!* Why?*—Please, Mother, tell me why a spider isn't blue.

31. *You shouldn't talk about a visitor's beard, Joyce, until he has gone!* Why?* Please tell me why.

32. Why don't you have a beard, Mother?

33. I want to cut my eyebrows in half! *Oh! You wouldn't want to do that!* Why? Because I would look funny?

34. Why do we have eyebrows?

35. Why must I hurry?

36. Why should I wait for candy until after supper?

37. Why did you speak to that man?

38. *Please don't bang the car-door!* Why?*

39. Why did the chickens walk in front of the car?

40. *It is time to go home for dinner now!* Why?*

A certain number of these questions are obviously motivated by the desire to attract attention or intended as a protest; others are quasi-automatic exercises of the questioning habit—they remind one of *Leerlauf* activities *in vacuo*. But others, such as Nos. 2, 9, 26, 32, are expressions of genuine curiosity; Lorimer put thirteen out of forty questions into this category, judging them by content and the child's expression. It is curiosity of a new type, no longer directed at the practical or playful uses of things only, but at the mystery of their 'becauses'.

The word 'because' now plays a similar part to that which the word 'name' did before: an abstracted relation has become a relatum, concretized in a verbal symbol. The child's concept of 'becauseness', i.e. causality, will undergo a series of changes, but not the verbal symbol which refers to it. Later on, the causal relation will enter as a relatum into the higher matrix of 'logical categories'; and even later this class, in its turn, will become a member of the matrices of epistomology, psychology, and so on.

Explaining and Understanding

This leads us to the question of the nature of explanation.

Earlier on I quoted Craik's suggestion that the nervous system's main function is 'to model or parallel external events', and that 'this process of paralleling is the basic feature of thought and explanation'.[18] In terms of the present theory the 'model' consists of hierarchies of flexible matrices with fixed codes, abstracted by the organism accord-ing to its lights. Insight and understanding then become relative terms, the degree of understanding depending on how many different aspects of reality have been abstracted, how sharply they are discriminated, to what extent the abstract codes lend themselves to explicit formulations, and the degree of precision and error which the model reveals when subjected to the test of empirical verification.

We have seen that it is necessary to distinguish between *progress* in understanding—the acquisition of new insights, and the *exercise* of understanding at any given stage of development. *Progress* in understanding is achieved by the formulation of new codes through the modification and integration of existing codes by methods already discussed: empirical induction, abstraction and discrimination, bisociation. The *exercise* or application of understanding—the explanation of particular events—then becomes an act of subsuming the particular event under the codes formed by past experience. To say that we have understood a phenomenon means that we have recognized one or more of its relevant relational features as particular instances of more general or familiar relations, which have been previously abstracted and encoded.

The conventional test of understanding is verbal explanation—the subject is invited to name the general rule of which the event to be explained is a particular instance. But the availablility of such neat and ready explanations is the exception rather than the rule—unless the explanation was learned by rote—because, in the first place, the codes which govern perception and cognition function below the level of focal awareness; in the second place because a great number of codes which govern thinking are unverbalized—including the codes of verbal thinking, grammar, and syntax; thirdly because there are emergent, 'nascent' codes which are still unstable and cannot be 'pinned down', but are sometimes nevertheless of decisive help to understanding. We thus arrive at a whole series of gradations in understanding and explanation—such as:

(a) *Unconscious* understanding mediated by the dream—a form of internal discourse in which specific experiences are subsumed under very old, emotion-charged matrices with pre-verbal codes. The transformations and disguises which people and events undergo in the dream may be described as acts of recognition of different appearances as the 'same thing' on the scales of symbolic relevance peculiar to the dream. Myth, folklore, fairy-tale, the fantasy world and magic causality of the child are mainly inspired by this type of understanding; and the explanations offered by primitives and children for their beliefs are true explanations in the sense defined.

(b) *Tentative* explanations, which indicate that the matrix into which the event is to be incorporated is still in the process of construction by trial-and-error learning and hypothesis-formation.

(c) *Half-understood* explanations referring to matrices *in statu nascendi* which, unlike (b), are being formed mainly by unconscious guidance, by unverbalized analogies, etc.

(d) Explanation by explicit *analogy*—its validity depending on whether it is arrived at by selective or Procrustean methods.

(e) *Implicit* understanding, when the phenomenon is recognized as an instance of a relation which has been abstracted but cannot be made verbally explicit.

(f) The same as (e) plus a verbal label. The abstracted pattern can now be *named* but not otherwise verbally described, ('sweet', 'pungent', 'beautiful'—visceral, kinesthetic, aesthetic experiences).

(g) *Explicit verbal* explanations and definitions which sound precise and convincing, but where the codes to which they refer contain some hidden axiom, *idée reçue*, unwarranted assumption.

(h) *Over-explicit*, rigid definitions which explain away problems as meaningless by taking the verbal components of the symbolic model to pieces—forgetting that the 'exact' sciences have always operated with fuzzy concepts, that good cooks work in dirty kitchens, and that the sterilization of verbal concepts leads to sterility.

Other headings could be interpolated into this list. Compared with the relatively few levels of understanding in the rat and even the chimpanzee, man's explanatory hierarchies represent a veritable tower of Babel; not merely because they reach higher, but because there are more finely graded levels between the unconscious processes at the base, and the abstract symbolism at the top.

Thus instead of talking of insight and understanding as all-or-nothing processes, and making verbal explanation a test for passing school exams, we should proceed by more cautious statements, such as: Johnnie has now understood that a phenomenon P is a particular instance of a general relation R which he can name; he has also understood that R is a particular instance of S, which he can also name. He may further have grasped that S is a particular instance of T which he has abstracted but which he cannot verbalize; or it may *dawn* on him that experiences of the type S have something in common, and are perhaps particular instances of some general relation T, which, however, he has not yet abstracted.

It follows that the degree of clarity and penetration of Johnnie's understanding must not be judged by the 'absolute height' he has reached in any 'vertical' abstractive hierarchy, but by the mastery he has attained on his own particular level. This depends on the factors already discussed, where the multi-dimensionality of experience (the intersection of several abstractive hierarchies in it) was taken for granted. Thus a garage mechanic may have a more complete understanding of the structure and function of motor cars than a theoretical physicist, in spite of the latter's more extended abstractive hierarchies; and an experienced Nanny may know more about children than an experimental psychologist. 'Vertical' progress in abstraction is of primary importance in the theoretical sciences only, but not in other domains of experience which are of greater significance to the majority. This may be the reason why the abstractive hierarchies were built up so very slowly in the learning process of the human species—although the native equipment for it was given millennia ago—and are acquired at an equally hesitant rate by the child.

Theoretically the building of the tower of Babel, of hierarchies of abstractions, can go on indefinitely, or until the most general patterns of events are subsumed as particular instances under one all-embracing law—a *lapis philosophorum*, or the unified field equations which Einstein hoped to find. But in fact individuals and cultures have their own ceilings of abstraction, where their quest for ultimates reaches saturation point—in theism, pantheism, vitalism, mechanism, or Hegelian dialectics. In less exalted domains the ceiling can be surprisingly low. Some primitive languages have words for particular colours but no word for 'colour' as a class. The abstraction of Space and Time as categories independent from the objects which occupy them (i.e. from duration and extension) is only some three hundred years old; so are the concepts of mass, force, etc. The slow, fumbling emergence of abstract concepts which in retrospect appear so self-evident, is best illustrated by the beginning of mathematics—a domain where pure abstraction seems to reign supreme.

The Dawn of Mathematics

To quote Russell's famous dictum once more, 'it must have required many ages to discover that a brace of pheasants and a couple of days were both instances of the number two'. In fact, evidence indicates that the discovery was not made in one fell swoop, but in several hesitant steps; and when it was achieved, some cultures were quite content to stop there and rest on their glories: Australian aborigines have only three number-words in their vocabulary: one, two, and many.[19] Most European languages show the traces of this stage of development: the Latin *ter* means both 'three times' and 'many' (cf. 'thrice blest').

At the earliest stage the number concept is not yet abstracted from the objects which are numbered: 'two-ness' is a feature situated in particular twosome objects, not a general relation. Language bears witness to this 'embeddedness': a 'brace' of pheasants is not a 'pride' of lions; a 'pair', when married, is a 'couple', when engaged in singing, a 'duo'. In some primitive languages not only the number two but all numerals adhere to the type of object counted; in the Timshian tongue of New Guinea there are seven different classes of number-words referring, respectively, to flat objects, round objects, long objects, people, canoes, and measures; the seventh, used for counting in general, was the latest to develop.[20]

Children go through a similar stage; Koffka mentions several three-year-olds who understood and used the words 'two apples', but did not understand 'two eyes', 'two ears'. One child, over four, when asked by his grandfather, 'How many fingers have I?', replied, 'I don't know; I can only count my own fingers.' There is an old joke about the new arithmetic teacher who, when he asked the class, 'How many oranges would Johnnie have if . . . etc.', received the indignant reply, 'Please, sir, we have only learned to count in apples'. The number-matrix, once adherent to the object-matrix, has gained such lofty independence, that their re-union is experienced as a bisociation of incompatibles.

The next step is the abstraction of *individual numbers*, which are not yet regarded as parts of a continuous series. The first 'personalized' number-concept abstracted by primitive and child alike is almost invariably the number two. Next follow the concepts 'one' and 'many'. Some cultures, as mentioned, stop there; others retain traces of this stage in their languages; Hebrew and Greek have retained separate grammatical forms for the singular, the dual, and the plural. Koffka mentions a child who played with combinations of 'two and one', 'two and two', etc., until early into its fifth year; only then did the number-word 'three' become firmly established.

These first individual number-concepts are only semi-abstract; they emerge as it were reluctantly from the womb, and retain for a long time the umbilical cord which attaches them to concrete objects or favourite symbols. In some primitive languages the word for five

is 'hand', for ten 'two hands'. Each number primarily refers to some
such 'model collection' of practical or mystical significance: the four
cardinal points, the Holy Trinity, the magic Pentagram. Each number
has its preferential connotation, its personality and individual profile;
it is as yet unrelated to other numbers and does not form a continuous
series with them. The number sense of Otto Koehler's birds who
can identify at a glance object-collections up to seven, and the same
faculty of human subjects (to whom heterogeneous objects are shown
on a screen for a time too short for counting) give us some idea of the
character of our own earliest number-concepts. They could be described as qualities rather than as quantities in a graded series; the identification of numbers in experiments where counting is excluded, consists apparently in recognizing the quasi-Gestalt quality of 'fiveness'
(I say 'quasi' because the objects are distributed at random and do not
provide coherent figural unity). In other words, each of the first
individual numbers up to perhaps seven or eight, is represented by
a separate matrix—its associative connotations—and a perceptual
analyser-code which enables us to recognize 'fiveness' directly, at a
glance. The analyser probably works by scanning, as in the perception
of triangles and squares; but this process is automatic and unconscious,
as opposed to conscious counting.

Thus the first 'personalized' number-concepts 'do not constitute a
homogeneous series, and are quite unsuited to the simplest logical or
mathematical operation'.[21] Those first operations are, apparently,
carried out not by counting, but by *matching* the collection of objects
to be counted against 'model collections' of pebbles, notches cut into
a stick, knots made in a string, and above all the fingers and toes. The
'model collections' are usually those to which the individual number-
concept originally referred. The earliest model collections seem to have
been pebbles; 'to calculate' is derived from calculus, meaning pebble;
to tally, from *talea*, cutting. Relics of other model-collections abound
in our weights and measures: feet, yards, furlongs, chains, bushels,
rods. The Ayepones in Australia hunt wild horses; when they return
from an excursion nobody asks them how many horses they have
caught but 'How much space will they occupy?'. Even Xerxes counted
his army by this method—at least, if we are to believe Herodotus:

All the fleet, being now arrived at Doriscus, was brought by its
captains at Xerxes' command to the beach near Doriscus . . . and
hauled up for rest. In the meanwhile, Xerxes numbered his army at

Doriscus. What the number of each part of it was I cannot with exact-
ness say, for there is no one who tells us that; but the count of the
whole land army showed it to be a million and seven hundred
thousand. The numbering was done as follows: a myriad [10,000]
men were collected in one place, and when they were packed
together as closely as might be, a line was drawn round them; this
being drawn, the myriad was sent away, and a wall of stone built on
the line reaching up to a man's navel; which done, others were
brought into the walled space, till in this way all were counted.[22]

It seems that as a general rule matching precedes counting in the
most varied cultures.

The next great advance was the integration of individual numbers
into a homogeneous series—the transition from cardinal to ordinal
numbers, from 'fiveness' to 'the fifth'. The activity of *counting* seems
to originate in the spontaneous, rhythmic motor activities of the small
child: kicking, stamping, tapping, with his hands and feet; and the
repetitive imitation of patterned series of nonsense syllables: 'Eeny
meeny miny mo'—a kind of pseudo-counting. Even more important
is perhaps the spontaneous, rhythmical stretching of fingers and tapping
with the fingers. Here was the ideal 'model collection' out of which,
in the course of something like a hundred thousand years, the skill of
finger-counting must have emerged. Danzig[23] calls attention to a
subtle distinction:

'In his fingers man possesses a device which permits him to pass
imperceptibly from cardinal to ordinal number. Should he want to
indicate that a certain collection contains four objects he will raise or
turn down four fingers *simultaneously*; should he want to count the
same collection he will raise or turn down these fingers *in succession*.
In the first case he is using his fingers as a cardinal model, in the second
as an ordinal system. Unmistakable traces of this origin of counting are
found in practically every primitive language.' A fascinating account
of counting methods in primitive societies can be found in Lévy-
Bruhl, *How Natives Think* (1926, Chapter V).

I have tried to re-trace the first two steps at the base of the mathematical hierarchy. The first was the slow and hesitant abstraction of
individual number concepts from the concrete objects to which they
relate; the second was the abstraction of the sequential relation between
numbers, which establishes the basic rule of the mathematical game:
counting. *A posteriori* it would seem that the road now lay open to the

logical deduction of the whole body of the theory of numbers; in fact each advance required the exercise of creative imagination, jumping over hurdles, following up crazy hunches, and overcoming mental blocks. Centuries of stagnation alternated with periods of explosive progress; discoveries were forgotten and re-discovered; within the same individual, brilliant insights could be followed by protracted snowblindness. It took several hundred years until the Hindu invention of zero was accepted in Christian Europe; Kepler detested and never accepted the 'coss'—i.e. algebraic notation; his teacher Maestlin showed the same hostility towards Napier's logarithms. Progress in the apparently most rational of human pursuits was achieved in a highly irrational manner, epitomized by Gauss' 'I have had my solutions for a long time, but I do not yet know how I am to arrive at them'. The mind, owing to its hierarchic organization, functions on several levels at once, and often one level does not know what the other is doing; the essence of the creative act is bringing them together.

The Dawn of Logic

Let us turn to the genesis of logical codes—and take as an example the so-called law of contradiction in its post-Kantian formulation: A is not not-A. To disregard this law used to be considered as a mortal sin against rationality; chief among the sinners were primitives and children, with their notorious imperviousness to contradiction—plus all of us who dream at night being A and not-A in a single breath.

Now in order to tell A from not-A, I must discriminate between them. Once I have discriminated between them 'A is not not-A' becomes tautologous, and you cannot sin against a tautology. But discrimination, as we saw, is a function of relevance. Functionally irrelevant differences between experiences may go either entirely unnoticed, or may be noticed but not retained, or they may be implicitly retained without arousing the need for explicit discriminatory responses, verbal or otherwise.

Once upon a time I had a sheep farm in North Wales, and my Continental friends kept addressing their letters to: Bwylch Ocyn, Blaenau Ffestiniog, near Penrhyndeudraeth, England. The postman, a Gaelic patriot, was much aggrieved. Had he consulted Lord Russell (who was my neighbour and lived in Llan Ffestiniog), he would no doubt have learned that since Wales is not-England and Ffestiniog is Wales, it followed that foreigners had a pre-logical mentality and were unable to understand the law of contradiction. Thus, if the criteria of relevance of X, determined by X's patterns of motivation, values, and knowledge, are significantly different from Y's, then Y's behaviour must necessarily appear to X as irrational and 'indifferent to contradiction'. Hence the mass of misinterpretations which missionaries have put on the mentality of primitives, and grownups on the mental world of the child.

To the primitive mind the most significant relations between persons, objects, and events are of magical character; in totemistic societies the existence of a magic link is assumed between members of the group and the totem. The Bororo tribe in northern Brazil, whose totem animal is the red *arara*, a kind of parakeet, affirm that they *are* red *araras*. Naturally, the Bororo can *see* the difference between a red bird and his fellow tribesman; but when referring to his conviction that both participate in a mystic unity, the difference between them is treated as irrelevant—just as the child who calls all pointed things 'nose', chooses to ignore the difference between noses and shoes as irrelevant for its purpose. The difference between primitive and modern mentality is not that the former is indifferent to contradiction, but that statements which appear as contradictory to one, do not appear so to the other, because each mentality abstracts and discriminates along different dimensions of experience or 'gradients of relevance', determined by different motivations. This applies not only to so-called 'primitive' cultures (which, of course, are often far from primitive). European thought in the Middle Ages, and Aristotelian physics in particular, appear to us full of glaringly evident self-contradictions. The same applies to the philosophical systems of Buddhism and Hinduism, which do not discriminate between object and subject, perceiver and perceived, and in which the value of the discriminatory act itself is discredited by the dogma of the unity of opposites.[24] Vice versa, if we tried to see ourselves through the eyes of a Buddhist or medieval Christian, our notion that random events exert a decisive influence on an ordered and lawful universe would appear as self-contradictory. To them—as to the pre-Socratians—apparent coincidences were the vital gaps in the trivial web of physical causation through which the *deus ex machina* manifested its will; these gaps caused a kind of porousness in the texture of reality through which destiny could infiltrate. In the modern European's universe, our critics would say, the figure-background relation in the porous texture is reversed.

In the magic world of the child, physical causation and abstract categories play an equally subordinate and uncertain part, and cannot be regarded as a test for contradiction. When a child makes contradictory statements, for instance, 'the sun is alive because it gives light' and 'the sun is not alive because it has no blood', this is simply due to the fact that the *word* 'alive' was learned before the *concept* of aliveness was formed; it is a case, as so often found at that age, of *a symbol in search of a referent*. Piaget, from whose experiments with a child of nine I have been quoting, emphasized that children are apt to forget their previous judgements and then give a contradictory one. Yet obviously the word 'alive' is used on each of the two occasions with a different meaning, based on different criteria: in the first case on the discrimination between hot and cold bodies (A and not-A), in the second between bodies with and without blood (B and not-B). Thus there is no contradiction between the two statements, only confusion regarding the meaning of the word 'alive'; what the child intended to say was: 'the sun is alive in so far as it is hot, but not alive in so far as it has no blood'. Implicit discrimination between contrasting alternatives is often blurred in the explicit statements of the child owing to its linguistic inexperience.

The child's attitude to its experiences is discriminatory within its framework of relevant relations, and its apparent contradictions are due partly to the fact that its scales of relevant values are different from the adult's, partly to the inadequacy of its symbolic equipment. But although the child *experiences* certain facts and relations as mutually exclusive and reacts accordingly, the relational concept of 'contradiction' itself is only abstracted at a much later stage of development; just as the child uses names before the name-thing relation as such is abstracted.

There seem to be three stages in the emergence of the 'law of contradiction'. The first is training the child to respond to the commands 'Yes' and 'No' and their equivalents; the second is the child's use of these symbols as levers to control the actions of others; the third is the use of 'Yes' and 'No' with reference to *verbal* activities. Stern's daughter used the word '*Nein*' at eighteen months in answer to the question, 'Shall we take Hilde away?'. But when she was asked 'Is this a doggie?' while the wrong animal was shown her, she remained silent, then echoed 'doggie'. Four months later, however, she began to contradict a wrong name by substituting the right one; and another two months later—at two years—she firmly said 'No' in denial of blatantly false verbal statements.

Thus we see that the principle of contradiction is applied to symbolic activities precisely at the stage where symbolic relations as such become relevant to the child and call out discriminatory reactions. Once this stage has been reached the child uses 'No' not only to prevent undesirable action, but to reject incorrect symbolic propositions. This new verbal device is for the child a source of satisfaction comparable to the discovery of the naming game. It is expressed by the frequent use of antithetic statements which are characteristic for this age; three-year-olds delight in phrases which sound as if they had been borrowed from the Proverbs of Solomon: 'I am fast runner, not slow runner', 'I not old boy, new boy', etc. The use of such paired antithetic statements marks the beginning of the process of abstracting the relation of mutual exclusion as such, followed by the other, now familiar, stages: the gradual downing of the generalized relation; the implicit grasp of the principle; and finally its explicit naming—though this last stage may never be reached. But regardless of whether or not the subject is able to give a verbal definition of it, the principle of the mutual exclusion of opposites previously discriminated as such, will enter as an important rule of the game into all matrices of rational thought.

Thus the so-called 'laws of thought' in traditional logic are, from the point of view of developmental psychology, merely the explicit formulations of implicit relations, abstracted by the usual procedures characteristic for all forms of learning. We may say that the principle of contradiction exists *a priori* in the organization of the nervous system, because the power to discriminate is built into that organization, and contradiction is merely an epi-phenomenon of discrimination. But we may also say that our judgements of what is a contradiction and what is not are empirically derived, because the gradients of relevance along which abstraction and discrimination proceed, are subjective and differ according to individual and culture.

But this subjectivity does not detract from the great power which the principle of contradiction exercises over the mind. And not only over the human mind; the experimental neuroses which Pavlov induced in his dogs testifies to it. The dog is trained to discriminate circles, or nearly circular ellipses, from flat ellipses, the former signalling food, the latter 'no food'. So long as the two types of signals are comfortably distinguishable from each other, the dog shows no sign of strain. But when intermediary forms are shown which could be interpreted as belonging to one class or its opposite, experimental neurosis sets in: the dog goes wild, then becomes apathetic, and seems to lose altogether its power of discrimination; it goes emotionally and intellectually to pieces. One might say that the dog has lost confidence in a world in which the law of the excluded middle has ceased to operate, and A is no longer not not-A.

It appears that dogs are not only emotionally more stable and loyal, but also more orthodox logicians than their masters. For the powers of discriminatory judgement are more diluted on the level of symbolic thought than in perception; and when thought is dominated by emotion and faith, the Red and White Queens always score against reasonable Alice, who asserts that 'One *can't* believe impossible things'; whereas the White Queen, after a little practice, managed to believe 'as many as six impossible things before breakfast'.

Which is, all things considered, quite a modest estimate.

NOTE

To p. 613. Once upon a time Lashley and Wade (1946) tried to make a distinction 'between the "so-called generalization" which means only a failure to observe differences and the generalization which involves perception of both similarities and differences. The amorphous figure, lacking in identity, is generalized in the first sense only.' The quotation is from Hebb (1949, p. 27), who seemed to share Lashley's view, although Lashley himself later dropped the distinction. The 'amorphous figure' in the quotation refers to 'an irregular mass of colour or a pattern of intersecting lines drawn at random'. Being amorphous it does *per definitionem* lack identity, i.e., the prerequisites for the formation of an object-concept; but it is nevertheless seen as some kind of figure on a background that is discriminated. In fact, abstraction without discrimination is a contradiction in terms. The abstracted quality—whether 'nose', 'dolly', or 'sound of the tuning fork' is always differentiated from non-nose and non-dolly and no-sound. (If the sound of the tuning fork is very weak, it will approach the limen of no-sound; about the effect of simple gradients of intensity, see Hebb (1958), p. 189; about pitch and octave gradients, see Osgood, op. cit., p. 361. Since perception of intensity, pitch, etc. is part of the animal's perceptual organization, they must influence the functioning of the analyser-codes.)

XVI

SOME ASPECTS OF THINKING

Multi-Dimensionality

In the preceding chapter we have discussed the processes by which the rules of the game of symbolic thought are acquired; let us now turn to adult thinking and problem-solving.

Thinking is a multi-dimensional affair. The Sterns recorded all the questions asked by their little daughter in the course of four days; but the record gives us only the scantiest pointers to what went on in the child's head. Perhaps one day a super-EEG will be constructed, which will record all the thoughts—or at least all verbalized thoughts —which the stream of consciousness carries through the subject's wired skull; yet even such a record, far more complete than anything James Joyce could dream of, would be but a poor pointer to the multi-dimensional patterns underlying the linear stream. The oscillating curve on the gramophone record needs a human auditory system to yield all the information it contains. The super-EEG would record larger units of information—entire words; but it would still need a psychoanalyst or a Joyce-interpreter to divine the meaning behind the meaning: the connotations of individual words, their unconscious echoes, the motivation behind it all, the rules of the patient's game, hidden to himself, and the memories which crop up as landmarks in his internal, mental environment.

We must nevertheless try to sort out some of the dimensional variables in this immensely complex, multi-dimensional activity; these variables will then yield gradients of different kinds; for instance:

(1) Degrees of consciousness;
(2) Degrees of verbalization;
(3) Degrees of abstraction;
(4) Degrees of flexibility;

(5) Type and intensity of motivation;
(6) Realistic versus autistic thought;
(7) Dominance of outer or inner environment;
(8) Learning and performing;
(9) Routine and originality.

Each of these headings has been repeatedly discussed in various contexts in various chapters. Most of them cut across the conventional classifications of thought such as 'associative' versus 'directional'. All variables are inter-dependent.

Now if variables depend on each other, there must be a function which defines their inter-dependence—a rule of the game. The question: 'If $y = f(x)$ and x is 7, how much is y?' is meaningless unless I define f. Similarly, if in the experimental laboratory the subject is given the stimulus word: $S =$ 'big' and is asked for the 'response', the question is meaningless unless f is defined as 'synonyms' or 'opposites' or 'rhymes', or whatever game is to be played.

One of the main contentions of this book is that organic life, in all its manifestations, from morphogenesis to symbolic thought, is governed by 'rules of the game' which lend it coherence, order, and unity-in-variety; and that these rules (or functions in the mathematical sense), whether innate or acquired, are represented in coded form on various levels, from the chromosomes to the structures in the nervous system responsible for symbolic thought. The codes are assumed to function on the trigger-release principle, so that a relatively simple signal-pattern releases complex, pre-set action-patterns, as the referee's whistle initiates or stops the activities of the football players. The rules are fixed, but there are endless variations to each game, their variability increasing in ascending order; this lends elasticity to habit, and gives rise to the subjective experience of freedom of choice between alternate possibilities of action. There is also an overall-rule of the game, which says that no rule is absolutely final; that under certain circumstances they may be altered and combined into a more sophisticated game, which provides a higher form of unity and yet increased variety; this is called the subject's creative potential.

Faced with the imaginary EEG record of the patient's stream of thoughts, the only way of interpreting it would be to find out what game the patient is playing at any moment, and why. This actually is the procedure of the free-association method in psychotherapy: the patient's words provide the record, and his dreams, it is hoped, will provide the interpretation of the underlying patterns of his individual matrices of thought. We follow, as we saw earlier on, similar methods in perceptual analysis: the sequence of pressure-variations reaching the ear-drum must be dismantled, analysed, and reassembled if we want to get at the underlying patterns of timbre, melody, and speech. The stream of sounds, like the stream of thoughts, yields its meaning only if the percipient knows the rules of the game.

The Experience of Free Choice

Let us consider some of the dimensions of thinking listed on pp. 630–1. Regarding *consciousness* I proposed to make a distinction between the 'linear scale' of awareness on the one hand, and hierarchic levels of consciousness on the other (Book One, VII, VIII). The former was to be regarded as a continuous gradient extending from completely self-regulatory physiological processes, through more or less automatized skills, to peripheral, and lastly, focal, awareness of events; the latter to be represented by quasi-parallel layers of mental organization—comparable to geological strata—which are discontinuous and governed by codes formed at different stages of phylogenetic and ontogenetic development. All this has been discussed at length in the previous volume, and need not be recapitulated; but I must append two additional points.

The first concerns 'linear' awareness. I have described, somewhat perversely, awareness as that dimension of experience which diminishes and shrinks away with the progressive automatization of a skill. For 'awareness' is an irreducible term, a black box like that other which contains the power of organic life to extract energy and information from its environment—and, in fact, continuous with the latter. On the other hand, the progressive automatization of motor skills, perceptual skills, verbal and mathematical skills, is an observable and to some extent even measurable factor of behaviour—epitomized on its lowest level by sensory habituation. Thus by expressing awareness by the inverse ratio of the automatization of the ongoing process, a certain strategic advantage is gained. Other things being equal (i.e. under stablized environmental conditions), automatization manifests itself in predictable, stereotyped performance, where the matrix has no degrees of freedom left for strategic decisions, because these are made by pre-set feedback controls, and do not require the attention of

higher centres. Conversely, the less automatized the skill, the greater
the freedom of choice between alternatives, to be decided on higher
levels according to more complex feedbacks—'loops within loops'—
from the outer and inner environment. Thus the logic of the argument
led first to a negative criterion of awareness as the reciprocal of habit-
formation, and now to the positive criterion of awareness as being
directly proportional to the degrees of freedom of the centre controlling the activity to make alternative choices, based on its estimate of
the lie of the land. We must assume that the higher in the hierarchy
the centre is placed, the more vivid will be the subject's experience of
his 'freedom of choice'. Freedom of the will is a metaphysical question
outside the scope of this book; but considered as a subjective datum
of experience, 'free will' is the awareness of alternative choices.

Degrees of Self-Awareness

The above was related to degrees of awareness on the continuous,
'linear' gradient. The second addendum relates to the hierarchic levels
of consciousness. At any moment of our existence, we carry on activities on various levels, simultaneously and more or less independently
from each: we breathe, metabolize, drive the car, and talk to the passengers all at the same time, 'in parallel' as it were.

But there are moments when a person perceives what he is doing
from a bird's eye view as it were; from a 'parallel' level of consciousness which is not at all involved in the activity in hand. Take a simple
example: you are absorbed in a game of chess; you concentrate on a
stratagem to defeat your opponent. You look up for a moment to
light a cigarette, and at that moment your awareness jumps to another
plane, as it were; you say to yourself 'what fun I am having playing
chess with old Henry on a Sunday afternoon'. Then you go back to
your game. It was a brief break-through from the activity in hand to
the contemplation of that activity from an upstairs balcony—a vertical
shift of awareness which enabled you to look down at the top of your
own head. To put it in a different way, attention has been displaced
from the object of the ongoing activity to the subject engaged in
carrying it out—that elusive entity, the self.

It is a paradox as old as Achilles and the Tortoise, that the subject
who is aware can never become the object of his awareness; at best he
can, if so inclined, achieve successive approximations which form a

convergent series. One may call this the paradox of the dog at dinner. The dog is eating his dinner; the wagging of his tail indicates that he is enjoying himself; but does he *know* that he is enjoying himself? . . . A little boy is watching a Western on the TV screen. He is enjoying himself. He knows perhaps that he is enjoying himself. Does he know that he knows? . . . The philosopher is thinking of a problem. He is aware that he is thinking of this problem. Is he aware that he is aware, etc. . . . ? The known is always one step ahead of the knower, and they chase each other up a spiral staircase, as it were. In Craik's terminology one might say that the model can never make a complete model of itself.* Regarding *verbal* models in particular, we have seen (pp. 592 ff.) that verbal statements are initiated by unverbalized intentions on higher levels, so that we again arrive at a receding series. This seems to indicate that the mind-body problem is not amenable to any solution in explicit, verbal terms.

On the other hand, the fact that the subject who is aware can nevertheless become, *to some extent*, the object of his own awareness, is of course of outstanding importance in mental life. Animals, apparently from planaria onwards, display attention and expectancy which indicate varying degrees of 'linear' awareness; primates, as well as domestic pets, may also have some rudiments of self-awareness. But the many-layered hierarchies of man, and particularly his symbolic hierarchies, place him on a lonely peak, and impose on him the impossible command to 'know thyself'. Awareness of awareness is a tantalizing gift; and 'I think therefore I exist' is a hopeful beginning. But the end, the identification of the knower and the known, which alone would constitute complete consciousness of existence, though always in sight, is never achieved. The successive forms of self-identification, starting from the child's fluid world of experience which knows as yet no firm boundary between self and not-self, can be likened to a mathematical series converging towards unity, or to a spiral curve converging towards a centre which it will only reach after an infinite number of involutions.

The aim of certain mystic practices—such as Hatha Yoga—is to permeate the self with awareness of itself by gaining voluntary control over visceral processes and isolated muscles. It would seem that this focussing of consciousness on the self, the inward core of the contracting spiral, is the direct opposite of the self-transcending aspirations of other schools of mysticism—the expansion of consciousness in an unfolding spiral, and its final dissolution in the 'oceanic feeling'. In fact, however, the Yogi's effort to gain conscious mastery of the body is considered as merely a detour towards attaining 'pure consciousness' —that is, 'consciousness without object or content other than consciousness itself'. Thus turned upon itself, pure consciousness is supposed to penetrate the Real Self—which, unlike the transient self, is part and parcel of the Atman, the universal spirit.[1] Both methods, therefore, each with a long historical ancestry, share the same ultimate aim— situated at the point where opposites meet; after all, as the bright little boy said, 'the infinite is where things happen which don't'.

'Self-awareness', in the sense of the preceding paragraphs, has of course nothing to do with 'self-consciousness' in the sense of gaucherie, stage-fright. The latter is our old friend, the paradox of the centipede —the disorganization of behaviour which results when higher centres interfere with the autonomous functioning of parts on lower levels. 'Self-consciousness', used in this sense, is a typically English coinage; it provides an amusing and rather revealing contrast to the equally malapropos German coinage '*Selbstbewusstsein*'—meaning self-confident, conscious of one's own value. As for the French, faithful to the Cartesian spirit, they use *conscience* to designate both consciousness and moral conscience.

Master-Switches and Releasers

Motivation has been discussed in Chapter VIII. It determines what kind of game the subject will engage in, and activates the proper codes. If he feels the need to build castles in Spain, day-dreaming will replace the routines of planning ahead. The rules of day-dreaming impose a minimum of restraints and leave a vast choice of strategies to reach the desired goal, wish-fulfilment. Thus even day-dreaming is 'goal-directed', but the direction of thought is determined by emotional gradients, not by a concrete target.

At the opposite end of the motivational spectrum are activities like problem-solving, governed by complex and precise rules. The goal to be reached is sharply defined, but has in itself no emotional significance; the reward is not contained in the target but in the act of reaching it. Some textbooks make a distinction between 'associative' and 'directive' thinking; but directiveness in the sense described is present even in the daydream, and controlled association enters into problem-solving; the difference is one of degree. Similar considerations apply to other classifications: abstract—concrete, realistic—autistic, etc.

Most ordinary thinking is of a mixed kind; it may pursue a set directional course for a while, according to strict rules, then go off at a tangent and drift along, until some higher centre enters into action, and discipline is restored. We have discussed these general aspects of ideation before; it remains to consider briefly some specific patterns of verbal thought.

At the base of all hierarchies which enter into our universes of discourse operate the implicit sub-codes of grammar and syntax; 'implicit' because they are automatized and we are not aware of their functioning. Lashley's dictum on perception is equally applicable to speaking and listening: 'We are aware of an organized structure; the organizing is never experienced.' The rules which determine how thoughts are put into words cannot themselves be put into words —except by the patient labours of logicians and semanticists to 'break the code'.

Next come the rules of common sense or common-or-garden logic, which are also empirically acquired, abstracted relations—codified *modus operandi* which the majority of people are no more able to define than they can define how they ride a bicycle. But as we move upward, towards more specific universes of discourse, the codes, too, become more explicit.

The simplest examples of explicit codes are the verbal commands in word-association tests, e.g.: 'name opposites!'. The experimenter then says 'dark', and the answer 'light' pops out promptly, as if produced by a slot-machine—although in a free-association test the subject would probably associate 'dark' with 'night' rather than with 'light', and 'hot' with 'Italy' rather than with 'cold'. Thus the verbal command 'opposites' has acted as a master-switch, as it were, which changed the entire pattern of verbal organization. Even more striking is what happens to my verbal matrices *si je continue de developer ma pensée en français*—if I continue to develop my argument, but use French words and French grammar to express it. My line of thinking has remained the same (or almost entirely so) but that single command-word 'French' has triggered off an instant reorganization affecting millions of neurons and their mode of inter-action. Not only has the vocabulary been changed, but also the method of converting ideas into syntactic language-units according to the sub-codes of French grammar.

I do not want to go into neuro-physiology, but let us note that the model of the telephone-switchboard plugging into another localized 'language-area' simply will not do. Let us return for a moment to word-association tests. 'Light-dark', 'hot-cold' are primitive examples of matrices governed by codes with a single parameter in semantic space. Even so, are we to assign, by analogy with the 'language-areas', different cortical territories to operations controlled by the commands 'opposites', 'synonyms', 'super-ordinate class', etc.; not to mention 'inter-polation', 'extra-polation', and the mighty hierarchies of symbolic logic or of mathematical operations? Moreover, if the command is again 'opposites', and the stimulus-word 'Napoleon'; or if the command is 'supraordinate class' in the species-genus game, and the stimulus-word 'nail' or 'birth'—what is the 'correct' response? Semantic space is multi-dimensional and cannot be represented by purely spatial connections activated by all-or-nothing signals in the three-dimensional rind of the brain; a model must include at least specific signals (e.g. frequency modulation pulses) and chemical (RNA) changes in the neurons to account for selectivity of response.[2]

In all controlled associations and symbolic operations we again find a principle confirmed which we found operating on all levels—namely, that a relatively simple 'releaser' signal from higher quarters ('opposites' 'speak French', 'find the square root of ...') triggers off the operation of a complex code—a whole universe of discourse in fact, with a hierarchy of implicit sub-codes, and a flexible strategy. (Even to find an 'opposite' to the word hairpin requires complex operations governed by individual 'strategies', perhaps involving visual images—a process continuous with problem-solving). The trigger-releaser may be a verbal or visual, or even chemical command—a tumblerful of gin or an amphetamin tablet: yet look what remarkably new rules of the game are triggered off by them.*

Explicit Rules and Implicit Codes

The implicit codes of grammar and syntax were, as we saw, acquired empirically 'as the gypsy learns to fiddle'. But the rules which govern more advanced symbolic skills—mathematics or chemistry, or Law—are learned in explicit verbal form. They may be acquired by rote-learning, or by guided learning, but at some stage they must be stated in explicit form. Take an example from elementary algebra: the average student learning the rule for solving quadratic equations:

$x_{1,2} = -p/2 \pm \sqrt{p^2/4 - q}$. For the next few days or weeks, every time he has to use the formula, he must look it up in his textbook (or, if he is very brilliant, derive it afresh). At this stage of the learning process the formula is not yet an automatically functioning rule of the game; it is not yet a 'code' impressed on his nervous system. But after some practice, a single glance at an expression of the form $x^2 + px + q = 0$ will tell him that it is a member of the matrix of quadratic equations and trigger off the rule—by now an automatized code—for solving it.

Thus rules which at first have to be looked up, or reconstructed by a conscious effort, become codified and automatized by routine. It is irrelevant in this particular context whether the student has by now forgotten the derivation of the formula and merely uses it as a mechanical gimmick; or whether he is aware of its binomial ancestry. This makes a vast difference in terms of understanding, but need not affect the process of automatization.

I have emphasized before that the term 'code' is used in this book not in the metaphorical way in which Freud, for instance, used the word 'censor', but to refer to concrete processes or patterns of organization in the central nervous system. However, it sounds somehow more plausible to attribute physiological reality to codes on lower levels of the organic hierarchy—the genetic code, the codes of instinct-behaviour and sensory-motor skills—than to claim that the rules of such esoteric games as non-Euclidian geometry or quantum mechanics are physiologically represented, by appropriate coding methods, in the nervous system, and can be triggered off by simple releasers (such as the command 'let's talk shop'). I must therefore underline once more that the term 'code' is meant to apply only to those rules of behaviour which govern established routines and function automatically without conscious effort. In the initial stages of learning a complex symbolic skill, the rules of the game (laws, theorems, mathematical or chemical formulae) must be constantly memorized, looked up, or consciously recalled; so long as this is the case they are not yet incorporated into the physico-mental organization and are not to be called 'codes'. Codes are only those fixed stable rules which, once switched on, automatically govern the thinking routine. The problem in problem-solving consists firstly in discovering which routine is appropriate to the problem—what type of game is to be played; and secondly, *how* to play it—i.e. which strategy to follow, which members of the flexible matrix are to be brought into play according to the lie of the land.

We learn, or discover, with strenuous effort, a new method of thinking; after a while, with practice, the novelty changes into semi-automatized routine, based on an invariant code with an adaptable matrix, and is incorporated into our repertory of habits. It is astonishing how soon, once a new railroad is built across desert and mountains, the passenger-trains start running on schedule.

But the process of habit-formation does not stop there: not only the *rules* of the newly learnt game become soon automatized to such an extent that it becomes increasingly difficult to go against them, but strategy, too, tends to become stereotyped and incorporated into the code. Take progress in chess, an example I have mentioned before. The beginner is uncertain about the rules; then the rules become automatic codes and it becomes almost impossible for him to move his men in impermissible ways; after protracted practice certain tactical principles, which are no longer 'rules' in the formal sense, also begin to operate automatically in his mind—e.g. to avoid pins, to seek open rook-files. But this reification of tactical pseudo-rules into automatized sub-codes contains a mortal danger, because considerations of strategy on a higher level demand that each of these tactical rules should be broken if the occasion warrants it. Sacrifices in material, and moves which look cockeyed (that is: positionally unsound), are signs of combinative power, i.e. originality; the mediocre player always remains a slave of habit and cautious orthodoxy.

At this point the argument merges into that of Book One (IX–XI), concerning the pitfalls of orthodoxy, over-specialization, and one-sided development in the history of science and philosophy. In biology or theoretical physics there are no clean-cut distinctions between canonical rules of the game and heuristic rules of strategy and tactics. We are inclined to believe, as popular books on science tell us, that the 'permissible moves' are laid down for ever by the laws of formal logic and the criteria for judging evidence; and that strategy is determined only by the lie of the land, that is, the data of observation. In fact, however, the rules turn out to be infiltrated with implicit assumptions and 'self-evident axioms' which as often as not are specious contraband; and the empirical strategies are often weighted by a stubborn adherence to methods of interpretation and biassed techniques, promoted to canonical status. Habit is heir to originality; without the hierarchies of organized habits life would be chaos; creativity means breaking up habits and joining the fragments into a new synthesis.

I have tried to outline the hierarchic organization of levels of under-standing, levels of consciousness, and levels of habit and flexibility—the last ranging from implicitly acquired codes, through the master-switches of controlled association, to the explicitly learned rules and pseudo-rules in the universes of discourse of science and philosophy. To avoid giving undue dominance to the abstractive hierarchies in the mental landscape, I must briefly mention some different types of language matrices—without aspiring at anything like a complete catalogue.

Phonetic matrices (of rhythm, meter, alliteration, assonance, rhyme, and euphony) do not properly belong to symbolic thought, though they interact with it not only in poetry and word-games but also in ordinary discourse, often more persistently than we are aware of.

Chronological matrices, naïvely regarded, seem to be linear chains of events, but are of course nothing of the sort. They are multi-dimen-sional structures in semantic space, governed by a diversity of selective codes, whose criteria of relevance are often quite indifferent to tem-poral order. This applies to personal memories, which always unfold within specific frames of reference, but also to written History: historians organize their material according to highly idiosyncratic rules for sifting and interpreting evidence, and for constructing causa-tive theories.

Classificatory codes in taxinomy, indexing systems and in certain branches of mathematical logic are hierarchic *par excellence* but rigid; they resemble stone pyramids in the mental landscape.

Dogmatic matrices could be described as closed systems with dis-torted feedback and impaired sub-skills of reasoning. They are ruled by a fixed code derived from an act of faith, a circular argument, or supposedly self-evident axioms. In other respects, however, they are remarkably adaptable, and their dialectical strategies are of great subtlety. Related to these are *frames of value* which determine ethical or aesthetic judgements or attitudes, and *emotion-dominated matrices* which need not be discussed as a separate category, since emotion enters in various guises and intensities into all form of thought.

Lastly, '*style codes*' represent a person's idiosyncrasies, mannerisms, etc., which, in their ensemble, constitute his individuality. Gait, gesture, voice, hand-writing are all governed by stable automatic codes. If a person, deprived by accident of the use of his right hand, learns to write with the left, his signature, before long, recovers its true character. 'Even the suspicious bank clerk will cash his cheque because the old form of signature returns,' wrote Penfield,[3] who had several such patients. 'The pattern of the signature and of the writing is in the brain, not in the hand.'

This applies, to a considerable extent, even to the *style* of writing. Hemingway or Proust can be identified—and parodied—after reading a few lines—as you identify the timbre of a drum or violin after a few transients. Even the language of common mortals whose style is undistinguished and seemingly indistinguishable, appears to have fixed characteristic ratios—.e.g. between the number of adjectives to verbs.

The *total matrix*, which comprises all these frames of behaviour, constitutes the personality structure. But even here, the code can apparently be triggered on and off by some super-master-switch—as the spectacular cases of multiple personalities indicate. Once more the hierarchy fades into a receding series.

NOTES

To p. 634. Cyberneticists have discussed at length models which are supposed to be capable of this feat. But they have no bearing on the question of awareness.

To p. 637. A summary of earlier work on controlled association tests, and the controversies around it (e.g. complex theory versus constellation theory) can be found e.g. in Woodworth (1939), pp. 790–800.

XVII

ASSOCIATION

'Multiple Attunements'

Associationism is dead, but association remains one of the fundamental facts of mental life. So far I have considered mental
organization chiefly in its 'vertical' aspect—hierarchic structures formed by abstractive processes in ascending series. But each
verbal concept, apart from being a member of a 'vertical' hierarchy,
is also a member of several connotative matrices, each of which could
be represented by an inclined plane. The concept's place in the vertical,
abstractive hierarchy provides the dictionary definition—as far as
that goes—of its meaning. But the concept as a psychological reality,
its aura of connotations, and its individual significance to the person
who actually uses it, is determined by the multitude of matrices which
intersect in it. Each of them provides an associative context governed
by a selective code; and the more there are of these inclined planes in
semantic space the richer and more multi-dimensional the concept.

If concepts are to be regarded as atoms of thought, they are certainly
not the hard lumps of classical physics. In the first place, they are unstable and subject to change—to change both in definition and in
connotation. My concept of a 'gene' or a 'seductress', or of 'President
Eisenhower' is certainly not the same as it was ten years ago, though
the verbal label attached to each of these concepts has remained the
same. It is strange to reflect that a major part of our scientific and
philosophical vocabulary consists of old Greek bottles filled and re-
filled with new wine; that *electron* once meant a piece of amber, and
Homer's *cosmos* a flat disc covered by a vault. It is even stranger that
the same Sanskrit root *matr* split, by mitosis, as it were, into *maya*—
the Oriental's web of illusions, and *metron*, metre, the Occidental's
yardstick to measure the world.

A concept has as many dimensions in semantic space as there are matrices of which it is a member. Let me return for a moment to the example of the parlour game mentioned before, 'towns starting with M'. In playing that game, I write down on my list 'Madrid'—which proves that the concept Madrid is a member of the phonetic matrix governed by the code 'initial M'. Since I am bored with the game, I permit my thoughts to wander, and at once an image arises: the crowd at the Puerta del Sol stampeding in the panic of an air bombardment—and off we go along the emotion-charged matrix of my memories of the Spanish Civil War. At this moment Brenda's little girl—who was watching the game, equally bored—asks, 'What is Madrid?'; and I oblige with the information: 'Madrid is the capital of Spain and of the Province of Madrid, situated on the left bank of the river Manzanares, which falls into the river Jarama'—whereby I have produced a definition of sorts of the concept 'Madrid'. A moment later I remember the Prado, with its Goyas, Velasquezes, and El Grecos—which are items in a mental catalogue indexed under the code 'Painters', sub-code 'Painters, Spanish' (but also under 'Spain', sub-code 'Spain, painters of'). These connotations presented themselves more or less automatically, but now my repertory of associations is nearly exhausted, and my mind a momentary blank. Add to the repertory the printed and auditory-vocal images of the word, plus the location of the town on a mental map, and you get about half a dozen matrices which will be activated by, and which will activate, the concept 'Madrid' without effort. The associative contexts of a concept that are firmly established in a person's repertory of thought-habits, are less numerous than we are inclined to believe—as free association tests demonstrate.

If, on the other hand, somebody asks me to talk about the geological foundations of Madrid, I shall make an embarrassed effort, and recall that the town stands on an undulating plateau and, by some inarticulate analogy, perhaps arrive at the conclusion that the soil consists chiefly of sand and clay. But that was an *inference* arrived at by the usual method of problem-solving, and not of a spontaneous association. My matrix of geological knowledge is scant; its code consists of the vague rule 'all that is relevant to the structure of the earth's crust'. This indicates the direction in semantic space of the search for an answer; but since the data of knowledge are lacking, there is little firm ground on which to move about. 'Madrid' was not a member of my geological matrix; after this embarrassing experience, it has been *recruited* to membership, but its ties to the matrix remain weak and tentative.

We have seen that the concept Madrid can be activated by any of the matrices to which it belongs (for instance 'Civil War'); and vice versa, that any of these matrices can be activated by it. If we assign to each matrix, metaphorically speaking, a specific 'wave-length' then the concept may be represented as *an aggregate of several oscillation-circuits*, each of which will receive and emit on the specific 'wave-length' of its matrix. We may call this the 'multiple attunement' of the concept to the various matrices of which it is a member.*

Now the aggregate of circuits, which is the concept, may *receive on one wave-length and emit on another*. 'Madrid' was evoked by the phonetic matrix 'initial M', and in its turn activated a different matrix, 'Civil War', which functions on a different wave-length. If the matrix of the incoming signal is of a complex or abstract character, the aggregate may tend to switch over to a circuit functioning on the wave-length of an emotionally more appealing matrix. Thus a concept is a member of several clubs, but it likes some clubs more than others. Its 'multiple attunements' may be represented as a line-spectrum of frequencies with a relatively stable energy-distribution. The frequencies of maximum energy—like the dominant partials in a sound-spectrum—would represent the concept's 'most-preferred' associative contexts. As the years go by, new lines would be added to the spectrum, while others would fade away, and the energy-distribution of associative preferences would change—getting mellower perhaps, like an old Stradivarius, or croaking, like an un-tuned piano. The effort to 'concentrate' on an abstract problem is probably proportionate to the energy required to inhibit preferential associative contexts of high energy-potential—i.e. 'habit strength'.

The preceding paragraphs may have given an exaggerated impression of the subjectivity of concepts—rather on the lines of Humpty Dumpty's 'a word means what I intend it to mean'. The connotations of concepts referring to individuals or places are of course largely personal; but on the other hand, there is experimental evidence to show that the associative priorities and the connotative 'aura' of concepts of a general character are surprisingly stable and standardized in individuals of the same culture. 'Marbe's Law' demonstrated the existence of a logarithmic relation between an individual's reaction-time in giving a certain response to a stimulus-word in an association test, and the frequency of the same response occurring in a group of people.** Osgood has invented an ingenious method of measuring 'semantic differentials'. The subjects were asked to assess the ratings of a concept —e.g. POLITE—on ten different graded scales: e.g. 'angular-rounded', 'cold-hot', 'good-bad', 'wet-dry'. Two groups of twenty subjects were used, and the mean ratings of each group were then plotted and compared. Surprisingly enough, the two graphs were almost identical; even more surprising, the greatest amount of disagreement (c. fifteen per cent) was found in the ratings of politeness as 'good' or 'bad': one group thought that to be polite deserved a 'goodness' rating of six points, the other of six and a half points, on a seven-point scale.[1]

To recapitulate: a concept may be regarded as a relatively stable aggregate or 'cluster' of receiving-transmitting circuits, with a kind of nuclear core: the verbal label ('MADRID'). Additional circuits may be recruited, others may fade with disuse, and the relative energy potentials of the circuits may be altered by long-term processes or the person's momentary mood; but the auditory-vocal (and visual) trace of the word MADRID remains unaltered, and thus preserves the identity of the concept through all these changes in time. We may further assume that any incoming signal, regardless through which circuit it is received, will activate the nuclear circuit—the auditory-vocal trace. If all goes well the response output will be emitted on the same wave-length on which the input was received, and I shall happily go on playing the 'towns with M' game. But since the cluster 'hangs together' it is likely that some amount of excitation has nevertheless spread to other circuits not concerned with the game—and thus caused the fleeting, fringe-conscious stirrings of my memories of the Civil War. This is a minor, permissible kind of distraction; and perhaps even a necessary one—without such ripples the stream of thought would be linear, colourless, all-too single-minded. But if one of the circuits with a high energy-potential gets excited, the control centres on higher levels of the hierarchy must prevent it from taking over if chaos is not to result; i.e., the code of the 'distracting' matrix must be blocked. During strenuous efforts to concentrate, one seems literally to 'feel' inside one's head the expenditure of energy needed to suppress diversional thoughts which keep popping up like jacks-in-the-box. 'A great part of our fatigue', Maxwell once remarked, 'often arises, not from those mental efforts by which we obtain the mastery of the subject, but from those which are spent in recalling our wandering thoughts'—particularly, one may add, during a long and boring lecture; while the reverse phenomenon is produced by the disinhibiting action of alcohol and drugs. All this seems to indicate that our preferential matrices of ideation are most of the time blocked by centres on higher

levels—which agrees well with the predominantly restraining function of the hierarchic controls in perceptual and motor organization.

Types of Association

I have used the word Association loosely, as it is nowadays mostly
used. In Drever's *Dictionary of Psychology*, for instance, we find:
  'Association: used generally of the principle in accordance with
which ideas, feelings, and movements are connected in such a way as
to determine their succession in the mind or in the actions of an individual, or of the process of establishing such connections.'
  Or take Humphrey (1951):
  'The term "association", or mental association, is a general name
often used in psychology to express the conditions under which
mental events, whether of experience or behaviour, arise.'[2]
  Hebb (1958) speaks at length about the association areas of the
cortex, but does not define association. Other authors, and textbooks,
differ widely in their definitions of the word, or prefer, wisely, not
to define it at all.
  Hobbes was probably the first to draw a distinction between what
came later to be called 'free association' and 'controlled' association:

> The train of thoughts, or mental discourse, is of two sorts. The first
> is unguided, without design, and inconstant ... in which case the
> thoughts are safe to wander, as in a dream. .... The second is more
> constant, as being regulated by some desire and design.[3]

However, free association is never entirely free: there are motivations, conscious or sub-conscious, which give it direction. On the
other hand, association controlled by some rule of the game, such as
'towns with M', is 'free' to the extent that the rule allows alternative
choices between permissible moves. The degrees of freedom of a
matrix vary from rigid automatism to the great adaptability of complex mental skills; and the flow of associative thought will accordingly
vary in character: it may move along fixed canals, or follow, like a
rivulet, the accidents of the terrain and make detours round obstacles
with an air of earnest goal-directedness.
  Since the attempts of the classic associationist school to reduce
thinking to association by contiguity and similarity (plus the 'secon-

dary laws' of facilitation) had to be abandoned, the principles supposedly underlying association have been classified and re-classified
over and again. Thus Wells[4] once made a catalogue of eighteen types
of association adapted from Jung, such as: 'egocentric predicate'
(example: lonesome—never); 'evaluation' (rose—beautiful); 'matter
of fact predicate' (spinach—green); 'subject-verb' (dog—bite), and
so forth, through 'object-verb', 'cause-effect', 'co-ordination', 'sub-
ordination', 'supraordination', 'contrast', 'coexistence', 'assonance',
etc. Woodworth (1939) suggested four classes: definition including
synonyms and supraordinates; completion and predication; co-
ordinates and contrasts; valuations and personal associations. He also
suggested an independent classification cutting across the one just
mentioned, according to a scale from 'meaningfulness' to 'super-
ficiality'.[5] Most of the *experimental* work refers to association tests
where the stimulus is a single word and the response is restricted to
one other word—a condition not exactly typical of ordinary verbal
discourse outside the laboratory.

The lesson which emerges from these elaborate and painstaking
attempts at classification is that the principles underlying associative
thinking are determined by the matrix in which the thinking takes
place; and that there are as many types of association as there are
codes which control verbal behaviour. In bilingual countries like
Switzerland, the response to a German stimulus-word will often be
its French equivalent; some people are addicted to metaphor, others
to punning; the chess player and the draughts player's associations
follow the rules of their respective games.

To sum up: associative thinking is the exercise of a habit. It may be
rigid or flexible, with a wide range of adaptability; yet it remains a
habit in so far as it observes certain invariant rules of the game. Association, *qua* exercise of a skill, is thus distinguished from *learning*, which
is the acquisition of a new skill, and from *bisociation*, which is the
combination, re-shuffling and re-structuring of skills. But these
categories overlap—as discussed in the next chapter.

NOTES

To p. 644. 'Wave-length' is of course used metaphorically for much more
complex processes, including both structural and functional characteristics of
nervous tissue. 'Excitation-clang' or 'frequency-modulation signals' or Hebb's
'phase-sequences in cell assemblies' would be closer approximations.

To p. 644. For a summary see Woodworth (1939) pp. 360 seq., Osgood (1960) pp. 722 et seq. Osgood (p. 722), discussing the relative frequencies and reaction times of verbal responses in association tests, speaks of a 'hierarchical structure of associations ; but he uses the word 'hierarchy' to refer to a linear scale of gradations.

XVIII

HABIT AND ORIGINALITY

roblem-solving is bridging a gap between the initial situation and the target. 'Target' must be understood in the widest sense —it may be an apple hanging high up on a tree, or a formula for squaring the circle, or inventing a honey-spoon which does not drip, or fitting a fact into a theory, or making the theory fit the facts.

Strictly speaking, of course, problems are created by ourselves; when I am not hungry, the apple ceases to be a target and there is no gap. Vice versa, the insatiable curiosity of Kepler made him see a problem where nobody saw one before—why the planets move as they do. But the motivational aspect of problem-solving, and the exploratory drive in general, have already been discussed.

There is also a different way of creating problems—for others to solve. Economy in art consists in implying its message in the gaps between the words, as it were. Words, we saw, are mere stepping-stones for thoughts; the meaning must be interpolated; by making the gaps just wide enough, the artist compels his audience to exert its imagination, and to re-create, to some extent, the experience behind the message. But this aspect has also been discussed already, and no longer concerns us.

Bridging the Gap

The process of bridging the gap between the perceived problem and its solution is described in an oft-quoted passage by Karl Mach:

The subject who wishes for a tree to be laid across a stream to enable him to cross it, imagines in fact the problem as already solved.

649

In reflecting that the tree must have previously been transported to the river, and previously to that it must have been felled, etc., he proceeds from the target-situation to the given situation, along a road which he will re-trace in the reverse direction, through a reversed sequence of operations, when it comes to actually constructing the bridge.[1]

This quotation has a long ancestry. It goes back—as Polya (1938) has shown in a remarkable paper—to Pappus' classic distinction between the analytical method, which treats the unknown solution of a geometrical problem as if it were already known, then inquires from what antecedent it has been derived, and so on backward from antecedent to antecedent, until one arrives at a fact or principle already known; and the synthetic method which, starting from the point reached last in the analysis, reverses the process.

However, the traditional distinction between analytical and synthetical method is full of pitfalls, and, though 'thinking backwards' from the unknown to the given plays an important role in mathematical reasoning, this is by no means always the case in problem-solving; moreover 'forward' and 'backward' are often quite arbitrarily used by taking topological metaphors too literally. If I aim my rifle at the target and then pull the trigger, it would be ridiculous to say that I was 'thinking backward' from target to trigger; I was merely demonstrating the trivial fact that in all goal-directed activities one always has to 'keep one's eyes on the target'—which can be taken either literally or metaphorically. The chess player's aim is to capture the opponent's king, either by directly attacking his defences, or by gaining such an advantage in material that the king will be at his mercy. But the player rarely reasons backward from an anticipated mate position—this happens only at dramatic combinative stages; as a rule he looks around the board to see 'what's in the position', explores the possibilities, and then considers what strategical or tactical advantages he can derive from it.

If I wanted to find out whether I am a descendant of Spinoza (as a crackpot uncle of mine once asserted), I could follow one of two methods, or a combination of both. I could trace Spinoza's descendants as they branch out downwards, or I could trace my own ancestors branching out and up; or start at both ends and see whether the branches meet. The example is a paraphrase from the *Logique de Port Royal*, whose authors seem to equate the upward process with analysis, the downward one with synthesis. Spinoza, incidentally, had no descendants.

Returning to Mach's example, the following would perhaps be a more realistic way of approaching the problem. To get to my target I must cross this stream. This conclusion is arrived at by keeping my eyes both on the target and on my own position—by glancing in alternation forward and back as it were. Since I must cross the stream, let's look for a bridge. There is no bridge. Is there perhaps a boat somewhere? No, there is not. Can I wade across? Yes—no, it's too cold. I have found three analogies with past methods of solving a problem, in my repertory of simple routines. If I wish to be pedantic I can say that the rules of the river-crossing skill allowed me three choices, three different stratagems, each of which I tried out implicitly, as a hypothesis. But surveying the lie of the land I find all three obstructed. What can be done? I must search for some other routine which fits the situation. Mach's suggestion to fell a tree is not a very practical one—I saw only once a bridge across a swollen gully built that way, by natives in Uzbekistan—but I have no axe and we are not in Uzbekistan. So, roll up your trousers, and let's hope the water is not too icy.

This is the hum-drum routine of planning and problem-solving in every-day life. It means, firstly, searching for a matrix, a skill which will 'bridge the gap'. The matrix is found by way of analogy (or 'association by similarity'), that is to say, by recognizing that the situation is, for my present intents and purposes, the same as some past situations. I then try to apply the same skill which helped in those past situations, to the present lie of the land. In the above example I have tried three successive stratagems—I have made three hypotheses—and after two have failed completely, I reverted to the third, which offered the only solution, though a far from perfect one. In other words, I have settled for an approximation. Most problems in practical life and in the history of science admit of no better solution.

A point to be noted is that even in this trivial example, the solution does not proceed in a single line from target to starting point, or vice versa, but by a branching out of hypotheses—of possible strategies— from one end, or both ends, until one or several branches meet, as in the Spinoza example. Furthermore, in a real geneaological search, the expert would eliminate unlikely branches and concentrate on those which for geographical or other reasons seem more promising. We have here, on a miniature scale as it were, that groping in a vaguely sensed direction, towards the 'good combination', the 'hooking of the proper atoms' (Poincaré), which I have discussed in Book One, VIII. However, in these trivial examples the groping and searching is done on the conscious or fringe-conscious level, and what we are looking for to bridge the gap is merely some routine trick in our repertory; a practical skill which will fit the particular lie of the land. In other words, the fanning out of hypotheses, the trial-and-check procedures in simple thinking routines, reflect the flexibility of the skill, which can operate through several sub-skills or equipotential lines of action, according to feedback from the environment.

These sub-skills of symbolic thought have been discussed in various contexts. They range from the implicit codes of grammar, syntax, and commonsense logic, through the operational rules of extrapolation, interpolation, transposition, schematization (exaggeration and simplification), and so forth, to the special rules of such special games as vector-analysis or bio-chemistry. But even these very special and complex skills can be practised by sheer routine; and vice versa some of the most original discoveries arose out of relatively simple problems. Complexity of thought is no measure of originality.

Searching for a Code

Polya defines a routine problem as one 'which can be solved either by substituting special data into a formerly solved general problem, or by following step by step, without any trace of originality, some well-worn, conspicuous example'.[2] He contrasts these routines with the 'rules of discovery': 'The first rule of discovery is to have brains and good luck. The second rule of discovery is to sit tight and wait till you get a bright idea.'[3] And he defines a 'bright idea' as 'a sudden leap of the imagination, a flash of genius'.[4]

However, most practical and theoretical problems are solved at some level between these two extremes. Polya's definition of routine is too narrow and rigid; it does not take into account the great flexibility, for instance, of sensory-motor skills such as rock-climbing, or glass-blowing, or playing an instrument in an uninspired but technically accomplished manner. In symbolic thinking we find equally flexible skills which are nevertheless routine: solicitors dictating a document or brief; interpreters at public congresses dictating *ad hoc* into the multi-lingual earphone-circuits; politicians on whistle-stop tours reeling off variations on well-worn themes. These are routine performances in Polya's sense of 'substituting special data into general equations'; but the equation, the code, leaves in these cases many more degrees of freedom than does a mathematical formula, and the act of 'substituting special data' has varying degrees of trickiness. Even to a skilled and expert translator, for instance, it often happens that he has no ready-made idiom or turn of phrase in his repertory to substitute for the original. He must improvise some approximation, perhaps a metaphor, to cover the meaning—which is a much higher skill, involving a degree of originality.

Turning to more difficult problems, of the type which Duncker and Maier put to their subjects, we find routine solutions combined with intimations of originality, and we shall recognize an increasing number of those factors, in embryonic shape as it were, which we saw at work in the creative process.

The degree of originality which a subject will display depends, *ceteris paribus*, on the nature of the challenge—that is, the novelty and unexpectedness of the situation. Familiar situations are dealt with by habitual methods; they can be recognized, at a glance, as analogous in some essential respect to past experiences which provide a ready-made rule to cope with them. The more new features a task contains, the more difficult it will be to find the relevant analogy, and thereby the appropriate code to apply to it. We have seen (Book One, VIII, XVII) that one of the basic mechanisms of the Eureka process is the discovery of a hidden analogy; but 'hiddenness' is again a matter of degrees. How hidden is a hidden analogy, and where is it hidden? And what does the word 'search' mean in this context? In the terms of the present theory it means a process of scanning, of bringing successive, perceptual or conceptual analyser-codes to bear on the problem; to try out whether the problem will match this type of filter or that, as the occulist tries out a series of lenses in the frame before the client's eyes. Yet the word 'search', so often used in the context of problem-solving, is apt to create confusion because it implies that I know beforehand what I am searching for, whereas in fact I do not. If I search for a lost collar-stud, I put a kind of filter into my 'optical frame' which lets only collar-studs and similar shapes pass, and rejects everything else—and then go looking through my drawers. But most tasks in problem-solving necessitate applying the reverse procedure: the subject looks for a clue, the nature of which he does not know, except that it should be a 'clue' (*Ansatzpunkt, point d'appui*), a link to a type of problem familiar to him. Instead of looking through a given filter-frame for an object which matches the filter, he must try out one frame after another to look at the object before his nose, until he finds the frame into which it fits, i.e. until the problem presents some familiar aspect—which is then perceived as an analogy with past experience and allows him to come to grips with it.

This search for the appropriate matrix, or rule of the game to tackle the process, is never quite random; the various types of guidance at the fumbling, groping, trying stages have been discussed before. Among the criteria which distinguish originality from routine are the *level of consciousness* on which the search is conducted, the *type of guidance* on which the subject relies, and the *nature of the obstacle* which he has to overcome.

Degrees of Originality

In one of Maier's ingenious experiments the problem set to the subject was to catch hold at the same time of two thin strings hung from the ceiling so wide apart that he could only get hold of one at a time. The only available tool was a pair of pliers. The solution is to tie the pliers to one string and set it into pendular motion. The crucial point of the experiment, however, is described as follows:[5]

'If the subject had not spontaneously solved the problem *within ten minutes*, Maier supplied him with a hint; he would "accidentally" brush against one of the strings, causing it to swing gently. Of those who solved the problem after this hint, the average interval between hint and solution was only *forty-two seconds*. . . . Most of those subjects who solved the problem immediately after the hint *did so without any realization that they had been given one*. The "idea" of making a pendulum with pliers seemed to arise spontaneously.' (My italics.)

Here we have a beautifully ambiguous example of what looks like 'unconscious' guidance. Obviously there is a world of difference between this kind of thing, and the nature of the sub-conscious processes which produce Kekulé's serpent dream or Poincaré's discovery of the Fuchsian functions. Maier's subjects seem to have 'cottoned on' to the solution on the pre-conscious or fringe-conscious level of awareness. Poincaré's inspiration was derived from the creative powers of the 'underground'.

Nevertheless, we notice that while trivial tasks, in so far as they require any reflection at all, are solved in full daylight as it were, with the focus of awareness on the target, even problems of moderate difficulty, such as Maier's, require a type of guidance on a different level. Frequently the difficulty arises not from the objective novelty of the problem, but from its 'embeddedness' in the subject's mind. In Book One (p. 189) I have described an experiment of Duncker's in which an object was so embedded in its visible role as a 'pendulum weight' that the student was unable to conceive of it in the role of a 'hammer'. 'Embeddedness' is a trivial version of the occasional 'snowblindness' of genius. In both cases the difficulty lies in going against routine—in discarding the most obvious or likely matrix that offers itself and thus gets into the way of the more unlikely one which will do the job. But again there is more than a mere difference in degrees between overcoming the perceptual attachment of the weight to the string, and overcoming the millennial attachment of the human mind to the all-too-plausible axioms of Aristotelian physics.

'Thinking aside' also occurs on all intermediate levels of difficulty. It may take the form of switching to visual imagery—as in the problem of the Buddhist monk (Book One, p. 183); or of re-stating the problem in different terms; or letting one's attention wander, guided by some nascent, cloudy analogy. A good example is the Duncker-puzzle about the two trains and the bird. Two goods-trains, a hundred miles apart, start moving towards each other, each at a speed of twenty miles per hour. A silly bird, frightened by the starting hiss of one of the trains, flies away at thirty miles per hour in a straight line along the railway track until it meets the other train; it reverses its direction until it meets the first train, then turns again, and so forth. What distance will the bird cover in its flight to and fro until the two trains meet?

To compute the sum of the series of flight-stretches is a rather complicated task. But if we think aside, forget about the distances covered by the bird, and compute the *time* until the two trains will meet—two and a half hours—we see at once that the bird has also flown for two and a half hours and hence covered a *total* of seventy-five miles. The puzzle reflects in miniature Galileo's epocal discovery of the laws of free fall—by switching his attention from the spatial to the temporal aspects of the process.

Another famous Duncker problem is how to bring up exactly six pints of water from a river, when you have only two containers, one measuring nine, the other four pints. You fiddle around, decant in your imagination the big container twice into the smaller one, throwing the water each time back into the river. This leaves you with one pint which you can keep in the bigger or put into the smaller container—but that does not help because now you cannot isolate the five pints to which the single pint must be added. The solution is simply to switch from *addition* to *subtraction*: you keep your pint in the smaller container, and fill it up from the larger one—it will now only take $4-1=3$ pints, leaving $9-3=6$ pints in the large jug. Different people solve this problem by different methods. Polya gives an analytical explanation; personally I found that with most people the click occurs through the reversal of the direction of thought from addition to subtraction—from figure to background—a phenomenon we frequently met in discovery.

At a certain level of problem-solving even a healthy kind of illogicality, of disregarding apparent contradictions, makes its appearance —as in the image of the monk meeting his alter-ego. But enough has been said to show that as the challenge becomes more provoking, the nature of the guidance which directs the search for the right type of matrix to bear on the problem, becomes more intuitive, more remote from the normal routine of thinking, and that extra-conscious processes play an increasingly important part. And thus, having started from the base of the hierarchy, we arrive at last at the roof, which we have surveyed in the first volume but had left hanging in the air: the act of discovery.

The term 'bisociation' is meant to point to the independent, autonomous character of the matrices which are brought into contact in the creative act, whereas associative thought operates among members of a single pre-existing matrix. But we have seen that this is a relative, not an absolute criterion, because the members of a matrix are subskills, i.e. matrices in their own right on a subordinate level of the hierarchy, and the degree of their integration, i.e. the coherence of the matrix, varies according to case. In matrices which have become fully automatized, the code alone determines which member shall act in which order—the pedant always takes the same route to his office, his strategy is fixed once and for all, and has become incorporated into the code. But the more flexible a skill, the greater the part played by strategy. Thus in the problem about the trains and the bird, the subject must compute the distance D flown by the bird, and he knows that distances are computed by the rule of the game $D = v.t$. The velocity v of the bird is given, and he could get the t in a jiffy by substituting for it the time taken by the trains until they crash ($t = 100/40 = 2\frac{1}{2}$). Both the formula, and the process of substitution, are familiar sub-skills in the subject's repertory of habits, and should function as members of the matrix. However, owing to the unusual lie of the land—i.e. the way the data are presented—his strategy breaks down, the matrix goes to pieces, and its members function as independent entities. Once this has occurred it would require a certain originality to combine them again. We might even be generous and say, that to re-combine them would be a minor bisociative act.

Thus the degree of independence of the matrices or submatrices which combine in the solution of a problem, can only be judged with reference to the subject's mental organization. Any boy of the sixth form can derive the Pythagorean theorem, which he has previously learned, as a matter of routine; but to discover it for himself would require a high degree of originality.

I hope I have laid sufficient emphasis on the fact that originality must be measured on subjective scales and that any self-taught novelty is a minor bisociative act. This taken for granted, let me recapitulate the criteria which distinguish bisociative originality from associative routine.

Association and Bisociation

The first criterion was the previous independence of the mental skills or universes of discourse which are transformed and integrated into the novel synthesis of the creative act. The student solving the train-bird problem is entitled to shout Eureka because his mathematical skills are so poorly integrated (or so easily dislocated) that the act of 'hooking them together' appears to him a novel discovery. The more unlikely or 'far-fetched' the mediating matrix M_2—i.e. the more independent from M_1—the more unexpected and impressive the achievement. The creative act could be described as the highest form of learning because of the high improbability (or anti-chance probability) of the solution.

If we now turn from subjective originality to discoveries which are new in actual fact, we again find the previous independence of the components that went into the 'good combination' to be a measure of achievement. Historically speaking, the frames of reference of magnetism and electricity, of physics and chemistry, of corpuscles and waves, developed separately and independently, both in the individual and the collective mind, until the frontiers broke down. And this breakdown was not caused by establishing gradual, tentative connections between individual members of the separate matrices, but by the amalgamation of two realms as wholes, and the integration of the laws of both realms into a unified code of greater universality. Multiple discoveries and priority disputes do not diminish the objective, historical novelty produced by these major bisociative events—they merely prove that the time was ripe for that particular synthesis.

Minor, subjective bisociative processes do occur on all levels, and are the main vehicle of untutored learning. But objective novelty comes into being only when subjective originality operates on the highest level of the hierarchies of existing knowledge.

The discoveries of yesterday are the truisms of tomorrow, because we can add to our knowledge but cannot subtract from it. When two frames of reference have become integrated into one it becomes difficult to imagine that previously they existed separately. The synthesis looks deceptively self-evident, and does not betray the imaginative effort it needed to put its component parts together. In this respect the artist gets a better deal than the scientist. The changes of style in the representative arts, the discoveries which altered our frames of perception, stand out as great landmarks for all to see. The true creativity of the innovator in the arts is more dramatically evident and more easily distinguished from the routine of the mere practitioner than in the sciences, because art (and humour) operate primarily through the transitory *juxtaposition* of matrices, whereas science achieves their permanent integration into a cumulative and hierarchic order. Laurence Olivier in Hamlet is perceived as Olivier and as Hamlet at the same time; but when the curtain goes down, the two personae separate again, and do not become amalgamated into a higher unit which is later combined with others into still higher units.

A further criterion of the creative act was that it involves several *levels of consciousness*. In problem-solving pre- and extra-conscious guidance makes itself increasingly felt as the difficulty increases; but in the truly creative act both in science and art, underground levels of the hierarchy which are normally inhibited in the waking state play a decisive part. It is perhaps significant that the German word for the Creator is *Schöpfer*, and for creating *schöpfen*—'to scoop' in the sense of drawing water in buckets from a well. The Creator is thus visualized as creating the world out of His own depth, and the creative mind with a small c is supposed to apply a similar procedure. But whatever the inner sources on which the Lord of Genesis drew while his spirit hovered over the dark waters, in the case of humble mortals the sources are in the phylogenetically and ontogenetically older, underground layers of his mind. He can only reach them through a temporary regression to earlier, more primitive, less specialized levels of mentation, through a *reculer pour mieux sauter*. In this respect the creative act parallels the process of biological regeneration —the liberation of genetic potentials normally under restraint, through the de-differentiation of damaged tissues. Thus the creative process involves levels of the mind separated by a much wider span than in any other mental activity—except in pathological states, which represent a *reculer sans sauter*. The emotional manifestations of the Eureka act—sudden illumination followed by abreaction and catharsis—also testify to its subconscious origins; they are to some extent comparable to the cathartic effects of the analyst's method of bringing 'repressed complexes' into the patient's consciousness.

The re-structuring of mental organization effected by the new discovery implies that the creative act has a revolutionary or *destructive* side. The path of history is strewn with its victims: the discarded isms of art, the epicycles and phlogistons of science.

Associative skills, on the other hand, even of the sophisticated kind which require a high degree of concentration, do not display the above features. Their biological equivalents are the activities of the organism while in a state of dynamic equilibrium with the environment—as distinct from the more spectacular manifestations of its regenerative potentials. The skills of reasoning rely on habit, governed by well-established rules of the game; the 'reasonable person'—used as a standard norm in English common law—is level-headed instead of multi-level-headed; adaptive and not destructive; an enlightened conservative, not a revolutionary; willing to learn under proper guidance, but unable to be guided by his dreams.

The main distinguishing features of associative and bisociative thought may now be summed up, somewhat brutally, as follows:

Habit	*Originality*
Association within the confines of a given matrix	Bisociation of independent matrices
Guidance by pre-conscious or extra-conscious processes	Guidance by sub-conscious processes normally under restraint

Habit	*Originality*
Dynamic equilibrium	Activation of regenerative potentials
Rigid to flexible variations on a theme	Super-flexibility (*reculer pour mieux sauter*)
Repetitiveness	Novelty
Conservative	Destructive-Constructive

And thus we are back where we left off in the first book; the circle is closed.

APPENDIX I: ON LOADSTONES
AND AMBER

I have compared (Book One, X) the constructive periods in the evolution of science to river-estuaries in which previously separate branches of knowledge merge in a series of bisociative acts. The present appendix is meant to illustrate the process by a few salient episodes from the history of magnetism and electricity—two fields of study which, until the beginning of the nineteenth century, had developed on independent lines, and seemed to be in no way related. Their merging was due to the discovery of unitary laws of a previously unsuspected kind underlying the variety of phenomena, and took physics a decisive step forward towards a universal synthesis.

The Greeks, fortunately perhaps, had not paid much attention to the antics of loadstones and amber; they had shrugged them off as freak phenomena. Aristotle had hardly anything to say about them— had he laid down the law on magnetism and electricity, as he did in other domains of physics, the story might have been different. As it happened, both sciences started from scratch in the seventeenth century, just at a time when scholasticism had to yield to the empirical approach. This smoothed their path of progress—but even so, progress was neither smooth nor continuous.

Apart from some casual references in earlier sources, the first landmark in the history of magnetism in Europe is a manuscript, dated 1269, by a French crusader, Petrus Peregrinus from Picardy. It gives a detailed description of two types of mariner's compass (which apparently had been in use for at least a century): a magnetized needle either floating on a stick in a bowl of water, or turning on a vertical axle. Peregrine further described his experiments with a spherical loadstone which he had fashioned, defining its poles and the attractive and repellent properties of its surface; yet he shared the contemporary belief that the source of the 'virtue' which attracted the compass needle was located in the sky—in the Polar Star or the Great Bear.

During the next three hundred years no further progress seems to have been made—except for some improvements of the compass and attempts to measure magnetic declination, caused by the puzzling discovery that the direction of the needle deviated at different places to different degrees from the direction of the Polar Star.

The next landmark is Dr. William Gilbert of Colchester, court physician to Queen Elizabeth, the first great English experimentalist. Gilbert put both magnetism and electricity on the map—or rather, on two separate maps; his influence on his younger contemporaries, Kepler and Galileo, was enormous. Gilbert's fundamental discovery— in fact the only important discovery made in the whole history of magnetism as an independent science—is again one of those which, in retrospect, appear deceptively simple. He found that the power which attracted the magnetic needle was not in the skies but in the earth: that the earth itself was a huge spherical loadstone. He arrived at this conclusion by making, as Peregrine had done, a spherical magnet, and exploring the behaviour of a minute compass-needle on its surface. As he moved the needle over his globe, he saw that it behaved exactly as the needle of the mariner's compass behaved on a sea journey—both with regard to its north-south alignment and to its 'dip', which increased the closer the needle approached either of the poles. He concluded that his spherical loadstone was a model of the earth which therefore must be a magnet.*

So the secret of the compass-needle was solved by ascribing magnetic properties to the earth—there remained only the secret of the nature of magnetism itself. Gilbert's book, *De Magnete*, was published A.D. 1600—the same year in which Kepler joined forces with Tycho de Brahe to lay the foundations of the new astronomy; the symbolic year which, like a watershed, divides medieval from modern philosophy. Gilbert, born in 1544, stood, like Kepler, astride the watershed: with one foot in the brave new world of experimental science, the other stuck in Aristotelian animism. His descriptions of how magnetism works are modern; his explanations of its causes are medieval: he regards the magnetic force as a living emanation from the spirit or soul of the loadstone. The earth, being a giant loadstone, also has a soul—its magnetic virtue—and so have the heavenly bodies.

'Magnetic force is animate, or imitates the soul; and in many things surpasses the human soul while this is bound up in the organic body.'[1]

The actions of the magnetic virtue are 'without error ... quick, definite, constant, directive, motive, imperant, harmonious ... it reaches out like an arm clasping round the attracted body and drawing it to itself. ... It must needs be light and spiritual so as to enter the iron'—but it must also be a material, subtle vapour, an ether or effluvium. Even the earth's rotation is somehow connected with magnetism: 'In order that the Earth may not perish in various ways, and be brought from confusion, she turns herself about by magnetic and primary virtue.'[2]

Thus Gilbert's book, which enjoyed uncontested authority for the next two hundred years, postulated on the one hand action at a distance, but asserted on the other the existence of an effluvium or ether which passes 'like a breath' between the attracting bodies. It was also a major factor in creating semantic confusion: the word 'magnetism', which originally referred to the properties of a type of ore mined in Magnesia, a province of Thessaly, came soon to be applied to any kind of attraction or affinity, physical, psychological, or metaphorical ('animal magnetism', 'Mesmerism', etc.). But as long as the study of the behaviour of magnets remained an isolated field of research, no further progress could be made. In 1621 van Helmont, and in 1641 Athanasius Kircher, published books on the subject which added nothing new to it, but dwelt at length on the alleged wound-healing properties of magnets; Kircher's book carried a whole section on the 'magnetism' of love, and ended with the dictum that the Lord is the magnet of the universe. Newton took no interest in magnetism except for some remarks in the third book of the *Principia*[3] to the effect that the magnetic force seemed to vary approximately with the inverse *cube* of the distance; while Descartes extended his theory of cosmic vortices to cover both magnetic and electric phenomena. The main subjects of interest were the variations in the positions of the earth's magnetic poles which, to the navigators' distress, were found to wander around like floating kidneys. This led to the kind of controversy characteristic of most periods of stagnation in the history of science; thus one Henry Bond of London town, a 'Teacher of Navigation', published in 1676 a book, *The Longitude Found*, based on the theory that the magnetic poles lagged behind the earth's daily rotation. This thesis was torn to pieces in another book, *The Longitude Not Found*, by Peter Blackborough.

Even the great Halley went haywire where magnetism was concerned: he proposed that the earth was a kind of solar system in miniature, with an inner core and an outer shell, both of them magnetized, and a luminous fluid between them to provide light for the people living on the surface of the inner core; this luminous effluvium escaping through the earth's pores gave rise to the *aurora borealis*. Halley was the greatest astronomer and one of the leading scientific minds of the age, who had published the first modern magnetic chart in Mercator's projection, based on his own patient observations; but his wild speculations indicate that the element of the fantastic was firmly embedded in the concept of magnetism—as it still is in our day. Children are still fascinated by compasses and magnets, governed by a force more mysterious than gravity—because the latter is taken for granted from earliest experience whereas magnetism cannot be sensed, and not only attracts but also repels. No wonder that this unique phenomenon, while considered in isolation, had led those who studied it round in circles in a blocked matrix.

But although, for nearly two centuries, the study of magnetism made no progress, Gilbert's work had a fertile influence on other branches of science. The loadstone became the archetype of action-at-a-distance, and paved the way for the recognition of universal gravity. Without the demonstrable phenomena of magnetic attraction, people would have been even more reluctant to exchange the traditional view that heavy bodies tended towards the centre of the universe, for the implausible suggestion that all heavenly and earthly bodies were tugging at each other 'with ghostly fingers' across empty space. Even the magic properties attributed to magnetism, and the very ambiguity of its concept, proved to be unexpectedly stimulating to the tortuous line of advance which led via Mesmerism and hypnosis to contemporary forms of psychiatry.

The next turning point is Coulomb's discovery, in 1785, that the inverse square law applied to magnetism too, as it applied to gravity. It must have looked at the time as if these two kinds of action-at-a-distance would soon turn out to be based on the same principle—as Kepler and Descartes thought they were; as if a great merger of sciences were in the offing. But that synthesis is still a matter of the future; instead of merging with gravity, magnetism entered into a much less obvious union with electricity.

The first mention of electricity on record occurs in the fragments of the *History of Physics* by Theophrastus, the successor of Aristotle at the head of the Athenean Lyceum. He innocently remarks that when amber is rubbed it acquires the curious virtue of attracting flimsy objects. The Greek word for amber is *elektron*. Although the Greeks were not interested in the *elektron*'s virtues, *Forever Amber* would be an appropriate motto for modern science.

For two thousand years little more is heard of electricity, until we again come to Dr. Gilbert, who demonstrated that the peculiar properties of amber were shared by glass, sulphur, crystals, resin, and a number of other substances, which he accordingly called 'electrics'. To account for electric attraction he created the concept of an electric effluvium, as distinct from the magnetic effluvium—but with an equally lasting influence on further developments.

During the next century, advance again was slow. Members of the Italian Academia del Cimento (a short-lived forerunner of the Royal Society) continued Gilbert's experiments, and added a few observations to them. The main events of the century were the discovery of electric repulsion and the construction, by Guericke, of the first machine for the continuous production of electricity. The machine consisted of a sulphur ball, the size of a child's head, which was rotated on an axle while the experimenter's hand was pressed against its surface, thus generating a frictional charge. Guericke also discovered, and described, the phenomena of electrical conduction and induction—but nobody paid any attention to them, and they had to be rediscovered in the next century. This illustration of discontinuity in progress was followed, almost immediately, by yet another one. In the first years of the eighteenth century an Englishman, Hawkesbee, invented a new machine to produce electricity by replacing Guericke's sulphur sphere with one of glass—which was a vast improvement, but again passed unnoticed. The glass-friction machine was re-invented and improved in the 1740s; the sphere was replaced by a cylinder, pads were used instead of the hand, and the machine was equipped with insulated wire conductors—the conductivity of metal having been meanwhile discovered by Gray and Du Fay, who also made the basic distinction between conductors and insulators.

The fact that the electric virtue produced by this machine could be carried by wires over distances of hundreds of feet led to the concept of a flow or *current*—the electric effluvium was now regarded as a kind of liquid, or liquid fire, flowing through the wire. But the phenomena of electric repulsion led Du Fay to assume two kinds of electric fluid—like kinds repelling, unlike kinds attracting each other, on the analogy of magnetic poles. Benjamin Franklin did not like the idea of two fluids; he believed that the polarity could be explained by a surplus or a deficiency of a single fluid, designated by a plus and a minus sign—a rather unhappy suggestion which, to this day, is apt to confuse the minds of hopeful students. A further complication arose from the fact that while the electric fluid was demonstrably unable to flow across insulating substances such as glass or air, it nevertheless induced electric charges on the other side of the insulator; so one now had to assume that there were two kinds of electricity: the first a fluid running through a wire, the second an etheric effluvium acting at a distance.

Thus by the middle of the eighteenth century the whole science was in a state of confused and creative anarchy—as cosmology and mechanics had been a hundred years earlier, before Newton. 'We cannot follow the twists of theory in the minds of these men', Pledge wrote about Franklin and his contemoraries;[4] yet they went happily ahead, theorizing in dirty kitchens and experimenting with kites, lightning rods, luminous discharges in vacuum tubes, detonating inflammable spirits, electrocuting birds, mice, and occasionally themselves. I have mentioned before (p. 204) the sensation created by the discovery of the condenser in the shape of the Leyden Jar—due to accidental shock; a few years later, the expression 'an electrifying effect' had already gone into metaphorical use. According to the *Oxford Dictionary*, armies were the first to be 'electrified'—by courage (Burke); theatre audiences came next (Emerson). Typical of the happy confusion was Gray's theory, which he confided to the secretary of the Royal Society on the day before his death, that the planets were moved round the sun by a simple electric force. To demonstrate this, a small pendulum weight was held on a string over an electrically charged globe, and lo! the weight began to describe circles and ellipses round the globe, always in the correct direction from west to east—due, of course, as was later proved, to small unconscious jerks which the experimenter imparted to the string.

The first indirect intimation of the shape of things to come was the demonstration (around 1780) by Cavendish and Coulomb that the action-at-a-distance type of electricity (i.e. the electrostatic field) was governed by the same inverse square law as magnetism and gravity. Thus mathematics entered into the study of electricity and magnetism, although their physical nature was anybody's guess. The mathematical tools were ready, in the shape of differential equations which French mathematicians of the eighteenth century—Lagrange, Laplace,

Legendre—had worked out for gravity and mechanics; then Poisson lifted the basic equations of the gravitational potential out of their original frame of reference, and applied them first to the electrostatic, then to the magnetic field. He was able to import these rules of the game from a foreign playing-field by the bold move of substituting 'electric charge' and 'magnetic pole strength' for 'gravitational mass' in the equation—and it worked. Newton's inverse square law, Lagrange's and Poisson's equations, were among the first striking instances revealing the unity of mathematical laws underlying the diversity of phenomena.

In the meantime, Luigi Galvani, Professor of Anatomy at the University of Bologna, had spent some fifteen years working on a theory of 'animal electricity'. On September 20th, 1786, he recorded one of his experiments, which was to make history. He attached a nerve-muscle preparation of a dissected frog to a copper hook and hung the hook on an iron railing. Whenever one of the frog's legs touched the iron, it jerked away and contracted violently. Now it was already known that electric discharges from Leyden Jars or lightning rods caused muscles to contract; but since the iron railing could not be a source of electricity, Galvani drew the logical conclusion that the electricity which caused the contraction was generated in the muscle itself under the stimulus of the metallic contact. Like so many neat and logical deductions it happened to be wrong; but it was an error which proved to be as immensely fruitful as Columbus' or Kepler's errors. The muscle convulsion had indeed been an electrical phenomenon; however, as Volta was soon to prove, the current had been generated not inside the muscle but by the contact of the two different metals, copper and iron—the prototype of the Voltaic battery (the frog's leg touching the railing closed the circuit). Galvani's theory had been a wrong move in the right direction, for the experiment *did* demonstrate the sensitivity of certain living tissues to minute electric currents; after a few decades of the usual detours, Sömmering compared nerves to electrical telegraph wires; and from the middle of the nineteenth century onwards electric phenomena played an increasing part in physiology, until finally the electro-chemistry of living tissues became a single, integrated matrix.

In the domain of inanimate matter, the Voltaic battery, inspired by Galvani's frogs, led to a parallel synthesis of electricity and chemistry. The battery gave the experimenters for the first time ample supplies of electric current—which neither the friction machines nor the

Leyden Jar had been able to do. It taught them not only that the chemical interaction of metals produced electricity; but also that an electric current sent through certain chemicals led to their decomposition. In 1806 Davy tentatively suggested that chemical affinity had an electrical basis. But nearly a century had to pass until, in 1897, Thompson discovered that a certain type of electrical discharge—the so-called cathode rays—consisted of particles smaller than atoms; and that in these particles 'matter derived from different sources such as hydrogen, oxygen, etc.—is one and the same kind, this matter being the substance from which the chemical elements are built up'.[5] Thompson's 'elementary corpuscles' were later named 'electrons'.

But let me return for a moment to the Voltaic battery. The abundant flow of current which it produced was so startling that it was at first doubted whether this 'electric fluid' was the same kind of thing which came in sparks out of the older contraptions. Comparison of their effects led to the realization that the discharges of static electricity from a Leyden Jar had a higher potential or tension, whereas the flow from the battery had a low potential but carried a greater quantity of current. Thus the distinction was made between the potential (voltage), roughly comparable to the gradient of a river-bed, and the quantity of liquid (amperage) that passed through it. But only fifty years later did Faraday realize that the spark from a Leyden Jar could be regarded as a short-lived current; then came Maxwell, who treated currents as moving charges, thus finally unifying the two kinds of electricity: 'frictional' and 'Voltaic'.

In the meantime, however, that other grand synthesis got underway: the unification of electricity and magnetism. There were several steps. The first link was established in 1820 by the observation of Hans Christian Oersted in Copenhagen that if an electric current flowed through a wire in the vicinity of a magnetic compass, the needle was deflected and turned into a position at right angles to the wire. The news created an immediate sensation in Paris, where Ampère's excitable brain gave off a spark bigger than any Leyden Jar: he realized in a single flash that if an electric current produced a magnetic field, as the reaction of the needle indicated, then *all magnetic fields* may be due to electric currents—that magnetism was a by-product of electricity. He let a current run through a spiral coil inside of which he placed a steel needle: it became magnetized, and the first electromagnet was born.*

But how, then, was the 'natural magnetism' of loadstones to be explained, which had no currents running around them? Ampère's answer was that minute currents were circulating in coils inside the atoms of the loadstone. These sub-atomic currents produced magnetic fields, which tended to align themselves with the magnetic field of the biggest loadstone, the earth. The theory at the same time dispensed with the necessity of explaining magnetism by the physical action of poles; it was perhaps the boldest and most surprising idea in this whole development. Unfortunately, Ampère's contemporaries were not 'ripe' for it. To quote D. L. Webster:

> Scientists should have reacted to this surprise better than they did—but scientists are human. The philosophical principle of parsimony in hypotheses should have been their guide. Instead their guide seems to have been habit. Parsimony would have dictated as follows:
>
> 1. Whatever we believe about magnets, we must recognize currents in wires as currents.
> 2. The pole theory of magnets requires us to believe in two types of field producers, poles and currents, whereas Ampère's theory requires only currents.
> 3. The pole theory requires two very different sets of laws for magnetic fields, one for fields due to poles and the other for fields due to currents, whereas Ampère's theory requires only one set of laws.
> 4. Therefore, we shall follow Ampère.

But poles were treated as real for nearly another century.[6]

Yet Ampère's idea was never entirely forgotten. Maxwell compared Ampère's sub-atomic coils to miniature spinning-tops which always tend to preserve the direction of their axes; he tried to magnetize a piece of iron by rotating it fast. In 1913, when Niels Bohr invented his model of the atom as a miniature solar system, it was thought that the orbital motions of the electrons round the nucleus provided the Ampèrean circuits. This turned out to be part of the truth; but the principal source of magnetism was found to be, even more surprisingly, a spinning motion of the electrons round their own axes. An electron, of course, can hardly be said to have an axis since it is now regarded as something in the nature of a blur; but mathematically the model worked, and that is all one can ask for in the present state of physics.

A century after Oersted, magnetism and electricity were finally reduced to a common source.

But I have been anticipating the happy end. The next stage, after Ampère had shown that an electric current will produce a magnetic field, was the discovery by Faraday (in 1831) that magnetism could be 'directly converted into electricity' by moving magnet and conducting coil relative to each other.* This led to the invention of the dynamo, and later of the electric motor; but we are concerned with theory, not with the ubiquitous applications of electric energy.

Faraday, as we know, was a visualizer, who saw the universe patterned by lines of force—like the familiar diagrams of iron filings grouped round a magnet. James Clark Maxwell, who inaugurated the post-Newtonian age in physics, was a super-visualizer. He took Faraday's imaginary lines of force and put them into imaginary tubes carrying a fluid; then he abolished the spaces between the tubes so that they became 'mere surfaces, directing the motion of a fluid filling up all space'—the ether. Next, he applied to this model the rules of a game which bore no relation at all to electro-magnetism—hydrodynamics, with its vortices and eddies and changing pressures.** One conclusion which emerged from this imaginary operation was that all changes in electric and magnetic force (for instance, those caused by an oscillating circuit) sent waves spreading through space; and that these waves had the same transverse character, and the same speed, as light. 'We can scarcely avoid the inference', he wrote in a monumental sentence, 'that light consists in the transverse undulations of the same medium which is the cause of electric and magnetic phenomena.'

Thus after electricity and magnetism had been united, both were now united to light. Electro-magnetic radiations came to be regarded as rapid alternations of electrical and magnetic stresses in space, where each change in the electric stress gives rise to a magnetic stress, which again gives rise to an electric stress and so on. Soon the range of these radiations was shown to comprise not only the visible spectrum between the ultra-violet and the infra-red of radiant heat, but to extend to the ultra-short gamma rays of radioactivity, and to the kilometre-long waves used in radio-communication.

Perhaps the most fascinating aspect of Maxwell's genius is that as soon as he had worked out the mathematical formulation of his theory, he discarded the model by means of which he had reached it. It was as if a man, after climbing a ladder to get a free view over his surroundings, had kicked out the ladder from under him, and remained freely suspended in the air. Gone were the tubes, the vortices, the ether; all that remained were 'fields' of an abstract, non-substantial nature, and the mathematical formalism which described the propagation of real waves in an apparently non-existent medium. It was the great turning point in physical science, when the aspiration to arrive at intelligible, mechanical models was abandoned. This renunciation, born of necessity, soon hardened into dogma—a secular version of the Commandment 'Thou shalt not make unto thee any graven image'—of gods or atoms.*

The transition from model-making to mathematical abstraction is strikingly illustrated by the fact that Maxwell himself left it to others (to Heinrich Rudolph Herz, as it came to pass) to give empirical proof of his electro-magnetic waves. As Crowther wrote:

> The General Equations of the Electro-magnetic Field were more real to him than material phenomena he could know in the laboratory. Physicists have often wondered why Maxwell made no attempt to prove experimentally the existence of electro-magnetic waves. He probably felt he was better acquainted with the waves through the medium of the General Equations, and would 'not have known them any better, perhaps not so well,' if he had met them in the laboratory.[7]

Yet even Maxwell had his blind spots. The electron as a basic, quasi-atomic unit of electricity was clearly implied in his model of ether-vortices, and in his theory of electrolysis. Yet he rejected the concept of 'particles' of electricity as Faraday before had rejected it. Thus, as already mentioned, it was left, to J. J. Thompson to take the next decisive step: the identification of the electron as an elementary unit of electricity, and at the same time an elementary particle of matter. Some fifteen years later Rutherford discovered that the atom had a positively charged nucleus; Moseley discovered that the number of electrons in an atom determined its place in the periodic system; and Bohr made his famous model of electrons circling round the nucleus like planets round the sun. Matter and electricity had merged into a single matrix.

We have followed, though only in the scantest outline, the successive confluences into a vast river-delta, of electricity, magnetism, light, heat, and other electro-magnetic radiations; of chemistry, biochemistry, and atomic physics. This development was, as we have seen

(p. 228), accompanied by the realization that the various 'powers of nature' were merely different forms of energy. In earlier days, and well into the nineteenth century, each of these 'powers' were thought to be contained in a material substance, a subtle fluid or vapour or effluvium: heat in the phlogiston; organic energy in the 'vital fluid'; gravity in the ether; electricity and magnetism in their separate effluvia. The word 'energy' from the Greek *en-ergos* (work) was for the first time used by Thomas Young in 1807 to designate kinetic energy only. But by that time Rumford had already shown by an ingenious experiment that mechanical energy could be converted into heat: he made a blunt boring machine, driven by horses, work against a metal cylinder underwater, and demonstrated that the heat thus produced actually brought the water to the boil. By the middle of the century it became evident that the powers of nature were convertible: mechanical motion into heat, heat into motion, motion into electricity, electricity into magnetism, and so forth. Thus one by one the various 'subtle fluids' dropped out of the game, and were replaced by equations determining the exchange rates, as it were, for the conversion of one kind of energy-currency into another. Lastly, Einstein and his successors taught us that mass and energy, particle and wave, are merely two aspects of one and the same basic process. Only in one respect have they failed so far: in their attempts to link the gravitational field and the electro-magnetic field in a single system of equations, a unified field theory.

NOTES

To p. 662. The 'dip', or magnetic inclination seems to have been discovered independently by Georg Hartmann, a German clergyman, in 1544, and by Robert Norman, a compass-maker from Wapping. Norman and Mercator also anticipated Gilbert by placing the source of magnetic attraction in the earth.

To p. 668. The experiment was actually suggested to Ampère by Arago.

To p. 670. Faraday's original formulation was indeed entirely relativistic. According to Newtonian mechanics, however, it did make a difference whether the wire was moved or the magnet. This paradoxical asymmetry was one of the pincipal considerations which led Einstein to the theory of special relativity (cf. Polànyi, 1957, pp. 10–11).

To p. 670. Vortices had already appeared in Kepler's and Descartes' explanations; and Helmholz, too, had compared the dynamics of fluids with electric currents and magnetic fields; but Maxwell's electro-hydro-dynamics were of an incomparably more refined order.

To p. 671. Maxwell himself was less dogmatic about it. 'For the sake of persons of different types of mind, scientific truth should be presented in different forms and should be regarded as equally scientific whether it appears in the robust form and vivid colouring of a physical illustration or in the tenuity and paleness of a symbolical expression.'

APPENDIX II: SOME FEATURES OF GENIUS

1. THE SENSE OF WONDER

In one of his essays—*The Cutting of an Agate*—William Butler Yeats voiced one of the silliest popular fallacies of our times:

> Those learned men who are a terror to children and an ignominious sight in lovers' eyes, all those butts of a traditional humour where there is something of the wisdom of peasants, are mathematicians, theologians, lawyers, men of science of various kinds.

The fallacy consists in the identification of 'men of science of various kinds' with the lowest kind: the figure of the uninspired pedant in the waxworks of popular imagination (p. 256). One might as well identify 'the artist' with the factory-girls who put in the colour on 'hand-painted' souvenirs.

It is a fallacy of relatively recent origin. Tillyard[1] and Marjorie Nicolson[2] have shown how profoundly the Pythagorean revival had influenced Shakespeare and transformed the Elizabethan world-picture. Perhaps the greatest experience of Milton's youth was peering for the first time through a Galilean telescope:

> Before [his] eyes in sudden view appear
> The secrets of the hoary Deep—a dark
> Illimitable ocean, without bound,
> Without dimension . . .

And we remember John Donne's excitement caused by Kepler's discoveries:

674

Man hath weav'd out a net, and this net throwne
Upon the Heavens, and now they are his owne . . .

The sense of wonder was shared by mystic, poet, and scientist alike; their falling apart dates only from the end of the nineteenth century. In Book One, XI, I have discussed the scientist's motivational drive, and the emotions to which it gives rise: the present appendix is meant to illustrate these general considerations by concrete examples from the lives of a few outstanding men.

Aristotle on Motivation

The mental image that one tries to form of a white-clad, sandalled member of the Pythagorean Brotherhood, living around 530 B.C. in Croton, southern Italy, is necessarily hazy. But at least we know that the Brotherhood was both a scientific academy and a monastic order; that its members led an ascetic communal life where all property was shared, thus anticipating the Essenes and the primitive Christian communities. We know that much of their time was spent in contemplation, and that initiation into the higher mysteries of mathematics, astronomy, and medicine depended upon the purification of spirit and body, which the aspirant had to achieve by abstinences and examinations of conscience. Pythagoras himself, like St. Francis, is said to have preached to animals; the whole surviving tradition indicates that his disciples, while engaged in number-lore and astronomical calculations, firmly believed that a true scientist must be a saint, and that the wish to become one was the motivation of his labours.

The Hippocratics followed a materialist philosophy; yet that wonderfully precise ethical commandment, the Hippocratic Oath, prescribed not only that the physician should do everything in his powers to help the sick, but also that he should refrain, in the patient's house, 'from any act of seduction, of male or female, bond or free'—a truly heroic act of self-denial. The motivation of Greek science in general was summed up in a passage by Aristotle, from which I have briefly quoted before (my italics):

Men were first led to study [natural] philosophy, as indeed they are today, by wonder. At first they felt wonder about the more superficial problems; afterwards they advanced gradually by perplexing themselves over greater difficulties; e.g., the behaviour of the moon, the phenomena of the sun, and the origination of the universe. Now he who is perplexed and wonders believes himself to be ignorant. Hence even the lover of myths is, in a sense, a philosopher, for a myth is a tissue of wonders. Thus if they took to philosophy to escape ignorance, it is patent that they were pursuing science for the sake of knowledge itself, and not for utilitarian applications. This is confirmed by the course of historical development itself. *For nearly all the requisites both of comfort and social refinement had been secured before the quest for this form of enlightenment began.* So it is clear that we do not seek it for the sake of any ulterior application. Just as we call a man free who exists for his own ends and not for those of another, so it is with this which is the only free man's science: it alone of the sciences exists for its own sake.[3]

It is amusing to note Aristotle's belief that applied science and technology had completed their task long before his time—as the italicized lines and other passages in his writings clearly indicate. His statement is somehow biassed, because it does not take into account the utilitarian element in the origin of geometry: land-surveying, and of astronomy: calendar-making. Nevertheless, his summing up of the motives which drove the Greek men of science seems to be by and large true. Thus Archimedes, the greatest of them, was compelled by necessity to invent a whole series of spectacular mechanical devices— including the water screw, and some engines of war which brought him all the fame and glory an inventor can dream of. Yet such was his contempt for these practical inventions that he refused to leave a written record of them. His passions were mathematics and pure science; his famous words, 'give me but a firm spot on which to stand and I will move the earth' reflect a metaphysical fantasy, not an engineer's ambitions. When Syracuse fell in 212 B.C. to the Roman general Marcellus, the sage, in the midst of the turmoil and massacre, was calmly drawing geometrical figures in the sand; according to tradition, his last words were—after being run through the body by a Roman soldier: 'Pray, do not disturb my circles'. Apocryphal or not, that tradition symbolizes the Greek attitude to science as a quest transcending the mortal self.

After the long dark interlude which came to an end with the Pythagorean Renaissance in Italy around A.D. 1500, four men stand highlighted on the stage of history: Copernicus, Tycho, Galileo, Kepler. They were the pioneers of the Scientific Revolution, the men on whose shoulders Newton stood: what do we know about their personal motives—which ultimately changed the face of this planet?

We know least about Copernicus (1473–1543); as a person, he seems to have been a pale, insignificant figure, a timid Canon in the God-forsaken Prussian province of Varmia; his main ambition, as far as one can tell, was to be left alone and not to incur derision or disfavour. As a student in Italy, he had become acquainted with the Pythagorean idea of a sun-centred universe, and for the next thirty or forty years he elaborated his system in secret. Only in the last year before his death, at the age of seventy, did he agree, under pressure of his friends and superiors, to publish it; the first printed copy of his book *On the Revolutions of the Heavenly Spheres* reached him on the day of his death. It is one of the dreariest and most unreadable books that made history, and remained practically unnoticed for the next fifty years, until Kepler took the idea up (the Church turned against it only eighty years after Copernicus's death).

Copernicus was neither an original nor even a progressive thinker; he was, as Kepler later remarked, 'interpreting Ptolemy rather than nature'. He clung fanatically to the Aristotelian dogma that all planets must move in perfect circles at uniform speeds; the first impulse of his long labours originated in his discontent with the fact that in the Ptolemaic system they moved in perfect circles but not at uniform speed. It was the grievance of a perfectionist—in keeping with his crabbed, secretive, stingy character (which every Freudian would gleefully identify as the perfect 'anal' type). Once he had taken the Ptolemaic clockwork to pieces, he began to search for a useful hint how to put it together again; he found it in Aristarchus's heliocentric idea which at that time was much in the air.* It was not so much a new departure as a last attempt to patch up an outdated machinery by reversing the arrangement of its wheels. As a modern historian has said, the fact that the earth moves is 'almost an incidental matter in the system of Copernicus which, viewed geometrically, is just the old Ptolemaic pattern of the skies, with one or two wheels interchanged and one or two of them taken out.'[4]

677

For 'four times nine years', as he later confessed, Copernicus had worked in secret on his book, hugging it to his aching heart—it was the timid Canon's only refuge from a life of frustrations. It was his version of the harmony of the spheres.

Tycho de Brahe (1546–1601) was an irascible, boastful Danish nobleman, trucculent and quixotic, born with a silver spoon in his mouth—to which a silver nose was added later, for his own had been sliced off in a duel with another noble Danish youth, who had the temerity to claim that he was the better mathematician of the two. Devotion to science could hardly assume more heroic proportions. But with Tycho everything was on a heroic scale: his figure (he kept, perhaps for the sake of contrast, a dwarf as a court jester); his eating and drinking, which led to his premature death from a burst bladder —because, with quixotic courtesy, he refused to leave the dinner table to pass water (even his pet animal, a temperamental elk, died of drinking too much beer); his quarrels with the kings he entertained, with the fellow astronomers whom he slandered, and with retainers whom he put in chains. On an even more gigantic scale were his observatories and the instruments—the likes of which the world had never seen—built on his island in the Sund.

At fourteen Tycho had witnessed a partial eclipse of the sun, and 'it struck him as something divine that men could know the motions of the stars so accurately that they were able a long time beforehand to predict their places and relative positions'.[5] From then onward his course was set, and he became the 'Phoenix of Astronomy'—against the resistance of his family who thought such plumage unworthy of a nobleman. The decisive revelation for him was the *predictability* of astronomical events—in contrast to the unpredictability of a child's life among the headstrong Brahes (Tycho had been kidnapped from his cot and brought up by his Uncle Joerge, a squire and admiral). His passion for astronomy began much earlier than Copernicus's and Kepler's, and took a direction almost opposite to theirs: it was not a passion for theory-making but for exact observation. Unlike those two, he was neither frustrated nor unhappy, merely irritated by the triviality of a Danish nobleman's existence among 'horses, dogs, and luxury'.

He took to astronomy not as an escape or metaphysical lifebelt but rather as a hobby—which then turned into the only thing held sacred by that Gargantuan heathen.

.   .   .   .   .

'You cannot help it, Signor Sarsi, that it was granted to me alone to discover all the new phenomena in the sky and nothing to anybody else.'[6] The most conspicuous feature in the character of Galileo (1564–1642) and the cause of his tragic downfall was vanity—not the boisterous and naïve vanity of Tycho, but a hypersensitivity to criticism combined with sarcastic contempt for others: a fatal blend of genius plus arrogance minus humility. There seems to be not a trace here of mysticism, of 'oceanic feeling'; in contrast to Copernicus, Tycho, and Kepler, even to Newton and Descartes who came after him, Galileo is wholly and frighteningly modern in his consistently mechanistic philosophy. Hence his contemptuous dismissal in a single sentence of Kepler's explanation of the tides by the moon's attraction: 'He [Kepler] has lent his ear and his assent to the moon's dominion over the waters, to occult properties and such like *fanciullezze*.'[7] The occult little fancy he is deriding is Kepler's anticipation of Newtonian gravity.

Where, then, in Galileo's personality is the sublime balance between self-asserting and self-transcending motives which I suggested as the true scientist's hallmark? I believe it to be easily demonstrable in his writings on those subjects on which his true greatness rests: the first discoveries with the telescope, the foundations of mechanics, and of a truly experimental science. Where that balance is absent—during the tragic years 1613–33, filled with poisonous polemics, spurious priority claims, and impassioned propaganda for a misleadingly oversimplified Copernican system—in that sad middle period of his life Galileo made no significant contribution either to astronomy or to mechanics. One might even say that he temporarily ceased to be a scientist—precisely because he was entirely dominated by self-asserting motives. The opposite kind of imbalance is noticeable in Kepler's periods of depression, when he entirely lost himself in mystic speculation, astrology, and number-lore. In both these diametrically opposed characters, unsublimated residues of opposite kind temporarily dominated the field, upsetting the equilibrium and leading to scientific sterility.

But in the balanced periods of Galileo, the eighteen happy years in Padua in which most of his epoch-making discoveries in the study of motion were made, and in the last years of resignation, when he completed and revised the *Dialogue Concerning Two New Sciences*—in these creative periods we seem to be dealing with a different kind of person, patiently and painstakingly experimenting and theorizing on the motions of the pendulum; on the free fall and descent along an inclined plane of heavy bodies; on the flight of projectiles; the elasticity, cohesion, and resistance of solid bodies, and the effects of percussion on them; on the buoyancy of 'things which float on the water', and a hundred related matters. Here we have a man absorbed in subjects much less spectacular and conducive to fame than the wonders of the Milky Way and the arguments about the earth's motion—yet delighting in his discoveries, of which only a select few friends and correspondents were informed; delighting in discovery for discovery's sake, in unravelling the laws of order hidden in the puzzling diversity of phenomena.

That order was for Galileo, as it was for Kepler, a mathematical order: 'The book of nature is written in the mathematical language. Without its help it is impossible to comprehend a single word of it.'[8] But unlike Kepler and the Pythagoreans, Galileo did not look at the 'dance of numbers' through the eyes of a mystic. He was interested neither in number-lore nor in mathematics for its own sake—almost alone among the great scientists of his period, he made no mathematical discoveries. Quantitative measurements and formulations were for Galileo simply the most effective tools for laying bare the inherent *rationality of nature*. The belief in this rationality (and in the rationality of nature's creation, the human mind) was Galileo's religion and spiritual salvation—though he did not realize that it was a religion, based on an act of faith.

His revolutionary methods of proving the rationality of the laws governing the universe was later called 'experimental philosophy'—and even later, by the much narrower terms 'experimental science' or 'empirical science'. It was a fertile combination of experimenting and theorizing, which had been tentatively used by some of Galileo's precursors since the fourteenth century—but it was Galileo who elevated it to a modern technique and a philosophical programme. It was a monumental bisociation of the valid elements in Greek thought, transmitted by the Schoolmen (and particularly by the Occamists) on the one hand, and of the experimental knowledge of engineers, artisans, and instrument-makers on the other. The *Dialogue Concerning Two New Sciences* characteristically opens with a most unusual suggestion by Salviati (Galileo's mouthpiece): that, as a philosopher, he had much to learn from mechanics and craftsmen.

Salviati: The constant activity which you Venetians display in your famous arsenal suggests to the studious mind a large field for investigation, especially that part of the work which involves mechanics;

for in this department all types of instruments and machines are constantly being constructed by many artisans, among whom there must be some who, partly by inherited experience and partly by their own observations, have become highly expert and clever in explanation.

Sagredo: You are quite right. Indeed, I myself, being curious by nature, frequently visit this place for the mere pleasure of observing the work of those who, on account of their superiority over other artisans, we call 'first-rank men'. Conference with them has often helped me in the investigation of certain effects including not only those which are striking, but also those which are recondite and almost incredible.[9]

We are reminded of Pythagoras visiting the blacksmith's shop to discover the secret of vibrating chords—to learn from those dark, sweaty, and ignorant men about the harmony of the spheres. This is the point where *hubris* yields to humility; in his best and happiest moments, Galileo achieves not only this transition, but is also transformed from a scientist into a poet. In the midst of his formidable polemical onslaught on the Platonist dualism of despair—which contrasted the perfect, immutable, crystalline heavens to the earthy corruption of generation and decay—his imagination and language suddenly grow wings:

Sagredo: I cannot without great wonder, nay more, disbelief, hear it being attributed to natural bodies as a great honour and perfection that they are impassible, immutable, inalterable, etc.: as, conversely, I hear it esteemed a great imperfection to be alterable, generable, mutable, etc. It is my opinion that the Earth is very noble and admirable by reason of the many and different alterations, mutations, generations, etc., which incessantly occur in it. And if, without being subject to any alteration, it had been all one vast heap of sand, or a mass of jade, or . . . an immense globe of crystal, wherein nothing had ever grown, altered, or changed, I should have esteemed it a wretched lump of no benefit to the Universe, a mass of idleness. . . . What greater folly can be imagined than to call gems, silver, and gold noble and earth and soil base? . . . If there were as great a scarcity of earth as there is of jewels and precious metals, there would be no king who would not gladly give a heap of diamonds and rubies . . . to purchase only so much earth as would suffice to plant a jessamine in a little pot or to set a tangerine in it, that he might see it sprout, grow up, and bring forth goodly leaves, fragrant flowers, and delicate fruit. . . . These men who so extol incorruptibility, inalterability, etc., speak thus, I believe, out of the great desire they have to live long and for fear of death, not considering that, if men had been immortal, they would not have had to come into the world. These people deserve to meet with a Medusa's head that would transform them into statues of diamond and jade that so they might become more perfect than they are.[10]

In another work, Galileo wrote a charming and profound allegory on the motives, methods, and limitations of the 'experimental philosophy' which he had created. The work is *Il Saggiatore*, 'The Assayer' —which has only recently been translated into English, presumably because most of it consists of a querulous, scientifically worthless polemics against the Jesuit scholar Grassi on the subject of comets (which Galileo insisted on treating as optical illusions—largely because Tycho and Grassi held the opposite views). Yet hidden in this nasty bunch of nettles are flowers of rare beauty:

> Once upon a time, in a very lonely place, there lived a man endowed by nature with extraordinary curiosity and a very penetrating mind. For a pastime he raised birds, whose songs he much enjoyed; and he observed with great admiration the happy contrivance by which they could transform at will the very air they breathed into a variety of sweet songs.
> One night this man chanced to hear a delicate song close to his house, and being unable to connect it with anything but some small bird he set out to capture it. When he arrived at a road he found a shephered boy who was blowing into a kind of hollow stick while moving his fingers about on the wood, thus drawing from it a variety of notes similar to those of a bird, though by a quite different method. Puzzled, but impelled by his natural curiosity, he gave the boy a calf in exchange for this flute and returned to solitude. But realizing that if he had not chanced to meet the boy he would never have learned of the existence of a new method of forming musical notes and the sweetest songs, he decided to travel to distant places in the hope of meeting with some new adventure.

Subsequently, the man discovered that there are many other ways of producing musical notes—from strings and organs, to the swift vibrations on the wings of mosquitoes and the 'sweet and sonorous shrilling of crickets by snapping their wings together, though they cannot fly at all'. But there was an ultimate disappointment waiting for him:

Well, after this man had come to believe that no more ways of forming tones could possibly exist ... when, I say, this man believed he had seen everything, he suddenly found himself once more plunged deeper into ignorance and bafflement than ever. For having captured in his hands a cicada, he failed to diminish its strident noise either by closing its mouth or stopping its wings, yet he could not see it move the scales that covered its body, or any other thing. At last he lifted up the armour of its chest and there he saw some thin hard ligaments beneath; thinking the sound might come from their vibration, he decided to break them in order to silence it. But nothing happened until his needle drove too deep, and transfixing the creature he took away its life with its voice, so that he was still unable to determine whether the song had originated in those ligaments. And by this experience his knowledge was reduced to diffidence, so that when asked how sounds were created he used to answer tolerantly that although he knew a few ways, he was sure that many more existed which were not only unknown but unimaginable.[11]

Hubris is temporarily submerged by humility. Galileo was the first of a race of modern experimental scientists convinced of the infallibility of their 'exact empirical methods'; in fact he created the type. It comes as a surprise to hear him talk about things 'not only unknown but unimaginable'. But this ultimate modesty, derived from a sense of wonder close to mysticism, is found in all great scientists—even if hidden by an arrogant façade, and allowed to express itself only on rare occasions.

About Kepler I have said enough, in this book and elsewhere, to show that mysticism was the mainspring of his fantastically laborious life—starting with the analogy between God the Father and the Sun, continued in his lifelong conviction that the universe was built around the frames of the five Pythagorean solids, and that the planetary motions were regulated by the laws of musical harmony. But his mystic convictions, and the disarmingly child-like streak in his character, did not prevent him from casting horoscopes for money—however much he despised himself for it; from indulging in naïve snobbery, and quarrelling like a fish-wife with the overbearing Tycho. His vanity had a perverse twist: he was very proud of himself when his astrological forecasts of a cold spell and an invasion by the Turks came true; but towards his real discoveries he was completely indifferent, and he was astonishingly devoid of professional jealousy. He naïvely expected the same of other astronomers; and when Tycho's heirs delayed publication of his priceless collection of observational data, Kepler simply stole the material to put it to proper use—his ethics did not include respect for private property in Urania's domains.

When Kepler had completed the foundations of modern astronomy by his Third Law, he uttered a long Eureka cry:

> The heavenly motions are nothing but a continuous song for several voices (perceived by the intellect, not by the ear); a music which, through discordant tensions, through syncopes and cadenzas, as it were (as men employed them in imitation of those natural discords), progresses towards certain pre-designed, quasi six-voiced clausuras, and thereby sets landmarks in the immeasurable flow of time. It is, therefore, no longer surprising that man, in imitation of his creator, has at last discovered the art of figured song, which was unknown to the ancients. Man wanted to reproduce the continuity of cosmic time within a short hour, by an artful symphony for several voices, to obtain a sample test of the delight of the Divine Creator in His works, and to partake of his joy by making music in the imitation of God.[12]

Here we have the perfect union of the two drives: the vain-glorious ego purged by cosmic awareness—*ekstasis* followed by *katharsis*.

Newton, Monster and Saint

From the end of the seventeenth century onward the scene becomes too crowded for a systematic inquiry into individual motivations; however, I have said enough to suggest the basic pattern—and though the character of the times changed, that pattern remained essentially the same.

Look at Newton, for instance: he has been idolized and his character bowdlerized to such an extent (above all in the Victorian standard biography by Brewster) that the phenomenal mixture of monster and saint out of which it was compounded was all but lost from sight. On the one hand he was deeply religious and believed—with Kepler and Bishop Usher—that the world had been created in 4004 B.C.; that the convenient design of the solar system—for instance, all planetary orbits lying in a single plane—was proof of the existence of God, who not only created the universe but also kept it in order by correcting from time to time the irregularities which crept into the heavenly motions —and by preventing the universe from collapsing altogether under the pressure of gravity. On the other hand, he fulminated at any criticism of his work, whether justified or not, displayed symptoms of persecution mania, and in his priority fight with Leibniz over the invention of the calculus he used the perfidious means of carefully drafting in his own hand the findings, in his own favour, of the 'impartial' committee set up by the Royal Society. To quote M. Hoskin:

> No one supposes that the committee set up by the Royal Society of which Newton had then been president for several years, was impartial. But we can only realize the extent of Newton's share in its conclusions when we examine a much-corrected draft summary of what were to be the findings of the committee. The draft is written in Newton's own hand, and it is fascinating to watch Newton debating with himself whether the committee ought to say 'We are satisfied that he [Newton] had invented the method of fluxions before' 1669, or whether it would sound better if they said 'We find that he invented the method of fluxions before' 1669; or deciding that to say 'We are satisfied that Mr. Newton was the first author of this method' was too terse, and that several more lines of explanation ought to be inserted before the conclusion 'for which reason we reckon Mr. Newton the first inventor'.[13]

Here is pettiness on a heroic scale—combined with a heroic vision of the universe worked out in minute detail: in other words, the mixture as before.

The Mysticism of Franklin

As we move on into the eighteenth century the towering genius of Benjamin Franklin sticks out of it like his lightning rod. Printer,

journalist, pamphleteer, politician, wire-puller, diplomat, and statesman; pioneer of electricity, founder of the physics of liquid surfaces,
discoverer of the properties of marsh gas, designer of the *chevaux de
frise* which halted the advance of the British fleet on the Delaware,
inventor of bifocal spectacles and of improved fireplaces, advocate of
watertight bulkheads on ships and of chimney-shafts for the ventila-
tion in mines—the list could be continued. And yet this 'first civilized
American', as one of his biographers called him,[14] for all his incompar-
able clarity of thought and lucidity of style, had formed his metaphysical outlook at the age of sixteen when he read a book by Tryon,
a member of the group of British Pythagoreans. The members of this
sect were chiefly known for their vegetarianism because, like the
ancient Brotherhood, they believed in the transmigration of souls and
wished to avoid the risk of feasting on some reincarnation of a human
being. Franklin became a convert to vegetarianism and believed in
transmigration to the end of his life. At the age of twenty-two he
composed a Pythagorean epitaph for himself; at the age of eighty-four,
the year of his death, he ordered that it should appear, unchanged, on
his tomb. It reads:

The Body
Of
BENJAMIN FRANKLIN
Printer
(Like the Cover of an Old Book
Its Contents Torn Out
And Stript of its Lettering and Gilding)
Lies Here, Food for Worms.
But the Work Shall Not Be Lost
For It Will (As He Believed) Appear Once More
In a New and More Elegant Edition
Revised and Corrected
By
The Author

His conviction that souls are immortal, that they cannot be destroyed and are merely transformed in their migrations led him, by
way of analogy, to one of the first clear formulations of the law of the
conservation of matter. The following quotations will make the
connection clear:

The power of man relative to matter seems limited to the dividing it, or mixing the various kinds of it, or changing its form and appearance by differing compositions of it, but does not extend to the making or creating of new matter, or annihilating the old.

This was written when he was seventy-eight. The following was written one year later:

I say that when I see nothing annihilated, and not even a drop of water wasted, I cannot suspect the annihilation of souls, or believe that He will suffer the daily waste of millions of minds ready made that now exist, and put Himself to the continual trouble of making new ones. Thus finding myself to exist in the world, I believe I shall, in some shape or other, always exist.

The argument seems to indicate that what one might call the principle of the 'conservation of souls' was derived from that of the 'conservation of matter'. But in fact it was the other way round. As Kepler had transformed the Holy Trinity into the trinity of Sun—Force—Planets, so in Franklin's case, too, a mystical conviction gave birth, by analogy, to a scientific theory. And could there be a more charming combination of man's vanity with his transcendental aspirations than to pray for a 'more elegant, revised, and corrected edition' of one's proud and humble self?

The Fundamentalism of Faraday

The nineteenth-century landscape is crowded with giants; I shall briefly comment on four of them. In the physical sciences Faraday and Maxwell are probably the greatest: Einstein, who ought to know, has put them on a par with Galileo and Newton; and Crowther, who wrote short biographies of both, makes the fine distinction of calling Faraday 'the greatest physicist of the nineteenth century' and Maxwell 'the greatest theoretical physicist of the nineteenth century'. To these let me add, from the biological sciences, Darwin and Pasteur, to make up a foursome.

Faraday, whom Tyndall described as 'the great mad child', was the most inhuman character of the four: the son of a sectarian blacksmith, self-taught, with a passionate temperament which was denied all human outlets except religion and science. This was probably the cause of the protracted episode of mental disorder, comparable to Newton's, which began when he was forty-nine. Characteristic of the coyness of science historians is the *Encyclopaedia Britannica*'s reference to Faraday's clinical insanity: 'In 1841 he found that he required rest, and it was not till 1845 that he entered on his second great period of research.'

At thirty, shortly after his marriage—which remained childless—Faraday joined an extreme fundamentalist, ascetic sect, the 'Sandemanians', to which his father and his young wife belonged, and whose services he had attended since infancy. The Sandemanians considered practically every human activity as a sin—including even the Victorian virtue of saving money; they washed each other's feet, intermarried, and refused to proselytize; on one occasion they suspended Faraday's membership because he had to dine, by royal command, with the Queen at Windsor, and thus had to miss the congregation's Sunday service. It took many years before he was forgiven and re-elected an Elder of the sect.

In his later years Faraday withdrew almost completely from social contacts, refusing even the presidency of the Royal Academy because of its too worldly disposition. The inhuman self-denials imposed by his creed made Faraday canalize his ferocious vitality into the pursuit of science, which he regarded as the only other permissible form of divine worship.

The Metaphysics of Maxwell

James Clerk Maxwell was of an altogether different, balanced, and happy disposition. In his case, too, religious belief became a spur to scientific activity, but in more subtle ways. He was a double-faced giant: he completed the classical edifice of the Newtonian universe, but he also inaugurated the era of what one might call the 'surrealistic' physics of the twentieth century.

As Kepler had embraced the Copernican system 'for physical or if you prefer, metaphysical reasons', so Maxwell confessed that the theories of his later period were formed 'in that hidden and dimmer region where Thought weds Fact. Does not the way to it pass through the very den of the metaphysician, strewed with the remains of former explorers and abhorred by every man of science?'

The metaphysician in Maxwell had by that time long outgrown the crude materialism of mid-nineteenth-century science, and its equally crude forms of Christianity. Maxwell's religious beliefs were conceived in symbolic, almost abstract, terms; they compared to Faraday's fundamentalist creed as his abstract equations of the electro-magnetic field compare with the lines of force which to Faraday were 'as real as matter'. The connection between Maxwell's religious and scientific views is indeed just as intimate as in the case of Franklin or Kepler. I have mentioned before how, once he had arrived at his twenty general equations, Maxwell kicked away the scaffolding from under him—the physical model of vortices in the ether—and thus inaugurated the post-Newtonian era in physics, with its renunciation of all models and representations in terms of sensory experience.

There is a characteristic passage in one of his letters to his wife:

'I can always have you with me in my mind—why should we not have our Lord always before us in our minds. . . . If we had seen Him in the flesh we should not have known Him any better, perhaps not so well.' In another letter to his wife, he says that he had been re-reading Ephesians vi. This is not a very inspiring chapter, dealing with relations between parents and children, masters and servants; yet Maxwell comments: 'Here is more about family relations. There are things which have meanings so deep that if we follow on to know them we shall be led into great mysteries of divinity. If we reverence them, we shall even see beyond their first aspect a spiritual meaning. For God speaks to us more plainly in these bonds of our life than in anything that we can understand.'

J. G. Crowther—who, as an adherent of the Marxist philosophy of history can hardly be accused of mystic inclinations—remarks on this curious passage: 'Here Maxwell accepts material relationships with the belief that acquaintance with them will lead to spiritual understanding. He proceeds from the contemplation of material relationships to spiritual truth, from the model of the electro-magnetic field to the equations. The influence of the New Testament is seen also in his interpretation of self-sacrifice. During the last years of his life, his wife was an invalid. He nursed her personally with the most assiduous care. At one period he did not sleep in a bed for three weeks, though he delivered his lectures and superintended the laboratory as usual. The modernity of Maxwell's science, and the antiquity of his sociology and religion appear incongruous. But it may be noted that though his views on sociology and religion were antique, they were superior to those of nearly all his scientific contemporaries. He at least thought about these problems, and if he was unable to find modern answers to them, he learned enough of them to avoid the intellectual phili-stinism of his time.'

It was the time when Berthelot proclaimed: 'The world today has no longer any mystery for us'; when Haeckel had solved all his *Welträtsel* and A. R. Wallace, in his book on *The Wonderful Century*, declared that the nineteenth century had produced 'twenty-four fundamental advances, as against only fifteen for all the rest of recorded history'. The Philistines everywhere were 'dizzy with success'—to quote once more Stalin's famous phrase of 1932, when factories and power dams were going up at great speed while some seven million peasants were dying of starvation. It had indeed been a wonderful century for natural philosophy, but at its end moral philosophy had reached one of its lowest ebbs in history—and Maxwell was well aware of this. He was aware of the limitations of a rigidly deterministic outlook; it was he who, in his revolutionary treatment of the dy-namics of gases, replaced mechanical causation by a statistical approach based on the theory of probability—a decisive step towards quantum physics and the principle of indeterminism. Moreover, he was fully aware of the far-reaching implications of this approach, not only for physics but also for philosophy: 'It is probable that important results will be obtained by the application of this the statistical method, which is as yet little known and is not familiar to our minds. If the actual history of Science had been different, and if the scientific doctrines most familiar to us had been those which must be expressed in this way, it is possible that we might have considered the existence of a certain kind of contingency a self-evident truth, and treated the doctrine of philosophical necessity as a mere sophism.'[15]

Already at the age of twenty-four he had realized the limitations of materialist philosophy: 'The only laws of matter are those which our minds must fabricate, and the only laws of mind are fabricated for it by matter.'[16] Twenty years later, at the height of his fame, he gave full rein to his hobby, satirical verse, to ridicule the shallow materialism of the Philistines. The occasion was the famous presidential address by John Tyndall to the British Association meeting in Belfast. Tyndall, a generous soul but a narrow-minded philosopher, attacked the 'theologians' and extolled the virtues of the brave new materialist creed. Maxwell's satire is still valid today:

In the very beginning of science,
    the parsons, who managed things then,
Being handy with hammer and chisel,
    made gods in the likeness of men;
Till Commerce arose, and at length
    some men of exceptional power
Supplanted both demons and gods by
    the atoms, which last to this hour.

From nothing comes nothing, they told us,
    nought happens by chance but by fate;
There is nothing but atoms and void,
    all else is mere whims out of date!
Then why should a man curry favour
    with beings who cannot exist,
To compass some petty promotion
    in nebulous kingdoms of mist? . . .

First, then, let us honour the atom,
    so lively, so wise, and so small;
The atomists next let us praise, Epicurus,
    Lucretius, and all;
Let us damn with faint praise Bishop Butler,
    in whom many atoms combined
To form that remarkable structure,
    it pleased him to call—his mind.

In another poem he wrote:

. . . While down the stream of Evolution
We drift, expecting no solution
But that of the survival of the fittest.
Till, in the twilight of the gods,
When earth and sun are frozen clods,
When, all its energy degraded,
Matter to aether shall have faded;
We, that is, all the work we've done,
As waves in aether, shall for ever run
In ever-widening spheres through heavens beyond the sun.

And thus in the nineteenth century's most advanced scientific mind we meet once again, in a sublimated and rarified form, the ancient belief in the indestructibility of the numinous.

The Atheism of Darwin

Dr. Robert Darwin was an atheist who chose for his son Charles the career of a country clergyman—simply because this seemed to be the most gentlemanly occupation for a youth so obviously devoid of any particular ambition and intellectual excellence. Charles himself fully agreed with this choice. As a student at Cambridge he had read *Pearson on the Creeds*, and had come to the conclusion that he did not 'in the least doubt the strict and literal truth of every word in the Bible'.[17] Even during the voyage of the *Beagle* he amused the officers by his naïve orthodoxy, and he was deeply shocked when one of his shipmates expressed doubts concerning the biblical account of the Flood. Such a rigid fundamentalist belief could not be reconciled with speculations about the origin of species; his loss of faith coincided with his conversion to the evolutionary theory. For a while he fought a rearguard action against his doubts by day-dreaming about the discovery of old manuscript texts which would confirm the historical truth of the Gospels; but this did not help much. In the months following his return from the voyage the new theory was born and his faith in religion was dead.

Darwin's arguments against religion were as crude and literal-minded as his belief had been: 'the miracles were not credible to any sane man'; the Old Testament gave a 'manifestly false history of the world, with the Tower of Babel, the rainbow as a sign, etc., etc.'[18] He took strong exception to the 'damnable doctrine' that non-believers, 'and this would include my Father, Brother and almost all my best friends', will be everlastingly punished. As for Hinduism or Buddhism, and the persistence of religious aspirations throughout human history, he explained them—in an oddly Lamarckian argument—as the result of 'inherited experience'.

Nor must we overlook the probability of the constant inculcation of a belief in God on the minds of children by producing so strong and perhaps an inherited effect on their brains, not as yet fully developed, that it would be as difficult for them to throw off their belief in God, as for a monkey to throw off its instinctive fear and hatred of a snake.

Before the great turning point in his life, 'the nuclear discovery' of his theory, he had not only been an orthodox believer, but at least on one occasion, in the grandeur of the Brazilian forest, he had also felt that quasi-mystical, 'deep inward experience' that there must be more in man than 'the mere breath of his body.'[19] But after the turning point such experiences did not recur—and he himself wondered sometimes whether he was not like a man who had become colour-blind. At the same decisive period, when he was about thirty, Darwin suffered, in his own words, a 'curious and lamentable loss of the higher aesthetic tastes'. An attempt to re-read Shakespeare bored him 'to the point of physical nausea'.[20] He preferred popular novels of the sentimental kind—so long as they had a happy ending. In his autobiography he complained:

> But now for many years I cannot endure to read a line of poetry. My mind seems to have become a kind of machine for grinding general laws out of a large collection of facts, but why this should have caused the atrophy of that part of the brain on which the higher tastes depend, I cannot conceive. The loss of these tastes is a loss of happiness, and may possibly be injurious to the intellect, and more probably to the moral character, by enfeebling the emotional part of our nature.

Darwin's 'religious tastes', if the expression may be permitted, had been of an equally unsubtle nature. 'His sensibility was of that inverted order that is unable to extend to human beings the same sympathy and respect it has for animals. As a zoologist Darwin was naturally more at home in the realm of animal behaviour than of philosophy. This may be why so much of his discussion of religion, morality and aesthetics seems painfully naïve.'[21] The concept of 'religious experience' did not mean to Darwin what it did to Maxwell—the intuition of an 'unknown reality which held the secret of infinite space and enternal time'; it meant to him believing the story told in Genesis, and also in eternal hellfire. In *The Descent of Man*, he had denied that language was a unique attribute of man because animals too use sounds and gestures to communicate emotions. This confusion of sign and symbol equally pervades his discussions of religion. In his youth he had believed in the 'strict and

literal truth of every word in the Bible'; later on he considered himself
an atheist because he did not believe in the Tower of Babel. Neither
attitude has much relevance to the unconscious, inner motivation of his
work. More relevant is the fact that the kind of undefinable intuition
which he had experienced in the Brazilian forest went out of his life at
the same time as the 'atrophy of the higher tastes' set in. This was at the
time when he made his basic discovery. The remaining forty odd years
were spent on the heroic labours of its elaboration.

Darwin, as we have seen, was like Copernicus, essentially a one-
idea man. Each had his 'nuclear inspiration' early in life, and spent the
rest of his life working it out—the ratio of inspiration to perspiration
being heavily in favour of the second. Both lacked the many-sidedness,
that universality of interest and amazing multitude of achievement in
unrelated fields of research which characterized Kepler, Newton,
Descartes, Franklin, Faraday, Maxwell, and hundreds of lesser but
equally versatile geniuses. It is perhaps no coincidence that both Darwin
and Copernicus, after the decisive turning point when their course
was set, led a life of duty, devotion to task, rigorous self-discipline, and
spiritual desiccation. It looks as if the artesian wells of their inspiration
had been replaced by a mechanical water supply kept under pressure
by sheer power of will.

In Darwin's case, the magnitude of this power must be measured
against the handicap of forty years of chronic ill health, which also
afflicted his large family. The sense of duty which kept him going
became his true religion. After the publication of the *Origin* and the
Descent, he became one of the most celebrated personalities in Europe,
but he continued to lead the same rigorously scheduled life, without
allowing himself to bask in the sun, without getting spoilt or distracted from his work. 'While others used the prestige of Darwinism
to promote their social or political views, Darwin himself forebore
doing so;'[21a] and when Marx proposed to dedicate to him the English
translation of *Das Kapital* Darwin refused the honour.

His last years were spent in churning out a number of technical
books and papers; his very last book was called *The Formation of Vegetable Mould through the Action of Worms*. He had started this research on
earthworms at twenty-eight, after his return from the voyage of the
Beagle; now, after this momentous detour, he finished it at the age of
seventy-two, one year before his death. It is a measure of the enormous
vogue which Darwin enjoyed that the worm book, in spite of its unprepossessing title, sold eight thousand five hundred copies in the first

three years after publication—which would be quite a respectable success for a novel in our own days.

On one occasion in his late years Darwin was asked to state his opinion on religion. He answered that while the subject of God was 'beyond the scope of man's intellect', his moral obligations were nevertheless clear: 'Man can do his duty.' On another occasion—in an addendum to his autobiography—he explained that, even without a belief in God, a man 'can have for his rule of life ... only to follow those impulses and instincts which are the strongest or which seem to him the best ones. .... By degrees it will be more intolerable to him to obey his sensuous passions rather than his highest impulses, which when rendered habitual may be almost called instincts. His reason may occasionally tell him to act in opposition to the opinion of others, whose approbation he will then not receive; but he will still have the solid satisfaction of knowing that he has followed his innermost judge or conscience.' He never realized that statements of this kind destroyed the very foundations of any strictly materialistic and deterministic philosophy, including his own—according to which human morality was derived from innate 'social instincts'. 'It can hardly be disputed', he wrote in his disastrous controversy against Mill, 'that the social feelings are instinctive or innate in the lower animals: and why should they not be so in men?' But from what source, then, would man derive the power to follow those instincts 'which seemed to him the best ones', to obey his 'highest impulses' as opposed to his 'sensuous passions'; and even 'to act in opposition to the opinion of others'? The source of that power must evidently be the 'innermost judge, or conscience'— concepts of a transcendental nature and quite heretical from the point of view of a purely materialist world-view.

It has been said that Darwin's philosophizing was 'painfully naïve'. Yet his life bore witness, not to his philosophical rationalizations, but to his transcendental beliefs—he was a *croyant malgré lui*. The proof is in the closing passages of his two great books:

It is interesting to contemplate a tangled bank, clothed with many plants of many kinds, with birds singing on the bushes, with various insects flitting about, and with worms crawling through the damp earth, and to reflect that these elaborately constructed forms, so different from each other, and dependent upon each other in so complex a manner, have all been produced by laws acting around us. ....
Thus, from the war of nature, from famine and death, the most

exalted object which we are capable of conceiving, namely, the production of the higher animals, directly follows. There is grandeur in this view of life, with its several powers, having been originally breathed by the creator into a few forms or into one; and that, whilst this planet has gone cycling on according to the fixed law of gravity, from so simple a beginning endless forms most beautiful and most wonderful have been, and are being evolved.[22]

Man may be excused for feeling some pride at having risen, though not through his own exertions, to the very summit of the organic scale; and the fact of his having thus risen, instead of having been aboriginally placed there, may give him hope for a still higher destiny in the distant future. But we are not here concerned with hopes or fears, only with the truth as far as our reason permits us to discover it; and I have given the evidence to the best of my ability. We must, however, acknowledge, as it seems to me, that man with all his noble qualities, with sympathy which feels for the most debased, with benevolence which extends not only to other men but to the humblest living creature, with his god-like intellect which has penetrated into the movements and constitution of the solar system —with all these exalted powers—Man still bears in his bodily frame the indelible stamp of his lowly origin.[23]

Here is humility and wonder, and a sense of participation which transcends not only the individual self but the collective pride of *homo sapiens*.

The Faith of Pasteur

Louis Pasteur's character and life is an almost perfect illustration of ambition, pride, vanity, self-righteousness, combined with self-sacrifice, charity, humility, romanticism, and religion, to make a happy balance of opposites. At the height of his fame, Pasteur related with evident relish that at an official reception the Queen of Denmark and the Queen of Greece had broken etiquette by walking up to him to pay their homage. But he also spent several months every year for five years in the mountains of Cevennes, to find a cure for an epidemic disease of silkworms. When he had found its cause, and saved the French silk manufacturing industry from ruin, the Minister of Agriculture sent him for examination three lots of eggs which a famous silk-worm breeder was distributing throughout the country, ignoring Pasteur's recommendations of his method to obtain healthy strains. Pasteur replied:

> *M. le Ministre*—These three samples of seed are worthless. . . . They will in every instance succumb to corpuscle disease. . . . For my part I feel so sure of what I affirm, that I shall not even trouble to test, by hatching them, the samples which you have sent me. I have thrown them into the river.

And to a sceptical breeder, he wrote about the same time:

> *M. le Marquis*—You do not know the first word of my investigations, of their results, of the principles which they have established, and of their practical implications. Most of them you have not read . . . and the others you did not understand.

In his polemics against scientific adversaries he used the same impassioned language—the style sometimes reminds one of Galileo. But, unlike Galileo, he engaged in controversy only after he had established his case beyond all possible doubt in his experimental laboratory, and had hardened it by countless painstaking repetitions. As a result, again unlike Galileo, he was invariably, and to his opponents infuriatingly, proven right. He even wrote an article in the Galilean dialogue style for a wine-growers trade journal. The dialogue was meant to be a report of Pasteur's conversation with the mayor of Volnay, M. Boillot—which resulted in the conversion of M. Boillot to the Pasteurization of Burgundy wines. This epic dialogue starts with:

> *Pasteur:* Do you heat your wines, M. Maire?
> *M. Boillot:* No sir. . . . I have been told that heating may affect unfavourably the taste of our great wines.
> *Pasteur:* Yes, I know. In fact it has been said that to heat these wines is equivalent to an amputation. Will you be good enough, M. Maire, to follow me into my experimental cellar?

For the next two pages M. Boillot is shown what's what. He has to taste the treated and untreated wines of a score of vintages and vineyards, until he capitulates and admits the superior quality of the pasteurized wines—including those which came from his own vine-yards:

M. Boillot: I am overwhelmed. I have the same impression as if I were seeing you pouring gold into our country.

Pasteur: There you are, my dear countrymen, busy with politics, elections, superficial reading of newspapers but neglecting the serious books which deal with matters of importance to the welfare of the country. . . . And yet, M. Maire, had you read with attention, you could have recognized that everything I wrote was based on precise facts, official reports, *degustations* by the most competent experts, whereas my opponents had nothing to offer but assertions without proof.

M. Boillot: . . . Do not worry, Monsieur. From now on I shall no longer believe those who contradict you and I shall attend to the matter of heating the wines as soon as I return to Volnay.[24]

Pasteur had grown up in the Arbois; he was a connoisseur of wine, and he despised beer. But after the defeat of France by the Prussians in 1871, he considered it his patriotic duty to improve the quality of French beer—with the declared intention to produce a '*bière de la revanche*', superior to the Germans' cherished national drink. He even invaded, armed with his microscope, the sacred premises of Whitbread's in London; his laconic account of that historic visit makes one appreciate the drama that took place.

Pasteur was reverently handed two casks of the famed brew. He put a drop of one under the microscope and—'I immediately recognized three or four disease filaments in the microscopic field. These findings made me bold enough to state in the presence of the master-brewer, who had been called in, that these beers would rapidly spoil . . . and that they must already be somewhat defective in taste, on which point everyone agreed, although after long hesitation. I attributed this hesitation to the natural reserve of a manufacturer whom one compels to declare that his merchandise is not beyond reproach. When I returned to the same brewery less than a week later, I learned that the managers had made haste to acquire a microscope.' It was not the least of the miracles that Pasteur achieved.

Silkworms, wine, beer—and before that studies on the souring of milk, the turning of wine into vinegar, of vinegar into acid, of beet-sugar into alcohol. 'Louis . . . is now up to his neck in beet-juice',

Madame Pasteur complained in a letter. Each of these campaigns was conducted with the same crusading zeal, the same showmanship, the same patience and precision in method. Pasteur's father had been a sergeant in the Napoleonic army; after Waterloo he had become a tanner in the Arbois. He had probably heard the Emperor's famous speech at the Pyramids: 'Soldiers, from these summits forty centuries look down upon you.' Louis Pasteur, crouching with his microscope on top of one of the gigantic vats at Whitbread's, may have spoken the same words to the awe-stricken master-brewers.

And that is hardly an exaggeration, for in Pasteur's work we see clearly how the trivial by a short step can lead to the momentous, and how the two are inextricably mixed up in the scientist's mind and motives. One of the landmarks of science is the publication, in 1877, of Pasteur's book with the unprepossessing title, *Etudes sur la Bière, Ses Maladies, Les Causes qui les Provoquent. Procédé pour la Rendre Inalterable* . . . followed, almost as an afterthought, by . . . *Avec une Théorie Nouvelle de la Fermentation*. It contains the first complete statement of Pasteur's revolutionary discovery that yeast and all other agents which cause fermentation and putrefaction, are *living beings* of very small size—that is, micro-organisms, germs. In a similar way, his work on the silkworms had confirmed that contagious diseases were caused by microbes of different varieties. The principles of sterilization and partial sterilization ('pasteurization'); of immunization, of antisepsis and asepsis; our knowledge of the causative agents of disease and of the general conditions which determine the organism's receptivity for those agents; lastly, the 'domestication' of microbes and their use as antibiotics—all this grew out of Pasteur's often far-fetched researches into some specific technical problem, undertaken for apparently trivial motives.

Yet there were other motivational factors at work which lent urgency and drive to each of these technical research projects, from the earliest (*On the Turning of Milk*) onward: the intuitive vision of a grand unitary design underlying all biochemical transformations, a design which embraced not only the utilization of energy by living organisms in health and disease, but also—as we shall see in a moment—the secret of the origin of life. And finally, each particular project—whether it was concerned with silkworms, wine, or the inoculation of cattle against anthrax—though carried through with consummate showmanship and a Gallic flourish, was nevertheless a crusade for the public benefit; the resulting self-gratification was no more than a delicious by-product. Through the same interaction of the trivial and monumental which led to Pasteur's intellectual triumphs, the proponent of the *bière de la revanche* became the greatest benefactor of mankind since Hippocrates.

I have mentioned Pasteur's hope to discover 'the secret of life'. This is to be taken quite literally.

The earliest discovery of Pasteur, and for him the most exciting in all his life, was the asymmetry of molecules as a specific characteristic of living organisms—in other words, the fact that the molecules of living matter come in two varieties which, though chemically identical, are in their spatial structure like mirror images to each other—or like right and left gloves. 'Left-handed' molecules rotate polarized light to the left, 'right-handed' molecules to the right; life substances are thus 'optically active'. Why this should be so we still do not quite know; but it remains a challenging fact that 'no other chemical characteristic is as distinctive of living organisms as is optical activity'.

'I am on the verge of mysteries, and the veil which covers them is getting thinner and thinner. The night seems to me too long. . . . Life as manifested to us is a function of the asymmetry of the universe. . . . The universe is asymmetrical; for, if all the bodies in motion which compose the solar system were placed before a glass, the image in it could not be superimposed upon the reality. . . . Terrestrial magnetism . . . the opposition between positive and negative electricity, are but resultants of asymmetrical actions and movements. . . . Life is dominated by asymmetrical actions. I can even imagine that all living species are primordially in their structure, in their external forms, functions of cosmic asymmetry.'[25]

These intoxicating speculations caused Pasteur to embark on a series of fantastic experiments, aiming at nothing less than the creation of life by means of imitating the asymmetric action of nature in the laboratory, using powerful magnets and all kinds of optical tricks. It was this alchemist's dream which gave birth to the 'grand design' which I have mentioned and which—like a blue-print drawn in invisible ink—remained the secret inspiration behind his researches. Luckily, circumstances compelled him to descend from the monumental to the trivial level: Pasteur had to give up trying to create life and had to get 'up to his neck in beet-juice'. He had been appointed Professor of Chemistry in Lille; and no sooner was he installed than Monsieur Bigo, an industrialist engaged in the production of alcohol from beet-sugar, came to consult him about certain difficulties encountered in the process. Since this was one of the main industries of the region, Pasteur embarked on the task with patriotic fervour—it was the first in the series of this type of venture, long before the silkworms, the wine, and the beer.

In examining the fermented juice of the beet, he found in it a component, amyl alcohol, which turned out to be optically active. Therefore its molecules must be asymmetrical; but according to the grand design, asymmetry is the privilege and secret of life; therefore fermentation came from the activity of living things, of microbes. At this point the chain reaction set in which fused the germ theory of fermentation to the germ theory of disease. Thus did the alchemist's pipe-dream give birth to modern medicine—as Kepler's chimerical quest for the harmonies led to modern astronomy.

Here, I believe, is the clue to the scientist's ultimate motivation—the equivalent of the meeting of the tragic and the trivial planes in the artist's mind. Peering through his microscope or polariscope, in a never-ending series of dreary, technical, specialized investigations of amyl acid, tartaric acid, butyric acid, Pasteur was attending on one level to the business in hand—the beets of Mr. Bigo; on another he was scanning the secret of life 'through veils getting thinner and thinner'. Thus did some early explorers nourish the secret, childish hope to find at the North Pole a crater revealing the axis on which the earth turns. So did the Phoenician seamen hope to find, beyond the Pillars of Hercules, the island of Atlantis.

When he was thirty and newly married, Pasteur, though almost penniless, embarked on an expedition through Central Europe—a treasure-hunt for an elusive commodity dear to his heart: paratartaric acid, a chemical derived from the deposit in the vats of fermented wine (p. 193 f). He returned and described this Odyssey in an article in the Strasbourg newspaper *La Verité*, ending with the epic words: 'Never was treasure sought, never adored beauty pursued over hill and dale with greater ardour.'

The dream which turned the tartar-crystals into a symbol of the secret of life proved immensely fertile. But since the actual experiments of creating life had failed, Pasteur, in his later years, reversed his opinions and embarked on another celebrated controversy to prove that the alleged 'spontaneous generation' of micro-organisms (without progenitors, out of fermenting or putrefying matter) was a legend. 'It is a striking fact,' writes Dubos, 'perhaps worthy of the attention of psychoanalysts, that Pasteur devoted much of his later life to demonstrating that nature operates as if it were impossible to achieve what he —Pasteur—had failed to do. . . . Just as he had failed in his attempts to create or modify life, so he proved that others, who had claimed to be successful where he had failed, had been merely the victims of illusion.'[26]

This may indeed have been a factor which contributed to his change of attitude, but only a superficial one, like his childish boastings and showmanship. The obsession with the secret of life had bitten into deeper strata, where opposites cease to be opposites, the law of contradiction no longer applies, and a plus and minus sign become interchangeable. Among his unpublished writings there is a passage written when he was approaching sixty:

I have been looking for spontaneous generation for twenty years without discovering it. No, I do not judge it impossible. But what allows you to make it the origin of life? You place matter before life and you decide that matter has existed for all eternity. How do you know that the incessant progress of science will not compel scientists . . . to consider that life has existed during eternity, and not matter? You pass from matter to life because your intelligence of today . . . cannot conceive things otherwise. How do you know that in ten thousand years one will not consider it more likely that matter has emerged from life . . . ?[26a]

At the age of forty-six Pasteur suffered a stroke which left his left arm and leg permanently paralysed. Yet his greatest work was done during the following two decades, when he was an invalid and had to use his assistants' hands to carry out his experiments. In old age he would often browse in his earlier publications. 'Turning the pages of his writings, he would marvel at the lands that he had revealed by dispelling the fogs of ignorance and by overcoming stubbornness. He would live again his exciting voyages, as he told Loir in a dreamy voice: "How beautiful, how beautiful! And to think I did it all. I had forgotten it." '[27]

2. INNOCENCE AND EXPERIENCE

I have been discussing the motivational drive of scientists. Can we make any generalizations regarding their intellectual characteristics—in addition to those described earlier on (Chapters V–X)?

Precociousness

In the first place, such data as we possess confirm the popular belief that scientists reach their peak of creativity at an earlier age than artists. Most scientists made their basic discoveries when they were under forty—exceptions like Faraday or Pasteur always granted. In a valuable study on Nobel Prize winners by L. Moulin[28] we find the average age at which a person is awarded the prize to be fifty-one; but for physicists it is forty-five. (The award, of course, often lags by a number of years behind the discovery.) It is interesting to note that the stupendous increase, over the last half-century, in the volume of knowledge to be mastered had no significant influence on the age at which the award is received: between 1901 and 1930 the average, for physicists, was forty-five years, between 1931 and 1960, forty-six years. The average for chemists was fifty years for the first, fifty-one for the second period; for the award-winner in medicine it fell from fifty-five in the first, to fifty-three in the second period—presumably as an effect of increasing team-work. The figures also indicate an age-gradient from the more 'theoretical' to the more 'empirical' or 'applied' sciences. This is in keeping with the well-known fact of the precociousness of mathematicians—the most 'theoretical' among scientists (unfortunately there is no Nobel Prize for mathematics).

A related phenomenon is the dazzling multitude of infant prodigies among scientists: for every Mozart there are about three Pascals, Maxwells, Edisons. To quote only a few examples: the greatest

Renaissance astronomer before Copernicus, Johann Mueller from Koenigsberg, called Regiomontanus (1436–1476), published at the age of twelve the best astronomical yearbook for 1448; was asked at fifteen by the Emperor Frederick III to cast a horoscope for the imperial bride; went to the University of Leipzig when he was eleven, and at seventeen enjoyed European fame; he died at forty. Pascal had laid the foundations for the modern treatment of conic sections before he was sixteen. Jeremiah Horrocks (1619–1641) applied Kepler's laws to the orbit of the moon and made other fundamental contributions to astronomy before his death at the age of twenty-one. Evariste Galois (1811–1832), one of the most outstanding geniuses in the history of mathematics, was killed in a duel at the age of twenty-one (cf. p. 111). The notes which he left behind amount to no more than sixty pages of his 'collected works'; but those sixty pages inaugurated a new epoch in the theory of equations, and 'contain more mathematics than is to be found in some libraries crammed with books bearing mathematical titles'.[29] Clerk Maxwell, who lived to forty-eight, had his first mathematical paper read before the Royal Society at the age of fifteen; in the discussion, the geometrical construction which was the subject of the paper was described as superior to Newton's and Descartes' discussion of the same problem.

In contrast to this streak of precocity, however, is the fact that the majority of geniuses seem to have done rather badly in the normal school curriculum—often including the very subject on which later on they were to leave their mark. 'In his student days Einstein had been a lazy dog,' his erstwhile teacher Minkovsky remarked: 'He never bothered about mathematics at all.'[30]

Scepticism and Credulity

But the paradox is not too difficult to resolve. I have emphasized before (Book One, X) that the scientific genius is a curious mixture of scepticism and credulity. At school he is frequently bored by and cynical about orthodox doctrines which unimaginative and tradition-bound masters try to cram into his head. To quote Einstein once more: 'Physics too [as taught in the classroom] were split into special fields each of which could engulf a short life's work without ever satisfying the hunger for deeper knowledge. For the examinations one had to stuff oneself with all this rubbish, whether one wanted to or not.

This compulsion had such a terrifying effect on me that after my finals the consideration of any scientific problems was distasteful to me for a whole year.'[31]

The student's matrices of thought are still fluid—later on, when they have hardened, he will only be able to recapture his erstwhile innocence at inspired moments. Under propitious conditions, inexperience can be an asset: it entices the novice into asking questions which nobody has asked before, into seeing a problem where nobody saw one before. That is what young Maxwell probably did when he was lying on the grass before his father's house, looking at the sky and *wondering*. That is what Einstein did when at the age of sixteen he indulged in the fantasy of travelling at the speed of light; and what Edison did when 'his demands for explanations of what seemed obvious to his elders created the belief that he was less than normally intelligent'.

Einstein has compared the intellectual appetite of youth 'to the voraciousness of a healthy beast of prey'. When the child has learned that everything has a name, it develops a 'naming mania'. When it has learned that all events have 'becauses' it develops the mania of asking 'Why?—Why?—Why?' A fool, says the Bible, can ask more questions in a minute than a sage can answer in a week. But sages are scarce, and the child soon learns to accept answers which are not real explanations but conventional formulae or evasions, and to be content with them; the keen edge of its appetite for knowledge has become blunted. Only geniuses preserve their infantile voracity for 'becauses' —and the naïve hope that there *are* real answers to every question. 'Why is the moon round? Why does the apple fall from the tree? Why are there five planets instead of twenty, and why do they move as they do? Why does milk go sour? Why could the dairymaid not get the pox? Why is the colour of a sailor's blood in the tropics a brighter red than in Hamburg? Why did the dead frog's legs twitch?' One of the hallmarks of genius is that he has never lost the habit of asking foolish questions like these—each of which led to a momentous discovery.

Abstraction and Practicality

The reasons for this peculiarity have already been discussed: scepticism towards the conventional answers, the refusal to take anything for granted, the freshness of vision of the unblinkered mind. Taken together, these create an acuity of perception, a gift for seeing the banal objects of everyday experience in a sharp individual light—as painters and poets do, each in his own way; to observe details and notice trivia which escape the attention of others. This leads us to a second pair of complementary qualities (the first was scepticism paired with credulity) in the scientist's make-up: the coexistence of abstract and concrete moulds of thought, the faculty of combining high flights of theory with a keen sense of the practical and down-to-earth—a knack for picking up trivial clues. Pythagoras in search of the harmony of the spheres enters the blacksmith's workshop; Archimedes gets his solution from observing a smudge in his bath-tub; Galileo exhorts his friends to learn natural philosophy from the craftsmen in the arsenals of Venice; Kepler notices that the slit in his roof which let the rain through can be used as the aperture of a camera obscura to observe the sun; Claude Bernard takes the temperature of a rabbit's denervated ear and is led to the discovery that blood-vessels are controlled by nerves.

Throughout history, genius displays these complementary qualities of making lofty generalizations based on humble clues. 'It is very necessary', wrote Maxwell, 'that those who are trying to learn from books the facts of physical science should be enabled to recognize these facts when they meet with them out-of-doors. Science appears to us with a very different aspect after we have found out . . . that we may find illustrations of the highest doctrines of science in games and gymnastics, in travelling by land and by water, in storms of the air and of the sea. This habit of recognizing principles amid the endless variety of their action . . . tends to rescue our scientific ideas from that vague condition in which we too often leave them buried among the other products of a lazy credulity.'[32]

To have one's head in the clouds does not prevent one from having one's feet firmly on the ground. The scientist, as the artist, must live on several planes at once—look at eternity through the window of time. All great geniuses of science were endowed with this particular dualism of their faculties: a head for generalizations and an eye for minute particulars; searching for the secret of life in the beet-juice of M. Bigo; tilting at windmills without falling off the horse.

Multiple Potentials

I must mention one more characteristic property shared, apparently, by most great scientists: one may call it the 'multiple potential'. It helps to explain the paradox of the apparently haphazard way in which scientists are often launched on their career or on a particular line of research.

Kepler was designated to become a theologian when he was unexpectedly offered the job of a mathematician at a provincial school. Haüey was a botanist when the accident of dropping his friend's precious spar crystal made him change to crystallography, and become a pioneer in that field. Darwin, preparing to become a country curate, had the good luck of being invited to join the expedition of the *Beagle* —without that chance it is extremely doubtful whether he would have written *The Origin of Species*. The direction of all of Pasteur's later researches was determined by his first discoveries about the optical activity of paratartaric acid: he himself said that he had become 'enchained to the inescapable logic' by which one discovery gave birth to the next. As for Alexander Fleming, the coincidences which determined his initial choice of career are about as fantastic as the actual circumstances of his discovery. He had adopted the medical profession because his brother was a doctor; he had gone to St. Mary's where he was to spend the whole of his life, because he had played against their water-polo team; and he chose bacteriology as his branch of research because Freeman, the assistant of Almroth Wright, wanted to keep Fleming, who was an excellent shot, in St. Mary's rifle club.

The answer to the paradox is, apparently, that given the type of mind which Fleming had, he would in all likelihood have left his mark on any other branch of experimental science into which the wind of chance had blown him. In Pasteur's case, for instance, Dubos has convincingly shown that 'the inescapable logic' which his researches followed was by no means inescapable; for in Pasteur's notebooks and casual remarks there are projects and germs of discoveries which, had he only had the time to follow them up, or had the wind of circumstance blown from a different direction, would have brought an equally fertile harvest.

True genius, according to Dr. Johnson, 'is a mind of large general powers, accidentally determined to some particular direction, ready for all things, but chosen by circumstances for one'. Dubos, after quoting the Doctor, fully concurs with his opinion: 'It is often by a trivial, even an accidental decision, that we direct our activities into a certain channel, and thus determine which of the potential expressions of our individuality become manifest. Usually we know nothing of the ultimate orientation or of the outlet towards which we travel, and the stream sweeps us to a formula of life from which there is no returning. Every decision is like a murder, and our march forward is over the stillborn bodies of all our possible selves that will never be.'[33]

This moving confession of a great scientist seems to be based on the assumption that creativity is a kind of convertible energy which can be applied to various forms of activity—as the pressure of steam can be converted into electricity or motion. Stated in this extreme form, it is certainly an exaggeration: you cannot convert the creative energy of a painter into the composition of an opera. But it is nevertheless true that the particular type of intuition which makes the scientific genius can be focussed on problems as wide apart as colour-theory and celestial mechanics in Newton's case, or electro-magnetism and the theory of gases in Maxwell's—with equally striking results. The versatility, the quicksilvery mobility of minds like Archimedes', Galileo's, Descartes', Franklin's, Faraday's, or Edison's is truly phenomenal; they seemed to walk through life charged with static electricity, so that whatever object they touched, they drew a spark. One-idea men, such as Copernicus or Darwin, seem to be the exceptions among the truly great, and multi-potentiality the rule. The ominous trend towards over-specialization, its dangers to the creative mind, and the educational and administrative reforms needed to remedy it, are outside the scope of this book.

NOTE

To p. 677. The Artistarchian system and the motion of the earth had been discussed or taught by Copernicus's forerunners, the astronomers Peurbach and Regiomontanus, by his teachers Brujewski and Novara, and by his colleagues at the University of Bologna, Calcagnini, Ziegler, etc. (cf. *The Sleepwalkers* pp. 205-10).

REFERENCES

BOOK ONE

The Art of Discovery and the Discoveries of Art

PREFACE

1, *The Sleepwalkers* (1959). 2, *The Lotus and the Robot* (1960).

PART ONE THE JESTER

I. THE LOGIC OF LAUGHTER

1, Sully, J. (1902). 2, Duchenne de Boulogne (1862). 3, Ribot, T. A. (1896). 4, Quoted in the 'This England' column of the *New Statesman and Nation*, January 1946. 5, December 31, 1946. 6, Polànyi (1958), p. 50. 7, Bartlett (1958). 8, Bergson (1916), p. 59. 9, Lorenz, K. L. in Whyte, L. L. ed. (1951), pp. 176–8. 10, Santillana ed. (1953), p. 469. 11, *Br. J. Psychology* (1962), *53*, 3, p. 229.

II. LAUGHTER AND EMOTION

1, Gregory, J. C. (1924). 2, Quoted by Gregory, op. cit. 3, Foss, B. in the *New Scientist*, 6.7.1961. 4, Bain, A. (1868). 5, Bergson (1916). 6, McDougall, W. (1920). 7, Freud, *Gesammelte Werke*, VI (1940). 8, Freud, op. cit. 9, *The Guardian*, 5.9.1962. 10, See Ref. 3. 11, Bergson, op. cit. 12, Huxley, Aldous, in *Control of the Mind*, Farber, S. M. and Wilson, H. L. ed. (1961). 13, Auden, W. H. (1944).

III. VARIETIES OF HUMOUR

1, *Love's Labour's Lost*, V. ii. 2, Sawyer, W. W. (1955), p. 143. 3, Gregory, op. cit.

IV. FROM HUMOUR TO DISCOVERY

1, Santillana (1955), p. 124.

PART TWO THE SAGE

V. MOMENTS OF TRUTH

1, Köhler, W. (1957), p. 35. 2, Ibid., pp. 93–4. 3, Ibid., p. 94. 4, Ibid., p. 97. 5, Merton, R. K. (1961). 6, Polànyi (1958), p. 11. 7, Hadamard (1949), p. 119. 8, Ibid, p. 120. 9, Dubos (1960), p. 117. 9a, Ibid, p. 336. 10. Quoted in *The Creative Process*, Ghiselin, ed. (1952). 11, Hadamard, op. cit., p. 8. 12, de Launay, L. (1925). 13, Montmasson (1931), p. 77. 14, Polya, G. (1954), p. 76. 15, Findlay A. (1948), pp. 36–8.

VI. THREE ILLUSTRATIONS

1, *Histoire de l'Invention de l'Imprimerie par les Monuments*, ed. Höfer, Paris 1840. 2, *Mysterium Cosmographicum*, Preface. 3, Ibid. 4, *Opera Omnia*, Vol. XIII, pp. 33 ff. 5, Ibid., Vol. I, cap. 20. 6, Ibid., Notes 2 and 3. 7, *Astronomia Nova*, II, cap. 18. 8, Ibid., cap 44. 9, *Op. Omnia*, Vol. XV, pp. 134 seq. 10, Letter of 5.9.1857. 11, Footnote to the Historical Introduction to *The Origin of Species*. 12, *Notebooks*, quoted by Himmelfarb, G. (1959), p. 153. 13, *Life and Letters*, II, p. 215. 14, To Lyell; ibid., II, p. 241. 15, To Fawcett, *More Letters*, I, 195. 16, Ibid., I, 36. 17, *Origin*, 6th ed., p. 2. 18, Ibid., p. 3. 19, Lamarck (1914), pp. 109–10. 20, Nordenskiöld, *History of Biology*, p. 42, quoted by Himmelfarb, op. cit., p. 153. 21, *British Medical Journal*, 4.8.1956. 22, Himmelfarb, op. cit., p. 156. 23, *Origin*, 6th ed., p. 3. 24, Himmelfarb, op. cit., p. 234. 25, *My Life*, I, p. 359. 26, Ibid., I, pp. 232, 362. 27, Ibid., I, pp. 362 ff. 28, Himmelfarb, op. cit., p. 239. 29, Ibid., p. 238. 30, Loc. cit. 31, Ibid., p. 331.

VII. THINKING ASIDE

1, Whyte, L. L. (1962), p. 25. 2, Ibid., p. 63. 3, Ibid., pp. 88–9. 4, Ibid., p. 90. 5, Ibid., p. 91. 6, Ibid., p. 93. 7, Ibid., p. 95. 8, Ibid., p. 107. 9, Ibid., p. 108. 10, Ibid., pp. 119–20. 11, Ibid., pp. 124–5. 12, Ibid., pp. 150–1. 13, Ibid., p. 104. 14, Ibid., p. 147. 15, Ibid., p. 154. 16, Ibid., p. 154. 17, Ibid., p. 152. 18, Ibid., pp. 160–1. 19, Herrigel (1959), 3rd ed., pp. 57–8. 20, Suzuki, D. T. (1959), p. 94. 21, *Principles of Psychology* (1890), Vol. I, p. 255. 22, *Inquiries into Human Faculty*, 1883. 23, Findlay, A., op. cit., p. 42. 24, Kendall, J. (1955), p. 138. 25, Crowther, J. G. (1940), I, p. 135. 26, Hadamard, op. cit., pp. 142–3. 27, Ibid., p. 85. 28, Quoted by Hadamard, p. 94. 29, Roman Jakobson, quoted by Hadamard, p. 97. 30, Seelig (1954), p. 71. 31, Ibid. 32, Sidney Hook, 'Consciousness in Japan', *Commentary*, New York, Jan. 1959. 33, Whyte, L. L. (1962), p. 41. 34, *Tractatus*, Prop. 4121.

VIII. UNDERGROUND GAMES

1, *Civilization and its Discontents* (1930). 2, *Albert Einstein: Philosopher-Scientist* (1949), p. 53. 3, Loc. cit. 4, *Scientific American*, June 1961. In fact the problem originates with Carl Duncker. 5, *The Integration of Personality* (1940), p. 16. 6, Crowther, J. G. (1940) p. 325. 7, Loc. cit. 8, '*On Psychic Research*', ed. Gardner Murphy and Bellon, R. O. (1961). 9, *Ueber den Gegensinn der Urworte*, *Ges. Werke* VIII, p. 216. 10, *Die Verneinung*, G. W. XIV, p. 11. 11, Montmasson (1931), p. 137. 12, *Enc. Brit.*, 13th ed., article on Photography. 13, Beveridge (1950), p. 69. 14, Sachs, H. (1946), p. 98. 15, Bronowski (1961) p. 31. 16, Crowther (1937), p. 77. 17, Ibid., p. 69. 18, Loewi, O. (1960). 19, Loc. cit.

IX. THE SPARK AND THE FLAME

1, Quoted by Ghiselin, op. cit. 2, Beveridge, op. cit., p. 5. 3, Ibid. 4, *Harmonice Mundi*, Introduction to Book V. 5, Quoted by Beveridge, op. cit., p. 105. 6, *Astronomia Nova*, IV. cap. 58. 7, *The Sleepwalkers* (1959). 8, Jones, E. (1953), Vol. I, p. 55. 9, Ibid., p. 103. 10, Ibid., p. 101. 11, Ibid., p. 104. 12, Ibid., p. 97. 13, Lorimer (1929), p. 91. 14, Markey (1928), p. 42. 15, *The Story of My Life* (1902).

X. THE EVOLUTION OF IDEAS

1, Whitehead (1953). 2, *The Sleepwalkers*, pp. 515–16. 3, Pyke, M. (1961), p. 215. 4, Pledge, H. T. (1939), p. 100. 5, Burnet, J. (1908), p. 29. 5a, Pope's Epitaph for Newton, and Hilaire Belloc's Answer to it. 6, Bartlett (1958), pp. 98, 122, 134,

136–7. 7, (1948), p. 167. 8, *The Sleepwalkers*, p. 70. 9, Taton, R. (1957), pp. 134–5. 10, Butterfield (1949), pp. 1–2. 10a, *The Sleepwalkers*. 11, Butterfield, p. 7. 12, Heath, Th. L. (1932), p. 170. 13, For a critical account of the Galileo conflict see *The Sleepwalkers*. 14, Polànyi (1958), pp. 156–8. 15, Dubos (1950), p. 121. 16, Polànyi, op. cit., p. 168. 17, Ibid., pp. 12–13. 17a, *Scientific American*, May 1963. 18, Popper (1959), p. 280. 19, Dubos (1960), pp. 133–5. 20, *Voyage to Laputa*.

XI. SCIENCE AND EMOTION

1, Quoted by Kretschmer (1931), p. 136. 2, Beveridge, op. cit., p. 75. 3, Jones, E. (1953), I, p. 348. 4, Quoted by Farrington, B. (1953), pp. 130–1. 5, Quoted by Seelig, op. cit., p. 45. 6, *Harmonice Mundi*, Lib. IV, cap I. 7, Whyte, L. L. (1962), p. 66. 8, Op. cit., p. 105. 9, Seelig, op. cit., p. 44. 10, *Planète*. Paris, No. 1, 1961.

PART THREE THE ARTIST

A. The Participatory Emotions

XII. THE LOGIC OF THE MOIST EYE

1, Hilgard (1957), pp. 129 f. 2, Cf. Gellhorn, E. (1943 and 1957). 3, *The Expression of the Emotions in Man and Animals*. 4, Cf. e.g. Valentine (1946), and Clarke, Hunt, and Hunt (1947). 5, Cf. Mutch, R. T. (1944). 6, Montagu, A., *Science*, Vol. 130, p. 1572. 7, Kling, C. (1933).

XIII. PARTNESS AND WHOLENESS

1, Penfield (1959), p. 249.

XIV. ON ISLANDS AND WATERWAYS

1, Piaget (1930). 2, *Civilization and its Discontents*, p. 13 ff. 3, Lévy-Bruhl (1923 and 1926). 4, Cf. Polànyi, op. cit., p. 55.

B. Verbal Creation

XV. ILLUSION

1, Compressed from *The Observer*, London, 2.12.1962. 2, Lévy-Bruhl (1926), p. 76. 3, Ibid., p. 385. 4, Fitzmaurice Kelly, J., article on 'Literature' in *Enc. Brit.*, 13th ed.

XVI. RHYTHM AND RHYME

1, (1927), p. 139. 2, *Le Côté de Guermantes*. 3, A.R.N.M.D. (1940), Vol. XX, p. 732. 4, *The Name and Nature of Poetry*. 5, Quoted from Ghiselin, ed. (1952).

XVII. IMAGE

1, Sachs, H. (1946). 2, (1925), p. 270 ff. 3, Kretschmer (1934).

XVIII. INFOLDING

1, *What is Art?* 2, Richards, I. A. (1924). 3, Cohen, J. (1958).

XIX. CHARACTER AND PLOT

1, *Memento Mori*. 2, Brandt, G. W., in *Cassell's Enc. of Literature* (1953), Vol. I, p. 422. 3, (1930), pp. 25 seq.

XX. THE BELLY OF THE WHALE

1, See, for instance, Jung, *Psychology of the Unconscious* (1916); M. Bodkin, *Archetypal Patterns in Poetry* (1934); Toynbee, *A Study of History* (1947). 2, Jung (1928), p. 395. 3, Op. cit.

C. Visual Creation

XXI. MOTIF AND MEDIUM

1, Cf. Newton, E. (1941). 2, Listowel (1933), p. 217. 3, *Beauty and Ugliness* (1912). 4, Jaensch (1930). 5, Gris, Juan, *Horizon*, August, 1946. 6, Picasso in a conversation with the editor of *Cahiers d'Art* (1935), quoted by Goldwater and Treves (1945). 7, Wollberg, L. R. (1945). 8, Quoted by Reid, L. (1931). 9, Quoted by Gombrich (1962B), p. 159. 10, *A New Method of Assisting the Invention in Drawing Original Compositions of Landscape* (1765). 11, Gombrich (1962B), p. 123. 12, Ibid., p. 122. 13, *Dürer und die italienische Antike* (1905). 14, Gombrich (1962B), p. 75. 15, Ibid., p. 12. 16, Ibid., pp. 61 ff. 17, Ibid., p. 145. 18, Ibid., p. 12. 19, Ibid., p. 10.

XXII. IMAGE AND EMOTION

1, Kepes, G. (1956), p. 102. 2, Ibid., pp. 286–7.

XXIII. ART AND PROGRESS

1, (1949), p. 97. 2, Quoted by Gombrich (1962B), p. 246. 3, (1949), p. 105. 4, Gombrich (1962B), p. 20. 5, Ibid., p. 169. 6, Ibid., pp. 174–5.

XXIV. CONFUSION AND STERILITY

1, Some lengthy passages in this chapter are lifted without acknowledgements from my essay on 'The Anatomy of Snobbery' in *The Trail of the Dinosaur* (1954). 2, *Time*, January 26, 1962. 3, See Note 1. 4, Quoted from 'This England', *The New Statesman and Nation*, August 14, 1954.

BOOK TWO

Habit and Originality

INTRODUCTION

1, Jeffress, A., ed. (1951), p. 113.

I. PRE-NATAL SKILLS

1, Woodger (1929), p. 327. 2, Hyden (1960), p. 307. 2A, Hyden (1962). 3, Bertalanffy (1952), p. 134. 4, Schrödinger (1944), p. 71. 5, Cf. e.g. Buttin, G. 1962. 6, Fischberg, M. and Blackler, A. W. (1961). 7, Willier, Weiss, and Hamburger (1955), p. 338. 8, Hamburger (1955A), p. 67. 9, Waddington (1932), quoted from Polànyi (1958), p. 356. 10, Weiss (1939), p. 290. 11, Hamburger (1955B), p. 978. 12, Brachet (1955), pp. 389 ff. 13, Hamburger, loc. cit. 14, Bertalanffy (1952), p. 47.

II. THE UBIQUITOUS HIERARCHY

1, e.g. Coghill (1929), Carmichael, L. (1954). 2, Needham, J. (1932). 3, Spencer H. (1870–2). 4, Heidenhain (1923). 5, Jeffress, A., ed. (1951), pp. 140 ff. 6, Pribram

(1960), p. 6. 7, Hyashi, T. (1961), pp. 184 seq. 8, Pribram (1960), p. 8. 9, Holst, V. (1937, 1948). 10, Petermann (1932), p. 124. 11, Quoted from Petermann, op. cit., pp. 127 ff. 12, Ibid., p. 130. 13, Ibid., pp. 131 f. 14, Ibid., p. 132. 15, Quoted by Miller et al. (1960), p. 92. 16, Jeffress, op. cit., p. 141. 17, Quoted from Tinbergen (1951), p. 129.

III. DYNAMIC EQUILIBRIUM AND REGENERATIVE POTENTIAL

1, Pribram (1960), p. 4. 2, Tinbergen (1951), p. 126. 3, Thorpe (1956), pp. 28–30. 4, Needham, A. E. (1961). 5, Child, C. M. (1924).

IV. 'RECULER POUR MIEUX SAUTER'

1, Child, C. M. (1924), p. 151. 2, Ibid., p. 150. 3, Smithers (1960), p. 108. 4, Ibid., pp. 106–7. 5, Lashley (1960), p. 239. 6, Lashley (1929). 7, Bertalanffy, op. cit., p. 114. 8, Loc. cit. 9, Kretschmer (1931), p. 138. 10, Miller et al, op. cit., p. 199. 11, Polànyi (1958), p. 400. 13, Needham, A. E. 1961.

V. PRINCIPLES OF ORGANIZATION

1, Pribram (1960).

VI. CODES OF INSTINCT BEHAVIOUR

1, Tinbergen (1951), pp. 189, 195. 2, e.g. Spurway and Haldane (1953), quoted by Thorpe (1956). 3, Tinbergen (1953), p. 55. 4, Tinbergen (1951), p. 9. 5, Sir Julian Huxley. 6, Kuo, Z. Y. (1932). 7, Lehrman, D. S. (1961). 8, Beach, F. A. (1961). 9, Tinbergen (1951), p. 142. 10, Hilgard (1958), p. 3. 11, Thorpe (1956), p. 133. 12, Ibid., p. 18. 13, Ibid., p. 28. The term 'innate releasing mechanism' is a translation by Tinbergen of the German 'das angeborene, auslösende Schema' (von Uexhüll —Lorenz). 14, Tinbergen (1951), p. 103. 15, Loc. cit. 16, Tinbergen (1953), p. 9. 17, For a brief survey see 'The Concept of "Ritualization"' by A. D. Blest in *Current Problems in Animal Behaviour*, ed. Thorpe and Zangwill (1961). 18, Thorpe (1956), p. 132. 19, Ibid., p. 31. 20, Woodworth (1918). 21, Tinbergen (1951), pp. 105–6. 22, Ibid., p. 110. 23, Ibid., pp. 104–5. 24, Thorpe (1956), p. 41. 25, Ibid. p. 42. 26, Ibid., p. 19. 27, Loc. cit. 28, Thorpe (1956), p. 26. 29, Ibid., p. 262. 30, Hingston (1927), quoted by Thorpe (1956), p. 38. 31, Hingston, op. cit., quoted by Thorpe (1956), p. 39. 32, Lindauer, M. (1952). 33, Tinbergen (1953), p. 102. 34, Ibid., p. 116.

VII. IMPRINTING AND IMITATION

1, Hilgard (1957), p. 125. 2, Heinroth, O. (1938). 3, Thorpe (1956), p. 375. 4, Thorpe (1956), p. 356. 5, Lashley (1913). 6, McDougall (1936). 7, Thorpe (1956), p. 375. 8, Ibid., p. 374. 9, Ibid., p. 356.

VIII. MOTIVATION

1, Mowrer, O. H. (1952). 2, Freud (1920), pp. 3–5. 3, Hilgard (1958), p. 428. 4, Hebb (1949), pp. 178–80. 5, Cf. i.a., Zener (1957); Loucks (1935, 1938); Hovland (1937); Hilgard and Marquis (1940); and for a concise summary Hebb (1949), pp. 174–6. 6, For a review of the literature, cf. e.g. Pribram (1960). 7, Miller et al., op. cit., p. 30. 8, Pribram (1960), p. 3. 9, Skinner (1938), p. 9. 10, Ibid., pp. 40. 11, Miller et al., op. cit., p. 22. 12, Hilgard (1958), p. 105. 13, Humphreys, L. G. (1939). 14, Hull (1952), p. 350. 15, Hilgard (1958), p. 177. 16, Berlyne, D. E. (1960), p. 225. 17, Allport, G. W. (1957). 18, Goldstein, K. (1939). 19, Cf. e.g., Jencks B. and Potter, P. B., *Journal of Psychology*, Vol. 49,

p. 139. 20, Nissen, H. W. (1954). 21, Berlyne, op. cit., p. 115. 22, Ibid., p. 116. 23, Ibid., p. 127. 24, Ibid., p. 117. 25, Ibid., p. 117. 26, Ibid., p. 119. 27, Ibid., pp. 133–4. 28, Lorenz (1956). 29, Compressed from *The Descent of Man* (1913 ed.), pp. 108–10; and *The Expression of the Emotions* (1872), p. 43. 30, Berlin, 1917; London and New York 1925. 31, Berlyne, op. cit., p. 148. 32, Harlow et al. (1950). 33, Harlow (1953), p. 25. 34, Woodworth (1947), p. 123. 35, Berlyne, op. cit., p. 170. 36, Loc. cit. 37, Pavlov (1927). 38, Darchen, R. (1952, 1954, and 1957), quoted by Berlyne, op. cit., p. 104. 39, Thacker, L. A. (1950). 40, Thorpe (1956), p. 9. 41, Ibid., p. 12. 42, Craik, K. J. W. (1943), p. 61. 43, Allport, G. W. (1955), p. 67.

IX. PLAYING AND PRETENDING

1, Thorpe (1956). 2, Berlyne, op. cit., p. 5. 3, Thorpe (1956), p. 87. 4, Loc. cit. 5, Ibid. p. 355.

X. PERCEPTION AND MEMORY

1, Galambos (1956). Cf. also 269. 2, Moray, N., *The Listener*, 19.4.1962. 3, e.g. Hilgard (1958), p. 442 seq. 4, Ittelson, W. H. (1952), quoted from Polànyi (1958), p. 96. 5, Wever, E. G. (1949). 6, Osgood (1960), p. 111. 7, Pringle, J. W. S. (1951). 8, Hyden (1960, 1962). 9, Whitfield (1949), p. 367. 10, Miller et al., op. cit., pp. 134 ff. 10A, Bartlett (1961), cap. V. 11, See e.g. Hebb (1949), cap. 2. 12, Ibid. 13, Ibid. 14, Ibid. 15, Exner (1891), quoted by Thorpe (1956), p. 129. 16, See, for instance, Miles's (1931) fascinating kinephantoscope. 17, Dubos, p. 94. 18, Babbage (1830), quoted by Hanson (1961), p. 184. 19, Barlow (1959), pp. 552 seq. 20, Quoted by Koffka (1935), p. 143. 21, Woodworth (1938), p. 561. 22, Cf. Osgood (1960), p. 641, Kluever, H. (1955) and Jaensch, E. R. (1930). 23, Kluever, op. cit. and Jaensch, op. cit. 24, Kluever, op. cit. 25, Pierre, T. H. (1955). 26, Kluever, op. cit. 27, Jaensch, op. cit. 28, Ibid., p. 97. 29, Semon, R. 1921), p. 149. 30, Woodworth (1938), p. 42. 31, Head (1926), p. 232. 32, Quoted by Penfield (1959), p. 226. 33, Fry, D. B. and Denes, P., in *Mechanization of Thought Processes* (1959), p. 378. 34, Paget (1930). 35, Fry and Denes, op. cit., p. 381. 36, Paget, op. cit. 37, Ladefoged, P., in *Mechanization of Thought Processes* (1959), p. 407. 38, Ibid., p. 411. See also Mackay, D. M. and Sutherland, N. S., ibid., pp. 607–9. 39, Drever, J., 2nd. in *Annual Review of Psychology* (1960), p. 131. 40, Ibid., pp. 153–4. 41, Thorpe (1956), p. 119. 42, Loc. cit. 43, Thorpe (1956), p. 411. 44, Ibid., p. 119. 45, Quoted by Wilenski, R. H. (1940), p. 202. 46, cf. Ladefoged, P., in *Mechanization of Thought Processes* (1959), p. 402. 47, Bartlett (1961), p. 200. 48, Ibid, p. 213. 49, *Time*, March 2, 1962.

XI. MOTOR SKILLS

1, *Psychological Review*, 1899, 6, pp. 345–75. 2, Woodworth (1938), p. 159. 3, Book, W. F. (1908). 4, Woodworth (1938), p. 45. 5, *New Scientist*, March 1, 1962. 6, Miller et al. (1960), p. 86. 7, Lashley in the Hixon Symposium, p. 123. 8, Ruch, T. C. (1951), p. 205.

XII. THE PITFALLS OF LEARNING THEORY

1, (1927), pp. 32–3. 2, Skinner, quoted by Hilgard (1958), p. 117. 3, Ibid., p. 106. 4, Ibid., p. 152. 5, Köhler: *The Mentality of Apes, Gestalt Psychology*. Koffka: *Principles of Gestalt Psychology, The Growth of the Mind*. 6, Watson (1928), pp. 198 ff. 7, Watson (1924), p. 281. 8, Watson (1928), p. 199. 9, Loc. cit. 10, Hilgard (1958), p. 121. 11, Guthrie (1935), p. 25. 12, Skinner (1953a), quoted by Hilgard (1958), p. 115. 13, Hull (1945), p. 56. 14, Hilgard (1958), p. 152. 15, Osgood (1953), p. 655. 16, Hebb (1949), p. 59. 17, Hilgard (1958), pp. 8 ff. 18, Ibid., p. 335.

19. Polànyi (1958), p. 71. 20, Craik (1943), p. 121. 21, Hebb (1949), p. 127. 22, Thorpe (1956), pp. 96, 100, 106. 23, Ibid., pp. 229, 231. 24, Ibid., pp. 229, 231, 232, 235. 25, Ibid., p. 227. 26, Russell (1927), p. 41. 27, Osgood (1953), p. 451. 28, Rosenthal, R., and Fode, K. L., 'The Effect of Experimenter Bias on the Performance of the Albino Rat' in Behavioral Science, Vol. VIII, 3, July 1963. 29, Earl Ubell in the *New York Herald Tribune*, January 1960. 30, Thorndike (1913–14), p. 134. 31, Osgood, op. cit., p. 604. 32, Hilgard (1958), p. 15. 32a, Tolman (1937), p. 11. 33, Hilgard (1958), p. 65. 34, Krechevsky (1932). 35, Ibid. 36, Hilgard (1958), p. 470. 37, Osgood, op. cit., p. 604.

XIII. THE PITFALLS OF GESTALT

1, Köhler (1957), p. 113. 2, Ibid., p. 113 n. 3, Osgood (1960), p. 637. 4, Köhler (1957), p. 164. 5, Yerkes (1943), p. 156. 6, Osgood, op. cit., p. 611. 7, Loc. cit. 8, Köhler (1957), p. 43. 9, Ibid, p. 44. 10, Ibid., cap VII. 11, Ibid., p. 44. 12, Ibid., p. 45. 13, Ibid., p. 167. 14, Yerkes (1943). 15, Birch H. G., in *J. Comp. Psychol.*, 1945, p. 382. 16, Thompson, W. R. and Heron, W. (1954), quoted by Hebb (1958), p. 219. 17, Köhler (1957), p. 164. 18, Ibid., p. 167. 19, Köhler (1930), p. 277. 20, Ibid., pp. 272 seq. 21, Craik (1943), pp. 52. 22, Cf. e.g. Köhler (1957), p. 27. 23, Piaget (1954), p. 359. 24, Craik, op. cit., p. 1. 25, Russell (1927), pp. 279–80. 26, Ibid, p. 83. 27, Köhler (1930), p. 225. 28, Petermann (1932). 29, Hixon Symposium, p. 69. 30, Polànyi (1958), p. 341. 31, Koffka (1935), p. 570. 32, Köhler (1930), p. 215. 33, Hebb (1949), p. 134. 34, Ibid., p. 164. 35, Hebb (1958), pp. 204–5. 36, Hilgard (1958), pp. 475–6, 477–8.

XIV. LEARNING TO SPEAK

1, James (1890), Vol. I, p. 253. 2, Ach quoted by Humphrey, G. (1951), p. 260. 3, Osgood, op. cit., p. 686. 4, Piaget (1954), p. 359. 5, Hilgard (1957), p. 315. 6, Piaget (1954). 7, Ibid., p. 92. 8, Penfield and Roberts (1959), pp. 228–9. 9, Quoted by Woodworth (1938), p. 148. 10, Thorpe, op. cit., p. 119. 11, Head (1926), pp. 111, 112. 12, Woodworth (1938), p. 809. 13, Humphrey (1951), p. 252. 14, Penfield and Roberts (1959), p. 226. 15, Loc. cit. 16, Ibid., p. 228. 17, Chapter on 'Language and Thought'.

XV. LEARNING TO THINK

1, Russell (1927), p. 58. 2, Lorimer (1929), p. 95. 3, Cf. Book One, p. 322. 4, Lorimer (1929), p. 94. 5, Markey (1928), p. 71. 6, Ibid., p. 50. 7, Hebb (1949), p. 118. 8, Ibid., pp. 117 ff. 9, Quoted by Humphrey, op. cit., p. 25. 10, Osgood, op. cit., 689. 11, Cf. e.g. Hebb (1949), p. 176. 12, Lorimer, op. cit., pp. 103 ff. 13, Koffka (1930), p. 347. 14, Piaget (1930), p. 243. 15, Piaget (1928), p. 229. 16, Ibid., p. 227. 17, Lorimer (1929), pp. 124–6. 18, Craik, op. cit., p. 121. 19, See Lévy-Bruhl (1926), pp. 181 seq. 20, Ibid. 21, Dantzig (1930). 22, Herodotus, *Historia*, Bk. VII. 23, Dantzig, op. cit., pp. 9 ff. 24, Cf. e.g. Haas, W. S. (1956).

XVI. SOME ASPECTS OF THINKING

1, Cf. Koestler (1960). 2, Cf. Hyden (1960, 1962). 3, Penfield and Roberts, op. cit., p. 233.

XVII. ASSOCIATION

1, Osgood, op. cit. 2, Humphrey, op. cit., p. 1. 3, Quoted by Woodworth (1938), p. 370. 4, Quoted by Woodworth (1939) pp. 350 ff. 5, Woodworth (1939) pp. 352 ff.

XVIII. HABIT AND ORIGINALITY

1, Quoted by Polya (1938), p. 164. 2, Polya (1948), p. 158. 3, Ibid., p. 58. 4, Loc. cit. 5, Osgood, op. cit., p. 633.

APPENDIX I. ON LOADSTONES AND AMBER

1, *De Magnette*, Book V, cap. 12. 2, Ibid., VI, 4. 3, Cap 6. 4, Pledge (1939), p. 121. 5, Quoted from F. Sherwood Taylor (1949), p. 258. 6, Article on 'Electricity' in *Enc. Brit.* (1955 ed.) VIII, p. 189. 7, Crowther (1940), p. 348.

APPENDIX II. SOME FEATURES OF GENIUS

1, *The Elizabethan World Picture* (1946). 2, *Science and Imagination* (1956). 3, Quoted by Farrington (1953), pp. 130–1. 4, Butterfield (1949), p. 29. 5, Dreyer, J. L. E. *Tycho Brahe* (1890), p. 14. 6, *Il Saggiatore*. 7, *Dialogue on the Great World Systems*, p. 469. 8, *Il Saggiatore, Opere*, VI, p. 232. 9, *Dialogue Concerning Two Sciences*, p. 1. 10, *Dialogue on the Great World Systems*, pp. 68–9. 11, Drake Stillman (1957), pp. 256–8. 12, *Harmonice Mundi*, cap. 7. 13, Hoskin, M., 'The Mind of Newton', *The Listener*, 19.10.61. 14, Philips, R. (1927). 15, Crowther, J. G. (1940), p. 129. 16, Ibid., p. 316. 17, Himmelfarb, G., op. cit., p. 26. 18, Ibid., pp. 314–17. 19, Ibid., p. 317. 20, Ibid., p. 119. 21, Ibid., pp. 307–8. 21A, Ibid. p. 357. 22, *Origin of Species* (1873), p. 429. 23, *The Descent of Man* (1913) ed., pp. 946–7. 24, Dubos (1950), p. 72. 25, Dubos (1960), p. 36. 26, Dubos (1950), p. 114. 26A, Ibid, p. 396, f. 27, Ibid, p. 87. 28, *La Personne du Prix Nobel* (in the press). 29, *Enc. Brit.*, 13th ed. on Jalois. 30, Seelig, op. cit., p. 28. 31, Ibid., p. 26. 32, Crowther (1940), pp. 356 ff. 33, Dubos (1950), p. 383.

WORKS MENTIONED IN THIS BOOK

ACH, N., *Analyse des Willens*. Berlin, 1935.
ALLPORT, G. W., *Personality: A Psychological Interpretation*. New York: H. Holt, 1937.
ALLPORT, G. W., *Becoming*. Yale Univ. Press, 1955.
A.R.N.M.D., *The Hypothalamus*, Vol. XX, p. 732. Baltimore, Md., 1940.
AUDEN, W. H., *The Sea and the Mirror*. New York: Random House, 1944.
BABBAGE, C., *The Decline of Science in England*. London: R. Clay, 1830.
BAERENDS, G. P., 'Fortpflanzungsverhalten und Orientierung der Grabwespe *Ammophila campestris*' in *Jur. Tijd. voor Entom, 84*, 71–275, 1941.
BAIN, A., *Manual of Mental and Moral Science*. London: Longmans, 1868.
BARD, ed., Macleod's *Physiology in Modern Medicine*. St. Louis: Mosby, 1941 (9th ed.).
BARLOW, H. B., in *Mechanisation of Thought Processes*. London: H.M. Stationery Office, 1959.
BARTLETT, SIR FREDERICK, *Thinking*. London: G. Allen & Unwin, 1958.
BARTLETT, SIR FREDERICK, *Remembering*. Cambridge Univ. Press, 1961.
BECK, E. See Gastaut, H.
BELLON, R. O. See James, William.
BERGSON, H. L., *Le Rire*. Paris: F. Alcan, 1916 (15th ed.).
BERLYNE, D. E., *Conflict, Arousal and Curiosity*. London, New York, Toronto: McGraw-Hill, 1960.
VON BERTALANFFY, L., *Problems of Life*. New York: Harper Torchbooks, 1952.
BEVERIDGE, W. I. B., *The Art of Scientific Investigation*. London: Heinemann, 1950.
BIRCH, H. G., in *J. Comp. Psychol., 382*, 1945.
BIRNEY, R. C. and TEEVAN, R. C., eds., *Instinct*. Princeton, N. J., and London: van Nostrand, 1961.
BLACKLER, A. W. See Fischberg, M.
BLEST, A. D., in Thorpe and Zangwill, eds., *Current Problems in Animal Behaviour*. Cambridge Univ. Press, 1961.
BODKIN, M., *Archetypal Patterns in Poetry*. Oxford Univ. Press, 1934.
BOOK, W. F., *The Psychology of Skill*. Missoula, Mont.: Univ. of Montana, 1908.
BRACHET, J. L. A., article on 'Embryology, Human' in *Encyclopaedia Britannica*, Vol. VIII, 389B (1955 ed.).
BRACHET, J. L. A., See Hyden, H., 1960.
BRAGG, SIR LAWRENCE, *The History of Science*. London: Cohen & West, 1951.
BRANDT, G. W., article on 'Plot' in *Cassell's Enc. of Literature*, Vol. I. London, 1953.
BRONOWSKI, J., *Science and Human Values*. London: Hutchinson, 1961.
BRYAN, W. L. and HARTER, N., in *Psychol. Review, 6*, 345–75, 1899.
BURNET, J., *Early Greek Philosophy*. London: Blackwell, 1908.

BURT, SIR CYRIL, 'The Structure of the Mind' in *Br. J. of Educ. Psychol.*, Vol. XIX, June and November, 1949.

BURT, SIR CYRIL, 'The Concept of Consciousness' in *Br. J. of Psychol.*, *53*, 3, 1962.

BURT, SIR CYRIL, 'The Psychology of Laughter', Health Education Journal, Vol. III, 1945.

BUTTERFIELD, H., *The Origins of Modern Science*. London: G. Bell, 1949.

BUTTIN, G., in *Discovery*. London, August 1962.

CALVIN, A. D., ed., *Psychology*. Boston, Mass.: Allyn & Bacon, 1961.

CANNON, W. B., *Bodily Changes in Pain, Hunger, Fear and Rage*. New York: D. Appleton & Co., 1929 (2nd ed.).

CARMICHAEL, L., in *Manual of Child Psychology*, pp. 43–166. New York: J. Wiley & Sons, 1954 (2nd ed.).

CHILD, C. M., *Physiological Foundations of Behaviour*. New York: H. Holt & Co., 1924.

COBB, S., *Emotions and Clinical Medicine*. New York: W. W. Norton & Co., 1950.

COGHILL, G. E., *Anatomy and the Problem of Behaviour*. Cambridge Univ. Press, 1929.

COHEN, J., in *The New Scientist*, pp. 950 ff. London, 2.10.1958.

COPERNICUS, N., *On the Revolutions of the Heavenly Spheres*. Tr. Wallis, C. G. Chicago Univ. Press, 1952.

COZENS, A., *A New Method of Assisting the Invention in Drawing Original Compositions of Landscape*, 1765.

CRAIG, W., in *Biol. Bull.*, *34*, 91–107, 1918.

CRAIK, K. J. W., *The Nature of Explanation*. Cambridge Univ. Press, 1943.

CRILE, W. G., *The Origin and Nature of the Emotions*. Philadelphia: W. B. Saunders, 1915.

CROWTHER, J. G., *Famous American Men of Science*. London: Secker & Warburg, 1937.

CROWTHER, J. G., *British Scientists of the Nineteenth Century* (2 vols.). London: Penguin Books, 1940.

DANTZIG, T., *Number the Language of Science*. London: G. Allen & Unwin, 1930.

DARCHEN, R., in *Z. Tierpsychol.*, *9*, 362–72, 1952.

DARCHEN, R., in *Z. Tierpsychol.*, *11*, 1–11, 1954.

DARCHEN, R., in *J. Psychol. Norm. Path.*, *54*, 190–205, 1957.

DARWIN, C. R., *The Expression of the Emotions in Man and Animals*. London: J. Murray, 1872.

DARWIN, C. R., *The Origin of Species*. London: J. Murray, 1873 (6th ed).

DARWIN, C. R., *Descent of Man*. London: J. Murray, 1913 ed.

DARWIN, C. R., *Life and Letters*, ed. Francis Darwin, 3 vols. London, 1887.

DARWIN, C. R., *More Letters*, ed. Francis Darwin and A. C. Seward, 2 vols. London, 1903.

DENES, P. See Fry, D. B.

DIRAC, P. A. M., in *Scientific American*, Vol. 208, No. 5, May 1963.

DRAKE, STILLMAN, *Discoveries and Opinions of Galileo*. New York: Anchor Books, 1957.

DREVER, J., 2nd, in *Annual Review of Psychol*. Palo Alto, Calif.: Annual Reviews Inc., 1960.

DREVER's *Dictionary of Psychology*. London: Penguin Books, 1962.

DREYER, J. L. E., *Tycho de Brahe*. Edinburgh: A. & C. Black, 1890.

DUBOS, R., *Louis Pasteur*. Boston: Little, Brown & Co., 1950.

DUBOS, R., *Pasteur and Modern Science*. New York: Anchor Books, 1960.

DUCHENNE (de Boulogne), G., *Le Mécanisme de la Physionomie Humaine*. Paris: P. Asselin, 1862.

Albert Einstein: Philosopher—Scientist. Illinois: Evanston, 1949.

EMPSON, W., *Seven Types of Ambiguity*. London: Chatto & Windus, 1930.

EVANS, S. M., in *The New Scientist*. London, 2.5.1963.

EXNER, S., *Die Physiologie der facettierten Augen von Krebsen und Insekten*. Leipzig und Wien: 1891.

FARBER, S. M. and WILSON, R. H. L., eds., *Control of the Mind*. New York and London: McGraw-Hill, 1961.

FARRINGTON, B., *Greek Science*. London: Pelican Books, 1953.

FINDLAY, A., *A Hundred Years of Chemistry*. London: Duckworth, 1948 (2nd ed.).

FISCHBERG, M. and BLACKLER, A. W., in *Scientific American*, September 1961, pp. 131–8.

FODE, F. L. See Rosenthal, R.

FOORD, E. N. See Hebb, D. O.

FOSS, B., in *The New Scientist*. London, 6.7.1961.

FREUD, SIGMUND, *Gesammelte Werke*, Vols. I–XVIII. London: Imago Publishing Co., 1940–52.

FRY, D. B. and DENES, P., in *Mechanisation of Thought Processes* (2 vols). London: H.M. Stationery Office, 1959.

GALAMBOS, R., in *J. Neurophysiol.*, 19, 424–37, 1956.

GALANTER, E. See Miller, G. A.

GALILEO, GALILEI, *Opere*. Florence: Ediz. Naz., 1929–39.

GALILEO, GALILEI, *Dialogue Concerning Two New Sciences*. Tr. H. Crew. Evanston, Ill., 1950.

GALILEO, GALILEI, *The Star Messenger, The Assayer*, etc. See Drake, Stillman.

GALLAGHER, J. J., in *Psychology*. Boston, Mass.: Allyn & Bacon, 1961.

GALTON, F., *Inquiries into Human Faculty*. London and New York: Macmillan, 1883 (1st ed.).

GARDNER MURPHY. See James, William.

GASTAUT, H. and BECK, E., in *The New Scientist*. London, 1.3.1962.

GELLHORN, E., *Autonomic Regulations*. New York: Inter-Science Publishers, Inc., 1943.

GELLHORN, E., *Autonomic Imbalance*. New York: Inter-Science Publishers, Inc., 1957.

GHISELIN, B., ed., *The Creative Process*. Univ. of Calif. Press, 1952.

GIBSON, J. J., in *Psychol. Bull.*, 38, 781–817, 1941.

GILBERT, W., *De Magnete*. London, 1600.

GOLDSTEIN, K., *The Organism*. New York: American Books, 1939.

GOLDSTEIN, K., *Human Nature in the Light of Psychopathology*. Cambridge, Mass.: Harvard Univ. Press, 1947.

GOLDWATER, R. and TREVES, M., eds., *Artists on Art*. London: K. Paul, 1947.

GOMBRICH, E. H., *The Story of Art*. London: Phaidon Press Ltd., 1962a.

GOMBRICH, E. H., *Art and Illusion*. London: Phaidon Press Ltd., 1962b.

GOODFIELD, J. See Toulmin, S.

GRAVES, ROBERT, *Poetic Unreason*. London: Cecil Palmer, 1925.

GREGORY, J. C., *The Nature of Laughter*. London: K. Paul, 1924.

GREIG, J. Y. T., *The Psychology of Laughter and Comedy*. London: G. Allen & Unwin, 1923.

GRIS, JUAN, in *Horizon*, London, August 1946.

GUTHRIE, E. R., *The Psychology of Learning*. New York: Harper, 1935.

HAAS, W. S., *The Destiny of the Mind*. London: Faber, 1956.

HADAMARD, J., *The Psychology of Invention in the Mathematical Field*. Princeton Univ. Press, 1949.

HALDANE, J. B. S. See Spurway, H.

HAMBURGER, V., article on 'Regeneration' in *Encyclopaedia Britannica*, Vol. XIX, p. 67 (1955 ed.).

HAMBURGER, V., article on 'Experimental Embryology' in *Encyclopaedia Britannica*, Vol. VIII, p. 978 (1955 ed.).

HAMBURGER, V. See Willier, B. H.

HANLEY, C., in *Psychology*. Boston, Mass.: Allyn & Bacon, 1961.

HANSON, N. R., *Patterns of Discovery*. Cambridge Univ. Press, 1961.

HARDY, G. H., *A Mathematician's Apology*. Cambridge Univ. Press, 1940.

HARLOW, H. F., in *Psychol. Rev.*, *60*, 23–32, 1953.

HEAD, SIR HENRY, *Aphasia and Kindred Disorders of Speech*. Cambridge Univ. Press, 1926.

HEAD, SIR HENRY, in *B. J. of Educ. Psychol.*, Vol. XIX, II and III, June and November, 1949.

HEATH, T. L., *Greek Astronomy*. London: Dent, 1932.

HEBB, D. O., *The Organisation of Behaviour*. New York: Wiley, 1949.

HEBB, D. O., in *Psychol. Rev.*, *62*, 1955.

HEBB, D. O., *A Textbook of Psychology*. Philadelphia and London: Saunders, 1958.

HEBB, D. O. and FOORD, E. N., in *J. Exp. Psychol.*, *35*, 335–48, 1945.

HEIDENHAIN, M., *Formen und Kräfte in der lebenden Natur*. Berlin, 1923.

HEINROTH, O., *Aus dem Leben der Vögel*. Leipzig, 1938.

HERON, W. See Thompson, W. R.

HERRICK, C. J., *The Thinking Machine*. Chicago Univ. Press, 1929.

HERRIGEL, E., *Zen in the Art of Archery*. London: Routledge & K. Paul, 1959 (3rd ed.).

HESSE, M. B., *Forces and Fields*. London: T. Nelson, 1961.

HILGARD, E. R., *Introduction to Psychology*. London: Methuen, 1957.

HILGARD, E. R., *Theories of Learning*. London: Methuen, 1958 (2nd ed.).

HILGARD, E. R. and MARQUIS, D. G., *Conditioning and Learning*. New York: Appleton-Century, 1940.

HIMMELFARB, G., *Darwin and the Darwinian Revolution*. New York: Anchor Books, 1959.

HINGSTON, R. W. G., in *J. Bombay Nat. Hist. Soc.*, *31*, 1926–7.

Hixon Symposium. See Jeffress, L. A., ed.

HOBBES, T., *Leviathan*, 1651.

HÖFER, ed., *Histoire de l'Invention de l'Imprimerie par les Monuments*. Paris, 1840.

VON HOLST, E., in *Naturwiss.*, *25*, 1937.

VON HOLST, E. in *Experientia*, *4*, 1948.

HOOK, SIDNEY, in *Commentary*, New York, January 1959.

HOOKER, D., in *Genetic Neurology*, ed. Weiss, P., 1950.

HOSKIN, M., in *The Listener*, London, 19.10.1961.

HOUSMAN, A. E., *The Name and Nature of Poetry*. New York: Cambridge Univ. Press, 1933.

HOVLAND, C. I., in *J. Genet. Psychol.*, *51*, 279–91, 1937.

HULL, C. L., *Principles of Behaviour*. New York: Appleton-Century-Crofts, 1943.

HULL, C. L., *A Behaviour System*. New Haven, Conn.: Yale Univ. Press, 1952.

HUMPHREY, G., *Thinking*. London: Methuen, 1951.

HUMPHREYS, L. G., in *J. Exp. Psychol.*, *25*, 141–158, 1939.

HUXLEY, ALDOUS, in *Control of the Mind*, eds. Farber, S. M. and Wilson, H. L., 1961.

HYDEN, H., Chapter 5 in *The Cell*, Vol. IV, eds. Brachet, J. and Mirsky, A. New York: Academic Press, 1960.

HYDEN, H., in *Macromolecular Specificity and Biological Memory*, ed. Schmitt, F. O., 1962.

ITTELSON, W. H., *The Ames Demonstration in Perception*. Princeton Univ. Press, 1952.

JAENSCH, E. R., *Eidetic Imagery*. London: K. Paul, 1930.

JAMES, WILLIAM, *The Principles of Psychology*. New York: H. Holt, 1890.

JAMES, WILLIAM, in *On Psychic Research*, eds. Gardner Murphy and Bellon, R. O., 1961.

JEFFRESS, L. A., ed. *Cerebral Mechanisms in Behaviour—The Hixon Symposium*. New York: Wiley, 1951.

JENCKS, B. and POTTER, P. B., in *J. of Psychol.*, 49, 139.

JONES, E., *Sigmund Freud* (3 vols.). London: Hogarth Press, 1953–7.

JONES, E., in *B. Med. J.*, 4, 8, 1956.

JONES, M. R. See Nissen, H. W.

JUNG, C. G., *Psychology of the Unconscious*. New York: Moffat, Yard, 1916.

JUNG, C. G., *Contributions to Analytical Psychology*. London: K. Paul, 1928.

JUNG, C. G., *Modern Man in Search of his Soul*. London: K. Paul, 1933.

JUNG, C. G., *The Integration of Personality*. London: K. Paul, 1940.

KELLER, HELEN, *The Story of my Life*. London: Hodder & Stoughton (1959 ed.).

KELLY, J. FITZMAURICE, article on 'Literature' in *Encyclopaedia Britannica* (12th ed.).

KENDALL, J., *Michael Farraday*. London: Faber, 1955.

KEPES, G., The New Landscape. Chicago: P. Theobold, 1956.

KEPLER, JOHANNES, *Opera Omnia*, ed. Ch. Frisch. Frankofurti et Erlangae, 1858–71.

KEPLER, JOHANNES, *Gesammelte Werke*, ed. Caspar, v. Dyck and Hammer. Munich, 1938.

KLUEVER, H., article on 'Eidetic Images', in *Encyclopaedia Britannica*, Vol. VIII (1955 ed.).

KOESTLER, A., *Insight and Outlook*. London and New York: Macmillan, 1949.

KOESTLER, A., *The Sleepwalkers*. London: Hutchinson, 1959.

KOESTLER, A., *The Lotus and the Robot*. London: Hutchinson, 1960.

KOFFKA, K., *The Growth of the Mind*. New York: Harcourt Brace, 1930.

KOFFKA, K., *Principles of Gestalt Psychology*. New York: Harcourt Brace, 1935.

KÖHLER, W., *Gestalt Psychology*. London: G. Bell, 1930.

KÖHLER, W., *Dynamics in Psychology*. New York: Liveright, 1940.

KÖHLER, W., *The Mentality of Apes*. London: Pelican Books, 1957.

KRECHEVSKY, I., in *Univ. Calif. Publ. Psychol.*, 6, 27–44, 1932.

KRETSCHMER, E., *The Psychology of Men of Genius*. London: K. Paul, 1931.

KRETSCHMER, E., *A Textbook of Medical Psychology*. Trs. with an introd. by Strauss, E. B. London: H. Milford, 1934.

KORTLANDT, A., in *Arch. Néerl. Zool.*, 4, 401–42.

KUO, Z. Y., in *J. Comp. Psychol.*, 14, 109–21, 1932.

LADEFOGED, P., in *Mechanisation of Thought Processes*. London: H.M. Stationery Office, 1959.

LAMARCK, J. B., *Zoological Philosophy*. London: Macmillan, 1914.

LASHLEY, K. S., in *J. Anim. Behav.*, 3, 361–6, 1913.

LASHLEY, K. S., *Brain Mechanisms and Intelligence*. Chicago Univ. Press, 1929.

LASHLEY, K. S., *The Neuro-Psychology of Lashley* (Selected Papers). New York: McGraw-Hill, 1960.

LASHLEY, K. S. and WADE, M., in *Psychol. Rev.*, 53, 72–87, 1946.

DE LAUNAY, L., *Le Grand Ampère*. Paris, 1925.

LAWRENCE, W., in *Mechanisation of Thought Processes*, p. 411, 1959.

LEE, VERNON (pseud. Paget, Violet), *Beauty and Ugliness, and Other Studies in Psychological Aesthetics*. London: J. Lane, 1912.

LEHRMAN, D. S., in *Instinct*, eds. Birney, R. C. and Teevan, R. C. Princeton, N. J. and London: van Nostrand, 1961.

LÉVY-BRUHL, L., *Primitive Mentality*. London: G. Allen & Unwin, 1923.

LÉVY-BRUHL, L., *How Natives Think*. London: G. Allen & Unwin, 1926.

LINDAUER, M., in *Z. vergl. Physiol.*, *34*, 299–345, 1952.

LINDSLEY, D. B., in *Handbook of Experimental Psychology*, ed. Stevens, S. New York: Wiley, 1951.

LISTOWEL (W. F. H.), Earl of, *A Critical History of Modern Aesthetics*. London: G. Allen & Unwin, 1933.

LOEWI, O., in *Perspectives in Biology and Medicine*, Vol. IV., No. 1. Chicago Univ. Press, 1960.

LORENZ, K. L., in *L'Instinct dans le Comportement de l'Animal et de l'Homme*. Paris: Masson et Cie, 1956.

LORENZ, K. L., in *Aspects of Form*, ed. Whyte L. L., 1951.

LORIMER, F., *The Growth of Reason*. London: K. Paul, 1929.

LOUCKS, R. B., in *J. Psychol.*, *1*, 5–44, 1935.

LOUCKS, R. B., in *J. Comp. Psychol.*, *25*, 315–32.

McCONNELL, J. V., in *Psychology*. Boston, Mass.: Allyn & Bacon, 1961.

McDOUGALL, W., *The Group Mind*. New York: Putnam, 1920.

McDOUGALL, W., *An Outline of Psychology*. London: 1936.

McGUIGAN, F. J., in *Psychology*. Boston, Mass.: Allyn & Bacon, 1961.

MACKAY, D. M. and SUTHERLAND, N. S., in *Mechanisation of Thought Processes*, 1959.

MACLEOD's *Physiology in Modern Medicine*, ed. Bard (9th ed.). St. Louis: Mosby, 1941.

MALLARME, S., *Enquête sur l'Evolution Littéraire*. Paris, 1888.

MARKEY, J. F., *The Symbolic Process*. London: K. Paul, 1928.

MARQUIS, D. G. See Hilgard, E. R., 1940.

MAUROIS, A., *Alexander Fleming*. London: Cape, 1959.

Mechanisation of Thought Processes. London: H.M. Stationery Office, 1959.

MERTON, R. K., in *The New Scientist*. London, 2.11.1961.

MILES, W. R., in *Am. J. Psychol.*, *43*, 1931.

MILLER, G. A., GALANTER, E. and PRIBRAM, K. H., *Plans and the Structure of Behaviour*. New York: Holt, 1960.

MIRSKY, A. See Hyden, H., 1960.

MONTAGUE, A., in *Science*, Vol. 130, p. 1572.

MONTMASSON, J.-M., *Invention and the Unconscious*. London: K. Paul, 1931.

MORAY, N., in *The Listener*. London, 19.4.1962.

MOWRER, O. H., in *Annual Review of Psychology*. Palo Alto, Calif.: Annual Reviews, 1962.

MUNN, N. L., *Handbook of Psychological Research on the Rat*. Boston: 1950.

MUTCH, T. R., in *B. J. Ophthal.*, *28*, 317–36, 1944.

NEEDHAM, A. E., in *The New Scientist*. London, 2.11.1961.

NEEDHAM, A. E., in *Nature*, 30.12.1961.

NEEDHAM, J., in *Scientia*, *26*, 1932.

NEWTON, ERIC, *European Painting and Sculpture*. London: Penguin Books, 1941.

NEWTON, ERIC, *An Introduction to European Painting*. London: Longmans, Green, 1949.

NEWTON, SIR ISAAC, *Opera Omnia*. London, 1779–85.

NICHOLSON, M., *Science and Imagination*. New York: Cornell Univ. Press, Great Seal Books, 1956.

NISSEN, H. W., in the Nebraska Symposium on Motivation, II, *Current Theory and Research in Motivation*, ed. Jones, M. R. Lincoln, Nebr.: Univ. of Nebraska Press, 1954.

NORDENSKIOELD, E., *History of Biology*. New York: K. Paul, 1928.

OLDS, J., in *Proceedings of the First International Congress of Neuro-Pharmacology*. Amsterdam-London-New York-Princeton: Elsevier Publishing Co., 1959.

OLDS, J., in *Psychiatric Research Reports of the American Psychiatric Association.* January, 1960.

OSGOOD, C. E., *Method and Theory in Experimental Psychology.* New York: Oxford Univ. Press, 1953, 1960.

PAGET, SIR RICHARD, Bt., *Human Speech.* London: K. Paul, 1930.

PAVLOV, I. P., *Conditioned Reflexes.* Oxford Univ. Press, 1927.

PENFIELD, W. and ROBERTS, L., *Speech and Brain Mechanisms.* Princeton Univ. Press, 1959.

PETERMANN, B., *The Gestalt Theory.* London: K. Paul, 1932.

PIAGET, J., *Judgment and Reasoning in the Child.* London: K. Paul, 1928.

PIAGET, J., *The Child's Conception of Physical Causality.* London: K. Paul, 1930.

PIAGET, J., *The Construction of Reality in the Child.* New York: Basic Books, 1954.

PICASSO. See Goldwater, R. and Treves, M.

PIERRE, T. H., article on 'Imagery' in *Encyclopaedia Britannica* (1955 ed.).

PLEDGE, H. T., *Science since 1500.* London: H.M. Stationery Office, 1939.

POLÀNYI, M., *Personal Knowledge.* London: Routledge & K. Paul, 1958.

POLYA, G., *Wie Sucht Man die Lösung Mathematischer Aufgaben? Acta Psychologica,* IV, 2, Haag-Martinus Nijhoff, 1938.

POLYA, G., *How To Solve It.* Princeton Univ. Press, 1945.

POLYA, G., *Mathematics and Plausible Reasoning.* Oxford Univ. Press and Princeton Univ. Press, 1954.

POPPER, K. R., *The Logic of Scientific Discovery.* London: Hutchinson, 1959.

PRIBRAM, K. H. See Miller, G. A., 1960.

PRIBRAM, K. H., in *Annual Review of Psychology,* Vol. II. Palo Alto, Calif.: Annual Reviews, 1960.

PRINGLE, J. W. S., in *Behaviour, 3,* 174-215, 1951.

PYKE, M., *The Boundaries of Science.* London: Harrap, 1961.

RAULIN, J. M., *Le Rire et les Exhilarants.* Paris, 1899.

REID, L. A., *A Study in Aesthetics.* London: G. Allen & Unwin, 1931.

RIBOT, T. A., *La Psychologie des Sentiments.* Paris: F. Alcan, 1896.

RICHARDS, I. A., *Principles of Literary Criticism.* London: K. Paul, 1924.

ROBERTS, L. See Penfield, W.

ROSENTHAL, R. and FODE, F. L., in *Behavioural Science,* Vol. 8, Part 3, July 1963.

RUCH, T. C., in *Stevens' Handbook of Experimental Psychology.* New York: Wiley, 1951.

RUSSELL, BERTRAND, *An Outline of Philosophy.* London: G. Allen & Unwin, 1927.

RUSSELL, PHILIPS, *Benjamin Franklin, The First Civilised American.* London: Benn, 1927.

SACHS, H., *Master and Friend.* London: Imago Publishing Co., 1946.

DE SANTILLANA, G., ed., *Galileo Galilei Dialogue on the Great World Systems.* Chicago Univ. Press, 1953.

DE SANTILLANA, G., *The Crime of Galileo.* Chicago Univ. Press, 1953.

SAWYER, W. W., *Prelude to Mathematics.* London: Penguin Books, 1955.

SCHLOSBERG, H. See Woodworth, R. S.

SCHMITT, F. O., ed., *Macromolecular Specificity and Biological Memory.* Cambridge, Mass.: M.I.T. Press, 1962.

SCHRÖDINGER, E., *What is Life?* Cambridge Univ. Press, 1944.

SCRIVEN, M., in *Psychology.* Boston, Mass.: Allyn & Bacon, 1961.

SEELIG, K., *Albert Einstein.* Zürich: Europa Verlag, 1954.

SEMON, R., *The Mneme.* London: G. Allen & Unwin, 1921.

VON SENDEN, M., *Raum- und Gestaltauffassung bei operierten Blindgeborenen vor und nach der Operation.* Leipzig: Barth, 1932.

SHERRINGTON, C. S., *Integrative Action of the Nervous System.* New York: Scribner, 1906.

SHERWOOD TAYLOR, F., *Science Past and Present*. London: W. Heinemann, 1949.

SKINNER, B. F., *The Behaviour of Organisms*. New York: Appleton-Century, 1938.

SKINNER, B. F., *Science and Human Behaviour*. New York: Macmillan, 1953.

SKINNER, B. F., in *Amer. Psychologist*, 8, 69–78, 1953.

SMITHERS, D. W., *A Clinical Prospect of the Cancer Problem*. Edinburgh and London: Livingstone, 1960.

SPEARMAN, C., *Creative Mind*. Cambridge Univ. Press, 1930.

SPENCER, H., *Principles of Psychology*. London: Williams & Williams, 1871.

SPENCER, H., in *Essays on Education and Kindred Subjects*. London: J. M. Dent, 1911.

SPURWAY, H. and HALDANE, J. B. S., in *Behaviour*, 6, 8–24, 1953.

STEVENS, S. S., ed., *Handbook of Experimental Psychology*. New York: Wiley, 1951.

SULLY, J., *An Essay on Laughter*. London: Longmans, Green, 1902.

SUTHERLAND, N. S. See Mackay, D. M.

SUZUKI, D. T., *Zen and Japanese Culture*. London: Luzac, 1959.

TATON, R., *Reason and Chance in Scientific Discovery*. London: Hutchinson, 1957.

TEEVAN, R. C., See Birney.

THACKER, L. A., in *J. Comp. Physiol. Psychol.* 43, 86–98, 1950.

THOMPSON, W. R. and HERON, W., in *Canad. J. Psychol.*, 8, 17–31, 1954.

THORNDIKE, E. L., *Educational Psychology*. New York: Lemcke and Buechner, 1903.

THORNDIKE, E. L., *Animal Intelligence*. New York: Macmillan, 1911.

THORPE, W. H., *Learning and Instinct in Animals*. London: Methuen, 1956.

THORPE, W. H. and ZANGWILL, O. L., *Current Problems of Animal Behaviour*. Cambridge Univ. Press, 1961.

TILLYARD, E. M. W., *The Elizabethan World Picture*. London: Chatto & Windus, 1946.

TINBERGEN, N., *The Study of Instinct*. Oxford: Clarendon Press, 1951.

TINBERGEN, N., *Social Behaviour in Animals*. London: Methuen, 1953.

TOLMAN, E. C., in *Psychol. Rev.*, 45, 1–41, 1938.

TOLSTOY, L., *What is Art?*, Vol XVIII. Oxford Univ. Press, 1929.

TOULMIN, S. and GOODFIELD, J. *The Architecture of Matter*. London: Hutchinson, 1962.

TOYNBEE, A., *A Study of History*. Oxford Univ. Press, 1947.

TREVES, M. See Goldwater, R.

WADDINGTON, C. H. in *Phil. Trans. Roy. Soc.*, B., 221, 1932.

WADE, M. See Lashley, K. S.

WALLACE, A. R., *My Life* (2 vols.). London: Chapman & Hall, 1905.

WATSON, J. B., *Psychology from the Standpoint of a Behaviourist*. Philadelphia and London: Lippincott, 1924.

WATSON, J. B., *Behaviourism*. London: K. Paul, 1928.

WEBSTER, D. L., article on 'Electricity' in *Encyclopaedia Britannica*, Vol. VIII (1955 ed.).

WEISS, P., *Principles of Development*. New York: Holt, 1939.

WEISS, P., in *The Hixon Symposium*. See Jeffress, L. A., ed.

WEISS, P., ed., *Genetic Neurology*. Univ. of Chicago Press, 1950.

WEISS, P. See Willier, B. H., 1955.

WELLS, F. L., in *Psychol. Rev.*, 18, 229–33, 1911.

WERNICKE, C., *Der aphasische Symptomen-Komplex*. Breslau: Cohn und Weigert, 1874.

WEVER, E. G., *Theory of Hearing*. New York: Wiley, 1949.

WHITE, J. C. and SMITHWICK, R. H., *The Autonomic Nervous System* (2nd ed.). New York: Macmillan, 1941.

WHITEHEAD, A. N., *Science and the Modern World*. Cambridge Univ. Press, 1953.

WHITFIELD, I. C., in *Mechanisation of Thought Processes*, 1959.

WHYTE, L. L., ed., *Aspects of Form*. London: Lund Humphries, 1951.

WHYTE, L. L., *The Unconscious Before Freud*. New York: Anchor Books, 1962.

WILENSKI, R. H., *Modern French Painters*. London: 1940.

WILLIER, B. H., WEISS, P. and HAMBURGER, V., *Analysis of Development*. Philadelphia and London: W. B. Saunders, 1955.

WILSON, R. H. L. See Farber, R. M.

WITTGENSTEIN, L., *Tractatus, Logico Philosophicus*. London: K. Paul, 1922.

WOLBERG, L. R., *Hypnoanalysis*. New York: Grune & Stratton, 1945.

WOLF, A., *A History of Science, Technology and Philosophy*. London: G. Allen & Unwin, 1950 (2nd ed.).

WOODGER, J. H., *Biological Principles*. London: K. Paul, 1929.

WOODWORTH, R. S., *Dynamic Psychology*. New York: Columbia Univ. Press, 1918.

WOODWORTH, R. S., *Experimental Psychology*. New York: Holt, 1938; London: Methuen, 1939.

WOODWORTH, R. S., in *Am. J. Psychol.*, *60*, 119–124, 1947.

WOODWORTH, R. S. and SCHLOSBERG, H., *Experimental Psychology* (revised ed.). New York: Holt, 1954.

YERKES, R. M., *Chimpanzees: A Laboratory Colony*. New Haven: Yale Univ. Press, 1943.

ZANGWILL, O. L. See Thorpe, W. H. (1961).

ZENER, K., in *Am. J. Psychol.*, *50*, 384–403, 1937.

SOME REFERENCES ON THE PSYCHOLOGY AND PHYSIOLOGY OF WEEPING

A. *General Psychology, Theories, etc.*

BARNETT, S. A., 'The expression of emotions', *New Biol.* *22*, 73–90, 1957

DANA, C. L., 'The Anatomic Seat of the Emotions—A Discussion of the James-Lang Theory', *Arch. Neurology and Psychiatry*, 1921.

DARWIN, C., *The Expression of Emotions*, D. Appleton & Co. 136, 208, 373, 1896.

ENROTH, E., 'Om Graat', *Finska LäkSällsk. Handl.* 77, 76–88, 1935.

KLINEBERG, *Social Psychology*, 196, 1940.

LUND, F. H., 'Why do we weep?', *J. Soc. Psychol.* *1*, 136–51, 1930.

LUND, F. H., *Emotions, etc.* Ronald Press Co., New York, 47 ff., 1939.

PLESSNER, H., 'Das Problem von Lachen und Weinen', *Tijdschr. Phil. 2*, 317–84, 1940.

PLESSNER, H., *Lachen und Weinen*, Arnheim, Netherlands, 1950.

RUCKMICK, C. A., *The Psychology of Feeling and Emotion*, McGraw Hill, New York, 338 ff., 1936.

SPITZ, C., *Zur Psychologie des Weinens*, Zeulenroda, Sporn., 1935.

SULLEY, J., *An Essay on Laughter*, Longmans Green, London, 67–70, 1902.

YOUNG, P. T., 'Laughter and weeping, etc. in students', *J. Soc. Psychol.* 8, 311–34, 1937

YOUNG, P. T., *Emotions in Man and animal,* J. Wiley and Sons, London, 1943.
Weeping in chimps, 22;
Utility of, 58;
Cultural determination, 184;
Patterns of, 254–8;
Developmental, 164, 167, 177–9, 254, 255.

B. *Physiology*

ARNOLD, M. B., *Emotion and Personality, Vol. 2, Neurological and Physiological Aspects,* Cassell, London, 1960;
Weeping in thalamic disease, 12, 13;
Weeping and eeg, 162.

CHOROBSKI, S., 'The Syndrome of Crocodile Tears', *Arch. Neur. and Psychiatry,* 1951.

FORD, 'Paroxysmal lacrimation etc.', *Arch. Neurol. Psychiat. Chicago,* 29, 1933.

GEOFFREY WALSH, E., *Physiology of the Nervous System,* Longmans Green, London, 1957.
Crocodile tears, 408.

KLING, C., 'The Role of the Parasympathetic in Emotions', *Psychol. Rev.,* 1933.

MUTCH, T. R., 'The lacrimation reflex', *Brit. J. Ophthal.* 28, 317–36, 1944.

ROWBOTHAM, G. F., 'Observations on the effect of trigeminal denervation', *Brain,* 62, 364–80, 1939.

WHITE, J. C. and SMITHWICK, R. H. *et al* (3rd ed.), *The Autonomic Nervous System,* 40, 41, 250, 1952

C. *Weeping and Personality Development*

HUNT, J. Mc. V. (ed.), *Personality and the Behaviour Disorders, Vol. 1,* Ronald Press, Chap. 3, Mowrer, O. H., Dynamic theory of personality, 89, 1944.

RIVIERE, *Interntl. J. of Psychoanal.* 17, 395–422 (Psychological development in infancy.) 1936.

SULLIVAN, H. S., *Conceptions of Modern Psychiatry,* Tavistock Pbns., London, 15, 17, 89, 1953.

SYMONDS, P. M., *Dynamic Psychology,* Appleton Century Crofts, New York, 48, 280, 1949.

SYMONDS, P. M., *The Ego and the Self,* Appleton Century Crofts, New York, 13, 1951.

D. *Ontogenetics of Weeping*

AMES, L. B., 'Motor correlates of infant crying', *J. Genet. Psychol.,* 59, 239–47, 1941.

BAYLEY, N., 'A study of crying in infants etc.', *J. Genet. Psychol,* 40, 306–29, 1932.

BORGQUIST, A., 'Crying', *Am. J. of Psychol.,* 1906.

CLARKE, HUNT and HUNT, *J. Gen. Psychol.* 17, 398–402 (Weeping and startle pattern.), 1937.

GOODENOUGH, F. L., *Anger in Young Children,* 66–9, 244–9, 1931.

GOODENOUGH, F. L., *J. Abn. Soc. Psychol.* 27, 328–33 (Weeping in blind and deaf children.), 1932.

GOODENOUGH, F. L., *Developmental Psychology* (2nd ed.), Appleton Century. 201, 257; Individual differences, 273, 1945

KANNER, L., *Child Psychiatry*, Tanner, Illinois. 35, 599, 1960

LANDIS, C. and HUNT, W. A., *The Startle Pattern*, Farrar and Rhinehart, New York, 141, 1939.

LANDRETH, C., 'Factors associated with crying in young children', *Child Dev. 12*, 81–97, 1941.

MOWRER, O. H. and MOWRER, W. M., 'The meaning and measurement of crying', *Child Study*, 15, 104–7, 1938.

MUNN, N. L., *Evolution and Growth of Human Behaviour*, Riverside Press, Cambridge, Massachusetts, 407 ff., 1955.

ROSENZWEIG, S., 'Babies are taught to cry; a hypothesis', *Ment. Hyg. New York, 38*, 81–4, 1954

RUJA, H., 'The relation between neonate crying and length of labour', *J. Genet. Psychol. 73*, 53–5 (Test of Rankian birth cry hypothesis.), 1948.

VALENTINE, C. W., *Psychology of Early Childhood* (3rd ed.), Methuen, London, 1946.
> Early Appearance, 86 ff.;
> Inhibition of, 117;
> Social, 293;
> Resentment of, 297;
> Sympathy, 298.

E. *Psychopathology and Weeping*

DAVISON, C. and KELMAN, 'Pathological laughing and crying', *Arch. Neurol. Psychiat. 42*, 595–633, 1939.

GREENACRE, P., 'Pathological weeping', *Psychoanal. Quart. 14*, 62–75, 1945.

GREENACRE, P., 'Urination and weeping', *Am. J. Orthopsychiat, 15*, 81–8, 1945.

KELLY, G. A., *The Psychology of Personal Constructs, Vol. 2, Clinical Diagnosis and Psychotherapy*, Norton and Co., New York, 896 ff., 1113 ff., 1955.

LACOMBE, P., 'A special mechanism of pathological weeping', *Psychoanal. Quart. 27*, 248–51, 1958.

F. *Depth Psychological Formulations*

ABRAHAM K., *Selected Papers on Psychoanalysis*, Hogarth Press, 483 (Weeping in women as unconscious wish to urinate like a man.), 1954

BREUER, J. and FREUD, S., *Studies in Hysteria*, Hogarth Interntl. Psycho-analytical Library No. 50, 162 ff., 163 fn. (Weeping and abreaction arrears.), 1956.

FELDMAN, S. S., 'Crying at the happy ending', *J. Am. Psychoanal. Ass. 4*, 477–85, 1956.

(See GREENACRE 1945, 2, in Section E above.)

HEILBRUNN, G., 'On weeping', *Psychoanal. Quart. 24*, 245–55, 1955.

MONTAGUE, M. F. A., 'On the physiology and psychology of swearing', *Psychiat.*, 189–201 (Weeping in women as aggression outlet, substitute for function swearing performs for men.), 1942.

PETO, E., 'Weeping and laughter', *Intern. J. of Psychoanal. 27*, 129–33, 1956.

WEISS, J., 'Crying at the happy ending', *Psychoan. Rev.*, 1952.

G. *Relation of weeping to Psychosomatic Pathology.*

ALEXANDER, F., *Psychosomatic Medicine etc.*, G. Allen and Unwin, London, 1952;
> and Asthma, 139;
> Hysterical, 58;
> and Urticaria, 203.

DUNBAR, F., *Emotions and Bodily Changes*, Columbia, New York, 43 (Weeping and neurosis in Urticaria.), 1954.

HALLIDAY, J. C., 'Approach to asthma', *Brit. J. Med. Psychol. 17*, 1, 1937.

SAUL, L. J. and BERNSTEIN, C., 'The emotional settings of some attacks of Urticaria', *Psychosom. Med. 3*, 349, 1941.

ACKNOWLEDGEMENTS

The author and publishers wish to thank the following for permission to quote from various works: Basic Books, Inc., New York (*The Unconscious Before Freud*, by L. L. Whyte); Doubleday & Co., Inc., New York (*Pasteur and Modern Science*, by Rene Dubos, © 1960, by Educational Services, Inc. (Anchor Science Study Series), and *Darwin and the Darwinian Revolution*, by Gertrude Himmelfarb, © 1959, 1962, by Gertrude Kristol); the Clarendon Press, Oxford (*The Study of Instinct*, by Dr. N. Tinbergen); John Wiley & Sons, Inc., New York (*Cerebral Mechanisms in Behaviour—The Hixon Symposium*, ed. L. A. Jeffress); Little, Brown & Co., Boston (*Louis Pasteur*, by Rene Dubos, © 1950, by Rene Dubos); George Allen & Unwin, Ltd., London (*Thinking*, by Sir Frederick Bartlett); Europa Verlag, Zürich (*Albert Einstein*, by Carl Seelig); Cambridge University Press, New York (*The Name and Nature of Poetry*, by A. E. Housman); G. Bell, London (*Gestalt Psychology*, by W. Köhler); Allyn & Bacon, Boston (*Psychology*, ed. A. D. Calvin, © 1961, by Allyn & Bacon); Methuen & Co., London (*Learning and Instinct in Animals*, by W. H. Thorpe); Routledge & Kegan Paul Ltd., London (*Personal Knowledge*, by Michael Polànyi, *Mentality of Apes*, by W. Köhler, *The Symbolic Process*, by J. F. Markey, *The Growth of Reason*, by F. Lorimer, and *Invention and the Unconscious*, by J.-M. Montmasson).

2A *

INDEX

731